International Series of Monographs in

Earth Sciences

Editor: *Dean Earl Ingerson*

Department of Geology, University of Texas, Austin, Texas, USA

Volume 31

Advances in Organic Geochemistry 1968

Advances in Organic Geochemistry 1968

Proceedings of the
4th International Meeting on Organic Geochemistry,
held in Amsterdam, September 16-18, 1968

Edited by
P. A. Schenck and *I. Havenaar*

THE QUEEN'S AWARD
TO INDUSTRY 1968

Pergamon Press

Oxford · London · Edinburgh · New York
Toronto · Sydney · Paris · Braunschweig

Pergamon Press Ltd., Headington Hill Hall, Oxford
4 & 5 Fitzroy Square, London W.1

Pergamon Press (Scotland) Ltd., 2 & 3 Teviot Place, Edinburgh 1

Pergamon Press Inc., Maxwell House, Fairview Park, Elmsford, New York 10523

Pergamon of Canada Ltd., 207 Oueen's Quay West, Toronto 1

Pergamon Press (Aust.) Pty. Ltd., 19a Boundary Street, Rushcutters Bay,
N. S. W. 2011, Australia

Pergamon Press S. A. R. L., 24 rue des Écoles, Paris 5^e

Vieweg & Sohn GmbH, Burgplatz 1, Braunschweig

Editorial Assistance: *Werner Schröder*

08 006628 3   Pergamon Press
8280   Vieweg

Preface

The present volume in the International Series of Monographs in Earth Sciences contains the papers presented at the 4th International Meeting on Organic Geochemistry, held in Amsterdam, 16–18 September 1968. This meeting was organised under the auspices of the European Branch of the Organic Geochemistry Division of the Geochemical Society. The Executive Committee of the European Branch referred the organisation of the meeting to a Committee, consisting of E. Eisma, chairman, P. A. Schenck, secretary/treasurer, Mrs. M. Brongersma-Sanders, and I. Havenaar.

The meeting assembled in Amsterdam some 125 delegates from sixteen different countries. Their names and affiliations are included in a list at the end of this volume. Dr. Warren G. Meinschein, chairman-elect of the Organic Geochemistry Division kindly delivered the opening address.

For the first time in the relatively short history of these meetings, four invited speakers presented a general review on the state of affairs in several fields of geochemistry, i. e. organic compounds in sediments, geochemistry of petroleum, geochemistry of coal, and organic geochemistry of the oceans. To these speakers, Dr. G. Eglinton, Dr. G. T. Philippi, Dr. H. Postma and Dr. J. Karweil, the meeting is greatly indebted for their valuable contributions.

Moreover thanks are due to all those who contributed to the success of the meeting as authors of submitted papers, chairmen of the sessions and participants in the discussion.

The Organising Committee gratefully acknowledges the generous gifts received from British Petroleum Trading Ltd., Esso Europe Inc., Koninklijke/Shell Exploratie en Produktie Laboratorium (Shell Research N.V.), and Mobil Producing Netherlands Inc., which greatly helped to strengthen the financial basis of the meeting.

It is furthermore a pleasure to mention here the help of Miss K. A. Boekhout, who took an active part in organising the meeting and also assisted in preparing the papers for publication.

The Editors' aim has been to arrange publication of this Proceedings' volume as soon as possible after the meeting. This has required keeping editorial changes in the texts of the papers to a minimum. Figures have been printed where possible in the form in which they were received from the authors. All efforts to speed up publication would have been useless, however, if the authors had not co-operated as they did.

In addition to the texts of the papers, the discussions are also included; they are given in the language in which they were delivered.

The pleasant way in which Friedrich Vieweg & Sohn, Braunschweig, Germany, an affiliate of Pergamon Press, co-operated with the Editors in the production of this volume was greatly appreciated.

The Editors hope that this volume will find its way into the hands of all those interested in the field of geochemistry and that it may stimulate both the "old hands" and the newcomers to such an extent that many of them will join in the 5th meeting, which is scheduled to take place in Hanover, Germany, in 1971.

P. A. Schenck

I. Havenaar

Contents

Preface

General Lectures

G. Eglinton: Hydrocarbons and Fatty Acids in Living Organisms and Recent and Ancient Sediments   1

G. T. Philippi: Essentials of the Petroleum Formation Process are Organic Source Material and a Subsurface Temperature Controlled Chemical Reaction Mechanism   25

H. Postma: Dissolved Organic Matter in the Oceans   47

J. Karweil: Aktuelle Probleme der Geochemie der Kohle   59

Papers

A. L. Burlingame, P. A. Haug, H. K. Schnoes and *B. R. Simoneit:* Fatty Acids Derived from the Green River Formation Oil Shale by Extractions and Oxidations — A Review   85

A. L. Burlingame, P. C. Wszolek and *B. R. Simoneit:* The Fatty Acid Content of Tasmanites   131

D. H. Hunneman and *G. Eglinton:* Gas Chromatographic — Mass Spectrometric Identification of Long Chain Hydroxy Acids in Plants and Sediments   157

F. M. Swain, J. M. Bratt, S. Kirkwood and *P. Tobback:* Carbohydrate Components of Paleozoic Plants   167

W. Henderson, V. Wollrab and *G. Eglinton:* Identification of Steranes and Triterpanes from a Geological Source by Capillary Gas Liquid Chromatography and Mass Spectrometry   181

B. Nagy and *L. A. Nagy:* Investigations of the Early Precambrian Onverwacht Sedimentary Rocks in South Africa   209

W. Heller: Enzyme aus bituminösen Schiefern, Braunkohlen und Torfen   217

D. B. Boylan, Y. I. Alturki and *G. Eglinton:* Application of Gas Chromatography and Mass Spectrometry to Porphyrin Microanalysis   227

M. Fabre, N. J. Guichard-Loudet et *J. G. Roucaché:* Etude de la répartition dans un pétrole brut des n-paraffines C par C de C_1 à C_{40} à l'aide des tamis moléculaires 5 Å et de la C. P. G.   241

P. A. Schenck: The Predominance of the C_{22} n-Alkane in Rock Extracts   261

D. H. Welte: Determination of C^{13}/C^{12} Isotope Rations of Individual Higher n-Paraffins from Different Petroleums   269

V. A. Sokolov, A. A. Geodekjan and *Z. A. Buniat-Zade:* The General Scheme of Petroleum and Gas Formation, Alteration and Migration in the Earth's Crust   279

W. Kisielow and *A. Marzec:* Some Aspects of the Chemistry of Crude Oil Metamorphism   289

M. Correia, J. Lacaze, M. Poulet et *J. Roucaché:* Interprétation des variations de composition chimique présentées par les bruts des horizons productifs du gisement de Tiguentourine   303

R. Byramjee and *L. Vasse:* Geochemical Interpretation of Libyan and North-Saharan Crude Oil Analysis   319

M. Bestougeff, R. Byramjee et *L. Vasse:* Classification et caractérisation des pétroles bruts soufrés 331

G. Deroo, B. Durand, J. Espitalie, R. Pelet et *B. Tissot:* Possibilité d'application des modelès mathématiques de formation du pétrole à la prospection dans les bassins sédimentaires 345

R. E. Gérard and *G. Feugère:* Results of an Experimental Offshore Geochemical Prospection Study 355

L. Bonoli and *P. A. Witherspoon:* Diffusion of Paraffin, Cycloparaffin and Aromatic Hydrocarbons in Water and some Effects of Salt Concentration 373

Y. Califet, J. L. Oudin et *B. M. van der Weide:* Evolution expérimentale d'huiles brutes et de fractions d'huiles brutes sous l'influence de la température, de la pression et de minéraux argileux 385

A. Petrov, T. V. Tichomolova and *S. D. Pustilnikova:* The Distribution of Hydrocarbons in the Gasoline Fraction obtained upon Thermocatalysis of Fatty Acids 401

H. J. Kisch: Coal Rank and Burial-Metamorphic Mineral Facies 407

P. H. Given: The Chemical Aspects of Coal Metamorphism (A prepared contribution) 427

D. Leythaeuser and *D. H. Welte:* Relation between Distribution of Heavy n-Paraffins and Coalification in Carboniferous Coals from the Saar District, Germany 429

H. Wehner und *D. H. Welte:* Untersuchungen zum Gasabspaltevermögen des organischen Materials in Gesteinen und Kohlen des saarländischen Karbons und Devons 443

P. Hanbaba und *H. Jüntgen:* Zur Übertragbarkeit von Laboratoriums-Untersuchungen auf geochemische Prozesse der Gasbildung aus Steinkohle und über den Einfluß von Sauerstoff auf die Gasbildung 459

V. A. Sokolov, Z. A. Buniat-Zade, A. A. Goedekjan and *F. G. Dadashev:* The Origin of Gases of Mud Volcanoes and the Regularities of their powerful Eruptions 473

W. Flaig: Über den Ursprung des Stickstoffs in den Kohlen 485

U. Colombo, F. Gazzarrini, R. Gonfiantini, E. Tongiorgi and *L. Caflisch:* Carbon Isotopic Study of Hydrocarbons in Italian Natural Gases 499

P. Hahn-Weinheimer, G. Markl and *H. Raschka:* Stable Carbon Isotope Compositions of Graphite and Marble in the Deposit of Kropfmühl/NE Bavaria 517

H. Kroepelin: Racemisation of Amino Acids on Silicates 535

R. Kranz: Organische Aminoverbindungen in den Gas- und Flüssigkeitseinschlüssen uranhaltiger Mineralien und deren Bedeutung für Transportreaktionen in hydrothermalen Lösungen 543

M. Louis, C. J. Guillemin, J. C. Goni et *J. P. Ragot:* Coloration rose-carmin d'une sépiolite éocène, la quincyte, par des pigments organiques 553

A. Szalay and *M. Szilágyi:* Accumulation of Microelements in Peat Humic Acids and Coal 567

M. Schidlowski: Critical Remarks on a Postulated Genetic Relationship between Precambrian Thucholite and Boghead Coal 579

G. P. Vdovykin: Carbon Polytypism in Meteorites 593

List of Delegates 605

Name Index 610

Subject Index 611

Hydrocarbons and Fatty Acids in Living Organisms and Recent and Ancient Sediments

Geoffrey Eglinton

Organic Geochemistry Unit, School of Chemistry, University of Bristol
Bristol, England

Straight and branched chain alkanes, alkenes, and fatty acids are now known to be very widely distributed in plants and animals, though the total amounts of hydrocarbons are often small. With few exceptions, the n-alkanes exhibit a high odd/even carbon number predominance while the n-acids show an inverse relationship. Biosynthetic studies provide partial explanations for these distribution patterns and also for those of the branched hydrocarbons and acids, including the isoprenoids. The carbon skeletons of some compounds, such as phytol, persist to various degrees through the food web and hence provide a new type of marker. Thus certain derivatives of the isoprenoid acids can be separated by high resolution capillary gas chromatography in terms of their stereochemistry which may be correlated in turn with their past history and origin.

Increasing sophistication of analytical techniques permits the firm characterisation of hydrocarbons and fatty acids in progressively smaller amounts. The review will include a survey of procedures in current use and examples of their application to geological problems. Many factors undoubtedly determine the pattern of hydrocarbons and fatty acids found in fossils, sediments, and crude oils, but the single most important factor would seem to be slow thermal maturation. Laboratory experiments indicate that this process would effect predictable alterations in an original biological pattern. The hydrocarbons and fatty acids of sediments known to have been exposed to metamorphic influences show comparable patterns.

Introduction

I am expected to survey the distribution of hydrocarbons and fatty acids in living organisms and in sediments, but I think it would be more valuable to examine the overall situation within organic geochemistry, as seen by the organic geochemist. So this will be a general lecture, with a great deal of emphasis on biological markers. We could use the other term, "chemical fossil", but I think "biological marker" is more useful for the purposes of those working in this field [1]. I shall leave out most inorganic geochemical and geological considerations, although we should like to know more about the significance of particular samples under study. Also, I shall not be giving detailed treatment to biological matters. Chemists could profitably work more closely with biologists in the study of organisms involved in the formation and alteration of sediments; in industry, certain organisms are already being studied intensively because of their potential for the conversion of petroleum into human and animal foodstuffs [2].

I shall discuss the organic geochemistry of lipids, particularly hydrocarbons and fatty acids. Organic chemistry is concerned with the chemistry of carbon and it derives its impetus from the chemistry of living organisms. We may call ourselves "natural product chemists", but Nature consists not just of individual plant or animal species, but the geosphere, hydrosphere, and biosphere, with their complement of interacting biological and nonbiological entities. For that matter, the term "Nature" will include, if there is such a thing, extraterrestrial life. I believe that the traditional definition of natural product chemistry should now be expanded to include geological materials and, also, natural environments. The natural product organic chemist can then investigate sediments without feeling that he has to label himself a geochemist. Already this interest of the natural product chemist in the extension of organic chemistry to geological matters has resulted in the biological marker concept. Compounds which we might term biological markers are at present definable only where they have been extracted as "solubles" from the rock or sediment. This does not mean to say that we should ignore the kerogen, which makes up something like 90 % of most organic matter in rocks. However, it is much more difficult to get structural information out of kerogen than it is out of soluble materials, and the easy course is, therefore, to work on the soluble (i. e., extractable) material. But we would be making a serious mistake if we assumed that significance lies only in the soluble materials. People are now working on the kerogen and some of the papers to be given at this meeting will deal with this aspect.

Biological Markers and the Carbon Skeleton Concept

A biological marker is a compound the structure of which can be interpreted in terms of a previous biological origin. To be useful, the compound must have sufficient stability to survive long periods of time and sufficient complexity of structure (positional, and relative and absolute configuration) to render it very distinctive. It can be a compound originally present in the organism, but it is more usually a related structure, being derived from the original biolipids by the operation of diagenetic processes in the forming sediment and later maturation processes in the ancient sediment. We can approach the study of biological markers from two directions: first, the characterization of organic compounds in geological materials, and secondly, the characterization of the products of living organisms in terms of what might be expected to contribute to a sediment.

Figure 1 indicates some of the relevant processes which have been postulated as leading to petroleum [3]. Some of these give rise to the well-known biological markers: the n-alkanes, singly-branched (i. e., mono-methyl-substituted) long chain alkanes, acyclic isoprenoid alkanes, cyclic diterpanes, triterpanes, and steranes and the porphyrins. These compounds demonstrate control of positional isomerism in that the carbon atoms are always attached to one another in the same precisely determined way. In these terms and also in regard to relative stereochemistry, the

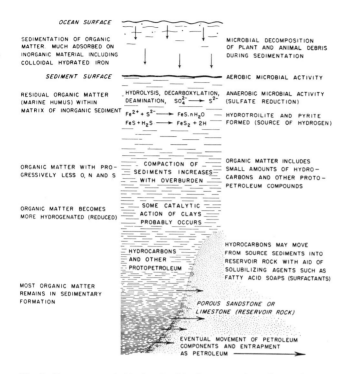

OCEAN SURFACE

SEDIMENTATION OF ORGANIC
MATTER. MUCH ADSORBED ON
INORGANIC MATERIAL INCLUDING
COLLOIDAL HYDRATED IRON

MICROBIAL DECOMPOSITION
OF PLANT AND ANIMAL DEBRIS
DURING SEDIMENTATION

SEDIMENT SURFACE

AEROBIC MICROBIAL ACTIVITY

RESIDUAL ORGANIC MATTER
(MARINE HUMUS) WITHIN
MATRIX OF INORGANIC SEDIMENT

HYDROLYSIS, DECARBOXYLATION,
DEAMINATION, $SO_4^{2-} \longrightarrow S^{2-}$

$Fe^{2+} + S^{2-} \longrightarrow FeS.nH_2O$
$FeS + H_2S \longrightarrow FeS_2 + 2H$

ANAEROBIC MICROBIAL ACTIVITY
(SULFATE REDUCTION)

HYDROTROILITE AND PYRITE
FORMED (SOURCE OF HYDROGEN)

ORGANIC MATTER WITH PRO-
GRESSIVELY LESS O, N AND S

COMPACTION OF
SEDIMENTS INCREASES
WITH OVERBURDEN

ORGANIC MATTER INCLUDES
SMALL AMOUNTS OF HYDRO-
CARBONS AND OTHER PROTO-
PETROLEUM COMPOUNDS

ORGANIC MATTER BECOMES
MORE HYDROGENATED (REDUCED)

SOME CATALYTIC
ACTION OF CLAYS
PROBABLY OCCURS

HYDROCARBONS
AND OTHER
PROTOPETROLEUM

HYDROCARBONS MAY MOVE
FROM SOURCE SEDIMENTS INTO
RESERVOIR ROCK WITH AID OF
SOLUBILIZING AGENTS SUCH AS
FATTY ACID SOAPS (SURFACTANTS)

MOST ORGANIC MATTER
REMAINS IN SEDIMENTARY
FORMATION

POROUS SANDSTONE OR
LIMESTONE (RESERVOIR ROCK)

EVENTUAL MOVEMENT OF PETROLEUM
COMPONENTS AND ENTRAPMENT
AS PETROLEUM

Fig. 1. Processes probably involved in the conversion of organic matter to petroleum
(W. Redfield, diagram based on an earlier one by Harold Smith, et al [3]

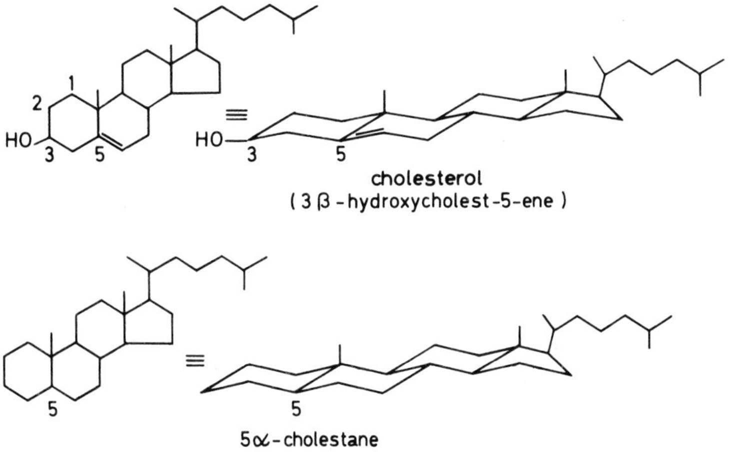

cholesterol
(3 β –hydroxycholest-5-ene)

5α-cholestane

Fig. 2. Structures of cholesterol and 5 α-cholestane

geologically occurring steranes have their biological counterparts in the steroids. In most steroids, the methyl groups and side chain point up, and the rings are trans-fused to give rather flat molecules. The absolute stereochemistry for naturally occurring cholesterol is as indicated, with the methyl groups up and the side chain at the right-hand side of the molecule. Cholesterol from one organism has the same absolute stereochemistry as cholesterol from another organism (i. e., it is the same enantiomer). This is important to the concept of the biological marker, because one should be able to show that the marker compound isolated from a sediment has retained the appropriate stereochemistry: for example, if cholestane is indeed formed geochemically from cholesterol or a related steroid, then it should not only be *cholestane* (i.e., have the right carbon skeleton and relative stereochemistry and magnitude of rotation of polarized light) but also be the correct *enantiomer* (i. e., have the correct absolute stereochemistry and sign of rotation). Should it be the other enantiomer, then there would have to be some explanation as to how such a whole scale inversion could occur: among the possibilities would be that organisms exist which provide the opposite absolute stereochemistry; another would be that there had been some catalysis or isomerization, but it is difficult to imagine an inversion process for the whole of the carbon skeleton of a sterane, for example.

With biological markers, we are concerned with the appropriate carbon skeletons as represented by the correct positions of the carbon atoms, the correct relative stereochemistry, and if we can determine it, the correct absolute stereochemistry. There are another two factors; carbon number dominance and isotopic composition.

In using carbon number dominance, we examine the abundance of series of compounds arranged in order of the number of carbons in their skeletons. Thus, if one examines the abundance of isoprenoid compounds from biological sources, we find that the pattern goes roughly as follows: C_5, C_{10}, C_{15} and C_{20} very abundant; C_{25} virtually unknown; C_{30} very abundant; C_{35} almost unknown; C_{40} quite abundant; C_{45}, C_{50} ... C_{110} rather less abundant. Similar patterns for isoprenoid hydrocarbons are found in sediments, and this is an important observation. An abiological production of isoprenoid hydrocarbons would tend to give a qualitatively smooth distribution of carbon number (i. e., 5, 10, 15, 20, 25, 30, 35, ... would be a smooth distribution of relative amounts, probably decreasing towards higher carbon numbers). Turning to the n-alkanes, we find that most organisms contain n-alkanes of carbon number around C_{30}, but that there is an alternation in abundance with successive homologues: the odd-carbon numbered n-alkanes are much more abundant than the even numbered homologues.

The principal example of isotopic composition is provided by ^{12}C: ^{13}C ratios, but I shall not discuss this because Dr. Welte will deal with it. Suffice it to say that the isotopic compositions of the original biolipid molecules must still be maintained in those portions of the molecules which have remained intact and have not been degraded or rearranged. In these cases, the isotopic fractionation induced during the formation of the carbon skeleton will still be preserved.

Living organisms examined so far do not appear to contain the saturated isoprenoid cycloalkanes, steranes, and triterpanes found in sediments and crude petroleums. Oxygenated and unsaturated analogues are, of course, present; for example, cholesterol. It is, of course, possible that these hydrocarbons are provided by as yet unexamined species of organisms. However, the more reasonable view is that they are formed during diagenesis of the oxygenated and unsaturated precursors. What is needed, therefore, for an understanding of the role of these particular biological markers is a summary of the carbon-skeleton content of the individual species of organisms. From this, one might assess the likely contributions to a sediment. Such surveys have yet to be made.

One type of biological marker where we do not use the carbon-skeleton concept, is of course, the protein or polypeptide structure. Individual amino acids are linked by amide bonds, and amino acid sequence analysis is necessary, rather than carbon skeleton analysis.

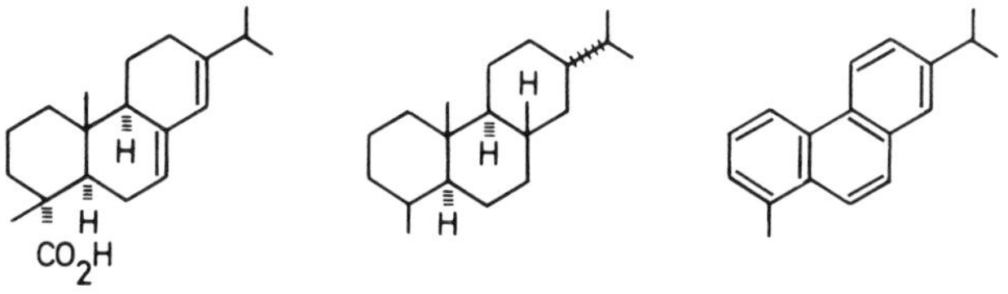

| Abietic Acid | Fichtelite | Retene |

Fig. 3. Structures of abietic acid, fichtelite and retene

The compounds indicated in Figure 3 illustrate the carbon skeleton approach. Fichtelite and retene are well-known as geolipids, though both are unknown as plant products. Abietic acid is a common constituent of tree resins and it is assumed that the abietic acid gives rise to the geolipids during diagenesis, for example, in a buried tree stump. Fichtelite retains the gross structure and relative stereochemistry of abietic acid. Retene, of course, retains most of the gross carbon skeleton, but none of the stereochemistry. Thus, the carbon skeleton of abietic acid is retained both in retene and in fichtelite, though the former is a fully dehydrogenated hydrocarbon and the latter is fully hydrogenated. Evidently a hydrogenation-dehydrogenation reaction occurs in sediments — or at least in the fossil tree stump from which these compounds were isolated. This relationship suggests that hydrogen is effectively transferred from one molecule to another. Both compounds are fairly stable. Both have similar gross carbon skeletons, but retene is planar and fichtelite is non-planar. These geogenetic relationships are, of course, still tentative and remain to be proven. The basic assumption is that the fossil hydrocarbons are not being formed by abiogenic processes; some of them presumably result from hydrogenation-dehydrogenation and other reactions carried out on the already existing carbon skeletons of compounds such as abietic acid. Thus, the carbon-carbon bonds present in the geolipids are in this case the same ones that were put there by the living organism. Such hydrocarbons may, therefore, be classed as biological markers, though further confirmation of their mode of formation is needed.

Distribution of Hydrocarbons and Fatty Acids in Living Organisms

This section will not present an exhaustive survey of the distribution of these classes of compounds in living organisms, but only a few carefully chosen examples. There are few biosynthetic pathways by which carbon skeletons are assembled in living organisms. Compounds isolated from living organisms must be explicable in terms of these pathways or of rearrangement and degradation reactions effected on the compounds first formed. The main routes are

(i) the acetate/malonate biogenesis for straight-chain carbon compounds and those bearing simple substituents, and

(ii) the isoprenoid biogenesis which produces branched and cyclic compounds built from repeating units of five carbon atoms.

In addition, single carbons, or, in some cases, two or three carbons, can be attached to these skeletons by methylation and alkylation processes involving methionine, etc. In spite of the simplicity of the products to be expected from the operation of these routes, some workers have reported very complex patterns of hydrocarbons from certain living organisms. It seems likely that these must represent contaminants or the products of alteration processes, rather than of the original biogenesis. The alternative view is that there are in such organisms major biosynthetic pathways about which we know nothing.

Generalized Carbon Skeleton	Common name	Comment
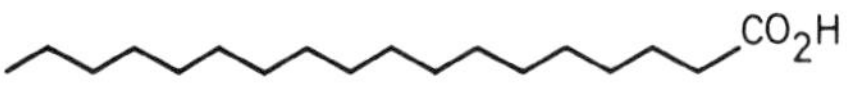 CO_2H	Normal	Abundant, widely distributed
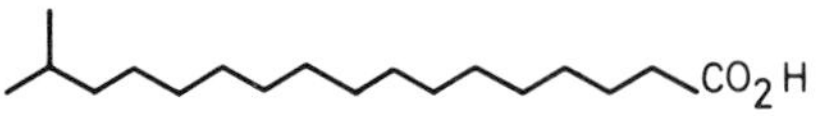 CO_2H	Iso	unusual as major constituents;
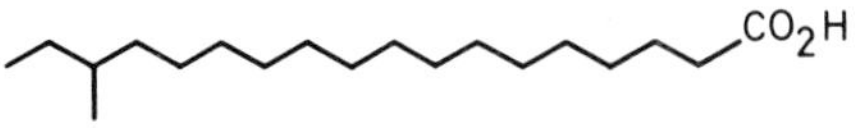 CO_2H	Anteiso	common in certain bacteria
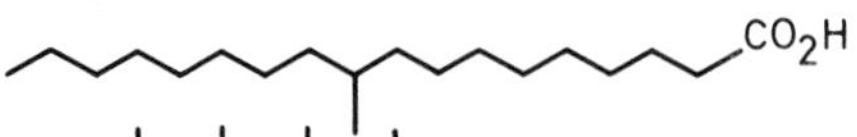 CO_2H	10-methyl	rare
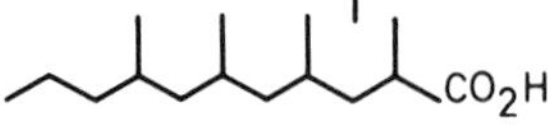 CO_2H	2,4,6,8 tetramethyl	unusual as major constituents; preen oils of birds.
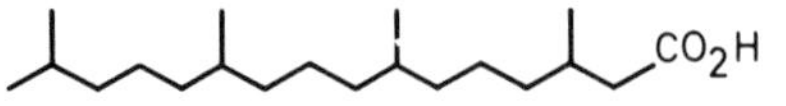 CO_2H	isoprenoid	Abundant, widely distributed, generally unsaturated, oxygenated and not as carboxylic acid.

Fig. 4. Structures of fatty acids typifying carbon skeletons produced by common biosynthetic pathways

Figure 4 exemplifies the carbon skeletons of typical acyclic fatty acids as synthesized by many different types of organism. The normal fatty acids are biosynthesized by malonate extension of acetate starter, while the iso- and anteiso-acids are the result of similar malonate extension of small, branched, starter acids. The 10-methyl acid is formed by methyl addition to the C_{18} straight-chain acid. The highly-branched acids exemplified by the 2, 4, 6, 8-tetramethylundecanoic acid result from chain extension with methylmalonyl units. It is an unusual type of acid, so far restricted to the preen glands of certain ducks and other birds. By contrast, the isoprenoids as a class of compounds are widely distributed: they are the result of the interlinking of C_5 units.

To some extent, the patterns of biological abundance of these skeletal types (i. e., as represented by the carbon skeletons only, disregarding any functionality) are mirrored in the composition of the extracts from sediments. Thus, the straight-chain and isoprenoid compounds are prominent constituents, but the singly-branched compounds, such as the iso-, anteiso- and mid chain methyl substituted compounds, are less abundant. Of course, the actual patterns of abundance in sediment extracts will reflect the operation of a variety of processes — for example, reduction and oxidation — which may have operated on the original biological material. The interpretation of this data must, of necessity, be complicated and there is much to investigate before one can read back with any certainty from the geolipid composition to the biolipids which originally contributed to the sediment.

The leaf waxes of higher plants contain interesting patterns of straight-chain compounds [4, 5]. The n-fatty acids are dominantly even-numbered whereas the n-hydrocarbons are dominantly odd-numbered. Further, both the hydrocarbons and the acids are mainly of chain-length around C_{30}. Thus, to restate the position, the carbon number distributions of the acids and hydrocarbons show a characteristic alternation of abundance, dominantly even in the case of the acids, and dominantly odd in the case of the hydrocarbons. Other constituents, such as the alcohols, show similarly characteristic patterns. In spite of the overall similarity of the patterns discussed, closely related species of plants can display rather different patterns of hydrocarbons and fatty acids: the patterns will still fit for odd or even dominance and also for general regions of major abundance. The differences may be sufficiently large for the patterns to be used as species indicators, but this chemotaxonomic approach must be used with caution. It is certainly too risky at present as a general approach to the interpretation of the origins of organic matter in sediments, since we know so little about the nature of the original biological material and the alteration processes taking place thereon.

The position with discrete fossils seems more hopeful. For example, Knoche and Ourisson [6, 7] have shown that the hydrocarbons which can be isolated from a modern species of *Equisitum* are very similar in their structures and pattern of abundance to those they were able to isolate from fossil specimens of *Equisitum*. This type of paleochemotaxonomic correlation may prove to be extremely useful.

Several groups of workers have turned their attention to the hydrocarbons and fatty acids of algae and bacteria [8–12]. Thus, the unicellular alga, *Nostoc muscorum* shows a very simple pattern of hydrocarbon constituents. The n-C_{17} hydrocarbon, which is the main constituent, is accompaneid by a small amount of branched C_{18} hydrocarbon. The hydrocarbon fraction does not contain higher or lower alkanes, at least in any significant quantity. Thus, if the C_{17} and C_{18} hydrocarbons contributed by this alga to a sediment persisted and were isolated at a later date, their presence could be interpreted as indicating contributions from *Nostoc*, rather than from higher plants. Of course, such inferences can only be very tentative for we do not know as yet how many different types of organisms display such hydrocarbon patterns. Incidentally, the branched C_{18} alkane, first encountered as a single peak on a 100' Apiezon-L capillary, turned out to be a mixture of two alkanes: the 7- and 8-monomethylheptadecanes. Almost certainly, these hydrocarbons are biosynthesized by methyl addition to the corresponding unsaturated straight chain acid [10, 11].

The distribution of the fatty acids of *Nostoc* are fairly typical of other algae. The C_{16} saturated acid is abundant, whereas the C_{18} homologue is not. However, the unsaturated C_{16} acid, which is also quite abundant, is matched by major quantities of unsaturated C_{18} acids, mono-, di-, and tri-unsaturated. The significance of such a distribution is that the saturated acid would be expected to survive interment very well, whereas the doubly-bonded compounds would be expected to undergo fairly rapid degradation under aerobic conditions and also polymerization by cross-linking. Alternatively, under reducing conditions, they might undergo reduction and so change the proportion of C_{16} and C_{18} acids very remarkably. Thus, under oxidizing conditions we might expect the n-C_{16} acid and not much else. On the other hand, under reducing conditions, we might expect a marked predominance of n-C_{18} over n-C_{16} saturated fatty acids. Parker and his colleagues [13] have shown that unsaturated fatty acids disappear quite rapidly from an algal mat and clearly, the biological marker concept may reveal whether conditions have been oxidizing, reducing, or both in succession.

From the above considerations of the hydrocarbons and fatty acids of higher plants and certain unicellular algae, we can see that the use of comparative biochemistry or chemotaxonomy, whereby the constituents of now-living species are studied, provides one approach to the study of the past environments. But we have little information on the passage of biological marker compounds through natural environments. Some progress has been made in following isoprenoid compounds in their passage through the marine foodweb. The complex inter-relationships between organisms in the sea might have been expected to befog any data relating to biological markers. However, recent researches indicate that this is not so. Some carbon compounds seem to pass along the food web relatively unchanged. Lipids present in one organism which is then consumed by another, may be deposited in the tissues of the latter organism. This process may continue through several steps, perhaps with some recycling through the initial stages. Blumer [14] at Woods Hole and Ackman [15] at Halifax in Nova Scotia and their collaborators, have shown that the carbon skeletons of isoprenoids may be preserved. The phytoplankton, which start the food chain, contain chlorophyll, wherein the C_{20} side chain of phytol is attached to the chlorin ring. Pristane and other C_{19} and C_{20} hydrocarbons are found in the copepods which feed upon the phytoplankton. Again, later sections of the food web contain fatty acids of an isoprenoid type which appear to be directly derived from the initial phytol of the phytoplankton. Thus, to some extent, these isoprenoid hydrocarbons and fatty acids illustrate the persistence of biological markers in a natural environment. A parallel situation is provided by industrial and urban pollution of environments [16].

We may expect that subsequent work will reveal series of compounds which will serve as indicators of terrestrial as against aquatic origin. Indeed, we can hope that it may be possible to classify an aquatic origin as freshwater, brackish, or marine. A partial answer for aquatic situations seems to be emerging from the work of Whitehead and his colleagues of British Petroleum at Sunbury, England [17]. The triterpenoids, which show a general preponderance in higher land plants, are not represented in marine or aquatic plants, though of course, further work may invalidate this generalisation. Hence, isoprenoids may provide biological markers characteristic of the environments in which sediments were laid down. The compounds would then be acting as "environmental markers". Of course, such markers based on other criteria, for example, those derived from inorganic chemistry, have been known for some time in other areas of geochemistry.

Methods for the Study of Geolipids

I shall deal only with the extractable geolipid fraction, especially the constituent hydrocarbons and fatty acids. Figure 5 indicates the procedures frequently used in obtaining crude geolipid extracts from a rock. The demineralization step is often omitted for, in most cases, it does not greatly increase the yield of geolipid. Incidentally, benzene and methanol are highly toxic and should be handled with care: the extraction and subsequent operations are best conducted in a fume hood. Toluene, which is much less toxic, can be used instead of benzene.

From there onwards, the geolipid extract can be examined in much the same way as a biolipid fraction. Figure 6 summarizes the procedures we have used in the isolation and purification of the fatty acids present in geolipid extracts. The column of potassium hydroxide-impregnated silica is convenient for the preliminary separation of the acids from the neutral fractions. The thinlayer plates of silver nitrate impregnated silica provide a further selection, based on the availability of unsaturation or of polar

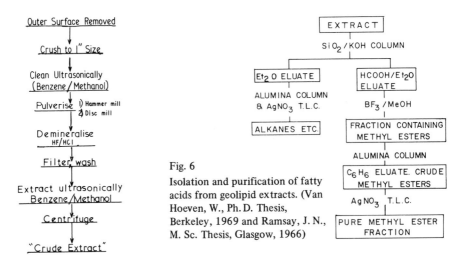

Fig. 5
Extraction of geolipids

Fig. 6
Isolation and purification of fatty
acids from geolipid extracts. (Van
Hoeven, W., Ph. D. Thesis,
Berkeley, 1969 and Ramsay, J. N.,
M. Sc. Thesis, Glasgow, 1966)

substituents in the compounds under study. Thus, unsaturated esters are held back on the plate relative to saturated analogues. The fastest-moving band when removed from the plate is generally found to be a fairly pure fraction comprised of saturated fatty acids, as their methyl esters. The esters of unsaturated fatty acids can be removed as a separate band, if they are present.

Chromatographic	Spectral	Physical
g. c.	i. r.	m. pt.
t. l. c.	n. m. r.	adduction
	u. v.	mol. sieve
	m. s.	x-ray
g. c.-m. s.	o. r. d.	

Fig. 7
Criteria for identification
of compounds

In Figure 7, I have indicated the criteria that are available for compound identification. Chromatographic methods provide identification by retention time, and in some cases, by color and other spot tests conducted on the relevant fractions. Both gas chromatography and thin layer chromatography operate at very low sample levels (i. e., in the microgram and submicrogram range).

The spectral methods generally require more material, with the exception of mass spectrometry. Infrared spectrometry provides very useful information about the presence or absence of functional groups, such as carbonyls, hydroxyls, etc. The spectra are also useful as "fingerprints" which sometimes enable identification of compounds by direct comparison with a reference library of spectra. We have found infrared useful also in examining the methyl substitution pattern of triterpanes isolated from geological materials. The quantities needed are generally of the order of a few hundred micrograms, though less can be managed. Nuclear magnetic resonance spectrometry is somewhat more demanding in regard to the quantity of sample needed, and for such study, it is generally not possible to obtain enough of a single geolipid component. It provides information on the distribution of hydrogens within the molecule and is extremely informative when it can be applied. Ultraviolet and visible spectroscopy are of particular value in dealing with compounds such as the porphyrins and aromatics, containing conjugated systems. It is of no value in dealing with hydrocarbons and fatty acids unless they contain light absorbing functions. Mass spectrometry requires an extremely small amount of substance (in the nanogram range) and is especially effective in indicating the gross structure of a compound, the position of substitution, etc. Stereoisomeric substances often give very similar, if not identical spectra. Fortunately, gas chromatography responds fairly well to some of the situations where mass spectrometry is in difficulty, so that a combination of the two, combined gas chromatography-mass spectrometry, is far more effective than either alone.

Melting points can be determined on a few micrograms of crystalline material sublimed onto a microscope slide. It is always difficult to obtain entirely pure crystals and this approach is, therefore, limited in its scope. However, should a good crystal be obtained, one may apply the elegant technique of X-ray crystallography. A "heavy atom" derivative is not essential and in a suitable case, the entire structure of the compound may be derived by mathematical analysis of the diffraction patterns, as has been demonstrated by Whitehead and his collaborators [18].

One of the most useful techniques for handling geolipids involves the formation of crystalline adducts with certain compounds, notably, urea and thiourea. These substances, when crystallized in the presence of the geolipids, can bring about fairly effective separations of straight-chain, branched, and cyclic compounds: urea forms adducts with straight chain compounds while thiourea includes acyclic branched compounds, but not straight chain or cyclic compounds. There are exceptions, however, and the separations effected are always incomplete. Molecular sieves are more precise in their operation and the 5 Angström sieve is now extensively used for the occlusion of normal alkanes thereby giving a clean separation between the normal alkanes on the one hand and the branched and cyclic alkanes on the other. We have recently studied a 7 Angström sieve which parallels the action of thiourea in occluding the branched alkanes and excluding the cyclic alkanes [19].

To summarize, it is our experience that the best method for the characterization of microquantities of geolipids is combined capillary gas chromatography-mass spectrometry [20, 21].The high efficiency of the capillary columns provides, first, a good separation between compounds, and second, high precision in specifying the retention time of a particular standard compound. Mass spectrometry, when

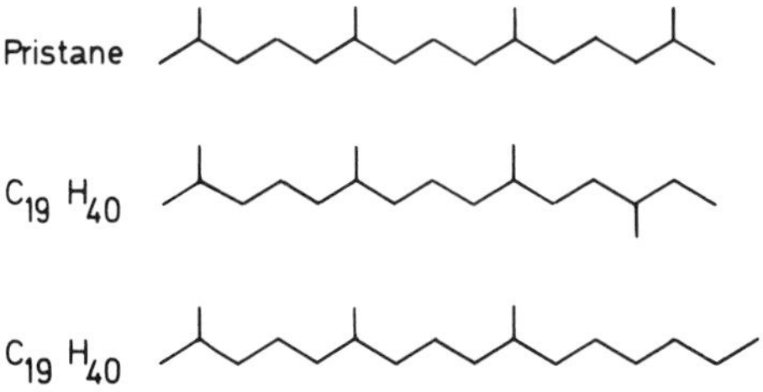

Pristane

$C_{19} H_{40}$

$C_{19} H_{40}$

Fig. 8
Structures of pristane and two isomeric C_{19} alkanes

conducted on a small segment of a gas chromatographic peak provides detailed information on the molecular structure. Figure 8 shows three isomeric hydrocarbons of formula $C_{19} H_{40}$ which are separable on a hundred foot Apiezon-L capillary. Of course, stereoisomers are not revealed here and would probably be inseparable under the conditions employed. The mass spectrum taken from each peak in turn, would provide the appropriate fragmentation pattern. The patterns may, on occasion, be similar, but here the combination of retention time and mass spectral fragmentation pattern is likely to be unique. Fortunately, low resolution mass spectrometers, which are equipped for fast scanning and are suitable for combining with gas chromatographs are now cheaper than they were in recent years, and are within the financial capabilities of some geochemical laboratories.

Complete characterization of geolipids should include the assignment of relative and absolute stereochemistry, where appropriate. One particular example which illustrates the problems and, also, the potential of this type of information is provided by phytol (Figure 9). As is well known, phytol is the alcohol esterifying the acid group of the chlorin nucleus in chlorophyll. Both methyl groups in phytol are on the same side of the carbon chain; this relative stereochemistry corresponds to 7R and 11R in absolute terms. Neither phytol nor dihydrophytol have been isolated from geological materials, but pristane [22] and phytanic acid [23] have. The pristane, which would result from decarboxylation of phytanic acid or by other routes from phytol, should be meso, but the behavioral differences for the different stereoisomers are expected to be slight and no gas chromatographic separation of the meso and d, l-forms has yet been achieved. Ackman, in collaboration with ourselves, Kates, and other workers, has shown that it is possible to distinguish more effectively between stereoisomers, by using an optically active alcohol, L-menthol, to bring about the formation of diastereoisomeric ester pairs. Thus, the series of acids indicated in Figure 10 has been studied using high resolution capillary gas chromatography of the L-menthyl esters [24]. With this approach, it should be possible to investigate the passage of isoprenoid compounds through the food web

PHYTOL (7R, 11R)

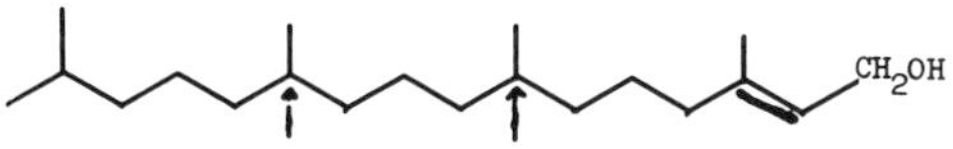

11R   7R   (Burrell et.al. 1959, 1966;
                         Crabbé et al. 1959.)

(Also in Chlorophyll, Vitamin K)

PRISTANE (Meso-6R, 10S)

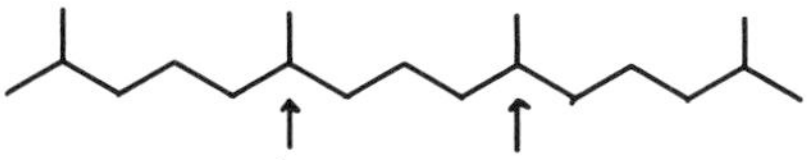

6R   10S   (Ibid.)

DIHYDROPHYTOL (3R, 7R, 11R)

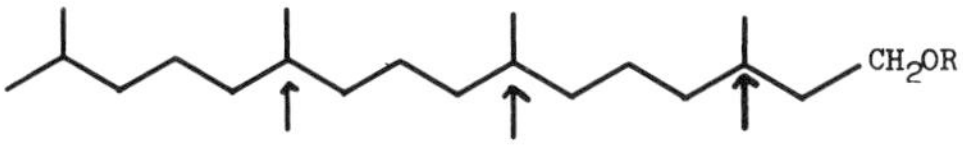

11R   7R   3R

(Kates et al. 1967)

(Also in α-Tocopherol)

PHYTANIC ACID

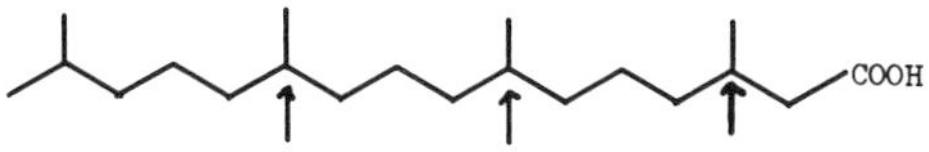

(a)   11R   7R   3S   - Animal (Lough, 1964)
(b)   11R   7R   3R   - Bacteria   (Kates et al. 1967)

Fig. 9. Absolute configuration of optical centers of phytol and related compounds (Note: two conventions are in use to define absolute configuration: in the molecules shown, R and S are equivalent to D and L, respectively). (For references cited, see Maclean, et al.[24])

of an environment, and provide the reference data needed for the interpretation of ancient sediments, which represent the end products of ancient environments. The isoprenoid acids isolated from an Eocene shale (Green River, see below) have been examined in this way.

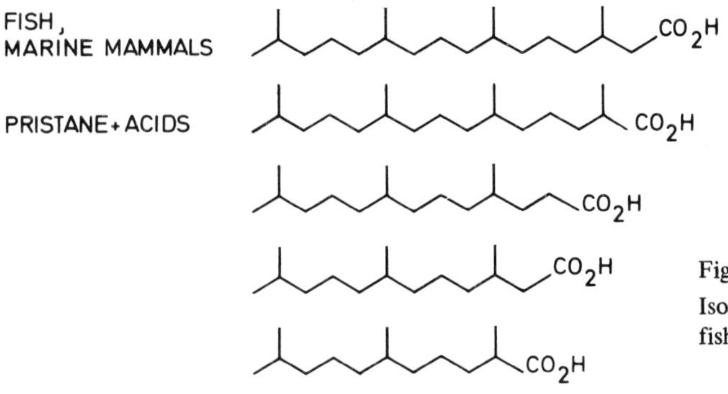

FISH,
MARINE MAMMALS

PRISTANE+ACIDS

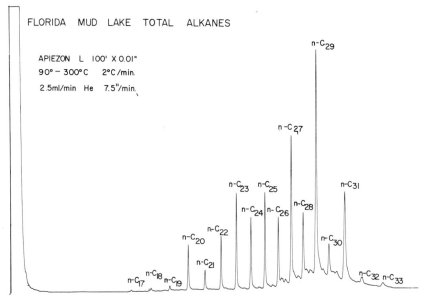

Fig. 10
Isoprenoid acids in
fish, marine mammals, etc.

An alternative approach to the separation of optically active compounds involves the use of optically active stationary phases, as demonstrated by Gil–Av and his collaborators [25].

Geolipids of Recent and Ancient Sediments

In the time available, I can provide only a few examples of the kind of data emerging from present researches.

In the first example (Figure 11), we see a gas chromatographic trace for the total alkanes extracted from one section of a core removed from Mud Lake in Florida

Fig. 11. Gas chromatograms (capillary column) of total alkanes from a portion (MW-2) of a core taken from Mud Lake, Florida (Recent). (Han, et al.[10])

[10]. This lake is entirely surrounded by semi-tropical vegetation. The undisturbed sediment is many feet deep and mainly consists of a very dark, finely-divided, somewhat gelatinous material. The study so far carried out reveals that different sections cut from the core do differ in their chemical composition. However, for the extract shown, we see that the dominant hydrocarbons are in the C_{30} region and are odd-numbered, in accordance with our findings for plant waxes. It is possible, therefore, that plant waxes made a prominent contribution at the time that particular section was laid down — a few thousand years ago. In addition, there are fair quantities of even-numbered alkanes, especially in the region just above C_{20}. This prevalence may be due in part to contributions from organisms which are known to provide even-numbered alkanes in addition to odd-numbered (for example, certain bacteria) and in part to geochemical reactions occurring in the sediment [26, 27]. As an example of the latter, I refer to the direct reduction of even-numbered acids and alcohols to the corresponding even-numbered hydrocarbons. Laboratory data are available, but the process has yet to be demonstrated for a natural sediment *in situ*. The n-C_{17} alkane is not abundant in this particular section which is, at first sight, rather puzzling because it has been said that this sediment consists largely of algal debris. However, other layers do show a more prominent n-C_{17} contribution and also an abundance of the isoprenoid hydrocarbons. Further work might take the form of a morphological examination of the debris in the sediment coupled with a chemical study of the same material.

For the second example, I have chosen the well-studied Green River shale. This shale, which is of Eocene age, is held to have been laid down in shallow inland lakes. It is not known what the actual contributions of the land plants and aquatic plants have been. The gas chromatograms of the alkane fractions from this shale are shown in Figure 12. The n-alkanes show the marked dominance of the odd carbon numbers in the C_{30} region, corresponding to the hydrocarbons of higher plants, while the n-C_{17} alkane, which is so prominent, may correspond to the hydrocarbon production of algae. Of course, these correlations are only tentative, and their main purpose should to be to serve as a stimulus for further research — for example, relating to other possible explanations for the presence of these compounds. The branched and cyclic alkanes, which are largely isoprenoid, show an elegant parallel with the known pattern of abundance of isoprenoids in plants and animals; thus, abundant C_{15}, C_{20}, C_{30} and C_{40}. The peak in the branched cyclic fraction around 40 minutes elution time corresponds to perhydrocarotene (C_{40}) [28]. The peaks in the C_{30} region are now being studied by combined, high resolution capillary gas chromatography-mass spectrometry [21]. We hope to clinch the identification of each of the steranes and triterpanes and then attempt a direct correlation with the steroids and triterpenoids present in various genera of contemporary plants and animals. Figure 13 shows a capillary gas chromatogram run with a lower boiling fraction taken from the Green River shale total alkanes [29]. The

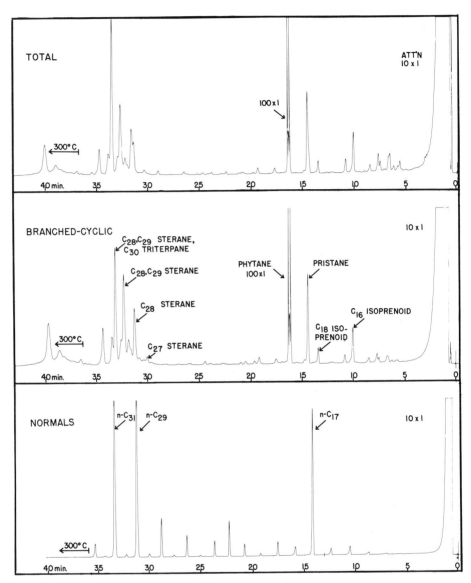

GREEN RIVER SHALE (COLORADO), ~60 X 10⁶ YRS. ALKANE FRACTIONS

Fig. 12. Gas chromatograms of alkane fractions from the Green River shale (Eocene).
[Johns, R. B., T. Belsky, E. D. McCarthy, A. L. Burlingame, P. Haug, H. K. Schnoes,
W. Richter and M. Calvin: Geochim. Cosmochim. Acta, **30**, 1191 (1966)]

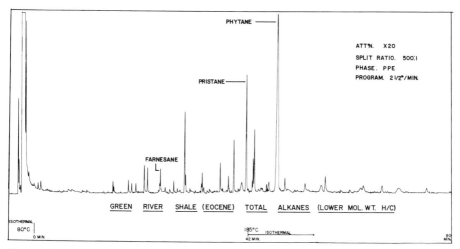

Fig. 13. Gas chromatogram (capillary column) for lower molecular weight range of alkanes from Green River Shale (Eocene). (McCarthy, p. 18 [29])

increased discrimination afforded by capillary columns is evident. One point of special interest concerns the pristane and phytane peaks. These are quite sharp and it is evident that the C_{19} and C_{20} alkanes to which they correspond are not mixtures of several positional isomers for these would have been resolved into separate peaks. Of course, the relative and absolute stereochemistries remain to be settled, but even the present results give strong support to the organic geochemist in his claim that these hydrocarbons are adequate biological markers.

I have chosen the Soudan shale (Precambrian, $> 2 \times 10^9$ years) as the final example of an extract from an ancient sediment. Figure 14 illustrates gas chromatograms obtained (capillary column) for the total alkane fraction [29]. The startling thing is the relative simplicity of this pattern, although, of course, greater detail is revealed when the chromatogram is run more slowly and under conditions of higher resolution. The normal alkanes are centered around C_{18} and are of a fairly narrow spread. The isoprenoids, pristane and phytane, are very prominent. The overall pattern is rather different from that of the Green River shale, and there is the further complication that the rock itself may have been heated by igneous contact at some time or other. In fact, this illustrates the difficulty with Precambrian samples where the history of the rock is so often little understood. These very old sediments yield only small quantities of extract, increasing thereby the ever-present possibility of contamination, either during past geologic eras, during Recent times, or even during the processes of extraction and separation of the geolipids. However, the importance of the information to be derived, especially in relation to the appearance and early development of life on this planet, will continue to serve as an incentive for further work.

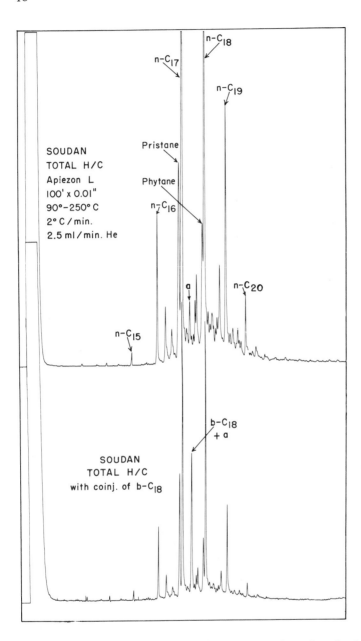

Fig. 14. Gas chromatogram (capillary column) of total alkanes from Soudan shale
(Precambrian, $> 2 \times 10^9$ years) [Han, J., unpublished data from Space Sciences Laboratory,
University of California, Berkeley; also Calvin, M., "Chemical Evolution", Oxford University
Press (1969)]

Geolipids — Abiogenic or Biogenic?

For the final part of this lecture, I should like to discuss the problem we face in trying to distinguish between abiogenic and biogenic lipids. By abiogenic compounds, I mean those which have been formed by completely non-biological processes. The situation is complicated by the alteration processes, which undoubtedly occur in sediments and which become especially significant in the neighborhood of thermal activity. To take an extreme case, let us consider a sediment in contact with an igneous intrusion. At the point of contact, the organic matter will be completely carbonized. At some distance from the intrusion, where the temperature range experienced has been much less, the degree of alteration will be correspondingly less and some of the biolipids may be unchanged or altered to only a small extent. This material we would class as altered or degraded biological material. So far, no case of the occurence of entirely abiogenic material has been authenticated, although numerous instances of organic matter occurring in geological situations of dubious biological origin have been examined. If we assume that abiogenic production of geolipids *is* possible, and in fact, may still be occurring somewhere in the earth's crust, then we are faced with the problem of distinguishing abiogenic material, biogenic material, and altered abiogenic and biogenic materials. This is not an easy task, but it must be resolved, for the results should have wide significance. For example, the answer is basic to successful unmanned planetary exploration, such as the proposed analysis of organic constituents of the Martian soil.

This lecture has been concerned principally with hydrocarbons and fatty acids, especially the former. Several investigators have examined the abiogenic production of hydrocarbons in the laboratory, and have shown that one cannot reproduce the patterns found in the extracts from sediments such as the Green River shale. Thus, Van Hoeven at Berkeley has demonstrated that the products of irradiation of frozen methane are extremely complex [30]. The gas chromatogram (Figure 15) apart from initial peaking at low molecular weights, displays an enormous "hump" extending to retention times corresponding to compounds of very high molecular weight. This vast mixture of hydrocarbons is the result of the radical processes occasioned by the impact of the high energy electron beam. The hydrocarbons are completely "abiogenic" for they have been formed in the laboratory without any part being played by the chemist other than to arrange the experiment: a carbon source is supplied and an energy source used to alter it. It is easy to distinguish such a mixture from a biologically-produced mixture of alkanes.

Recently, Ponnamperuma and his colleagues at Ames, California, have conducted experiments designed to bear on the possibility of hydrocarbon formation on the primitive earth [31]. Such experiments may also help to indicate possible present-day sites for terrestrial abiogenic synthesis. Isoprene can be polymerized on a clay

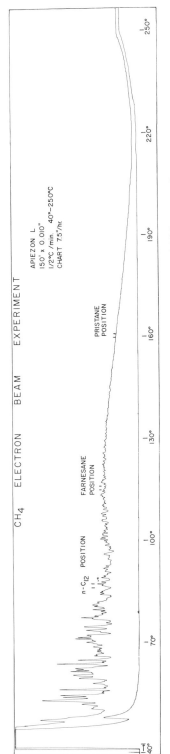

Fig. 15. Gas chromatogram (capillary column) of product from irradiation of frozen methane with high energy electrons [Van Hoeven, W., Ph. D. Thesis Berkeley (1969), unpublished]

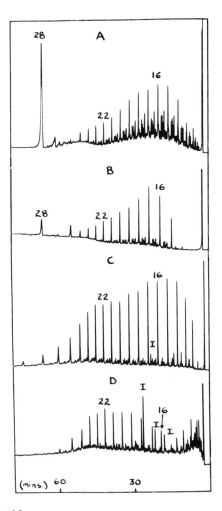

Fig. 16

Gas chromatograms of the alkane fractions from heat treatment of n-octacosane and from certain crude oils. A and B: fractions formed by the heat treatment (375 °C for 60 h) of n-octacosane in the presence of: A, bentonite, and B, bentonite and water. Alkane fractions from C, Nonesuch seep oil, and D, Boscan crude oil. Conditions 200 foot x 0.01 inch stainless steel capillary column coated with 7-PPE and "Gas Quat L" (from Amour Industrial Chemical Co., Illinois), temperature programmed from 100 °C to 250 °C at 3°/min, helium flow rate 3 ml/min. I indicates prominent peaks corresponding to isoprenoid hydrocarbons. (W. Henderson, et al. [33]).

catalyst, therby furnishing a series of isoprenoids of chain-length C_{10}, C_{15}, C_{20}, C_{25} etc. Of course, each carbon number is characterized by a series of peaks corresponding to a number of positional (structural) and stereochemical isomers. Further, each carbon number is part of a pattern of abundance which is distributed fairly smoothly from low to high carbon numbers. Hence, the result does not parallel at all the distribution patterns for the isoprenoid alkanes isolated from the Green River shale. The specificity shown by the geolipids lies in the paucity of the positional isomers present and in the relative abundances of the different carbon numbers, thereby paralleling the biological distribution of isoprenoids. Nothing like this is seen in the abiogenic mixture. McCarthy and Calvin [32] have discussed the polymerization of isoprene in theoretical terms and have indicated the large numbers of positional isomers which could arise in an abiogenic process. The biologically produced isoprenoids have very specific carbon-carbon linking enforced on them by the biosynthetic processes, i. e., the C_5 units are linked specifically head to tail and tail to tail, depending on the particular carbon number involved. Further work should demonstrate that geolipids also possess the appropriate relative and absolute stereochemistry, as indicated earlier in this talk. Hence, it would appear at this stage that we can distinguish purely biogenic and abiogenic patterns of alkanes, particularly in the isoprenoid series. But this still leaves open the question of the recognition of thermally or otherwise altered materials.

We are continuing our laboratory experiments involving the deliberate thermal alteration of geolipids alone and present in the sediments [33]. In recent experiments, we have heated a single n-alkane, n-C_{28}, alone and in the presence of bentonite and water. Figure 16 illustrates the gas chromatograms for the alkane fractions in the products. Only the saturated alkanes are shown, although aromatic and olefinic hydrocarbons and polymeric products are formed in addition. The significant result, in our opinion, is that a single n-alkane degrades thermally to give a smooth series of n-alkanes of lower carbon number, together with a certain proportion of branched and cyclic alkanes. The parallelism between these chromatograms and those of the crude oils also shown in Figure 16 is quite instructive. Petroleum chemists have known for a long time that some such process occurs in petroleum formation and that maturation is the likely explanation for the smooth pattern of n-alkanes shown by many crude oils [3, 27, 34, 35]. The inference is that biological patterns, represented *inter alia* by odd over even predominances of n-alkanes, are destroyed by thermal processes over long periods of time. With our experiments, the temperatures have been high, in the region of 375 °C down to 200 °C, but lower temperatures would almost certainly show the same trends. Hence, deeply-buried sediments exposed to temperatures of, say, around 100 °C to 150 °C for very long periods of time would almost certainly show a slow loss of the odd over even predominance for the n-alkanes.

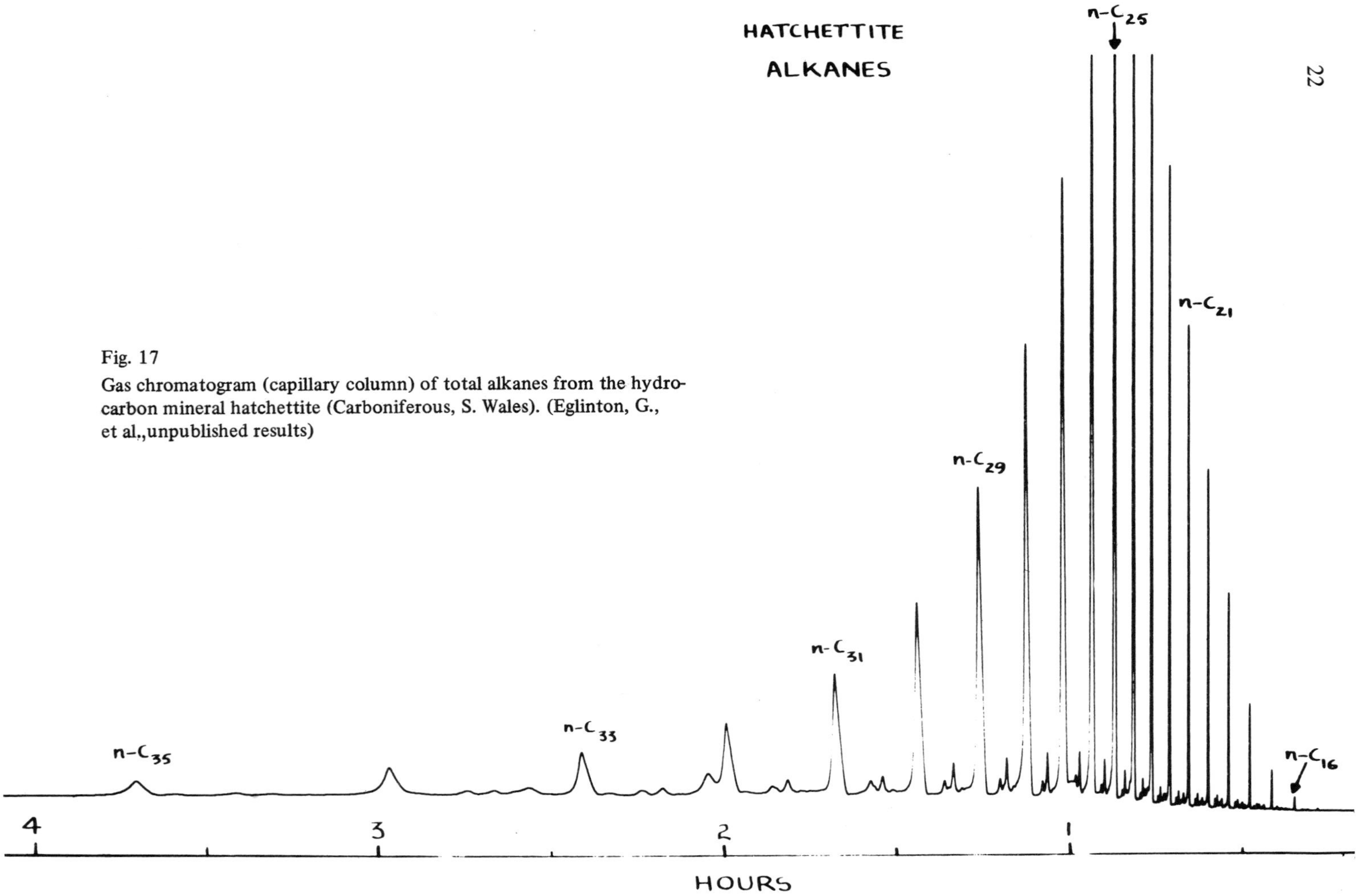

Fig. 17

Gas chromatogram (capillary column) of total alkanes from the hydro-carbon mineral hatchettite (Carboniferous, S. Wales). (Eglinton, G., et al.,unpublished results)

We are attempting a geological parallel for the laboratory experiments by studying the distribution of hydrocarbon minerals in the South Wales coal field. Mr. Naylor Firth has collected a number of samples of the hydrocarbon mineral hatchettite, which occurs in siltstone nodules within the coal seams and associated strata. These nodules often contain various inorganic minerals, such as nickel sulfide, in addition to the small, semi-crystalline masses of hydrocarbon. Figure 17 shows the gas chromatogram for one sample of hatchettite and the smooth envelope of n-alkanes is very marked.We would interpret this gas chromatogram as representing the products of thermal alteration of biogenic material originally present in the coal seams when they were laid down in Carboniferous times. At present, we know of no way in which we can demonstrate a biological origin for the hatchettite, but careful examination may still reveal some relatively unaltered hydrocarbons, acceptable as biological markers.

In summary, we now know more about the fate of biolipids in sediments than we did a few years ago and the biological marker concept still appears to be useful. There are difficulties in distinguishing between biological, altered biological, and possibly abiological materials. Further research will extend our knowledge of the different forms of occurrence of organic compounds in the earth's crust. We are approaching gradually a more complete understanding of the path of carbon compounds in Nature and their fate as they pass from the biosphere into the geosphere and back again.

Acknowledgements: Some of the information given in this talk has been kindly provided by colleagues at the University of Bristol and by Professor Melvin Calvin and his colleagues at the University of California, Berkeley. I am grateful to them all, and to the sponsors of our work at Bristol, namely, the Natural Environment Research Council, the Science Research Council, Shell International, the National Aeronautics and Space Administration (NsG 101–61, to the University of California, Berkeley) and the Petroleum Research Fund.

References

[1] Eglinton, G. and Calvin, M.: Scientific American. **216**, 32 (1967).

[2] Davis, J. B.: "Petroleum Microbiology". Elsevier Publishing Company, Amsterdam (1967).

[3] Smith, H. M., Dunning, H. N., Rall, H. T. and Ball, J. S.: American Petroleum Institute Meeting, New York, May (1959).

[4] (a) Eglinton, G. and Hamilton, R. J.: Science, **156**, 1322 (1967).

[4] (b) Kolattukudy, P. E.: Science, **159**, 498 (1968).

[5] Stransky, K., Streibl, M. and Herout, V.: Coll. Czech. Chem. Commun., **32**, 3213 (1967).

[6] Knoche, H., Ourisson, G.: Angew. Chem. Internat. Edit., **6**, 1085 (1967).

[7] Knoche, H., Albrecht, P. and Ourisson, G.: Angew. Chem. Internat. Edit. 7, 631 (1968).

[8] Oro, J., Tornabene, G., Nooner, D. W. and Gelpi, E.: J. Bacteriol., **93**, 1811 (1967).

[9] Gelpi, E., Oro, J., Schneider, H. J. and Bennett, E. O.: Science, **161**, 700 (1968).

[10] Han, J., McCarthy, D., Van Hoeven, W., Calvin, M. and Bradley, W. H.: Proceedings of the National Academy of Sciences, **59**, 29 (1968).

[11] Han, J., McCarthy, E. D. and Calvin, M.: J. Chem. Soc. In press.

[12] Maxwell, J. R., Douglas, A. G., Eglinton, G. and McCormick, A.: Phytochemistry, **7**, 2157 (1968).

[13] Parker, P. L., Van Baalen, C. and Maurer, L.: Science, **155**, 707 (1967).

[14] Blumer, M., Mullin, M. M. and Thomas, D. W.: Helgoländer Wiss. Meeresunters. Bd. **10**, 187 (1964).

[15] Ackman, R. G. and Hansen, R. P.: Lipids, **2**, 357 (1967).

[16] Robinson, J., Richardson, A., Crabtree, A. N., Coulson, J. C. and Potts, G. R.: Nature, **214**, 1307 (1967).

[17] Hills, I. R. and Whitehead, E. V.: Nature, **209**, 977 (1966).

[18] Hills, I. R., Smith, G. W. and Whitehead, E. V.: Nature, **219**, 243 (1968).

[19] Curran, R., Eglinton, G., Maclean, I., Douglas, A. G. and Dungworth, G.: Tet. Letters, 1669 (1968).

[20] Eglinton, G.: Proc. Soc. Analyt. Chem., **4**, 111 (1967).

[21] Henderson, W., Wollrab, V. and Eglinton, G.: Chem. Comm., **13**, 710 (1968).

[22] Blumer, M. and Snyder, W. D.: Science, **150**, 1588 (1965).

[23] Eglinton, G., Douglas, A. G., Maxwell, J. R., Ramsay, J. H. and Stallberg-Stenhagen, S.: Science. **153**, 1133 (1966).

[24] Maclean, I., Eglinton, G., Douraghi-Zadeh, K. and Ackman, R. G.: Nature, **218**, 1019 (1968).

[25] Feibush, B. and Gil–Av, E.: Advances in Gas Chromatography, ed. A. Zlatkis, **100** (1967).

[26] Blumer, M.: Science, **149**, 722 (1965).

[27] Brooks, J. D. and Smith, J. W.: Geochim. Cosmochim. Acta, **31**, 2389 (1967).

[28] Murphy, Sister Mary T. J., McCormick, A. and Eglinton, G.: Science, **157**, 1040 (1967).

[29] McCarthy, E. D., Thesis, Ph. D.: University of California, Berkeley, 1967.

[30] Van Hoeven, W., Thesis, Ph. D.: Universitiy of California, Berkeley, 1969.

[31] Munday, C., Pering, K. and Ponnamperuma, C.: Science. In press.

[32] McCarthy, E. D. and Calvin, M.: Nature, **216**, 642 (1967).

[33] Henderson, W., Eglinton, G., Simmonds, P. and Lovelock, J. E.: Nature, **219**, 1012 (1968).

[34] Welte, D. H.: Bull. Amer. Assoc. Petrol. Geol., **49**, 2246 (1965).

[35] Phillippi, G. T.: Geochim. Cosmochim. Acta, **29**, 1021 (1965).

Essentials of the Petroleum Formation Process are Organic Source Material and a Subsurface Temperature Controlled Chemical Reaction Mechanism

George Theodor Philippi

Shell Development Co.
Houston, Texas, USA

In the past various theories have been proposed to explain the origin of petroleum. The inorganic theory has been discarded, as an increasing number of observations point towards an exclusive origin of petroleum from the organic matter of sediments. Additional evidence for this theory is presented in this paper. Comparison of oil hydrocarbons with the hydrocarbons extracted from a sequence of Upper Pliocene to Upper Miocene shales indicated that the Los Angeles basin oils originated in organic-rich Upper Miocene (D) and (E) shales, and not in younger shales.

Three mechanisms have been proposed for the formation of petroleum from sediment organic matter: (1) biological, (2) by radioactive bombardment, and (3) by low temperature chemical reactions. Definite proof for mechanism (3) follows from the author's research. In the Los Angeles and Ventura basins, California, hydrocarbon content and hydrocarbon/noncarbonate carbon ratio increase slowly with depth and age in upper and lower Pliocene shales and more rapidly in the deeper and warmer upper Miocene shales. During the oil generation process, and simultaneous with the increase of the hydrocarbon/noncarbonate carbon ratio, the composition of the shale normal paraffins and naphthenes boiling above 325 $^\circ$C changes gradually and significantly. Eventually these components become very similar to those of the waxy oils of the basin.

In the Los Angeles as well as in the Ventura basin the bulk of petroleum is generated at depths where the subsurface temperature is above 115 $^\circ$C and where, therefore, the shales are sterile to bacteria. The conclusion that petroleum is formed from sediment organic matter essentially by thermal, nonbiological, processes is inescapable. Since petroleum generation is a chemical process, it is strongly temperature dependent. This explains the strong increase of the hydrocarbon/noncarbonate carbon ratio at greater depths, where the temperature is higher. It also explains why in the Ventura basin a greater depth is required for significant oil generation and for similarity of shale and oil hydrocarbons than in the Los Angeles basin. This is caused by the lesser temperature gradient in the Ventura basin. The importance of the temperature history of potential oil source rocks is stressed. Appreciable amounts of oil are formed only if the temperature of the source sediments has been sufficiently high over a sufficiently long period of time. Also the chemical nature of the source material must be favourable and its amount adequate. Good evidence is now available that lipids are a major source material of petroleum.

Introduction

Of the two major concepts of petroleum origin, organic versus inorganic origin, the position of the organic theory is very strong and the position of the inorganic theory is very weak. Geologists have pointed out for many years that the occurrence of petroleum is systematically related to sequences of sedimentary rocks and not systematically related to igneous rocks. We will see later in this presentation that presently there are conclusive chemical indications for the origin of petroleum from sedimentary organic matter. For this reason the inorganic theory of petroleum origin will not be further discussed in this paper because it is considered out of date.

Since the discovery of petroleum essentially three mechanisms have been proposed for the formation of petroleum from sediment organic matter:

(1)   biological,
(2)   by radioactive bombardment, and
(3)   by chemical reactions occurring at relatively low temperatures.

During the 1940–1952 period American Petroleum Institute Project 43, entitled "Transformation of Organic Materials into Petroleum" was engaged in a thorough study of possibilities (1) and (2). Project 43 a "The Role of Microorganisms in Petroleum Formation" was headed by Claude F. Zobell of Scripps Institution of Oceanography, La Jolla, California. Project 43 c, "Studies of the Effect of Radioactivity in the Transformation of Marine Organic Material into Petroleum Hydrocarbons," was headed by W.C. Whitehead of Massachusetts Institute of Technology, Cambridge, Massachusetts. Conclusions from the Final Report of API Research Project 43 (1952–1953) may be summarized as follows:

1. Methane is the only hydrocarbon formed by bacteria as a metabolic product,
2. Some bacteria form a small amount of hydrocarbons as part of their cell structure,
3. Many bacteria will attack and destroy hydrocarbons, but appreciably only in an oxidizing environment. *The most significant conclusion suggested by the results of API Project 43a is that bacteria alone cannot transform naturally occurring materials into petroleum.*
4. Research of Project 43 c confirmed Lind's results (1926, 1928) that radioactive bombardment of methane would yield hydrogen and some saturated gaseous hydrocarbons heavier than methane. No saturated liquid hydrocarbons resulted from the bombardment of methane or other gaseous paraffins. The liquids which were formed were unsaturated hydrocarbons such as have not been identified in crude oil. A small amount of saturated liquid hydrocarbons resulted when certain organic acids were bombarded by α-particles. The principal products were hydrogen, carbon monoxide, carbon dioxide and water.

5. It was possible to compute the energy available in the form of α-particles and to estimate the yield of hydrocarbons in an average shale. These estimated yields are much too small to account for the petroleum known in nature. Also, the most abundant product of radioactive bombardment is elemental hydrogen, which is not found in natural gas. *Thus, the results of API Research Project 43c strongly suggest that radioactive bombardment of organic materials of sediments does not contribute significantly to the formation of petroleum*

From the results of API Project 43 it appears that petroleum origin from sediment organic matter is neither the result of microbial activity nor of radioactive bombardment. Hence, the third of the three suggested mechanisms of petroleum formation should be considered more seriously, namely *the generation of petroleum by chemical reactions occurring at relatively low temperatures.*

Based on laboratory experiments Engler (1888–1912) was the first to suggest that petroleum originates from thermal decomposition of organic matter. He demonstrated that optically active oily products, somewhat resembling petroleum, are formed from fats and waxes at elevated temperatures of about 400 °C. Engler assumed that time and high pressure offset the fact that the temperature in oil source rocks is much lower than that used in the experiments. An attempt was made to explain the difference in chemical composition of the oily laboratory products and natural petroleum but this attempt is unsatisfactory from the present point of view.

In Engler's days techniques for petroleum analysis were primitive by modern standards. It is not surprising therefore that cracking experiments of organic matter have been repeated using more modern techniques. A few recent experiments may be briefly mentioned. Jurg and Eisma (1964) studied the hydrocarbons formed by heating behenic acid (normal $C_{21}H_{43}COOH$) to 200 °C in the presence of bentonite, with and without water. There was a strong predominance of the C_{21} n-paraffin, which can be attributed to decarboxylation of the fatty acid. Interestingly, a small amount of n-paraffins with 24–36 carbon atoms was formed also. If petroleum does originate from heating of organic matter, this suggests that the n-paraffins present in crude oil need not necessarily be derived from fatty acids with longer chain lengths. Without the bentonite clay, behenic acid did not yield detectable amounts of hydrocarbons at 200 °C. Hoering and Abelson (1962–1963) did heating experiments with Green River oil shale at temperatures ranging from 185 °C–400 °C. Among other things it was found that the relative proportions of hydrocarbons produced by heating the shale are influenced by the temperature at which the process occurs. Such laboratory cracking experiments, starting with those of Engler, are of great interest. However, suggestive as such experiments may be, they do not *prove* that natural petroleum is formed by heating of sediment organic matter. Proof that petroleum originates as a result of subsurface temperature controlled chemical reactions is based on the comparison of analyses of sediment hydrocarbons and petroleum hydrocarbons. This work was published three years ago (Philippi, 1965). Because of their relevance to the subject of petroleum origin, some of the essential results of this study will be presented here.

Difference in Hydrocarbon content of Ancient and Recent Sediments

From a study of Recent sediments for API Project 4, entitled "Origin and Environment of Source Sediments," Trask and Wu (1930) concluded that "liquid petroleum probably does not occur in sediments at the time of their deposition, and that if it is present, it is in very small amounts, certainly less than 3 parts per 100,000." Although no accurate hydrocarbon analyses of sediments were feasible in 1930, the inference of Trask and Wu, in a general way, was correct and has since been confirmed. Smith (1954) was the first to recognize and measure quantitatively the occurrence of very small quantities of hydrocarbons in Recent sediments. For three Orinoco Delta Recent sediments, Smith found hydrocarbon values of 25–82 parts per million by weight, based on dry sediment. For four deep-water marine sediments off the coast of West Africa, hydrocarbon values of 28–36 parts per million were found. Similar low hydrocarbon contents of Recent sediments have been observed by Blumer (1958), see the top of Table I.

At the bottom of Table I examples are presented of several ancient sediments with a moderately high to high indigenous hydrocarbon content. Comparison of the data of Table I shows that the indigenous hydrocarbon content of several ancient sediments is much higher than that of Recent sediments. Even more significant is the fact that for many ancient sediments the values of the hydrocarbon/noncarbonate carbon ratio are much higher. The large difference in hydrocarbon/noncarbonate carbon ratio of certain ancient sediments and of Recent sediments strongly suggests that the generation of petroleum is essentially a subsurface process. The depth at which this process takes place and its mechanism and duration will be discussed in the following section.

The Composition of the High-Boiling Normal Paraffins from Recent Sediments

Smith (1954) has shown that the hydrocarbons from Recent sediments contain the three major types – aromatics, naphthenes and paraffins – as do crude oils. Although gross composition of Recent sediment hydrocarbons resembles that of crude oils, a closer study of their detailed composition reveals very significant differences. Stevens, Bray and Evans (1956) and Bray and Evans (1961) were the first to point out the extreme difference in composition of the normal paraffins of the $C_{22}-C_{34}$ carbon-number range from Recent sediments on the one hand and of those from

Table I: Noncarbonate Carbon Content, Content of Indigenous Hydrocarbons Boiling Above 325 $^{\circ}$C, and Hydrocarbon/Noncarbonate Carbon Ratio of Some Recent and Ancient Sediments

| Environment (Location) | Recent Sediments | | |
	Average Non-carbonate Carbon %	Average Hydro-carbons ppm	Hydrocarbons / Noncarbonate Carbon
Shallow Marine (Gulf of Mexico Mud Flat, Lagoon, Carbonate Mud, Delta, & Shelf)	0.8	35	1:230
Deep Marine Basins	2.4	88	1:270

| Age-Formation (Location) | Source Rocks | | |
	Average Non-carbonate Carbon %	Average Hydro-carbons ppm	Hydrocarbons / Noncarbonate Carbon
U. Miocene – Div. D & E (Ventura & Los Angeles Basins, Calif.)	3.28	1640	1:20
Miocene – Telissa (Sungei Taham Field, S. Sumatra)	0.89	896	1:9.9
Cretaceous – 2nd White Specks (Alberta, Canada)	2.02	1572	1:13
Cretaceous – Graneros (Northeast Colorado)	3.08	1239	1:25
Cretaceous – La Luna Equivalent (Casabe Field, Columbia, S.A.)	1.54	1146	1:13
Permian – Leonard Facies A	2.14	3235	1:6.6
Facies B (Delaware Basin, Texas)	1.66	875	1:19
Mississippian – Lodgepole Eastern Montana)	0.79	267	1:30
Ordovician – Winnipeg (Eastern Montana)	0.53	394	1:13

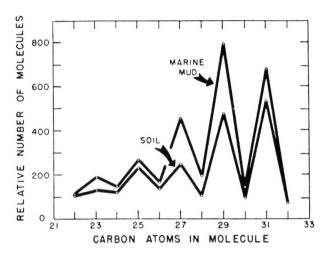

Fig. 1. Carbon number distribution curves of the normal paraffins from a Recent marine mud and from a soil sample. (after Stevens, Bray and Evans, 1956)

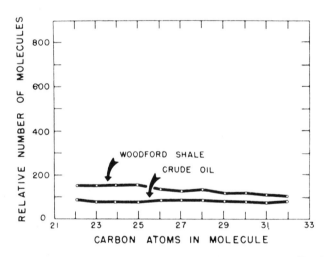

Fig. 2. Carbon number distribution curves of the normal paraffins from a crude oil and from an Ancient shale (after Stevens, Bray and Evans, 1956)

crude oils and ancient sediments on the other hand. As shown in Figure 1, in Recent sediments normal paraffin molecules with an odd number of carbon atoms strongly predominate over those with even numbers. By contrast, the normal paraffins from crude oils and several ancient sediments have approximately equal concentrations of odd- and even-carbon-number molecules, as is demonstrated in

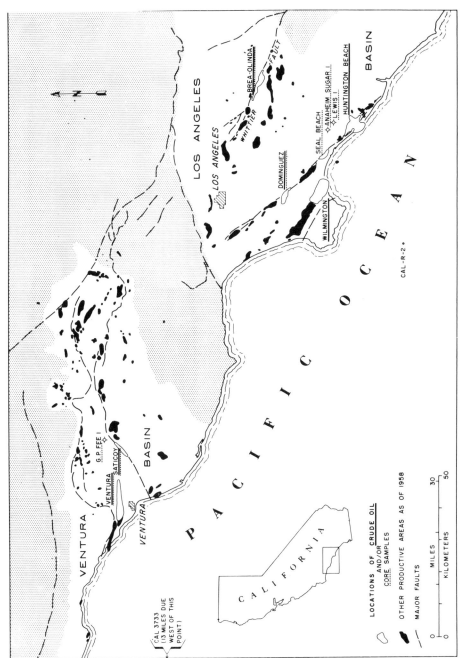

Fig. 3. Map of the oil fields of the Los Angeles and Ventura basins, California

Figure 2. The explanation of the strong odd-carbon-number predominance of the normal paraffins from Recent sediments is that the normal paraffins synthesized by many living organisms contain practically only normal paraffin molecules with odd carbon numbers. The fact that the normal paraffins from many ancient sediments and from crude oils are so very different from Recent sediment paraffins and exhibit smooth carbon-number distribution curves is due primarily to the oil generation process, as will be explained in a later section.

Subsurface Generation of Petroleum in the Los Angeles and Ventura Basins of California

Figure 3 is a map of the oil fields of the Los Angeles and Ventura basins of California. On this general map the names have been indicated of the fields and wildcat wells which are discussed in the text of this paper. Figure 4 shows the stratigraphic subdivisions used in Los Angeles and Ventura basin geology.

All subsurface samples discussed in this paper are conventional core samples which have been scraped and cleaned thoroughly before analysis. Only those samples are reported for which the indigenous nature of the hydrocarbons has been determined (Philippi, 1956).

AGE*				VENTURA BASIN		LOS ANGELES BASIN
	QUAT.	PLEIST.	UPPER	"TERRACE DEPOSITS"		PALOS VERDES
-1			LOWER	SAN PEDRO / SAUGUS		SAN PEDRO
		PLIOCENE	UPPER	SANTA BARBARA / PICO		PICO
-11	TERTIARY		LOWER	REPETTO		REPETTO
		MIOCENE	UPPER	SANTA MARGARITA / MODELO / MONTEREY		PUENTE
			MIDDLE	TOPANGA / TEMBLOR		MONTEREY / TOPANGA
			LOWER	RINCON / VAQUEROS		VAQUEROS
-25			OLIGOCENE	SESPE / COLDWATER / COZY DELL / MATILIJA		SESPE
-40 -60			EOCENE	LLAJAS / JUNCAL / SANTA SUSANA		SANTIAGO
-70			PALEOCENE	MARTINEZ		SILVERADO
			CRETACEOUS	CHICO		WILLIAMS / LADD / TRABUCO
-135			JURASSIC OR OLDER	"BASEMENT COMPLEX"		

* TIME IN MILLIONS OF YEARS SINCE BEGINNING OF PERIOD (ACCORDING TO HOLMES, 1960)

Fig. 4. Stratigraphic subdivisions and generalized correlation of formation names in the Los Angeles and Ventura basins, California

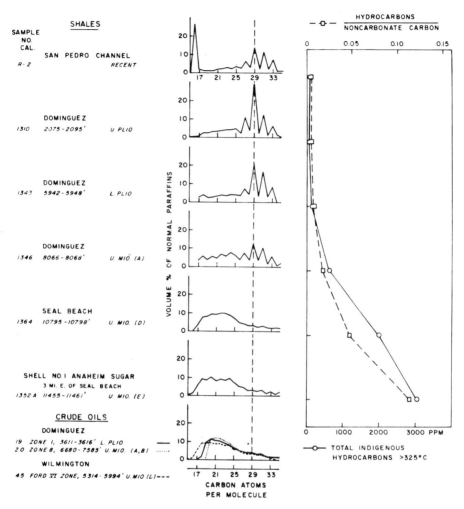

Fig. 5. Origin and development of petroleum n-paraffins and heavy hydrocarbons as a function of depth of burial and time in the Los Angeles basin, California

The graph of Figure 5 shows the changes with increasing depth and age of indigenous hydrocarbons boiling above 325 °C of (1) normal paraffin composition, (2) total hydrocarbon content and (3) hydrocarbon/noncarbonate carbon ratio. The graphs shown at the extreme right of Figure 5 demonstrate that both hydrocarbon content and hydrocarbon/noncarbonate carbon ratio increase strongly with depth of burial and age of the sediments. However, the increase is quite slow. It is not until well into the Upper Miocene shales (divisions D and E, approximately 15 million years old according to the time scale of Holmes, 1960) that enough hydrocarbons have been formed to raise the hydrocarbon/noncarbonate carbon ratio to the range of 0.030–0.120 which we have often observed in ancient oil source rocks (see Table I). At the top of Figure 5, left, the normal paraffin distribution curve of a typical Recent sample from the San Pedro Channel, offshore from the Los Angeles basin, has been plotted. From Figure 5 it appears that in the Los Angeles basin even in the lower Pliocene shales at 5942–5948 feet, hardly any change has taken place in the composition of the normal paraffins (Blumer, 1958). However, as hydrocarbons begin to form, as indicated by the increase of the hydrocarbon/noncarbonate carbon ratio, the composition of the normal paraffins begins to change. An example is the Upper Miocene division A sample of Figure 5. In such deeper and geologically older samples the oil generation process has started but is by no means completed. Normal paraffins in the $C_{18}-C_{22}$ interval have formed, and the odd-carbon-number predominance in the $C_{27}-C_{33}$ bracket has been reduced simultaneously but is still more pronounced than in crude oil.

Eventually, during the later stages of the oil generation process the concentration of normal paraffins formed in the subsurface (without odd predominance) is much greater than that which was originally present in the same sediments at the time of deposition. As a consequence, the strong odd-carbon-number predominance of the original normal paraffins, present from the time of deposition, is strongly diluted and almost disappears. A small ripple usually remains, as indicated by values of the odd/even ratio $2C_{29}/(C_{28}+C_{30})$ of $1 \cdot 1 - 1 \cdot 3$. The maximum value of this ratio which we have observed for crude oils is $1 \cdot 41$. This is exceptional.

As is apparent from Figure 5, in the Los Angeles basin it is not until Miocene division D shales that the composition of the sediment normal paraffins begins to equal that of the oils.

Change in Composition of Sediment Isoparaffins and Naphthene Hydrocarbons During Subsurface Oil Generation

In addition to normal paraffins, the high-boiling naphthenes from Recent through upper Miocene sediments have been studied because of their importance in the problem of the origin of oil. For this purpose, an isoparaffin-naphthene concentrate was prepared by carefully removing the aromatics by liquid chromatography from the total hydrocarbons extracted from the sediment, and then the normal paraffins were removed by urea adduction. The isoparaffin-naphthene concentrates obtained in this way were distilled in an efficient microstill, designed by Blumer (1962), into the following fractions:

Fraction 1	Fraction 2	Fraction 3	Fraction 4
$-325\,°C$	$325-370\,°C$	$370-420\,°C$	$420-470\,°C$

Because fraction 1 suffers from evaporation losses as a result of the experimental procedure, only fractions 2, 3 and 4 have been investigated in detail. They represent the $C_{19}-C_{32}$ carbon-number interval, which is within the light-to-medium lubricating oil range. Isoparaffin-naphthene fractions 2, 3, and 4 were analyzed by mass spectrometric parent peak methods (O'Neal, 1954; O'Neal et al., 1955; Schissler et al., 1957; Hood and O'Neal, 1959). Thus, the percentages of isoparaffins (zero rings) and of naphthenes with one ring, two rings, three rings etc., up to eight rings per molecule have been determined. Rings per naphthenic molecule were determined with the methods used.

Simultaneous with the increase of total hydrocarbon content and hydrocarbon/noncarbonate carbon ratio and the change of normal paraffin composition, the composition of the isoparaffin-naphthene concentrate also changes. Some of the

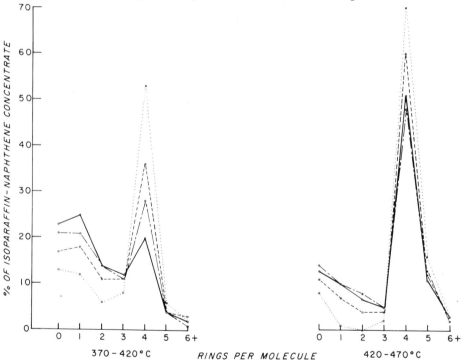

Fig. 6. Evolution of isoparaffins and naphthenes of the lube-oil range in shales of the Los Angeles basin, California

	Shales	Crude
	Shell, Anaheim-Sugar #	◇	Huntington Beach Field
. . . . . .	Cal. 1349, U. Mio. (A), 9613'	—— Cal. 36, U. Mio. (D), 4410'
- - - - - -	Cal. 1351, U. Mio. (D), 11,000'	
— · — ·	Cal. 1352 A, U. Mio. (E), 11,455'	

differences in isoparaffin-naphthene composition may be due to differences in environment of deposition of the sediments of different ages considered. However, the very significant changes in composition which take place in the lower Pliocene and upper Miocene shales, where oil is formed at an appreciable rate, are undoubtedly due to the oil generation process. In lower Pliocene and in upper Miocene A, B, C and D shales, in fractions 3 and 4, the percentage of naphthenes with four rings per molecule decreases with increasing depth and age of the sediments, and the relative concentration of naphthenes with one and two rings per molecule increases. Figure 6 illustrates this interesting phenomenon. The mass spectra of these and similar California samples, according to a method developed by Schissler et al. (1957), strongly suggest that the high fourring-per-molecule peaks are due to a large extent to the presence of sterol derivatives. The presence of sterols in a variety of Recent sediments has been demonstrated by Erdman and Schwendinger (1964).

The shale samples of Figure 6 are all from one wildcat well, Shell No. 1 Anaheim Sugar, which is located east and downdip from the Seal Beach and Huntington Beach oil fields (see Figure 3). Also plotted in Figure 6 is the analysis of the isoparaffin-naphthene concentrate from a typical waxy oil from nearby Huntington Beach field. As is apparent from Figure 6, in upper Miocene E shales at 11,455 ft depth, the oil formation process has finally reached the point at which the composition of the sediment isoparaffin-naphthene concentrate is very similar to that of the waxy oils of the area. As has already been pointed out, in upper Miocene division D and E shales the shale normal paraffins have become identical with those of the oils. This suggests that upper Miocene D and E shales are the source of the oil of the Los Angeles basin. More supporting evidence for this conclusion is presented in the next section.

Relationship Between Oil-Source-Rock Hydrocarbons and Crude-Oil Hydrocarbons: Source Beds of the Los Angeles Basin Oils

To facilitate the following discussion, some of the essential changes which, during the oil generation process, take place in the organic matter of subsurface shales are shown in Figure 7. In Figures 7 (a), (b) and (c) data for the Los Angeles basin have been plotted, and in Figures 7 (d), (e) and (f) data for the Ventura basin have been plotted. In Figure 7 analytical data of considerably more core samples have been used than in Figures 5 and 6.

Figure 7 (a) shows in detail the increase of the hydrocarbon/noncarbonate carbon ratio with depth and age of the Los Angeles basin shales. Figure 7 (b) shows the continuous decrease of the normal paraffin odd/even ratio with depth and age. The end value of the odd/even ratio $2C_{29}/(C_{28} + C_{30})$ of shale normal paraffins is close to 1.0, the same as in the majority of crude oils. The change with depth and age of the "naphthene index", shown in Figure 7 (c), is even more interesting.

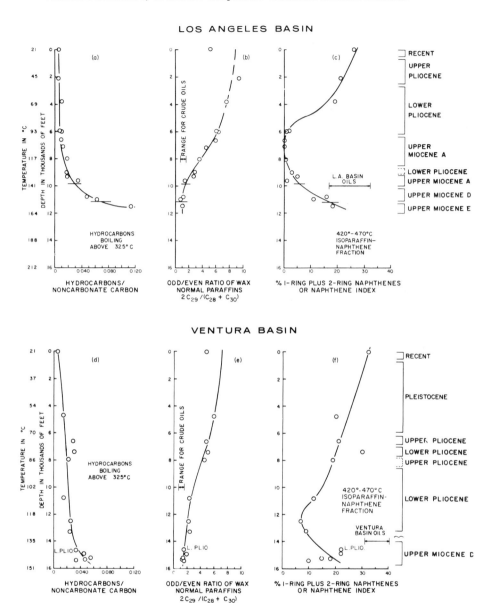

Fig. 7. Change of the heavy hydrocarbon/noncarbonate carbon ratio, the normal paraffin odd/even ratio, and the naphthene index with depth, subsurface temperature and age in shales from the Los Angeles and Ventura basins, California

"Naphthene index" is an abbreviated term for the sum per cent of one-ring and two-ring naphthenes in the 420 °C–470 °C isoparaffin-naphthene concentrate. The value of the naphthene index starts relatively high in Recent sediments, then drops essentially to zero, and later in the final stages of oil generation rises again to values identical with those for the crude oils of the same area. The range of values of the naphthene index as well as of the normal paraffin odd/even ratio for crude oils is shown on Figure 7. In the Los Angeles basin, only in upper Miocene D and E shales which have been buried at least 10,500 ft do the naphthene index and the normal paraffin odd/even ratio values *simultaneously* equal the values of crude-oil hydrocarbons. As is demonstrated in Figure 7, with increasing depth the hydrocarbon/noncarbonate carbon ratio of the shales increases strongly and the composition of the shale hydrocarbons gradually approaches that of the crude oil hydrocarbons. From these observations, and from the similarity in composition of shale hydrocarbons and crude oil hydrocarbons in upper Miocene divisions D and E shales, it is concluded that upper Miocene divisions D and E shales are the major source of the Los Angeles basin oils (Philippi, 1965). Middle Miocene shales, for instance, those of division F, may have contributed to the oil-generating process, but in the Los Angeles basin these strata are absent in many locations and, for this reason, are probably not important as a source of oil. In the Los Angeles basin, sediments older than middle Miocene consist of conglomerates, sandstones, red shales and schists, which are extremely unlikely to be oil source rocks. For these reasons the conclusion that in the Los Angeles basin the upper Miocene divisions D and E shales are the major source of the oil is well founded.

As far as we know this Los Angeles basin example is the first successful attempt of an oil source rock identification based on comparison of the composition of shale and crude oil hydrocarbons. *This first rigorous oil source rock identification may mark the first time the organic origin of petroleum is definitely proven.*

Discussion of the Mechanism and the Influence of Temperature and Time on the Subsurface Generation of Petroleum

The increase of the temperature in the subsurface of the Los Angeles and Ventura basins is shown in Figure 8. The average temperature gradient in the Los Angeles basin of 3.91 °C/100 m (2.15 °F/100 ft) is considerably greater than in the Ventura basin, where it is only 2.66 °C/100 m (1.46 °F/100 ft). The basic data for Figure 8 are from papers by Van Orstrand (1934, 1939) and by Moses (1961), see Philippi (1965).

Figure 7 demonstrates that in the Los Angeles basin the bulk of the oil generation takes place below 8000 ft depth and that in the Ventura basin it takes place below 12,000 ft. On the basis of the temperature-depth relationships of Figure 8, this

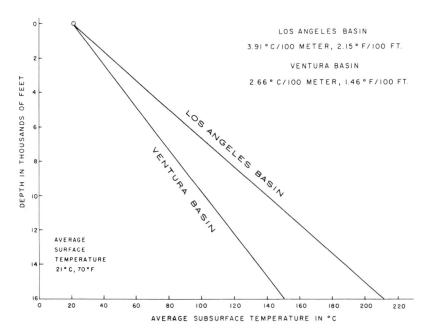

Fig. 8. Average temperature gradients in the Los Angeles and Ventura basins, California

means that in both the Los Angeles and Ventura basins the bulk of the oil generation takes place at temperatures above 115 °C (239 °F). Therefore, petroleum generation is a process occurring in an environment which has become sterile to bacteria because of the raised subsurface temperature. The conclusion that petroleum is formed essentially by nonbiological, thermal processes is inescapable. A shallow origin of petroleum in very young sediments, as has been considered by several investigators (Smith, 1954; Meinschein, 1959; Baker, 1960), is not compatible with the evidence presented.

The petroleum generation process, being chemical, consists of a multitude of subsurface reactions which convert part of the nonhydrocarbon components of the sediment organic matter both into hydrocarbons and into simple nonhydrocarbons, viz. compounds with a small percentage of sulfur or nitrogen which resemble hydrocarbons. As with other chemical reactions, the rates of these oil-forming reactions depend on both temperature and pressure. For the petroleum generation process, of these two factors, temperature is by far more important. The rate of different chemical reactions differs but, quite generally, increases exponentially with the absolute temperature. Because of this feature, the rate of most chemical reactions is increased by a factor of 2–3 for each rise in temperature of 10 °C (or 18 °F).

Pressure, because of its effect on gas-liquid equilibria and component concentrations, influences the rate of part of the oil-forming reactions. However, the effect of increase of pressure on the reaction velocities involved is far less than exponential.

The strong increase of the hydrocarbon/noncarbonate carbon ratio at greater depths and temperatures, shown in Figures 7 (a) and (d), is supporting evidence for the chemical, temperature-controlled nature of the petroleum generation process. Additional and very convincing evidence for this conclusion is the much shallower depth of maximum oil generation and of equal composition of shale and oil hydrocarbons in the Los Angeles basin compared with the Ventura basin. This is undoubtedly caused by the considerably greater temperature gradient in the Los Angeles basin (Figure 8). The present depth of equal composition of shale and oil hydrocarbons in normal positions in the Los Angeles basin, away from strongly uplifted fault blocks, is around 11,000 ft, where the temperature is about 150 °C (302 °F). Even at 15,000 ft depth in the Ventura basin the upper Miocene D shale hydrocarbons are slightly immature, see Figures 7 (e) and (f). Therefore, in the Ventura basin the level at which upper Miocene D shale hydrocarbons mature is somewhat below 15,000 ft, or, in other words, at temperatures somewhat above 143 °C (289 °F). This suggests that the temperature at which hydrocarbons of oil source beds of the same age (upper Miocene D) mature is much the same in the Los Angeles and Ventura basins.

During the upper Miocene D and E period the present Los Angeles and Ventura basins were united and existed as one large basin where organic rich shales of very similar facies were deposited. Because of this, in the present Los Angeles and Ventura basins the upper Miocene divisions D and E source rock shales have a very similar organic content and facies. However, the source rocks of the two basins are exposed to different temperature gradients. Because the environment of deposition of the Los Angeles and Ventura basin source rocks is so similar, the influence of the nature of the organic matter on the generation of petroleum is practically identical in the two basins. This is the reason why the influence of the temperature gradient on the oil generation process stands out so clearly in this study.

In summary, definite proof that natural petroleum originates by subsurface temperature controlled, nonbiological chemical reactions is based upon two observations (Philippi, 1965):

1. the observation that the bulk of the Los Angeles and Ventura basin petroleum originates at subsurface temperatures above 115 °C, and
2. the observed influence of the temperature gradient on the oil generation process.

It should not be inferred that the high temperature and the great depths at which the bulk of the oil generation occurred in the Los Angeles and Ventura basins are general. This is not necessarily true for much older source rocks than those of upper

Miocene age. In older source rocks more time has been available for the oil generation to proceed, and the same amount of petroleum may have been generated at a
lower average temperature over a longer period of time. However, the amount of
oil generated increases only linearly with time but exponentially with the absolute
temperature. Because of this, *neither a fixed depth nor a fixed duration of the oil
generation process exists.* The following factors influence the amount of petroleum
which is formed in subsurface sediments:

(1)   The amount and nature of the organic matter of the source beds.
(2)   The temperature history of the source beds.
(3)   The effect of catalysts, if present.

The importance of the temperature history of potential oil source sediments should
be stressed. In the Los Angeles and Ventura basins oil generation is barely noticeable
around 5000 ft depth. At the temperatures inherent to this depth the generation
process is too slow to be of significance, even over a few epochs. The important
thing is whether a potential source sediment has been exposed for a sufficiently
long time to subsurface temperatures at which the rate of oil generation is sufficiently
rapid. The temperature history of a potential source sediment is determined to a
large extent by the tectonic history, i.e. how deeply the sediment has been buried,
once or several times, and for how long.

Precursors of Petroleum

Research on the precursors of petroleum is not possible without a thorough knowledge of the structure of individual hydrocarbon and nonhydrocarbon components
known to be present in petroleum. A very good survey of the literature on this
interesting topic, up to date to May 1965, has been given by Smith (1966).

Nier and Gulbransen (1939) discovered that the carbon isotope ratio C^{13}/C^{12} of
sedimentary carbonate rocks is about 2–3 percent above that of natural organic
compounds. Craig (1953) extented these studies and showed that plant and animal
tissues, coals, petroleums and the organic matter of sediments all exhibit C^{12} enrichment. Silverman (1965) has made an extensive study of C^{13}/C^{12} ratios of crude
petroleum, petroleum fractions and natural gases. These studies widen and confirm
Craig's results and show that petroleum definitely falls into the biologic or organic
isotopic range. This result is compatible with the organic theory of petroleum origin.
In Figure 9, which is taken from Silverman's paper, C^{13}/C^{12} ratios of carbon containing natural materials are illustrated. The data of Figure 9 are from papers by
Craig (1953) and by Silverman and Epstein (1958). Figure 9 demonstrates that the
highest C^{13}/C^{12} ratios are found in carbonate rocks. From Figure 9 it is evident
also that the C^{13}/C^{12} ratio of petroleums is similar to that of the lipids from marine
plants and from land plants and dissimilar to the C^{13}/C^{12} ratios of the *total* substance of marine plants and marine invertebrates. Based on these observations Silverman (1965) suggests that lipids are the major source material of petroleum.

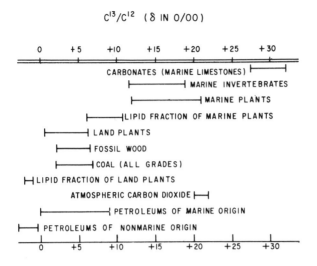

Fig. 9

C^{13}/C^{12} δ-value ranges in natural carbonaceous materials (after Silverman, 1965)

Guided by the similarity in chemical structure of lipid molecules and many petroleum hydrocarbons, Mair (1964) also concluded that lipids are precursors of petroleum. Mair stresses the importance of the terpenoids in this respect. Quote: "By hydrogenation or dehydrogenation, with, in most cases, partial fragmentation of the terpenoid molecules, it is possible to account for most of the structures found in those petroleum hydrocarbons which contain aromatic or cyclohexane rings. Indeed, no other source material can explain in as satisfactory a manner the presence of large amounts of short chain, principally methyl, substituents on the rings of the "average" 6-membered cyclic hydrocarbon molecule in the gasoline fraction of petroleum." Mulik and Erdman (1963) suggest that low boiling aromatics may be formed from carotenoids, compounds which also belong to the lipid category. Cooper and Bray (1963) have published a theory for the formation of n-paraffins from fatty acids, another category of lipids. Bendoraitis, Brown and Hepner (1962, 1963) have suggested phytol as the precursor of phytane and pristane, two isoprenoid hydrocarbons present in petroleum. Phytol is a diterpenoid alcohol and a lipid, and represents about 30 percent by weight of the chlorophyll molecule.

In Figures 10 and 11 illustrations are presented of several lipid molecules and of their most likely hydrocarbon derivatives. These derivatives have been suggested by the authors cited and by others. n-Paraffins and isoparaffins most likely originate from fatty acids and fatty alcohols, isoprenoid isoparaffins from phytol and farnesol, high molecular naphthenes from steroids like cholesterol, and low molecular aromatics and naphthenes from carotenoids.

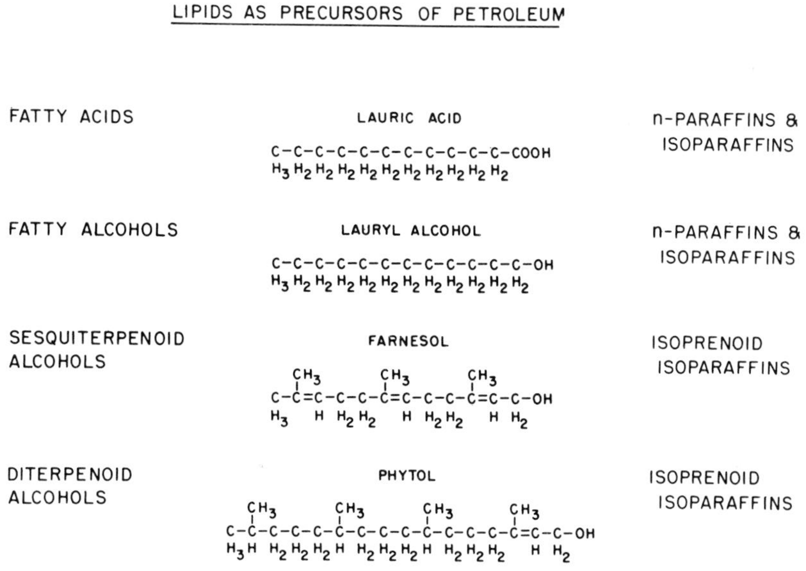

LIPIDS AS PRECURSORS OF PETROLEUM

FATTY ACIDS   LAURIC ACID   n-PARAFFINS &
ISOPARAFFINS

C−C−C−C−C−C−C−C−C−C−C−COOH
H3 H2 H2 H2 H2 H2 H2 H2 H2 H2 H2

FATTY ALCOHOLS   LAURYL ALCOHOL   n-PARAFFINS &
ISOPARAFFINS

C−C−C−C−C−C−C−C−C−C−C−C−OH
H3 H2 H2 H2 H2 H2 H2 H2 H2 H2 H2 H2

SESQUITERPENOID
ALCOHOLS   FARNESOL   ISOPRENOID
ISOPARAFFINS

     CH3   CH3   CH3
C−C=C−C−C−C=C−C−C−C=C−C−OH
H3   H   H2 H2   H   H2 H2   H   H2

DITERPENOID
ALCOHOLS   PHYTOL   ISOPRENOID
ISOPARAFFINS

    CH3   CH3   CH3   CH3
C−C−C−C−C−C−C−C−C−C−C−C−C=C−C−OH
H3H H2 H2 H2 H H2 H2 H2 H H2 H2 H2   H H2

Fig. 10. Examples of lipid molecules and their most likely hydrocarbon derivatives (1)

LIPIDS AS PRECURSORS OF PETROLEUM

STEROIDS   CHOLESTEROL   HIGH MOLECULAR
NAPHTHENES

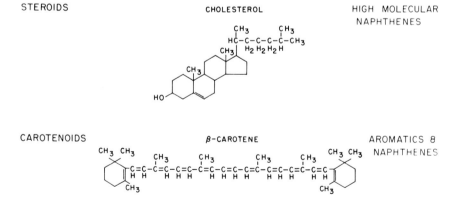

CAROTENOIDS   β−CAROTENE   AROMATICS &
NAPHTHENES

Fig. 11. Examples of lipid molecules and their most likely hydrocarbon derivatives (2)

Conclusions

1. Adequate proof has been obtained for the origin of petroleum from sediment organic matter on the basis of rigorous oil source rock identification.
2. It has also been proven that the general reaction mechanism of petroleum formation in the Los Angeles and Ventura basins of California consists of subsurface temperature controlled, nonbiological, chemical reactions. This general reaction mechanism of petroleum formation may very well apply in other oil basins also.
3. Lipids are extremely likely as major precursors of petroleum.
4. The information lacking mostly in our understanding of the origin of petroleum problem is precise data about the chemistry of the conversion of lipids into petroleum components.

Acknowledgement: I am much indebted to the management of Shell Development Company for permission to present this paper.

References

API Research Project 43, "Transformation of Organic Materials into Petroleum," Final Report, in: Report of Progress. Fundamental Research on Occurrence and Recovery of Petroleum, API 1952–1953.

Baker, E.G. (1960): A Hypothesis Concerning the Accumulation of Sediment Hydrocarbons to Form Crude Oil. Geochim. et Cosmochim. Acta 19, 309–317.

Bendoraitis, J.G., Brown, B.L., and Hepner, L.S. (1962): Isoprenoid Hydrocarbons in Petroleum. Isolation of 2, 6, 10, 14-Tetramethylpentadecane by High-Temperature Gas-Liquid Chromatography. Anal. Chem. 34, 49–53.

Bendoraitis, J.G., Brown, B.L., and Hepner, L.S. (1963): Isolation and Identification of Isoprenoids in Petroleum. Proceedings 6th World Petrol. Congress, Section V, Paper 15, p. 13–29. Frankfurt, Germany.

Blumer, M. (1958): Unpublished results.

Blumer, M. (1962): An Efficient Still for Milligram Samples of High Boiling Materials. Analyt. Chem. 34, 704–708.

Bray, E.E., and Evans, E.D. (1961): Distribution of n-Paraffins as a Clue to Recognition of Source Beds. Geochim. et Cosmochim. Acta 22, 2–15.

Cooper, J.E., and Bray, E.E. (1963): A Postulated Role of Fatty Acids in Petroleum Formation. Geochim. et Cosmochim. Acta 27, 1113–1127.

Craig, H. (1953): The Geochemistry of the Stable Carbon Isotopes. Geochim. et Cosmochim. Acta 3, 53.

Engler, C. (1888): Berichte, 21, 1816.

Engler, C. (1889): Berichte, 22, 592.

Engler, C. (1893): Berichte, 26, 1436.

Engler, C. (1897): Berichte, 30, 2358.

Engler, C. (1888): Chem. Ztg. 12, 842.

Engler, C. (1901): Chem. Ztg. 25, 1116.

Engler, C. (1906): Chem. Ztg. 30, 711.

Engler, C. (1911, 1912): Petroleum Zeit. 7, 399–403.

Erdman, J.G., and Schwendinger, R.B. (1964): Sterols in Recent Aquatic Sediments. Science 144, 1575–76.

Hoering, T.C., and Abelson, P.H. (1962–1963): Hydrocarbons from Kerogen, Carnegie Inst. Washington, Year Book 62, 229–234.

Holmes, A. (1960): A Revised Geological Time Scale. Trans. Edinb. Geol. Soc. 17, 183–215.

Hood, A., and O'Neal, M.J. (1959): Status of Application of Mass Spectrometry to Heavy Oil Analysis, in Advances of Mass Spectrometry, pp. 175–192, Pergamon Press, London.

Jurg, J.W., and Eisma, E. (1964): Petroleum Hydrocarbons: Generation from Fatty Acid, Science, 144, 1451–1452.

Lind, S.C. (1928): The Chemical Effects of Alpha Particles and Electrons, published by the Chem. Cat. Co., New York.

Lind, S.C., and Bardwell, D.C. (1926): Chemical Action of Gaseous Ions Produced by Alpha Particles: IX-Saturated Hydrocarbons, J. Am. Chem. Soc. 48, 2335–2351.

Mair, B.J. (1964): Terpenoids, Fatty Acids and Alcohols as Source Materials for Petroleum Hydrocarbons. Geochim. et Cosmochim. Acta, 28, 1303–21.

Meinschein, W.G. (1959): Origin of Petroleum. Bull. Amer. Assoc. Petrol. Geol. **43**, 925–43.

Moses, P.L. (1961): Geothermal Gradients, in Drilling and Production Practice, pp. 57–63, Amer. Petr. Inst.

Mulik, J.D., and Erdman, J.G. (1963): Genesis of Hydrocarbons of Low Molecular Weight in Organic Rich Aquatic Systems. Science, **141**, 806–807.

Nier, A.O., and Gulbransen, E.A. (1939): Variations in the Relative Abundance of the Carbon Isotopes. Journ. Amer. Chem. Soc. **61**, 697.

O'Neal, M.J. (1954): Application of High Molecular Weight Mass Spectrometry to Oil Constitution, in Apllied Mass Spectrometry, pp. 27–46. Institute of Petroleum.

O'Neal, M.J., Hood, A., Clerc, R.J., Andre, M.L., and Hines, C.K. (1955): The Determination of Heavy Oil Composition by Mass Spectrometry. Proc. Fourth World Petrol. Congr., Section V, 307, Carlo Columbo, Publ., Rome.

Philippi, G.T. (1956): Identification of Oil Source Beds by Chemical Means. Proc. Intl. Geol. Cong., Mexico City, Section III, Petr. Geol., 25–38.

Philippi, G.T. (1965): On the Depth, Time and Mechanism of Petroleum Generation, Geochim. et Cosmochim. Acta, **29**, 1021–1049.

Schissler, D.O., Stevenson, D.P., Moore, R.J., O'Donnell, G.J., and Thorpe, R.E. (1957): Steranes in Petroleum, A.S.T.M. Committee E–14, New York.

Silverman, S.R., and Epstein, S. (1958): Carbon Isotopic Compositions of Petroleums and Other Sedimentary Organic Materials. Bull. Amer. Assoc. Petr. Geol. **42**, 998.

Silverman, S.R. (1965): Investigations of Petroleum Origin and Evolution Mechanisms by Carbon Isotope Studies. In: Isotopic and Cosmic Chemistry, North-Holland Publishing Co., Amsterdam.

Smith, H.M. (1966): Crude Oil – Qualitative and Quantitative Aspects. The Petroleum World. U.S. Bureau of Mines, Inform. Circ. 8286, pp. 1–41.

Smith, P.V. (1954): Studies on Origin of Petroleum. Occurrence of Hydrocarbons in Recent Sediments, Bull. Amer. Assoc. Petrol. Geol. **38**, 377–404.

Stevens, N.P., Bray, E.E., and Evans, E.D. (1956): Hydrocarbons in Sediments of Gulf of Mexico. Bull. Amer. Assoc. Petrol. Geol. **40**, 975–983.

Trask, P.D., and Wu, C.C. (1930): Does Petroleum Form at the Time of Deposition. Bull. Amer. Assoc. Petrol. Geol. **14**, 1451–63.

Van Orstrand, C.E. (1934): Temperature Gradients, in Problems of Petroleum Geology, pp. 989–1021, American Association of Petroleum Geology.

Van Orstrand, C.E. (1939): Temperature of the Earth in Relation to Oil Location, in Temperature – Its Measurement and Control in Science and Industry, pp. 1014–1033. Amer. Inst. Phys., Reinhold, New York.

Dissolved Organic Matter in the Oceans

Hendrik Postma

Netherlands Institute for Sea Research
Den Helder, The Netherlands

Attempts to determine the total amount of dissolved organic matter in the sea
have been made for more than 50 years, but only recently analytical methods
have become sufficiently accurate to provide reliable data about its concentrations and distribution. Simultaneously a considerable number of organic compounds have been detected, although the chemical composition of a large fraction
remains unknown.

Besides differences in the organic components in various water masses, principal
questions concern the rate of supply and the composition of dissolved organic
matter from the land, production by marine plankton and plankton debris,
transport into the deep sea either by water movements or sinking of particulate
organic matter, age and rate of decomposition of various fractions. This lecture
discusses possible answers to these questions, taking into account the distribution
of other chemical properties in the ocean, such as yellow substances and fluorescence, the possible relation to production of organic matter in surface waters and
the rate of oxygen consumption in the deep sea.

Introduction

About 60 years ago the biologist Pütter carried out a series of investigations to show
that dissolved organic matter is present in natural waters in considerably larger
amounts than particulate matter and that it can be used as food by marine animals
(Pütter, 1909). He compared the concentration of plankton in a certain volume of
water with the amount of food in solution. To cite an extreme example, he found
for a certain marine protozoan that the amount of plankton necessary for the
energy requirements of the animal in one hour was present in 10 litres of sea water
and the equivalent quantity of dissolved organic substance in only 0.5 ml. Since
the volume of the animal in question is only 0.1 ml, it could impossibly live on
plankton, while the amount of dissolved material would be sufficient.

It has subsequently been shown that Pütter seriously overestimated the amounts
of dissolved carbon and underestimated the amounts of plankton. Especially Krogh
(1931) has carried out much work to refute the idea that dissolved matter would
play such a central rôle in the food chain. As a result, this material to-day is given
a less distinguished place, although Pütter's ideas tend to come back in one form
or another.

The determination of small concentrations of dissolved organic substances in the
presence of large quantities of salt is a technically difficult procedure. Pütter's
results, obtained by oxydation of the material with $KMnO_4$, gave values which are

very much too high. Krogh (1934), in a series of measurements near the Bermudas, found an average of 2.4 mg/1 of carbon along the vertical. Skopintsev and Timofeeva (1962) arrived at an average of 1.5 mg/l in the North Atlantic Ocean. Duursma (1961), Menzel (1964) and Holm Hansen, Strickland and Williams (1966) find values around 0.5 mg/l.

Numerical considerations in this review will be based on the last-mentioned data, since they have been obtained by a number of independent investigators. Some doubt the actual concentrations remains, since in all analytical procedures which are applied blank determinations are high.

In addition, it is difficult to distinguish sharply between dissolved and suspended organic matter, since there is a gradual transition from compounds in true solution to colloidal matter and suspended particles. For all practical purposes, dissolved organic matter can be defined as material which is not retained by a membrane or glass fiber filter with very small pores (one micron or less) and which is not easily separated from sea water by centrifugation or settling (Duursma, 1965).

In this paper present-day knowledge of the distribution of dissolved organic matter in the oceans will be reviewed and problems of origin, stability and composition will be discussed. It should be stressed that our knowledge is far from complete and that various interpretations of the available data seem possible.

Distribution and Residence Time

Organic matter present in the sea comes from two main sources: phytoplankton production and run-off from the land. Even in the most transparent water no net production takes place below a depth of 100–150 metres. Organic matter from the land will also be introduced near the sea surface, mainly with rivers. Hence, all or nearly all dissolved organic matter must be derived from organic compounds originally present in the surface water layers. Since breakdown of organic matter generally proceeds rapidly, one might expect that the concentration of dissolved organic matter would decrease rapidly, perhaps even logarithmically, with depth.

Indeed, relatively large amounts of dissolved organic carbon are found near the water surface, but below the photosynthetic zône and at least below 400–500 metres the vertical distribution is surprisingly homogeneous. Examples for various parts of the ocean are shown in Fig. 1 a-d. Not only vertical differences, but also differences from place to place are rather small. Even in a relatively isolated basin like the Mediterranean Sea (Fig. 1 d) the concentrations are not essentially different from the open ocean. At a closer look there are certain distinct geographical patterns, which will be discussed later on. To begin with we will consider average conditions. For the greater part of the water column a concentration of 0.5 mg/l C seems a good estimate. Nearly all values for deep water are between 0.2 and 0.8 mg/l.

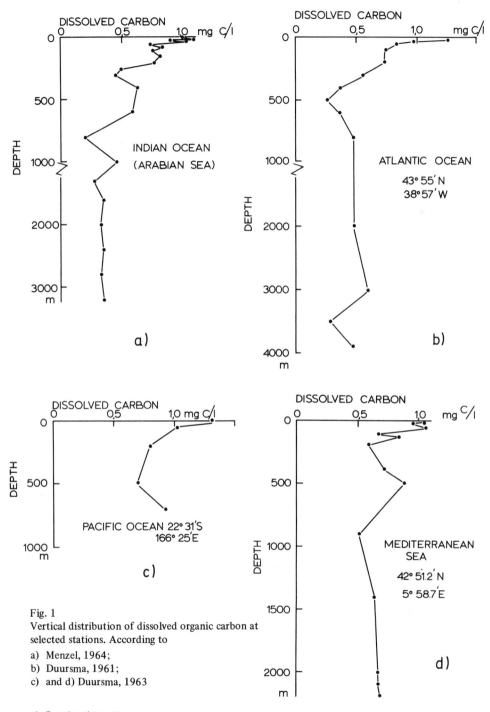

Fig. 1
Vertical distribution of dissolved organic carbon at
selected stations. According to

a) Menzel, 1964;
b) Duursma, 1961;
c) and d) Duursma, 1963

4 Geochemistry 68

Krogh (1934) was the first to note the homogeneous vertical distribution and he concluded that the material must be very stable. Indeed, deep water renewal by mixing processes and currents in the oceans proceeds very slowly. The "age" of deep water in the Atlantic Ocean must be measured in hundreds of years and in the Pacific in a thousand years or more. Hence, to arrive at a relatively homogeneous distribution of a dissolved substance the residence time of the material must surpass these time spans.

This argument, of course, strictly holds only for dissolved substances or particles with a very slow sinking rate. It is in principle conceivable that the material is formed by the breakdown of particulate organic matter which settles through the water column before all of it is decomposed. To give a simple example: if grains of a soluble substance are dropped through a vertical tube filled with water, the amount of material going into solution at every depth is about the same. This is caused by the fact that settling velocity is about directly proportional to the surface of the grains, whereas the amount going into solution is approximately inversely proportional to this surface. A similar relationship could exist between organic detritus and dissolved organic matter in the ocean and in that case a homogeneous distribution could be explained without assuming a great age.

There is, however, another argument against a short lifespan of the organic matter. A slow rate of decomposition can be derived from data about oxygen consumption. Estimates about deep water oxygen consumption have been made by a number of authors (Riley, 1951; Postma, 1958; Munk, 1966). The average rate of oxygen utilisation is about 0.003 ml/l/year, which corresponds with about 0.001 mg/l/year of carbon. If only dissolved organic matter is oxidized, the "age" of this material is therefore 500 years. Of course, this "age" would increase if a considerable part of the oxygen is used for decomposition of particulate organic matter.

Terrigenous Sources

It seems possible to explain the origin of dissolved organic matter from the land as well as from the sea itself. Many rivers contain much larger concentrations of organic matter than the sea. This leads to an elevated concentration of dissolved organic matter in many coastal seas into which rivers debouch.

There are insufficient data for a reliable estimate of the average concentration of dissolved organic matter in rivers. Moreover, many rivers carry a heavy load of organic matter derived from sewage, which makes an evaluation of concentrations in the past impossible. A conservative average value is probably 5 mg/l. The total runoff from rivers is 4×10^{13}/year, so that the total supply would be 2×10^{14} g/year. The total volume of the oceans is 1.4×10^{18} m^3; the content of dissolved organic matter is therefore 700×10^{15} grams. Hence, about 3500 years would be needed to supply all dissolved organic matter to the sea by rivers. Since the "age" of the material is of the order of 500 years, this means that at most only 10–20 % of the material could originate from the land.

The assumption of terrigenous origin of part of the dissolved organic carbon has some attraction, since in the sea as well as in fresh water part of the organic matter has the properties of humic substances. These cause a yellowish colouring of the water and can be detected by their blue fluorescence in ultraviolet light (Fig. 2).

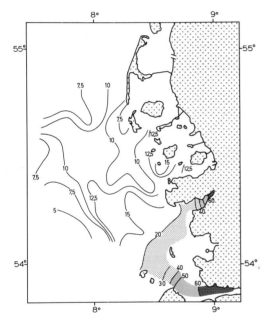

Fig. 2

Distribution of fluorescence, measured in ultraviolet light, in the surface water of the German Bight. Note the increase towards the estuary of the river Elbe (below, right). On unit corresponds with the fluorescence of 0.75 mg chininebisulphate in 1000 ml of distilled water; after Kalle (1956)

Kalle (1962) has shown, however, that at least in the North Sea basin and in the North Atlantic Ocean the spectrum of the fluviatile humic material is different from that of the marine material. He classifies the former as chiefly phenolic humic acids and the latter as carbohydrate humic acids. Only a beginning has been made, however, with a spectral classification of dissolved organic matter and much more work has to be done before reliable conclusions can be drawn.

In any case stable humic acids form only a small part of the dissolved organic material present in the surface layers of the sea, since considerable seasonal concentration variations occur here, which are not correlated with terrestrial supply, but depend on biological processes in situ. It seems therefore improbable that a considerable fraction of terrigenous dissolved organic matter would reach the deep sea.

Marine Sources

More promising is the possibility of the production of dissolved organic matter by
marine phytoplankton. Net production of organic carbon by photosynthesis in the
oceans is about 60 grams/m^2/year (Steemann Nielsen, 1960). The average depth of
the ocean being 4000 metres, about 2000 g of dissolved organic carbon is present
under every m^2 of water. Hence, if all organic matter produced in the sea would go
into solution, the average "age" of this material would be $\frac{2000}{60}$ or 35 years. Since
the actual residence time, as we saw earlier, is of the order of 500 years, only about
5—10 % of the organic matter photosynthesized has to be converted into the dissolved state. There are two possibilities: the dissolved material may be excreted directly by living phytoplankton, or it orginates from organic detritus.

The direct production of dissolved organic matter by living algae in fresh as well
as in salt water has in recent years been studied by a number of authors. Already
in 1930 Krogh and Lange carried out a series of experiments with Scenedesmus,
which showed that in periods of vigorous growth about 5 % of the assimilated
carbon went into solution. In other experiments somewhat higher percentages
were found. Modern investigations confirm that under optimal conditions the
amount of dissolved organic matter formed is indeed relatively small (Hellebust,
1965). However, if conditions become less favourable, this amount may increase
considerably.

Among the factors which cause a percentual increase are: a high population density; a low and especially a high light intensity; low concentrations of carbon dioxide and possibly of nutrient salts; sudden environmental changes such as a rapid
change in salinity. Examples are given by Nalewajko (1966).

Under natural conditions mostly one or a combination of these factors are exerting
their influence, so that in general the excretion of dissolved organic carbon will be
greater than 5 %. We may note that a positive relationship between rate of photosynthesis and production of dissolved organic matter does not necessarily exist,
since in periods of plankton blooms the environmental conditions may favour relatively low losses of dissolved carbon from the cells. Mostly, however, high rates of
photosynthesis will cause high production of dissolved organic matter. Duursma
(1961) has shown that in the southern North Sea near the Dutch coast the concentrations of dissolved organic carbon indeed go up and down with primary production with a time log of two weeks to a month. High values occur in spring and
early summer and low values in winter and fall. Total annual production of dissolved organic matter in spring is estimated at least 2.6 mg C/l or 52 g/m^2 (water depth
20 metres). According to a tentative estimate by the present author annual primary
production in the area is between 150 and 200 gC/m^2/year, so that 25—30 % of
this production would be transformed into organic matter. Similar and somewhat

lower percentages were found by Hellebust (1965) in the Gulf of Maine and in coastal water near Woods Hole. This investigator further observed that apparently healthy populations of natural phytoplankton excreted 4 — 16 % of assimilated carbon, whereas at the end of a diatom bloom, when a large number of plankton debris was present, 17–38 % was formed. In the North Sea, and in fact in most ocean waters, a very considerable part if not the majority of organic particles consist of organic detritus. Therefore, the percentual increase of the formation of dissolved organic matter in comparison with healthy plankton cultures will be caused by the production from organic debris as well as by an increase of excretion by phytoplankton.

It is premature to apply the percentages mentioned above to the open ocean. However, since 5–10 % excretion or solution would already be sufficient to cover the demand there is enough room to explain the presence of dissolved organic matter in the oceans by transformation of marine organic materials.

Relation with particulate Organic Matter

Returning to the problem of the vertical distribution of dissolved organic matter in the deep sea, it is clear that there are two possible ways to explain the presence of dissolved organic material in the deep sea. One is formation from sinking debris, the other downward transport by vertical movements of water masses. Regarding the first possibility it is interesting to consider the concentration and vertical distribution of particulate organic matter. As in the case of dissolved materials one might assume that this concentration will decrease rapidly from the water surface downward. Indeed, concentrations of particulate organic matter in the surface layers are relatively high, but optical measurements in deep water (Jerlov, 1959) and in recent years direct weight determinations show that below the photosynthetic zone and at least below 500 metres the material is distributed rather homogeneously, although with a more pronounced decrease with depth than dissolved matter (Menzel and Goering, 1966; Menzel, 1967; Riley et al., 1965).

The average concentration of particulate organic matter in deep water, expressed as carbon, is 10 mg/m^3; this is 40 g below one m^2 and about equal to the annual production per m^2 of organic carbon by photosynthesis. Hence, contrary to dissolved organic carbon the total amount present could in principle easily be produced in a few years. To give a numercial example, let us assume that the average age of the particulate organic material is 10 years. In that case 1 mg/m^3/year or 4 g/m^2/year must be renewed, which is only about 7 % of the net annual photosynthetic production of 60 g/m^2. In addition, it could be assumed that the 1 mg/m^3/year which disappears is completely transformed into dissolved carbon. This would in its turn give an average age of dissolved carbon of 500 years, which is the minimum age found previously. In principle it seems not impossible to consider the particulate organic carbon as an intermediary between the living organic matter near the water surface and the homogeneously distributed dissolved organic matter in the deep sea.

For a more realistic picture one would have to take into account that part of the particulate organic matter settles to the deep sea floor before it is decomposed and that another part of it will be used in the water by zooplankton and bacteria. This would necessarily increase the age of dissolved organic matter to more than 500 years.

The essential question is whether an average age of say 10 years for the suspended material is realistic. Only direct age determinations by means of the C 12/C 14-method can provide a definite answer. Meanwhile, to explain the relatively homogeneous vertical distribution a considerable part of the material must reach the ocean bottom, so that an important fraction of the organic particles must have a setting velocity which carries them through the water column in less than 10 years. No reliable estimates of sinking rates are at present available, but the organic conglomerates can obtain diameters of many tenths of microns.

An alternate theory has been developed by Riley and coworkers (Riley, 1963; Riley et al. 1965), who assume that just the opposite happens of what has been described above. They suppose, and obviousiy have some experimental evidence, that organic aggregates grow by adsorption of dissolved organic carbon from the surrounding water. Of course, taking into account the gradual transition between dissolved and particulate matter, this does not seem impossible, but in this manner the question of the origin of the dissolved organic matter remains unanswered.

A third suggestion has been made by Menzel and Goering (1966) and Menzel (1967), who suppose that the suspended organic matter, like the dissolved organic matter, is of great chronological age. The rather homogeneous distribution is then the result of large scale oceanic mixing. If this assumption is right, both the distribution of dissolved and particulate matter must be explained essentially in the same way and their spatial distribution may be rather similar.

The meagre and partially contradictory information available about the regional distribution of dissolved and particulate organic matter is not sufficient to decide between these theories. There is some evidence that the southern ocean may be a relatively rich source both for particulate and dissolved organic matter. The distribution of dissolved organic carbon along a meridional section of the Indian Ocean shows a distinct increase from north to south (Menzel, 1964). In the southern Pacific Ocean dissolved organic phosphorus has two distinct maxima: one near the depth of the Antarctic intermediate water and one in very deep water. (Rochford, 1963). These two water masses originate in the southern ocean. The same is the case of particulate organic matter in the Tasman Sea. (Dal Pont and Newell, 1963). In all these cases, values are well above the oceanic average.

Chemical Composition

Up to now chiefly the distribution of organic carbon has been discussed. There is a large amount of information available, which shows that dissolved organic matter is a mixture cf a large number of organic compounds. Many of these compounds have been identified and it may be expected that a better knowledge of their distribution will lead to a better understanding of their genesis.

An important indication for the composition of organic matter is the C-N-P-ratio. For living phytoplankton this ratio, expressed by weight, is 100:18:2.5 (Sverdrup et al. 1942). For dissolved organic matter ratio's between 100:10:1 and 100:50:1 have been found in different water masses (compare Duursma, 1965). Holm-Hansen et al (1966), in a recent investigation, find a ratio of 100:11:1 near the coast of California for the water column between 100 and 1300 metres. The ratio for dissolved inorganic compounds in the Pacific Ocean is 100:13:1.8 (compare Postma, 1964). The differences may be explained by assuming that organic matter loses relatively large amounts of N and P already in the upper water layers. For material that is hundreds of years old, however, the changes of the ratio's are not very spectacular. Evidently, the composition of the dissolved organic matter in the deep sea does not differ dramatically from that of living material.

This conclusion is confirmed by studies of the vertical distribution of individual compounds or groups of compounds. It must be taken into account,however, that components which have actually been classified chemically do not make up more than about 10 % of the dissolved organic matter present.

Summarizing, it appears that dissolved organic matter in the deep sea is hundreds of years old, but has a chemical composition which does not essentially differ from that of fresh organic material. The same holds, perhaps in a lesser degree. for organic particles (compare Holm-Hansen et al. 1966).

The surprising stability of the material is not caused by fundamental resistance against bacterial attack: if water from the deep sea is stored in a bottle, the dissolved organic matter is utilized by bacteria. This rapid breakdown is greatly furthered by a fixed substrate, in this case the glass walls of the bottle. Such a substrate is lacking in the ocean. Total available particle surface in the deep sea is of the order of 5 mm^2/l (Riley et al. 1965), which is about 10.000 times less than the wall surface in a bottle of this volume.

Jannasch (1967) has suggested that the dissolved organic matter in the deep sea is unavailable for microbial breakdown because its concentration, although high in comparison with other forms of organic material, is extremely low if compared with that in other biological media. Experiments in steady state cultures show that below a certain substrate concentration the bacterial population collapses. For the organic substrates used (lactate, glycerol, glucose) the threshold concentration veried between 0.5 and 100 mg/l or generally higher than concentrations encountered in the deep sea. The collapse is ascribed to lack of production of an essential growth substance at low population densities.

Of course, the environmental conditions created in experiments cannot simply be translated into those of the deep sea. They point to the possibility, however, that dissolved organic matter is preserved there because this water mass forms an unfavourable environment for bacterial life.

References

Dal Pont, G. and Newell, B., 1963: Suspended organic matter in the Tasman Sea. Aust. J. Mar. Freshw. Res., 14, 155–165.

Duursma, E. K., 1961: Dissolved organic carbon, nitrogen and phosphorus in the sea. Neth. J. Sea Res., 1, 1–148.

Duursma, E. K., 1963: The production of dissolved organic matter in the sea, as related to the primary gross production of organic matter. Neth. J. Sea Res., 2, 85–97.

Duursma, E. K., 1965: The dissolved organic constituents of sea water. Chemical Oceanography, chapter 11, 433–475, ed. J. P. Riley and G. Skirrow, Acad. Press. London.

Hellebust, J. A., 1965: Excretion of some organic compounds by marine phytoplankton. Linmn. Oceanogr., 10, 192–206.

Holm Hansen, O., Strickland, J. D. H. and Williams, P. M., 1966: A detailed analysis of biologically important substances in a profile off Southern California. Limn. Oceanogr., 11, 548–561.

Kalle, K., 1955: Chemische Untersuchungen in der Irminger See in Juni 1955. Ber. Dtsch. Wiss. Komm. Meeresf., 14, 313–328.

Kalle, K., 1956: Chemisch-hydrographische Untersuchungen in der inneren Deutschen Bucht. Deutsch.Hydr. Zeitschrift, 9, 55–65.

Kalle, K., 1962: Ueber die gelösten organischen Komponenten im Meerwasser. Kieler Meeresf., 18 (3), 128–131.

Jannasch, H. W., 1967: Growth of marine bacteria at limiting concentrations of organic carbon in seawater. Limn. Oceanogr., 12, 264–271.

Jerlov, N. G., 1959: Particle distribution in the ocean. Reports Swedisch deep-sea exp., III (3), 1–97.

Krogh, A., 1931: Dissolved substances as food of aquatic organisms. Biol. Rev., 6, 412–442.

Krogh, A., 1934: Conditions of life in the ocean. Ecol. Monogr., 4, 421–429, 430–439.

Menzel, D. W., 1964: The distribution of dissolved organic carbon in the Western Indian Ocean. Deep-Sea Res., 11, 757–765.

Menzel, D. W. and Goering, J. J., 1966: The distribution of organic detritus in the ocean. Limnol. Oceanogr., 11, 333–337.

Menzel, D. W., 1967: Particulate organic carbon in the deep sea. Deep Sea Res., 14, 229–238.

Munk, W. H., 1966: Abyssal recipes. Deep-Sea Res., 13, 707–730.

Nalewajko, C., 1966: Photosynthesis and excretion in various planktonic algae. Limn. Oceanogr., 11, 1–10.

Postma, H., 1958: Shellius Expedition 1929–1930, Vol. II, part 8, 1–116.

Postma, H., 1964: The exchange of oxygen and carbon dioxide between the ocean and the atmosphere. Neth. J. Sea Res., **2**, 258–283.

Pütter, A., 1909: Die Ernährung der Wassertiere und der Stoffhaushalt der Gewässer. Fischer Verlag, Jena.

Riley, G. A., 1951: Oxygen, phosphate and nitrate in the Atlantic Ocean. Bull. Bingham Oceanogr. Coll., **13**, 1–126.

Riley, G. A., 1963: Organic aggregates in sea water and the dynamics of their formation and utilization. Limn. Oceanogr., **8**, 372–381.

Riley, G. A., van Hemert, D. and Wangersky, P. J., 1965: Organic aggregates in surface and deep waters of the Sargasso Sea. Limn. Oceanogr., **10**, 354–363.

Rochford, D. J., 1963: Some features of organic phosphorus distribution in the south-east Indian and south-west Pacific Oceans. Aust. J. Mar. Feshw. Res., **14**, 119–138.

Skopintsev, B. A. and Timofeeva, S. N., 1962: Content of organic carbon in the waters of the Baltic Sea, North Sea and subtropical zones of the North Atlantic Ocean. Akad. Nauk. USSR, **25**, 110–117.

Steemann Nielsen, E., 1960: Productivity of the oceans. Ann. Rev. Plant Physiol., **11**, 341–362.

Aktuelle Probleme der Geochemie der Kohle

Joachim Karweil

Mitteilung aus der Bergbau-Forschung GmbH, Forschungsinstitut des Steinkohlenbergbauvereins
Essen-Kray, Germany

The author examines the influence of the expansion of the earth on the conditions
obtaining during the genesis and the metamorphism of coals. Acceleration of
gravity, air pressure, the maximum height of the clouds and the length of the
day differed substantially, though not on principle, from their present values. The
high biochemical productivity in that period caused the oxygen content of the
atmosphere to rise above its present level, and this accounts for the origin of fires
in the swamp forests and, as a result, for the formation of fusain.

The changes of the coal during the coalification process and their reasons are
explained, attention being called to the heterogeneity of the initial material. As
this heterogeneity was conserved for a long period of time, it is difficult to get a
detailed insight into the chemism of the coalification process and to determine
the rank of the coal. The coalification process leads to the formation of water and
gassy reaction products, such as CO_2 and hydrocarbons, the quantity of which
can be roughly calculated. The quantity of methane exceeds the storage capacity
of the seams. In consequence, a current of methane ascends from the lower seams
and expels the heavier hydrocarbons from the overlying ones.

The calculation of the speed of reaction of the coalification process must be based
on a rather simplified model, separating roughly into two groups easily and weakly
reacting substances. In this way the coalification problem is restricted to reactive
substances the metamorphism of which can be defined by temperature and
time. The pressure does not exert any influence upon the speed of reaction.

As the temperature of the seams during their subsidence has played a very important part, the author markes an attempt to estimate the geothermal gradient during this period of time. With this end in view he explains the formation of a geo-
syncline by reactions which in part effect also the expansion of the earth, that is
to say by differentiation processes in the interior of the earth which are induced
by unbalanced sedimentation, vapour acting as a catalyst. The calculations lead
to the conclusion that in the carboniferous period the geothermal gradient of the
Ruhr strata has been higher than today.

Der Einfluß der Erdexpansion auf die Verhältnisse bei der Entstehung und Umwandlung der Kohlen wird untersucht. Erdbeschleunigung, Luftdruck, maximale
Wolkenhöhe und Tageslänge im Karbon unterschieden sich merklich, wenn auch
nicht grundsätzlich von ihren heutigen Werten. Die hohe biochemische Produktivität in diesem Zeitabschnitt ließ den Sauerstoffgehalt der Atmosphäre über seinen
heutigen Wert ansteigen. Dies macht Waldbrände in den karbonischen Sumpfwäldern
verständlich und damit die Bildung von Fusit.

Die Veränderungen der Kohle im Lauf der Inkohlung und ihre Ursachen werden
geschildert und auf die Heterogenität des Ausgangsmaterials hingewiesen. Diese
bleibt während eines großen Teils des Inkohlungsprozesses erhalten und erschwert

nicht nur detaillierte Aussagen über den Chemismus der Inkohlung, sondern auch über die Angabe eines ,,Inkohlungsgrades''. Bei der Inkohlung entstehen Wasser, Kohlendioxid und Kohlenwasserstoffe als gasförmige Reaktionsprodukte, deren Menge rechnerisch abgeschätzt werden kann. Die Methanmenge ist größer als das Speichervolumen der Flöze. Infolgedessen entsteht ein Methanstrom aus den tieferen durch die darüberliegenden Flöze, der die schweren Kohlenwasserstoffe aus den oberen Flözen herausspült.

Zur Berechnung der Reaktionsgeschwindigkeit des Inkohlungsprozesses muß man sich eines stark vereinfachten Schemas bedienen, bei dem auf der einen Seite die reaktionsträgen, auf der anderen Seite die reaktionsfreudigen Stoffe zusammengefaßt werden. Das Inkohlungsproblem wird dadurch auf die reaktionsfähigen Stoffe beschränkt, deren Stoffumsatz durch Temperatur und Zeit beschrieben werden kann. Druck hat keinen Einfluß auf die Reaktionsgeschwindigkeit.

Da die Temperatur in den Flözen zur Zeit der Versenkung eine sehr wichtige Rolle gespielt hat, wird versucht, die geothermische Tiefenstufe in diesem Zeitraum abzuschätzen. Dazu wird die Bildung einer Geosynklinale durch Reaktionen erklärt, die auch z.T. die Erdexpansion bewirken, nämlich durch Differentiationsvorgänge, die im Erdinnern auftreten als Folge fehlenden Sedimentationsgleichgewichtes, und bei denen Wasserdampf die Rolle eines Katalysators spielt. Aus den Berechnungen folgt, daß im Ruhrkarbon eine höhere geothermische Tiefenstufe geherrscht haben muß als heute.

1. Problemstellung

Es ist eine Eigenart wissenschaftlicher Forschungstätigkeit, daß sie sich nicht in geregelten Bahnen stetig vorwärtsbewegt, sondern in Form von Sprüngen, deren Richtung nicht immer von vornherein zu erkennen ist. Irgendein Gebiet rückt plötzlich in den Mittelpunkt allgemeinen Interesses und wird intensiv bearbeitet. Nach einer gewissen Zeit erlahmt das Interesse daran, um sich an einer anderen Stelle erneut zu konzentrieren. Der Grund für diese Verhaltensweise ist entweder in Fortschritten auf dem Gebiet der apparativen Untersuchungsmethoden zu suchen oder in der Konzeption neuer theoretischer Vorstellungen.

Auch auf dem Gebiet der Kohlenforschung kann man diesen Schwerpunktwechsel beobachten. Anfangs interessierte man sich vorwiegend für das Ausgangsmaterial, für die Pflanzen und Tiere der Karbonzeit und für die damaligen klimatischen Verhältnisse. Dann wandte sich das Interesse mehr der Metamorphose zu. Die Mazerale und ihre Umwandlung im Laufe der Inkohlung rückten in den Blickpunkt. Mit Beginn der vierziger Jahre setzte eine intensive Grundlagenforschung ein, die zunächst mehr physikalisch orientiert war und sich mit Problemen der Benetzungswärme, der Porosität, den Kristallitdimensionen und ähnlichem beschäftigte, die sich dann aber im Laufe der Zeit auch den überaus schwierigen Fragen der chemischen Konstitution der Kohlen erfolgreich zuwandte.

Der Anreiz für diese Folge von Schwerpunktbildungen ging überwiegend vom technischen Fortschritt auf dem Gebiet physikalischer Analysenmethoden aus. Impulse aufgrund neuer theoretischer Vorstellungen sind auf dem Gebiet der Kohlenforschung nur selten zu beobachten. Die Kohle hat sich gegenüber allen Versuchen einer theoretischen Behandlung als recht unzugänglich erwiesen.

Wenn die Anstrengungen der letzten vierzig Jahre fas ausschließlich dem Endprodukt, den Kohlen, galten, so ist es eigentlich an der Zeit, sich auch wieder einmal des Ausgangsmaterials zu erinnern. Die auf allen Gebieten der Wissenschaft in den letzten Jahrzehnten gewonnenen neuen Forschungsergebnisse sind auch für die mit den Kohlen verbundenen Probleme von Bedeutung und lassen es angebracht erscheinen, unsere Vorstellungen über Entstehung und Umwandlung der Kohlen an Hand eben dieser auf Nachbargebieten gemachten Fortschritte zu prüfen und zu vervollständigen.

Dazu ist es zunächst notwendig, sich mit den Bedingungen zu befassen, unter denen sich das organische Ausgangsmaterial ablagert, wobei die überaus aktuelle Vorstellung von einem sich im Laufe der Zeit ausdehnenden Erdkörper zu Hilfe genommen werden muß. Als nächstes wären einige Bemerkungen zur biochemischen Produktivität und zu den Strukturänderungen während der Umwandlung notwendig. Das Problem der Gasabspaltung während der Inkohlung leitet schließlich zu reaktionskinetischen Fragen über, bei denen die Temperatur und damit wieder die Erdexpansion eine wichtige Rolle spielt.

2. Ablagerungsbedingungen

Wenn man sich ein Bild über die Ablagerungsbedingungen zur Karbonzeit machen will, muß man wissen, wie groß die Erde zu dieser Zeit war. Bild 1 zeigt, wie man sich das bereits erwähnte Wachstum der Erde vorstellen muß. Durch die radioaktive Zerfallswärme dehnt sich der Erdkern aus. Wenn die Zugfestigkeit des Mantels überschritten wird, reißt dieser auf. Dabei gelangen Kern- und Mantelmaterial in Zonen geringeren geostatischen Druckes, so daß eine zusätzliche Volumenvergrößerung durch Umwandlung kristalliner Hochdruckphasen in Niederdruckphasen erfolgt. Bei diesem Vorgang entsteht im Mantel eine Strömung, die der einer Quelle ähnlich ist. Diese Quellströmung hat in dem gezeigten Beispiel Afrika und Südamerika im Laufe von 10^8 Jahren auseinander getrieben. Die Corioliskraft verursachte eine starke Westdrift der Strömung, so daß man die Folgen der Expansion auf dem amerikanischen Kontinent besser erkennen kann als auf dem afrikanischen.

Wie man sieht, ist die Erdexpansion kein stetiger, sondern ein periodischer Vorgang, der keineswegs radialsymmetrisch verläuft und deshalb zu der unsymmetrischen Form der Erde geführt hat. Nach einer Zusammenstellung von Creer (1967) wächst der Erddruckmesser im Mittel jährlich um 1,2 mm. Mit diesem Wert ergeben sich die im Bild 2 zusammengestellten Daten für die Sedimentationsbedingungen zur Karbonzeit.

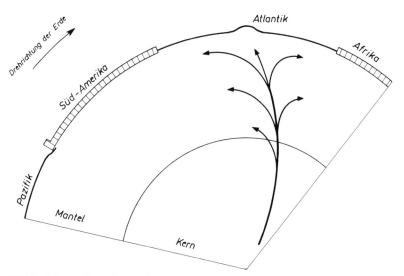

Bild 1. Schema der Erdexpansion

Vergangenheit	a	$325 \cdot 10^6$	$290 \cdot 10^6$	0
Durchmesser	km	12350	12392	12740
g/g_0	–	1,064	1,057	1
Luftdruck	kg/cm^2	1,23	1,12	1
max. Wolkenhöhe	km	11,7	10,9	10
Tageslänge	h	< 22,6	< 22,7	24

Bild 2
Veränderungen einiger Größen
bei der Abnahme des Erddurchmessers um 1,2 mm/a

Aus dem Gang der auf den heutigen Wert bezogenen Erdbeschleunigung g/g_0
folgt, daß zur Karbonzeit alle Gegenstände 6 % schwerer waren als heute. Auch
der geostatische Druck war damals um diesen Betrag größer. Der Luftdruck ist –
wenn man die nicht sehr wahrscheinliche Voraussetzung macht, daß die Luftmenge
in den vergangenen 300 Millionen Jahren konstant geblieben ist – um rund 20 %
höher gewesen und entsprach damit einem Wert, der heute in einem Schacht von
1.300 m Teufe herrscht. Die maximale Wolkenhöhe beträgt heute etwa 10 km.
Das entspricht einem Luftdruck von knapp einer drittel Atmosphäre. Nimmt man

an, daß dieser Luftdruck die Grenze der Tragfähigkeit der Atmosphäre für Wasserdampf kennzeichnet, so läßt sich die maximale Wolkenhöhe während der Karbonzeit zu 11 km bestimmen. Die Tageslänge betrug damals etwa 22,7 Stunden.

Aus dem Vorstehenden folgt, daß Wind und Regen — und damit die Erosion — sowie der Wellengang auf dem Meer etwas heftiger gewesen sein müssen als heute. Gewitter waren häufiger und auch intensiver. Das ist von Interesse für die Entstehung von Waldbränden. Die Pflanzen, insbesondere die Bäume, wurden durch den Schwerkraft- und Wettereinfluß stärker strapaziert. Es wurden also mehr Pflanzenteile abgeschlagen und dadurch die Sedimentmenge vergrößert. Die Wolkenschicht war im Karbon im Mittel 10 % dicker. Das dürfte allerdings allein zur Erklärung des Fehlens von Jahresringen nicht ausreichen.

Die aus der Erdexpansion abzuleitenden Produktionsbedingungen zur Karbonzeit decken sich mit den auf anderem Wege gewonnenen. Wichtig für die Inkohlungsgeschwindigkeit war möglicherweise die höhere Verdichtung des sedimentierten organischen Materials infolge des höheren geostatischen Druckes. Dieser Einfluß ist leider auf Grund unserer heutigen Kenntnisse nicht abzuschätzen.

Die schnelle Zunahme der biochemischen Produktivität vor und während des Karbons ließ den Sauerstoffgehalt der Atmosphäre sprunghaft nach oben schnellen, vermutlich sogar über seinen heutigen Wert hinaus (Berkner und Marshall 1963, Rutten 1965). Hohe Sauerstoffgehalte in der Atmosphäre der Karbonzeit erleichtern das Verständnis für den kalten Abbau organischer Substanz zu Zersetzungsfusinit, sowie — im Zusammenhang mit der bereits erwähnten größeren Häufigkeit von Gewittern — die Entstehung ausgedehnter Waldbrände trotz heftiger Regengüsse.

3. Biochemische Produktivität

Man fragt jetzt natürlich nach den Gründen, die einerseits zur Bildung der festen Kohlen, andererseits zur Bildung des flüssigen Erdöls geführt haben.

Die biochemische Produktivität ist durch die Fotosynthese gegeben, also durch die Reaktion zwischen Wasser und Kohlendioxid mit Licht als Energiequelle. Die beiden Ausgangsmaterialien und die Energie stehen normalerweise auf dem Lande und im Wasser gleichermaßen zur Verfügung. Die Absorption des Lichts ist aber ein Volumeneffekt. Die Oberflächen der Organismen absorbieren das auffallende Licht nicht vollständig, sondern reflektieren einen Teil. Um auch dieses reflektierte Licht auszunutzen, müssen die absorbierenden Organe in vielen Stockwerken übereinander angeordnet werden. Das ist im Wasser leicht möglich, denn die unter Lichteinfluß sich vermehrende Substanz schwimmt und kann sich infolgedessen in vielen Schichten übereinander anordnen. Die Schichtdicke entspricht theoretisch der Tiefe des Gewässers. Die Hauptmenge des Lichts wird freilich schon in den obersten 10—20 Metern absorbiert.

Auf dem Lande ist es viel schwieriger, eine Schichtdicke einzustellen, die zur vollen Ausnutzung des Lichts und damit zur optimalen biochemischen Produktivität führt. Die niederen Organismen können in der Luft nicht schwimmen, sondern sind an den Boden gefesselt. Erst als es der Natur gelang, aus der mechanisch nicht sehr festen Zellulose durch Zufügen von Lignin eine stabile Gerüstsubstanz herzustellen, mit der die lichtaufnehmenden pflanzlichen Organe, wie z.b. die Blätter, in vielen Etagen übereinander angeordnet werden konnten, stieg die biochemische Produktivität auch zu Lande auf optimale Werte an. Die absorbierende Schichtdicke ist durch die Höhe der Bäume gegeben. Sie entspricht mit einer Höhe von 10—20 Metern dem Wert, der auch im Wasser zu beobachten ist.

Die biochemische Produktivität im Wasser erzeugte vorwiegend reaktionsfreudige, wasserstoffreiche Zellinhaltsstoffe, die sich manchmal gut geschützt in einem streng anaeroben Milieu ablagerten und aus denen sich das flüssige und deshalb technisch leicht zu gewinnende Erdöl bildete. Auf dem Lande wurden vorwiegend Gerüstsubstanzen erzeugt, die wegen ihres geringen Wasserstoffgehaltes wenig reaktionsfähig sind und sich in die technisch nur umständlich zu gewinnenden Kohlen verwandelten.

Die Kohlen entstanden somit als Folge des Strebens der Natur nach optimaler biochemischer Produktivität auf dem Lande.

4. Umwandlung und Struktur

Um die vielfältigen Veränderungen verstehen zu können, die während der Inkohlung auftreten, muß man sich die Kohlen vorstellen als ein Gemisch aus den chemisch inerten Aromatkomplexen, die aus dem Lignin entstanden sind, und den zwischen diesen Komplexen befindlichen wasserstoffreichen reaktionsfreudigen Substanzen, die im folgenden „Zwischenraumsubstanz" genannt werden sollen. Diese Zwischenraumsubstanz ist aus den „öligen" Anteilen, wie den Wachsen und Harzen, sowie aus den Umwandlungsprodukten von Zellulose und Eiweißstoffen hervorgegangen, und geht im Laufe der Inkohlung in Form von Wasser, Kohlendioxid und gasförmigen Kohlenwasserstoffen verloren. Die Zwischenraumsubstanz muß keineswegs für sich isoliert vorliegen, sondern es können auch chemische Bindungen zu den Aromatkomplexen bestehen.

Bild 3 zeigt dieses Gemisch in einer freilich keineswegs maßstabsgerechten Aufteilung. Die Aromatkomplexe sind grau schattiert eingezeichnet. Sie dürfen nicht mit den röntgenografisch festgestellten Kristalliten identifiziert werden. Es handelt sich bei diesen Komplexen wahrscheinlich um Anhäufungen von zueinander unvollständig orientierter Aromatsubstanz mit Durchmessern von 10—20 AE (J. Karweil, 1966). Im kolloidchemischen Sinn sind es Aromatmizellen, die in der schraffiert dargestellten Zwischenraumsubstanz schwimmen.

	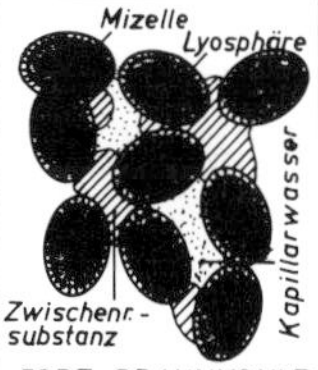 Mizelle Lyosphäre Zwischenc-substanz TORF BRAUNKOHLE	$CH_4, H_2O, CO_2, N_2,$ 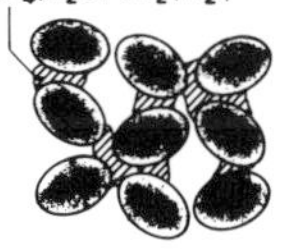 35-40% FB GASFLAMMKOHLE	$CH_4, N_2,$ 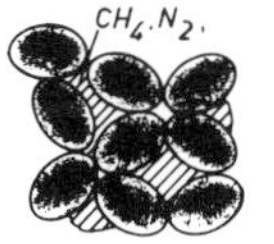 19-28% FB FETTKOHLE	Chemische Bindung CH_4 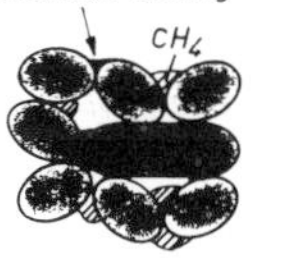 <10% FB ANTRAZIT
gasförmige Inkohlungsprodukte	–	H_2O, CO_2, CH_4 SKW, N_2	CH_4, SKW, N_2.	CH_4
Porensystem	sehr weit	weit	eng bis sehr eng	eng bis weit
Zugänglichkeit der inneren Oberfläche	sehr gut	gut	schlecht	schlecht bis gut
Benetzungswärme	–	groß	klein	mittel
Extrahierbarkeit	–	groß	klein	fehlt wegen Vernetzg.
Festigkeit	–	groß durch H-Brücken	klein	groß durch Vernetzg.
Dielektrizitäts-konstante	–	mittel durch polare Gruppen	klein	groß durch el. Leitfähigkeit
Verhalten beim Erhitzen		weites Porensystem beeinträchtigt Back- u. Bläheigenschaften	enges Porensystem u. fehlende Vernetzung bewirkt starkes Blähen und Backen	starke Vernetzung u. weites Porensystem verhindern Blähen und Backen

Bild 3. Änderungen der Mizellstruktur der Kohlen während der Inkohlung

Die Braunkohlen stellen ein Lyogel dar (G. Agde und H. Schürenberg 1942). Die Mizellen sind von einer Schicht nach außen gerichteter Wasserdipole umgeben. Zwischen den Mizellen befindet sich das punktiert gekennzeichnete Kapillarwasser sowie die schraffiert eingetragene Zwischenraumsubstanz. Braunkohlen enthalten in ihren Karboxylgruppen austauschfähigen Wasserstoff und wirken daher als Ionentauscher. Diese Eigenschaft ist für die Anreicherung von Metallen in Kohlen wichtig. Darüber werden auf dieser Tagung A. Szalay und M. Szilagyi[1]) berichten.

Die Inkohlung besteht im Braunkohlenstadium im wesentlichen aus Verdichtung und Entwässerung, so daß sich der Inkohlungsgrad durch den Wassergehalt der Kohlen oder durch ihre Verbrennungswärme charakterisieren läßt.

Wenn das Wasser im Lauf der Inkohlung durch Verdichtung und Temperaturanstieg entfernt worden ist, entstehen die gasreichen Steinkohlen deren Eigenschaften durch eine sehr sauerstoffreiche Zwischenraumsubstanz bestimmt werden. Die mechanische Festigkeit in diesem Inkohlungszustand wird durch Wasserstoffbrücken hervorgerufen. Geht der Sauerstoff im Verlauf der Inkohlung verloren, so verschwinden die Wasserstoffbrücken, und der Zusammenhalt wird dann durch die weniger

[1]) A. Szalay and M. Szilágyi, Accumulation of Microelements in Peat Humic Acids and Coal; in diesem Band.

festen van der Waals'schen Kräfte bestimmt. Das ist bei den Fettkohlen der Fall. Ist soviel Zwischenraumsubstanz verloren gegangen, daß sich die Mizellen berühren, so entstehen zwischen ihnen chemische Bindungen. Die Festigkeit steigt deshalb nach den Anthraziten hin wieder an.

Der kritische Punkt, an dem sich die Mizellen berühren, macht sich bei vielen Kohleneigenschaften bemerkbar. Er liegt bei einem Gehalt von etwa 21 % an Flüchtigen Bestandteilen bzw. 90 % an Kohlenstoff.

Im Bild sind noch einige andere Beispiele angeführt. So wird beispielsweise die Benetzungswärme anfangs durch innere Oberfläche und Wasserstoffbrücken bestimmt. Bei den Fettkohlen fehlen beide, so daß die Benetzungswärme hier durch ein Minimum geht. Nach den Anthraziten hin steigt sie wieder an, weil die Gasabspaltung während der Inkohlung neuen Porenraum und damit neue Oberfläche schafft.

Die Inkohlung spielt sich vornehmlich innerhalb der Zwischenraumsubstanz ab und ist daher durch die Menge an eben dieser Substanz zu charakterisieren. Das erfolgt bei jeder inkohlungsmäßigen Einstufung einer Kohle durch ihren Gehalt an Flüchtigen Bestandteilen. Man kann natürlich auch umgekehrt vorgehen und die Aromatkonzentration als Maßstab benutzen. Das geschieht bei der Einstufung einer Kohle durch ihr Reflexionsvermögen, denn mit dem Reflexionsvermögen mißt man die Konzentration an freien Elektronen im Aromatsystem der Kohle und damit die Größe dieser Systeme.

5. Gasabspaltung

Die Inkohlung ist mit einer Gasabspaltung verbunden, die wiederholt berechnet worden ist (H. Jüntgen und J. Karweil, I 1966). Die Resultate sind auf Bild 4 wiedergegeben. Neben Methan und Kohlendioxid entstehen auch Wasser und Stickstoff sowie geringe Mengen schwerer Kohlenwasserstoffe. Die Ergebnisse der verschiedenen Autoren unterschieden sich ziemlich stark voneinander. Das liegt z.T. an den benutzten Kohlenanalysen, z.T. an den unterschiedlichen Rechenverfahren.

Während des gesamten Inkohlungsverlaufs wird Stickstoff abgegeben. Man weiß nicht recht, wie er entsteht. Es ist zu vermuten, daß er bei der Reaktion von stickstoffhaltigen mit sauerstoff- und schwefelhaltigen Gruppen gebildet wird. Über den Ursprung des Stickstoffs in den Kohlen wird W. Flaig berichten[1].

Bei der Umwandlung von 1 kg Ausgangsmaterial mit 40 % Flüchtigen Bestandteilen zu einer Kohle mit 20 % Flüchtigen Bestandteilen wird neben rd. 70 m^3 Methan noch etwa die gleiche Menge Kohlendioxid abgespalten. Bis zum Anthrazit werden weitere 80 m^3 Methan gebildet. Kohlendioxid entsteht in diesem Bereich nicht mehr.

[1] W. Flaig, Über den Ursprung des Stickstoffs in den Kohlen; in diesem Band.

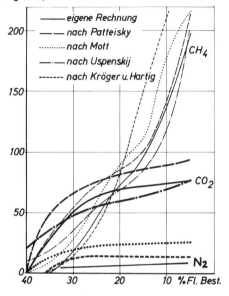

Bild 4

Integrale Gasabspaltung von CH_4, CO_2 und N_2 in Liter/kg Ausgangsmaterial mit 40 % Flüchtigen Bestandteilen

Es wird viel mehr Methan gebildet als in den Flözen gespeichert werden kann (H. Jüntgen und J. Karweil 1966 II). Das überschüssige Methan durchströmt die auflagernden Schichten und gelangt schließlich in die Atmosphäre. Die zu oberst liegenden Flöze werden infolgedessen ständig von einem Methanstrom aus den darunterliegenden durchflossen. Innerhalb eines 30 Meter hohen Schichtpaketes mit Gehalten an flüchtigen Bestandteilen zwischen 40 und 5 % wird jeder Quadratmeter des obersten Flözes im Laufe der Umwandlung von 5.000 m³ Methan durchflossen. Das entspricht theoretisch im Mittel einem jährlichen Durchfluß von 20 ml je Quadratmeter. Unter günstigen Bedingungen, d.h. bei einem dichten Deckgebirge, können sich infolgedessen auch aus den gasförmigen Inkohlungsprodukten der Steinkohlen große Gaslagerstätten bilden.

Der Spülgasstrom hat das Kohlendioxid und die schweren Kohlenwasserstoffe aus den oberen Flözen vollständig herausgespült. Diese Flöze sind zudem wegen ihres geringen Inkohlungsgrades sehr porös und behindern den Spülvorgang nur wenig. Mit zunehmender Inkohlung werden die Poren in den Kohlen immer enger, und die Kohlen deshalb immer weniger gasdurchlässig. Außerdem nimmt die Spülgasmenge mit der Teufe ab. Deshalb können in den tiefer liegenden Flözen noch schwere Kohlenwasserstoffe nachgewiesen werden (R. Gedenk, H.A. Hedemann und W. Rühl 1964). Kohlendioxid ist hier freilich nicht mehr zu finden, weil es nur zu Beginn der Inkohlung entstanden und durch den Spülvorgang sofort entfernt worden ist. Mit ständig weiter fortschreitendem Inkohlungsgrad nimmt schließlich auch die Menge der nachweisbaren schweren Kohlenwasserstoffe ab, weil die im Laufe der Zeit durch den Spülvorgang entfernten in diesem Inkohlungszustand nicht mehr nachgebildet werden können.

Wegen der extrem langen Reaktionszeiten sind weder in den Kohlen noch in den Flözgasen ungesättigte Kohlenwasserstoffe enthalten. Über die speziellen Bedingungen, unter denen auch ungesättigte Kohlenwasserstoffe bei der Ausgasung auftreten können, werden P. Hanbaba und H. Jüntgen berichten[1]).

Das $^{12}C/^{13}C$-Verhältnis in dem von den Kohlen adsorbierten Methan verschiebt sich mit zunehmendem Inkohlungsgrad immer mehr zum schweren Isotop, denn dieses ist chemisch fester gebunden (U. Colombo u.a. 1968). Das Verhältnis kann sich außerdem durch Fraktionierung während der Migration ändern. Die Ähnlichkeit des $^{12}C/^{13}C$-Verhältnisses bei Flözgasen und trocknen Erdgasen spricht dafür, daß letztere als Inkohlungsprodukte anzusprechen sind (U. Colombo u.a. 1968, W.J. Stahl 1967).

Selbstverständlich werden auch aus den kohligen Inhaltstoffen der anorganischen Sedimente Kohlenwasserstoffe gebildet, und zwar in Mengen, die nicht unterschätzt werden dürfen (W.P. Koslow und L.W. Tokarew 1960).

Für die Geschwindigkeit, mit der die bei der Inkohlung abgespaltenen Gase wandern, spielt zunächst die Loslösung der im Feinstporensystem festgehaltenen Gasmolekel eine Rolle. Das ist ein Problem der Desorptionskinetik. Die beweglich gewordenen Molekel müssen dann durch die Kohle wandern, wobei ihre Geschwindigkeit durch einen Diffusionsvorgang bestimmt wird (H.D. Schilling 1965). Auf ihrem Wege können die Molekel natürlich immer wieder durch Engpässe aufgehalten werden. Es ist eine sehr mühsame Wanderung, die die Gasmolekel in der Kohle ausführen müssen. Die Ausgasungszeiten für eine nichtrissige Kohle sind sehr lang und dem Quadrat der Teilchendurchmesser proportional. Beispielsweise verliert ein Kohlenteilchen von 1 Millimeter Durchmesser die Hälfte seines adsorbierten Gases erst in 200 Stunden. Wenn die Kohle stark rissig ist, etwa infolge tektonischer Beanspruchung, wird die Ausgasungsgeschwindigkeit um 1–2 Zehnerpotenzen erhöht (P. Grüneklee, H. Jüntgen und M. Teichmüller 1968).

Die Diffusionsgeschwindigkeit von Gasen ist außerordentlich stark von der Molekülgröße abhängig, wie erstmals durch die Anwendung einer nichtisothermen Untersuchungsmethode nachgewiesen werden konnte (P. Hanbaba, H. Jüntgen und W. Peters 1968). Die Diffusionskoeffizienten der einzelnen Glieder der homologen Reihe der Paraffine nehmen von Methan bis zum Isobutan um sechs Zehnerpotenzen ab.

---

[1]) P. Hanbaba und H. Jüntgen, Zur Übertragbarkeit von Laboratoriums-Untersuchungen auf geochemische Prozesse der Gasbildung aus Steinkohle und über den Einfluß von Sauerstoff auf die Gasbildung; in diesem Band.

Diese Ergebnisse lassen sich für den Gastransport in unverritzten Flözen anwenden,
sofern man größere Spalten infolge tektonischer Beanspruchung ausschließt. In
diesem Fall sind die auf Bild 5 angegebenen Ausgasungszeiten für eine 90 %ige
Gasentbindung aus einer Kugel aus Kohle von 1 Meter Durchmesser zu erwarten
(P. Hanbaba und H. Jüntgen, private Mitteilung).

Gas	Zeit für 90%ige Ausgasung bei 30° C in Jahren
Methan	$5 \cdot 10^4$
Äthan	$3 \cdot 10^6$
Propan	$2 \cdot 10^7$
n – Butan	$1 \cdot 10^9$
iso – Butan	$5 \cdot 10^{10}$

Bild 5

Ausgasung einer Kohlekugel
von 1 Meter Durchmesser

Die Ergebnisse über die Diffusion deuten an, daß es nicht möglich ist, die in den
Kohlen adsorbierten öligen Substanzen auf einfachem Wege zu desorbieren, weil
die Desorptionstemperatur über der Zersetzungstemperatur liegt. Nur bei extrem
schneller Erhitzung besteht die Aussicht, diese Substanzen wenigstens teilweise
unzersetzt zu gewinnen. Dem Austreiben der schweren Kohlenwasserstoffe aus den
Flözen entspricht die Migration des Erdöls. Im Erdölmuttergestein werden Gase
abgespalten durch Reaktionen, die denen der Inkohlung ähnlich sind, die aber in
Anbetracht einer flüssigen Phase und einer andersartigen stofflichen Zusammensetzung schon bei niedrigen Temperaturen, und dort relativ schnell, ablaufen. Das
Volumen der abgespaltenen Gase ist — genau wie bei den Kohlen — größer als das
Speichervolumen des Gesteins. Die Gase drücken deshalb die in den Poren gespei-
cherten flüssigen Öle in Richtung des geringsten Strömungswiderstandes aus dem
Muttergestein heraus, bis durch den nachlassenden Gasdruck oder die Auffüllung
eines weitporigen Gesteins, das eine Trennung von Gas und Flüssigkeit erlaubt, die
Wanderung endet und sich die eigentliche Lagerstätte bildet.

Damit das Öl herausgedrückt werden kann, muß der Kapillardruck überwunden
werden. Die Poren im Erdölmuttergestein sind einige μm weit. Der Kapillardruck
liegt dann bei einigen Atmosphären. Theoretisch wäre auch bei den Kohlen eine
Ölmigration möglich. Leider sind die Poren in den Steinkohlen tausendmal enger
als die im Erdölmuttergestein, so daß von den Inkohlungsgasen Kapillardrücke von
1.000 Atmosphären überwunden werden müßten, um die öligen Inhaltsstoffe aus
der Kohle herauszudrücken. Die Gasdrücke in den Flözen betragen aber maximal
nur 100 Atmosphären, sind also um eine Zehnerpotenz zu klein (J. Karweil 1966).

6. Inkohlungsgeschwindigkeit

Von großem Interesse ist die Geschwindigkeit, mit der sich das Ausgangsgemisch
in Kohle verwandelt. Es handelt sich bei diesem Prozeß um eine Folge chemischer
Reaktionen, deren Umsatz von Zeit und Temperatur abhängt. Übrigens hängt nicht
nur die Umwandlung der Kohle von Zeit und Temperatur ab, sondern auch die der
Gesteine. Wenn man daher Kohlen und Gesteine als Thermometer für geologische
Ereignisse benutzen will, müssen stets Temperatur und Zeit gemeinsam berücksichtigt werden, es sei denn, die Erhitzung erfolgte so schnell, etwa durch ein Pluton,
daß die Zeit vernachlässigt werden kann.

Druck kann die Reaktionsgeschwindigkeit nur bei solchen Stoffen beschleunigen,
die ungesättigte Doppelbindungen enthalten. Solche Bindungen sind aber viel zu
reaktionsfreudig, um in den Kohlen bestehen bleiben zu können. Da bei der Inkohlung Gase abgespalten werden, wie z.B. Methan, kann Druck die Inkohlung nur
behindern. Huck und Patteisky (1964) konnten das experimentell nachweisen.

Wenn man die Gesetze der Reaktionskinetik auf Kohlen anwenden will, muß man
sich eines extrem vereinfachten Modells über den Aufbau und die Umwandlung
der Kohlen bedienen. Dazu faßt man auf der einen Seite alle jenen Substanzen zu
einem Kollektiv zusammen, die sich an der Inkohlung wegen ihrer Reaktionsträg-
heit nicht beteiligen. Das sind im wesentlichen die hocharomatischen Systeme, die
aus dem Lignin entstanden sind. Auf der anderen Seite steht dann die Zwischenraumsubstanz, also die Wachse und Harze, die Eiweißreste und andere, die das
Kollektiv der reaktionsfähigen Stoffe bilden. Die Inkohlung besteht darin, daß die
reaktionsfähigen Stoffe das Kohlenflöz unter Bildung von Methan, Kohlendioxid
und Wasser verlassen.

Da sich die Menge der reaktionsfähigen Stoffe als Funktion des Inkohlungszustan-
des ermitteln läßt (G. Huck und J. Karweil 1953), kann man den üblichen reaktionskinetischen Ansatz machen, wonach die Reaktionsgeschwindigkeit der Zahl der
jeweils vorhandenen reaktionsfähigen Gruppen proportional ist, und den Inkohlungszustand als Funktion von Temperatur und Verweilzeit bei eben dieser Temperatur ermitteln (G. Huck und J. Karweil 1955).

Die Reaktionsgeschwindigkeit wird durch zwei Parameter bestimmt, nämlich durch
die Aktivierungsenergie – das ist ein Maß für die Temperaturabhängigkeit der
Reaktion – und durch die Stoßkonstante, die angibt, wieviel Gruppen in der Zeit-
einheit miteinander reagieren.

Für Steinkohlen wurde eine Aktivierungsenergie von 8,4 kcal/mol und eine Stoßkonstante von $3,9 \cdot 10^{-10}$ min^{-1} gefunden. Das sind Werte, die im Bezug auf die
Aktivierungsenergie eine knappe Zehnerpotenz, für die Stoßkonstante mehr als
zwanzig Zehnerpotenzen kleiner sind als die Werte, die man normalerweise für chemische Reaktionen findet.

Es gibt zwei Möglichkeiten, diese Diskrepanz zu erklären. Bei der einen schließt man folgendermaßen: Die Inkohlung ist eine Feststoffreaktion, bei der die reaktionsfähigen Stoffe durch inertes Material voneinander getrennt sind. Damit die reaktionsfähigen Moleküle zueinander finden können, sind komplizierte Drehungen und Verschiebungen notwendig. Die Reaktionsgeschwindigkeit wird in diesem Fall durch eine Diffusion im festen Zustand bestimmt. Es ist bekannt, daß man in diesem Fall sehr kleine Reaktionskonstanten beobachtet.

Nun sind in den vergangenen Jahren große Fortschritte auf dem Gebiet der Pyrolyse erzielt worden, und es liegt daher nahe, diese Ergebnisse für die Deutung der Inkohlung mit heranzuziehen. Jüntgen und van Heek (1968) haben experimentell und theoretisch gezeigt, daß die Gasabspaltung sich mit sinkender Aufheizgeschwindigkeit zu immer niedrigeren Temperaturen verlagert, und daß der geschwindigkeitsbestimmende Schritt bei einer sehr weitgehenden Änderung der Aufheizgeschwindigkeit von $10^{+5} - 10^{-3}$ Grad pro Minute stets in der Auftrennung chemischer Bindungen besteht. Das legt den Gedanken nahe, auch den Inkohlungsprozess, der freilich noch neun Zehnerpotenzen langsamer verläuft, als der langsamste Laborversuch, als Pyrolysereaktion aufzufassen. Aus der Theorie folgt, daß sich bei dieser niedrigen Aufheizgeschwindigkeit die methanbildenden Reaktionen in den Temperaturbereich zwischen 200 und 300 °C verlagern. Hanbaba (1967) hat dieses Konzept durch quantitative Rechnungen unter Verwendung von experimentell gemessenen Aktivierungsenergien näher ausgeführt. Der Grundgedanke besteht darin, daß die Inkohlungsreaktion sich zusammensetzt aus sehr vielen verschiedenen parallel miteinander ablaufenden Einzelreaktionen mit Aktivierungsenergien zwischen 50 und 62 kcal/mol und entsprechend gestuften Stoßkonstanten. Die Überlagerung aller dieser Reaktionen führt dann zu scheinbaren Reaktionskonstanten der Bruttoreaktion, die sehr kleine Werte in der oben angegebenen Größenordnung besitzen. Dies wäre eine rein chemische Erklärung der Inkohlung, und zwar als Folge von Reaktionen, die zumindest teilweise im adsorbierten Zustand ablaufen. Reaktionen im fest adsorbierten Zustand stellen eine Besonderheit dar, die eigentlich nur bei der Inkohlung beobachtet wird.

Welche von diesen beiden Deutungen für die kleinen Werte der Reaktionskonstanten richtig ist, kann zur Zeit nicht entschieden werden. Vielleicht spielen beide Einflüsse eine Rolle. Die Hanbaba'sche Deutung hätte den großen Vorteil, daß es reaktionskinetisch gesehen keinen Unterschied mehr gibt zwischen Inkohlung und Pyrolyse, zumindest nicht, solange keine Phasenumwandlungen erfolgen, wie z.B. ein Schmelzen der Kohle. Diese Deutung eröffnet möglicherweise einen Weg, die Reaktionskonstanten der Inkohlung aus Pyrolyseversuchen im Labor zu ermitteln.

Zur leichteren Durchführung von Inkohlungsrechnungen kann man sich eines Diagramms bedienen, das auf Bild 6 wiedergegeben ist (J. Karweil 1955), und dessen Gebrauch an Hand der Moskauer Braunkohlen erläutert sei. Diese Kohlen sind

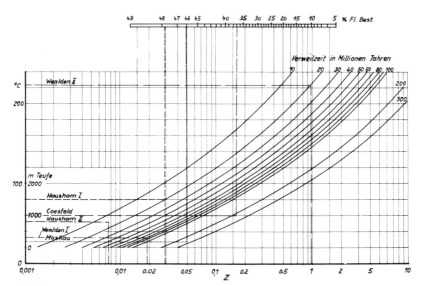

Bild 6. Berechnung der Inkohlung

etwa 300 Millionen Jahre alt und waren nicht tiefer als 200 m versenkt. Man sucht
auf der Ordinate den Wert für die Versenkungstiefe von 200 m auf, geht dann nach
rechts, bis man auf die Kurve für eine Verweilzeit von 300 Millionen Jahren stößt,
und dann nach oben, wo man einen diesem Inkohlungsverlauf zugehörigen Gehalt
an Flüchtigen Bestandteilen von 45,5 % ablesen kann. Gefunden wurden 45 %. Der
geringe Inkohlungszustand dieser an sich sehr alten Kohle ist eine Folge der niedrigen Inkohlungstemperatur.

Dieses Diagramm gilt nur für „normale" Kohlen. Fusit oder Kohlen, die während
des Inkohlungsverlaufs oxidiert worden sind, wie z.B. die Kohlengerölle, lassen
sich nicht mit dem hier angegebenen Diagramm behandeln, denn ein stofflich anders
geartetes Ausgangsmaterial bedingt andere Reaktionskonstanten als sie für die
Berechnung des Diagramms angenommen worden sind.

7. Temperaturverhältnisse während der Inkohlung

Für die Inkohlung sind — wie gesagt — Zeit und Temperatur die entscheidenden
Parameter. Die Reaktionszeiten sind aus geologischen Überlegungen bekannt. Pro-
blematisch sind die Reaktionstemperaturen, insbesondere die während der Zeit der
tiefsten Versenkung. Die Tiefe der Versenkung läßt sich zwar aus geologischen
Unterlagen ermitteln, wie kommt man nun aber zu Aussagen über die geothermische
Tiefenstufe zur Karbonzeit? Bisher hat man allen Rechnungen den heutigen Wert
zugrunde gelegt. Das ist sicher nicht ganz richtig.

Die Temperatur an der Erdoberfläche wird durch die Sonneneinstrahlung bestimmt, durch die der Erde im Mittel 285 kcal/m^{2}h zugeführt werden. Die gleiche Wärmemenge wird wieder in den Weltraum zurückgestrahlt. Die Erde befindet sich im Strahlungsgleichgewicht mit ihrer Umgebung. Der natürliche Wärmefluß aus dem Erdinnern ist mit 0,05 kcal/m^{2}h um vier Zehnerpotenzen geringer als die Sonneneinstrahlung. Die Wärmeerzeugung innerhalb der Flöze im Laufe der Inkohlung ist nochmals vier Zehnerpotenzen kleiner und deshalb in jedem Fall zu vernachlässigen.

Der Wärmeverlust der Erde mit 0,05 kcal/m^{2}h bestimmt die geothermische Tiefenstufe in der Erdkruste und damit die Temperatur, der die Kohlen während der Versenkung ausgesetzt waren. Dieser Wärmestrom stammt aus dem radioaktiven Zerfall von Uran, Thorium und Kalium. Die Konzentration dieser Elemente in der Erdkruste ist bekannt, so daß sich die radioaktive Wärmeerzeugung berechnen läßt. Man findet dafür 8 kcal/m^{2}h. Die Wärmeerzeugung ist also 150 mal größer als der Verlust. Zwar ist die Konzentration an den genannten radioaktiven Stoffen in der Kruste durch Anreicherungsprozesse, auf die später nochmals hingewiesen wird, etwas größer als die durchschnittlich zu erwartende Konzentration im gesamten Erdinnern, einen Unterschied von zwei Größenordnungen kann man aber durch Anreicherung allein nicht erklären.

Nun ist mit der Expansion der Erde eine Umwandlung von kristallinen Hochdruckphasen in Niederdruckphasen verbunden, denn der geostatische Druck verringert sich bei der Expansion mit dem Quadrat des Erddurchmessers. Die kristallinen Phasengleichgewichte werden daher ständig in Richtung größerer Volumina verschoben. Dabei wird Wärme verbraucht.

Als Beispiel für eine kristalline Phasenumwandlung sei die Umwandlung von Stichovit einer Dichte von 4,35 g/cm^3 zu Quarz mit einer Dichte von 2,65 g/cm^3 genannt. Kalorische Unterlagen für die Umwandlung kristalliner Phasen in den hier interessierenden Druckgebieten liegen nicht vor, so daß man auf eine Schätzung angewiesen ist, die sich freilich nur auf die Größenordnung beziehen kann. Für diese Schätzung soll das Bild 7 benutzt werden. Dort ist ein Schnitt durch die Erde gezeichnet mit innerem und äußerem Kern, Mantel und Kruste. Im oberen Teil des Bildes sind Dichte und Druck als Funktion der Tiefe nach Clark und Ringwood (1964) eingetragen.

Im Bereich der Kruste kann man die Umwandlungswärme der Schmelzwärme des Gesteins gleichsetzen. Das sind ungefähr 100 kcal/kg. Unter Berücksichtigung der Erdausdehnung um 1,2 mm/a und einer Volumenvergrößerung bei der Phasenumwandlung von 15 %, wie sie aus Angaben von Binge (1962) abzuleiten ist, errechnet sich ein auf die heutige Erdoberfläche bezogener Wert von 0,05 kcal/m^{2}h.

Bei der Expansion der tieferen Schichten entsteht eine Abkühlung durch Volumenarbeit, die im oberen Teil der Figur mit eingezeichnet ist. Der auf die Erdoberfläche bezogene Kühleffekt steigt danach von 0,05 kcal/m^{2}h in der Kruste auf über

J. Karweil

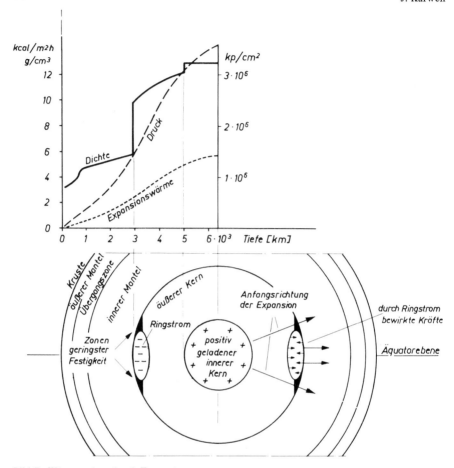

Bild 7. Wärmeverlust durch Expansion

5 kcal/m²h im Kern an. Dazu kommen noch die Wärmetönungen durch Phasenumwandlungen, insbesondere an den Dichtesprüngen, die nicht bekannt sind, sich
aber in der Größenordnung der Ionisierungsenergieen bewegen dürften, d.h. zwischen
etwa 10 und 30 eV entsprechend 5–10 kcal/m²h. Sie sind damit ungefähr genau so
groß wie die durch die adiabatische Volumenexpansion verursachten.

In dem hier vorliegenden Zusammenhang interessieren weniger die genauen Werte
der Umwandlungswärmen als vielmehr ihre Größenordnung. Es zeigt sich, daß der
Wärmeverbrauch durch die Phasenexpansion vergleichbar ist mit der radioaktiven
Wärmeerzeugung. Das Temperaturgefälle im Erdinnern wird infolgedessen in erster
Linie durch das Gleichgewicht zwischen Erzeugung und Verbrauch und erst in
zweiter Linie durch die Wärmeleitfähigkeit des Gesteins bestimmt.

Wenn auch die Wärmeerzeugung beim radioaktiven Zerfall sofort entsteht, während beim Wärmeverbrauch durch die Expansion mit einer sterisch bedingten Verzögerung zu rechnen ist, kann man doch zunächst annehmen, daß sich das Gleichgewicht zwischen Erzeugung und Verbrauch eingestellt hat. Der radioaktive Beitrag zur geothermischen Tiefenstufe wird dann in erster Näherung zeitunabhängig und muß zur Karbonzeit den gleichen Wert gehabt haben wie heute. Die Einschränkung „in erster Näherung" ist notwendig, weil zur Karbonzeit – wie bereits ausgeführt – ein höherer geostatischer Druck herrschte und deshalb der Endpunkt der Phasenexpansion auf einem höheren Druckniveau lag als heute.

Wie das Bild zeigt, werden durch den hohen Druck Elektronen aus dem inneren Kern in den äußeren gepreßt. Der Kern lädt sich dabei positiv auf, und die Elektronen bilden einen Ringstrom, der den Erdmagnetismus verursacht. Die vom Ringstrom ausgeübten Kräfte vergrößern die Polabplattung und verfestigen die Materie rings um den Kernäquator. Der Erdmagnetismus hängt in hohem Maß von den Druck- und Temperaturverhältnissen im Kern ab, insbesondere von den Vorgängen, die mit der Erdexpansion verknüpft sind, so daß eine Abschätzung der Größe der Erdexpansion auf Grund paläomagnetischer Messungen nicht ohne weiteres möglich ist. Diese Messungen, die eine größenordnungsmäßig schnellere Expansion ergeben als die paläogeografischen, sind deshalb hier nicht berücksichtigt worden.

Aus aktuellem Anlaß – wir befinden uns zur Zeit in einer Periode intensiver Sonnenaktivität – sei noch darauf hingewiesen, daß durch die Kopplung zwischen irdischem Magnetfeld und den mechanischen Spannungen im Erdinneren mit der höheren Sonnenaktivität auch eine höhere Wahrscheinlichkeit für Erdbeben verbunden ist.

Aus dem Zusammenwirken von Ringstrom mit Temperatur, Dichte und Phasenumwandlungen in Kern und Mantel ist im übrigen auf eine unstetige periodische Erdexpansion zu schließen.

Das hier entwickelte Schema kann man übrigens auch auf die Sonne anwenden. Die Quellströmungen äußern sich dort als Sonnenflecken, deren Temperatur als Folge der Phasenexpansion rund 1.000° niedriger liegt als die der Fotosphäre. Die Expansion ist also keineswegs eine Sondererscheinung, die nur auf die Erde beschränkt ist. Die Phasenumwandlungen sind in den Sonnenflecken besser zu beobachten als im Erdinneren. Es ist deshalb zu hoffen, daß die Sonnenfleckenforschung auch Einblicke in die Verhältnisse im Erdinneren vermittelt, und daß man daraus zu genaueren Unterlagen über die für die Inkohlung so wichtige geothermische Tiefenstufe gelangen kann, als sie zur Zeit zur Verfügung stehen.

Neben der radioaktiven ist die plutonische Aktivität von Einfluß auf die Temperatur. Um diesen Einfluß zu erfassen, muß man sich mit den Ursachen der Versenkung der Kohlen befassen. Die Kohlen des Ruhrkarbon entstanden in einer nassen sich langsam vertiefenden Senke am Fuße des variszischen Gebirges. Wenn sich die

Senke nur langsam vertiefte, so hob sich die Sedimentoberfläche über den Wasser-
spiegel, der Luftsauerstoff hatte Zutritt und baute die organischen Sedimente zu
ihren Ausgangsstoffen Kohlendioxid und Wasser ab. Sie verschwanden also vollständig. Ging die Senkung zu schnell vor sich, so überflutete das Wasser die Moore,
brachte sie zum Absterben und begrub die organischen unter anorganischen Sedimenten. Die Aufeinanderfolge von organischen und anorganischen Sedimenten
ist ein Ausdruck für das unstetige Wirken geophysikalischer Kräfte und für die
sehr speziellen Ablagerungsbedingungen, unter denen die Bildung von Kohlenlager-
stätten möglich war.

Nach einer gewissen Zeit kam die Senkung zur Ruhe, es trat im Gegenteil eine
Hebung ein, bei der die Schichten durch seitlichen Schub gefaltet wurden.

Dieser ganze Vorgang hat eine gewisse Ähnlichkeit mit der Bildung einer Geosynklinalen nebst anschließender Auffaltung eines Gebirges. Man sollte ihn daher einmal unter diesem Gesichtspunkt diskutieren. Die konventionelle Erklärung von
Geosynklinale und Orogen setzt geschlossene, großräumige Strömungen im Erdinnern voraus, die physikalisch leider nicht möglich sind. Zu einer physikalisch
einwandfreien Erklärung von Synklinale und Orogen gelangt man, wenn man die
Vorgänge heranzieht, die mit der Erdexpansion im Zusammenhang stehen. Dadurch
wird auch eine Abschätzung der Wärmeverhältnisse möglich.

Bei der Bildung der Erde wurden in ihrem Innern große Mengen von Wasserstoff
eingeschlossen. Da die Gesteine mit zunehmender Tiefe immer undurchlässiger
werden für Gase aller Art, ist sein Oxidationsprodukt, der Wasserdampf, aus dem
oberflächennahen Schichten der Erde verschwunden. In den tieferen Schichten ist
er noch vorhanden. Zur Abschätzung der Tiefe, bis zu der eine vollständige Desorption des Dampfes erfolgt ist, kann man davon ausgehen, daß der Wassergehalt der
oberen Schichten der Erde ursprünglich schätzungsweise 1–2 % betragen hat. Um
das auf der Erdoberfläche befindliche Wasser zu produzieren, ist dann eine Desorptionszone von 50–100 Kilometern Dicke erforderlich. Das ist ein Höchstwert,
denn zum Oberflächenwassern haben sicherlich auch die tieferen Regionen unterhalb der Desorptionszone beigetragen.

In der Desorptionszone muß die Wellengeschwindigkeit mit zunehmender Tiefe
ansteigen. Man kann infolgedessen das Maximum der Wellengeschwindigkeit mit
der Grenze der Desorptionszone identifizieren. Dieses Maximum, das unter dem
Namen Moho-Diskontinuität bekannt ist, liegt in etwa 40 km Tiefe, also an der
unteren Grenze des oben errechneten Wertes.
Der sich an dieses Maximum in Richtung zunehmender Tiefe anschließende Abfall
der Wellengeschwindigkeit, der als Gutenberg-Kanal bezeichnet wird, ist dann als
die beginnende Aufweichung des Gesteins durch die unterhalb der Desorptionszone
zunehmende Wasserdampfkonzentration zu deuten.

Wenn nun im Rahmen der großräumigen Erdexpansion, wie sie auf dem ersten
Bild gezeigt worden ist, Spalten aus größerer Tiefe aufreißen, das heißt solche, die
mindestens aus dem Gutenberg-Kanal kommen, so diffundiert Wasserdampf längs
dieser Spalte zur Erdoberfläche empor (Bild 8a). Wenn der Wasserdampf auf
seinem Weg ausgetrocknete Gesteinsschichten erreicht, deren Temperatur über etwa
700 °C liegt, so erweichen diese, denn der Wasserdampf erniedrigt ihren Schmelz-
punkt (Bild 8 b). Je mehr Wasserdampf emporsteigt, um so größer wird das erweichende Volumen. Mit dem Erweichen ist eine Volumenvergrößerung verbunden, für
die man im Mittel 15 % ansetzen kann.

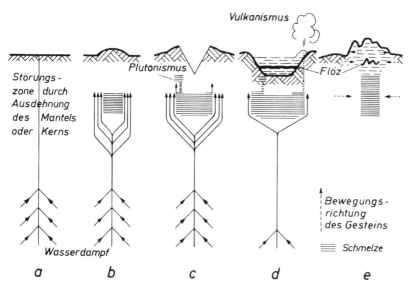

Bild 8. Geosynklinale und Gebirgsbildung

Die mit dem Erweichen verbundene Erhöhung der Beweglichkeit der Atome erlaubt
es, daß sich die durch die Erdexpansion verschobenen, aber zunächst noch eingefro-
renen kristallinen Phasengleichgewichte einstellen. Damit ist nach einer Abschätzung
von Binge (1962) eine Volumenvergrößerung um nochmals 15 % verbunden. Kürz-
lich hat Neuhaus (1968) eine Zusammenstellung über Phasenumwandlungen gegeben,
bei denen z. T. noch größere Volumenänderungen auftreten. Durch Erweichen und
Phasenumwandlung dehnt sich das aufschmelzende Volumen somit um rund 1/3
aus.

Wenn die Expansion anfangs sehr langsam verläuft, bildet sich eine Beule (Bild 8 b).
Mit wachsenden Mengen von aufsteigendem Wasserdampf nimmt auch die Expan-
sionsgeschwindigkeit zu, bis schließlich die Fließgeschwindigkeit überschritten wird,

und die Kruste unter Bildung einer Spalte aufreißt (Bild 8 c), die sich schließlich
zu einer Senke ausweitet (Bild 8 d). Bei diesem Vorgang dringt ein Teil des in großer
Tiefe unter Druck stehendem basischen Magmas nach oben. Auf den Bildern 8c und
8 d sind Vulkanismus und Plutonismus angedeutet. In einer derartigen Senke, die
sich mit zunehmender Expansion des aufgeschmolzenen Herdes vertiefte und mit
Sedimenten füllte, muß man sich die Moore der Karbonzeit vorstellen.

Erschöpft sich der Wasservorrat, der die Störung speist, so diffundiert der in dem
aufgeschmolzenen Volumen gelöste Dampf zur Atmosphäre und das Volumen
beginnt, sich unter Kontraktion zu verfestigen. Die tangentiale Komponente der
Fliehkraft auf der Erdoberfläche oder eine andere in der Nähe sich bildende Synklinale pressen die noch weiche Masse zusammen. Die in der Senke angehäuften
Sedimente werden nach oben gepreßt und dabei gefaltet (Bild 8e). Die
Falten werden dabei auseinander gezerrt, so daß sich die Größe des Zusammen-
schubes nicht durch Ausplätten der Falten feststellen läßt. Bei diesem Herausquet-
schen steigt ein Teil der eingeschmolzenen Sedimente als saures Magma nach oben.
Der aufsteigende Wasserdampf wird von radioaktiven Zerfallsprodukten wie Radon
und Helium begleitet und schleppt außerdem wasserdampfflüchtige Verbindungen
wie Kieselsäure, Alkalisalze und Metalloxide aus der Tiefe mit nach oben. Die Bildung der kieselsäurereichen Sial-Schicht und die großen Mengen von Alkalisalzen
auf der Erdoberfläche verdanken diesem Mechanismus ihre Entstehung. Durch auf-
steigenden Wasserdampf haben sich auch Uran und Thorium in der Erdkruste angereichert. Aber diese Anreicherung darf freilich nicht überschätzt werden, weil sie
durch die Verdünnung mit Kieselsäure zum Teil wieder rückgängig gemacht wird.
Sie kann deshalb nicht als Erklärung für den großen Unterschied zwischen Wärmeerzeugung und Wärmeverbrauch herangezogen werden.

Bei dem Vorgang tritt naturgemäß in der basaltischen Sima-Schicht eine Verarmung an den genannten Substanzen auf, so daß die Zusammensetzung dieser
Schicht nicht als repräsentativ für das Erdinnere betrachtet werden darf.

Die vorstehenden Angaben über den Mechanismus der Entstehung einer Geosynklinale gestatten eine Abschätzung des Beitrages des Plutonismus zur geothermischen Tiefenstufe, wobei freilich eine Reihe von starken Vereinfachungen vorge-
nommen werden muß.

Die Bildung der Ruhrkohlen vollzog sich in einem flachen Trog von ca. 100 km
Länge, 50 km Breite und etwa 3 km Tiefe. Das Volumen dieses Troges möge dem
halben Volumen eines Kastens mit senkrechten Wänden entsprechen. Auf Bild 9a
ist der einfachste Fall für die Bildung einer Geosynklinalen aufgezeichnet. Der
schräg schraffiert eingezeichnete erweichende Körper möge sich gleichmäßig nach
allen Seiten ausdehnen, wobei die Begrenzungswände parallel zu sich verschoben
werden, z.B. wird die durch die Punkte A und B gehende zur Zeichenebene senkrecht
stehende Wand nach rechts verschoben. Dadurch entsteht ein waagerecht schraffiert

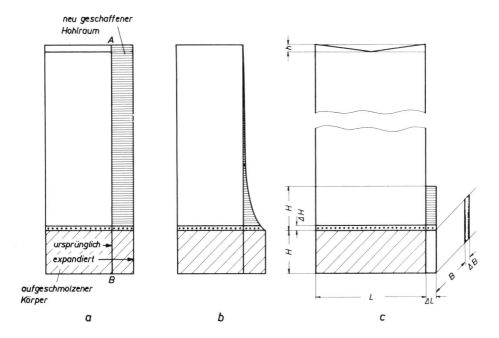

Bild 9. Schema der Vortiefe

eingezeichneter Hohlraum, bei dessen Auffüllung die Synklinale entsteht. Das
Volumen der sich bildenden Synklinale besteht aus dem gebildeten Hohlraum-
volumen abzüglich des punktiert eingezeichneten Volumens, das bei der Expansion
des aufgeschmolzenen Körpers nach oben hin verbraucht worden ist.

Bei der Expansion des aufschmelzenden Körpers werden die Gesteinswände natürlich nicht parallel zu sich verschoben, sondern es wird eine Deformation der Wand
entstehen, ähnlich der auf Bild 9b gezeichneten. Für die Rechnung kann man nun
näherungsweise annehmen, daß die Basis des durch die Expansion geschaffenen
Hohlraumvolumens durch Längen- und Breitenänderung der Synklinale gegeben
ist und daß die Höhe des Hohlraumvolumens gleich der Höhe des aufgeschmolzenen
Körpers ist.

Mit den Bezeichnungen

   L Länge

   B Breite   der Geosynklinale

   h maximale Tiefe

Δ L   Längenzunahme

Δ B   Breitenzunahme   bei der Expansion des

Δ H   Höhenzunahme   aufschmelzenden Körpers

H   Höhe des Körpers vor dem Aufschmelzen

und dem auf Bild 9c dargestellten Schema ergibt sich die Volumenbilanz mit einigen Vernachlässigungen zu

$$\Delta \text{ L.B.H.} + \Delta \text{ B.L.H.} - \Delta \text{ H (L} + \Delta \text{ L)} \cdot \text{(B} + \Delta \text{ B)} = 0{,}5 \text{ h.B.L.}$$

Setzt man eine Volumenexpansion um 1/3 voraus, also eine Änderung von Länge, Breite und Höhe des Körpers beim Aufschmelzen von je rd. 10 %, so findet man H = 6,35 · h.

Das aufgeschmolzene Volumen ist also 19 Kilometer hoch.

Für die Berechnung des von dem aufgeschmolzenen Körper erzeugten zusätzlichen Wärmestromes soll nur die Volumenmenge herangezogen werden, die bei der Ausdehnung nach oben in Richtung zur Erdoberfläche entstanden ist. Ferner wird angenommen, daß der Körper in einer Tiefe von 30 km entstanden ist, entsprechend einer Temperatur von 1.000 °C, und daß die darin enthaltene Wärme (spez. Wärme c = 0,3 kcal/kg, Dichte d = 3.000 kg/m^3) innerhalb der Versenkungsdauer (t = 20 · 10^6 a) abgeflossen ist. Für den Wärmefluß gilt dann

$$W = \frac{(B + \Delta B)(L + \Delta L) \cdot \Delta H \cdot d \cdot c \cdot T}{B \cdot L \cdot t}$$

Mit den oben angegebenen Werten findet man W = 0,017 kcal/m^{2}h.

Die zum Aufschmelzen notwendige Wassermenge läßt sich aus Angaben über den Paricutin auf 0,3 − 0,5 % der Masse des aufgeschmolzenen Körpers, also auf 1 − 2 · 10^{12} t schätzen (J. Karweil 1968). Diese Wassermenge bewirkt einen zusätzlichen Wärmestrom von ca. 1,8 · 10^{-3} kcal/m^{2}h.

Im Verlauf der Hebung, die der Senkung folgte, sind die Flöze auf etwa die halbe Versenkungstiefe aufgestiegen. Daraus errechnet sich ein Zusammenschub der Synklinale um 5 km.

Wahrscheinlich hat der Wasserdampf, der die oberkarbonische Vortiefe verursachte, zuvor die variszische Geosynklinale mit entstehen lassen. Er dient ja bei dem ganzen Vorgang eigentlich nur als Katalysator.

Es sei an dieser Stelle noch darauf hingewiesen, daß die hier vorgetragene Art der Behandlung der Wärmeverhältnisse einer Synklinale nicht ohne weiteres verallgemeinert werden darf. Mit zunehmendem Alter der Erde verlagern sich die aufschmelzenden Körper in immer größere Tiefen, weil die Schicht, die den Endzustand der Expansion erreicht hat, immer dicker wird, und weil die Grenze der Desorptionszone immer tiefer absinkt. Dadurch treten Komplikationen auf, deren Behandlung hier zu weit führen würde.

Die Abschätzung über den Wärmebeitrag des aufgeschmolzenen Körpers zeigt, daß der Temperaturgradient im Ruhrkarbon während der Zeit der tiefsten Versenkung höher gewesen sein muß als heute und vermutlich um $5-6°/100$ m gelegen hat. Die Folgen, die sich hieraus für die kinetischen Inkohlungsrechnungen ergeben, bedürfen noch einer eingehenden Prüfung. Diese Prüfung stellt einen sehr langwierigen Vorgang dar, der nur an Hand vieler Inkohlungsrechnungen für Flöze durchgeführt werden kann, deren geologische Vorgeschichte gut bekannt ist.

Es sei zum Schluß noch darauf hingewiesen, daß man aufgrund der hier vorgetragenen Auffassung die anorganische Entstehung von Erdöl ablehnen muß. Der Wasserdampf hat auf seinem Wege aus dem Erdinnern zur Erdoberfläche Stickstoff mitgenommen und allen reaktionsfähigen Kohlenstoff zu Kohlendioxid, Kohlenmonoxid, Methan und Wasserstoff verwandelt. Nun ist aber die Wassermenge auf der Erdoberfläche stöchiometrisch fünfzigmal größer als die Kohlenstoffmenge, die vom Wasserdampf vergast und zur Erdoberfläche transportiert worden ist. Das ist ein Zeichen dafür, daß in der Erdkruste ein stark wasserdampfhaltiges oxidierendes Milieu herrschen muß, in dem sich keine flüssigen Kohlenwasserstoffe in nennenswerten Mengen bilden können.

Die Kühlung durch Phasenexpansion war übrigens von entscheidender Bedeutung für die Entstehung und Erhaltung des Lebens auf der Erde. Sie hat nämlich die Aufheizung des Erdinnern verhindert und dadurch der Erde das Wasser erhalten. Die Temperatur im inneren Kern dürfte wegen der starken Kühlung nur einige hundert Grad betragen und im äußeren Kern auf wenig über tausend Grad ansteigen. Der innere Kern ist deshalb fest, der äußere flüssig oder doch zumindest weich. Am großen Dichtesprung zwischen äußerem Kern und innerem Mantel ist ein steiler Temperaturabfall in den Mantel hinein zu vermuten.

Die Expansionskühlung fehlt bei allen Himmelskörpern, deren Masse gleich oder kleiner ist als die der Venus, vorausgesetzt natürlich, daß diese Körper eine der Erde ähnliche chemische Zusammensetzung haben. Die nicht oder nur wenig expansionsfähigen Körper sind unmagnetisch, und die geothermische Tiefenstufe steigt bei ihnen auf einige hundert Grad je hundert Meter an. Unter einer hauchdünnen festen kalten Oberflächenschicht befindet sich bereits glutflüssiges Magma, und die Temperatur steigt mit der Tiefe immer weiter an. Das Wasser kocht unter diesen Umständen aus dem Inneren heraus und diffundiert in den Weltraum. Die Folgen fehlender Expansionskühlung sind auf dem Mond und dem Mars zu beobachten.

8. Schluß

Die hier geschilderten Methoden zur Untersuchung von Bildung und Umwandlung der Kohlen mögen manchmal reichlich kühn erscheinen, etwa wenn man daran denkt, daß für die Bestimmung der Reaktionskonstanten der Inkohlung aus Pyrolyseversuchen eine Spanne von 9 Zehnerpotenzen in der Aufheizgeschwindigkeit zu überspringen ist, und die Art, wie die Temperatur zur Zeit der Versenkung mit Hilfe der Erdexpansion ermittelt wird, mag fremdartig wirken. Die Vorgänge in der Vortiefe, in der sich die Kohlen bildeten, sind aber für die Chemie der Kohle so wichtig, und es ist sowenig bekannt darüber, daß man sich damit einmal etwas gründlicher befassen sollte als das bisher geschehen ist. Die Bestimmung der Reaktionskonstanten der Inkohlung aus Labormessungen, und die Ermittlung der geothermischen Tiefenstufe zur Karbonzeit, die man braucht, um die Kenntnis der Reaktionskonstanten praktisch anwenden zu können, gehören zu den derzeit aktuellsten Problemen der Inkohlung.

Das Ziel der hier geschilderten Bemühungen besteht darin, die Probleme der Kohlenbildung und -umwandlung quantitativ zu erfassen. Es genügt auf die Dauer nicht, sich mit einer reinen Phänomenologie zu begnügen, wie etwa der Messung von 20 oder 30 Stoffkonstanten von Kohle, sondern das Ziel muß der Antwort auf die Frage gelten „Warum ist das so? ". Dazu ist ein unverhältnismäßig größerer Aufwand an Theorie und Experiment notwendig als für reine Phänomenologie. Es müssen Methoden und Ergebnisse sehr unterschiedlicher wissenschaftlicher Disziplinen miteinander verknüpft werden. Deswegen ist aber auch zu hoffen, daß dabei Resultate gewonnen werden, die nicht nur für die Kohlenforschung, sondern auch für benachbarte Wissenschaftsgebiete, insbesondere die Reaktionskinetik und die Geophysik, von Nutzen sind.

Literatur

Agde, G. und Schürenberg, H.: Untersuchungen über die Kolloidstruktur der erdigen Braun-kohlen.-Braunkohle **41**, 41–48 1942.

Berkner, L.V. und Marshall, L.G.: in "The Origin and Evolution of Atmospheres and Oceans". John Wiley and Sons, New York 1963, S. 102–126.

Binge, H.J.: Folgerungen der Diracschen Hypothese für die Physik des Erdkörpers. – Dissertation Hamburg 1962.

Clark, S.P. und Ringwood, A.E.: Rev. Geophys. **2**, 35–88, 1964.

Colombo, U., Gazzarini, F., Gonfiantini, R., Kneuper, G. sowie Teichmüller, M. und R.: Das Verhältnis der stabilen Kohlenstoffisotope von Steinkohlen und kohlenbürtigem Methan in Nordwestdeutschland. – Z. angew. Geol. **14**, 257–65, 1968.

Creer, K.M.: Die Expansion der Erde. – Umschau in Wiss. und Techn. **67**, 13–16, 1967.

Gedenk, R., Hedemann, H.A. und Rühl, W.: Oberkarbongase, ihr Chemismus und ihre Beziehungen zur Steinkohle – Cinquième Congrès International de Stratigraphie et de Géologie du Carbonifère, Paris, 9–12. September 1963, S. 431–450.

Grüneklee, P., Jüntgen, H. und Teichmüller, M.: Brennstoff-Chemie, in Vorbereitung.

Hanbaba, P.: Reaktionskinetische Untersuchungen zur Kohlenwasserstoffentbindung aus Steinkohlen bei niedrigen Aufheizgeschwindigkeiten – Dissertation Aachen 1967.

Hanbaba, P. und Jüntgen, H.: Physikalische und chemische Vorgänge bei der Gasentbindung aus Steinkohle. – Erdöl und Kohle – Erdgas – Petrochemie, im Druck.

Hanbaba, P., van Heek, K.H., Jüntgen, H. und Peters, W.: Gasabspaltung bei Pyrolyse von Steinkohlen unter extrem verschiedenen Aufheizgeschwindigkeiten – Vortrag auf der 7. Internationalen Kohlenwissenschaftlichen Tagung in Prag 1968.

Hanbaba, P., Jüntgen, H. und Peters, W.: Nichtisotherme instationäre Messung der aktivierten Diffusion von Gasen an Festkörpern am Beispiel der Steinkohle. – Berichte Bunsenges. f. phys. Chem. **72**, 554–62, 1968.

Huck, G. und Karweil, J.: Versuch einer Modellvorstellung vom Feinbau der Kohle – Brennstoff-Chemie **34**, 97–102, 129–135, 1953.

Huck, G. und Karweil, J.: Physikalisch-chemische Probleme der Inkohlung – Brennstoff-Chemie **36**, 1–11, 1955.

Huck, G. und Patteisky, K.: Inkohlungsreaktionen unter Druck. – Fortschr. Geol. Rheinld. und Westfalen **12**, 551–558, 1964.

Jüntgen, H. und van Heek, K.H.: Gas Release from Coal as a Function of the Rate of Heating. – Fuel XLVII, 103–117, 1968.

Jüntgen, H. und Karweil, J.: Gasbildung und Gasspeicherung in Steinkohlenflözen I. Gasbildung – Erdöl und Kohle – Erdgas – Petrochemie **19**, 251–258, 1966.

Jüntgen, H. und Karweil, J.: Gasbildung und Gasspeicherung in Steinkohlenflözen, II. Gasspeicherung – Erdöl und Kohle – Erdgas – Petrochemie **19**, 339–344, 1966.

Karweil, J.: Die Metamorphose der Kohlen vom Standpunkt der physikalischen Chemie – Z. deutsch. geol. Ges. **107**, 132–139, 1955.

Karweil, J.: Inkohlung, Pyrolyse und primäre Migration des Erdöls – Brennstoff-Chem. **47**, 161–169, 1966.

Karweil, J.: Bildung der Kohlen, Umwandlung der Kohlen und Expansion der Erde. – Vortrag im Kolloquium der Bergbauforschung GmbH., Essen-Kray, am 15.5.68.

Koslow, W.P. und Tokarew, L.W.: Gasbildung in sedimentären Schichten. − Z. Angew. Geologie 6, 537−544, 1960.

Neuhaus, A.: Über Phasen- und Materiezustände in den tieferen und tiefsten Erdzonen. − Geologische Rundschau 57, 972−1001, 1968.

Peters, W. und Jüntgen, H.: Einfluß der Hohlraumstruktur auf Gas-Feststoffreaktionen an Steinkohle. − Chem. Ing. Techn. 40, 1039−44, 1968

Rutten, M.G.: Geologic Data on atmospheric History. − Vortrag auf dem internationalen Symposium über Luftchemie und Radioaktivität, Visby, August 1965.

Schilling, H.D.: Die Sorptionskinetik von Methan an Steinkohlen als physikalisch-chemisches Grundphänomen der Ausgasung hereingewonnener Steinkohle −− Dissertation Aachen 1965.

Schilling, H. D., Jüntgen, H. und Peters, W.: Die Sorptionskinetik von Methan an Steinkohlen als Grundlage des Ausgasungsprozesses. − Glückauf-Forschungshefte 27, Nr. 5, 203−214, 1966.

Stahl, W.J.: Zur Methodik der $^{12}C/^{13}C$-Isotopen-Untersuchungen an Erdgasen − Erdöl und Kohle − Erdgas − Petrochemie, 20, 556−559, 1967.

van Heek, K.H., Jüntgen, H. und Peters, W.: Nichtisotherme Reaktionskinetik der Kohlenpyrolyse − Brennstoff-Chemie 48, 163−170, 1967.

Fatty Acids Derived from the Green River Formation Oil Shale by Extractions and Oxidations[1]) — A Review

A. L. Burlingame, Patricia A. Haug[2]), Heinrich K. Schnoes[3]) and Bernd R. Simoneit

Space Sciences Laboratory, University of California
Berkeley, California, USA

The Green River Formation oil shale (Eocene - - 52 x 10^6 years) is a carbon rich sedimentary rock thought to be the end result of sedimentation of algae and protozoa in a series of freshwater lakes. An extensive investigation of the carboxylic acids occurring in this shale has been undertaken to elucidate the nature and biopaleontological relationships of these components and to allow correlations with previous studies on the alkanes isolated from this formation.

The exhaustive benzene/methanol extract consisted of 2.2 percent (0.04 % of the shale) acids which, after successive GLC separations of the methyl esters, were identified individually by low resolution mass spectrometry. The major components found were C_7-C_{12} normal carboxylic acids; C_9-C_{10} isoprenoid acids; $C_{12}-C_{18}$ normal a, ω-dicarboxylic acids; C_{16}, C_{18} and C_{19} β-methyl-n-a, ω-dicarboxylic acids; and C_{10} and C_{12} ketoacids. In minor amounts were found benzoic-, phenyl alkanoic-, naphthoic-, cyclic-, mono-unsaturated- and cycloaromatic acids.

The acids liberated from the mineral-kerogen matrix after HF/HCl treatment of exhaustively extracted shale amounted to 31.5 percent of the extract (0.06 percent of the shale). Again, separations were carried out by GLC techniques and structural identification of individual components, as well as homologous series by high and low resolution mass spectrometry. This fraction consisted mainly of C_5-C_{32} normal acids; C_8-C_{22} branched-chain acids; and C_3-C_{18} n-a, ω-dicarboxylic acids. In small amounts were found: C_4-C_{16} methylketoacids; C_5-C_{18} mono-unsaturated and/or cyclic acids; C_7-C_{15} benzoic acids; $C_{11}-C_{14}$ naphthoic acids; and $C_{10}-C_{15}$ cycloaromatic acids.

Subsequent oxidation of the kerogen concentrate with chromic acid successively for 3,6 15 and 24 hours yielded substantial quantities of fatty acids (0.60 percent of the shale), which were identified by the same techniques used for the previous fractions. The major homologous series found were: C_3-C_{35} normal acids; C_3-C_{27} branched-chain acids; and C_4-C_{22} a, ω-dicarboxylic acids. The minor constituents were: C_4-C_{20} methylketoacids; C_5-C_{26} monounsaturated and/or cyclic acids; C_7-C_{18} benzoic acids; $C_{11}-C_{13}$ naphthoic acids; $C_{10}-C_{18}$ cycloaromatic acids; di- and tricarboxylic aromatic acids; and tetracyclic- and pentacyclic monocarboxylic acids.

---

[1]) This review represents Part XXVII in the Series High Resolution Mass Spectrometry in Molecular Structure Studies. For Part XXVI, see A.L. Burlingame and B.R. Simoneit, Nature, in press.

[2]) Present address: Department of Chemistry, Rice University, Houston, Texas

[3]) Present address: Department of Biochemistry, University of Wisconsin, Madison, Wisconsin

Introduction

The Green River Formation Oil Shale, a sedimentary rock of Eocene age (ca. 52×10^6 years) was presumably formed by deposition of organic debris from a non-marine environment. The sediment is extremely rich in organic carbon (The carbon-hydrogen analysis of the oil shale used in these studies is 20.1 percent Carbon, 2.3 percent Hydrogen, 0.6 percent Nitrogen, 0.3 percent Sulphur and 67.0 percent residue) yielding an average of 40 gallons of crude oil per ton of shale. The organic matter, which is thought to derive mainly from algae (Bradley, 1966) and protozoan remains, is sedimented with silt consisting predominantly of carbonate minerals. Available geologic and geochemical evidence supports the view that the shale has not been subjected to either high temperatures or pressures, suggesting that the organic matter should be relatively well preserved.

Partly because of its potential economic value as a rich source of petroleum and partly because of its intrinsic scientific interest, the sediment has been quite actively investigated in recent years. Chemical studies have been concerned with both the shale oil resulting from retorting of bulk sediment, and the organics solvent extractable from the oil shale. Results based on the former method, which must involve considerable degradation of the organic material, are of lesser interest from the paleobiochemical viewpoint, and most of the detailed structural and stereochemical data are derived from extraction experiments.

Chemical analyses, although far from complete, are in agreement with the general assumption that biological precursors are a major source of the fossil organic matter. Thus, the presence of homologous series of normal and isoprenoidal hydrocarbons has been established. Normal alkanes ranging from C_{13} to C_{33} (lower homologues are probably lost in extraction procedures) exhibit an odd over even predominance not unlike the pattern observed for present-day biological alkane mixtures (Eglinton, Scott, Belsky, Burlingame, Richter and Calvin, 1966). Isoprenoidal alkanes (C_{15}, C_{16}, C_{18} to C_{20}) have been identified (Eglinton, Scott, Belsky, Burlingame, Richter and Calvin, 1966; Robinson, Cummins and Dinneen, 1965; Cummins and Robinson, 1964). Steranes, triterpanes and C_{40}-terpenoidal hydrocarbons, among which cholestane, ergostane, sitostane, lupane (Burlingame, Haug, Belsky and Calvin, 1965), gammacerane (Hills, Whitehead, Anders, Cummins and Robinson, 1966) and perhydro-β-carotene (Murphy, McCormick, Eglinton, 1967) are fairly convincingly characterized.

The fact that the aliphatic isoprenoidal, steroidal, triterpenoidal and tetraterpenoidal alkanes are prominent components of the saturated hydrocarbon fraction (Haug, 1967) represents excellent evidence for the biological origin of the organic matter extractable from this oil shale.

Next to the hydrocarbon fraction, the acidic constitutents of the extractables and those formed upon demineralization and matrix oxidation have received most experimental attention and comprise the subject of this review. A homologous series of straight-chain carboxylic acids from C_{10} to C_{34} was reported by Lawlor and Robinson (1965); normal acids of similar or more limited range have also been found by several other investigators (Haug, 1967; Abelson and Parker, 1962). Oxidation experiments of shale kerogen have yielded a series of normal acids up to C_{35} (Burlingame and Simoneit, 1968). The presence of *iso* and *anteiso* acids has been claimed on the basis of g.l.c. and infrared data in one study (Leo and Parker, 1966), but this finding has not yet been confirmed by other workers. The occurrence of isoprenoidal acids (C_8, C_9, C_{14} to C_{17}, C_{19} to C_{21}) is well established (Haug, 1967; Eglinton, Douglas, Maxwell, Ramsay and Ställberg-Stenhagen, 1966; Douglas, Douraghi-Zadeh, Eglinton, Maxwell and Ramsay, 1968); phytanic and norphytanic acids are major components of this fraction, paralleling to some extent the distribution of isoprenoidal alkanes. The isoprenoidal skeleton also occurs linked to the kerogen matrix — a finding of importance in correlation of the organic polymer structure to the extractables in this oil shale (Burlingame and Simoneit, 1968). A recent study of the isoprenoid acid methyl esters by gas chromatography has shown a diastereoisomeric composition which is compatible with a chlorophyll derivation for these acids (MacLean, Eglinton, Douraghi-Zadeh, Ackman and Hooper, 1968). In addition, the occurrence of oxo-acids (Haug, Schnoes and Burlingame, 1967) and several series of aromatic carboxylic acids (Haug, Schnoes and Burlingame, 1968) has been reported.

Porphyrin constituents of the shale and its shale oil have been investigated recently. Homologous series of alkylated etio-porphyrins, carboalkoxy porphyrins, cycloalkyl- and alkylbenzoporphyrins appear to be present (Morandi and Jensen, 1966; Baker, Yen, Dickie, Rhodes and Clark, 1967).

Much of the chemical work thus far has been directed toward the discovery and structural elucidation of compounds thought to be directly related to common biological precursor material. The emphasis on the search for isoprenoidal and triterpenoidal alkanes and isoprenoidal acids is a reflection of current interest in this field. For a deeper understanding of both the biological and diagenetic processes which contributed to the genesis of shale organics, a broadening of the research effort would appear desirable. Such should include the study of additional compound classes, the kerogen material, quantitative data on the occurrence and distribution of certain compounds as well as compound classes relative to others, and data detailing the nature of isolated organics in the rock matrix.

Some data bearing on the distribution of hydrocarbons as a function of depth of deposition are available from the work of Robinson, Cummins and Dinneen (1965) who found that the chain length of isoprenoidal alkanes tended to decrease with depth (while total content increases), and the interesting finding of Eglinton,

Douglas, Maxwell, Ramsay and Ställberg-Stenhagen (1966) of the predominance of the C_{12} acid at the 1200 ft. level of the shale. However, in most cases data presently available do not permit sound speculation as to specific sources of the compounds found, diagenetic transformation pathways, or the relationships between different compound classes.

Since previous investigations were aimed usually at the isolation of specific compounds or compound classes and are based on one method of extraction and isolation, giving thus perhaps a somewhat distorted picture of the amounts and range of certain compound types present, we thought it of some interest to obtain data on the total distribution of compounds resulting from different extraction methods.

Table I. Organic acid fractions of the Green River Formation, per 100 g oil shale sample ($\sim$ 45 % kerogen concentrate).

1. **First Extract** (ϕ H $-$ MeOH)

   | totals: | 1300 mg |
   | acids: | 8 mg |

2. **Exhaustive Extract** (ϕ H $-$ MeOH)

totals:	440 mg
acids: (heptane)	30 mg
(ether)	18 mg

3. **Matrix Entrapped Acids** (after demineralization HF/HCl)

totals:	190 mg
acids: (heptane)	60 mg
(ether)	1.5 mg

4. **Oxidation** (3 hour, CrO_3- H_2SO_4)

totals:	145 mg
acids: (heptane)	60 mg
(ether)	34 mg

5. **Oxidation** (9 hour, CrO_3- H_2SO_4)

totals:	225 mg
acids: (heptane)	35 mg
(ether)	150 mg

6. **Oxidation** (24 hour, CrO_3- H_2SO_4)

totals:	398 mg
acids: (heptane)	48 mg
(ether)	320 mg

7. **Oxidation** (48 hour, CrO_3- H_2SO_4)

totals:	685 mg
acids: (heptane)	274 mg
(ether)	360 mg

We chose to investigate the carboxylic acids obtainable from the oil shale of the Green River Formation by three experimental procedures:

(a)   direct extraction of the whole shale with organic solvents,
(b)   demineralization of the exhaustively extracted shale followed by extraction, and
(c)   successive oxidations of the residue remaining after demineralization ("kerogen").

Our data are as yet of a preliminary nature, requiring in many cases verification by identification of individual compounds only partly accomplished by this study, but they provide information on the total acid content, range and nature of acids contained in, and bound to, the polymer and mineral matrices (Table I).

The oxidation experiments were carried out in a stepwise fashion up to 48 hour total duration, at which time all organic matter was essentially degraded. These results do not bear on the acids occurring as such in the shale, but give some insight into the composition of the kerogen material.

Part I: Exhaustive Extraction of Shale

Experimental

In order to minimize contamination, several precautions were followed throughout these studies. All microlabware was treated with chromic acid, rinsed with distilled water and distilled organic solvents; this same procedure was applied to most of the glassware used in the large scale workup. All solvents used were A.C.S. reagent grade and redistilled in all glass stills. Other reagents used were checked for organic contaminants and treated to remove any that were present.

Shale samples from the Colorado Green River Formation were collected from a cliff-outcrop at Parachute Creek, 8 miles northwest of Grand Valley, Colorado, latitude N 39° 37', longitude W 108° 7', at an elevation of 7300 feet. After removal of the outer one-half inch of rock surface from several large pieces and rinsing with solvent, 5.3 kg of shale was broken into small fragments (3—20 mesh) and ultrasonically extracted in batches with benzene/methanol (4:1 v/v). These extracts were not further investigated. Further treatment of the shale is illustrated in an abbreviated form by the flowsheet of Figure 1. The shale was pulverized (about 200 mesh) and extracted twice (in batches of 500 g of shale to 2 1 of 4:1 benzene/methanol) for twenty minutes with mechanical stirring and sonication. From this extract, 55 g of hexane soluble material was obtained. This material was divided into two portions of 26 and 29 g respectively, each dissolved in 500 ml of hexane and extracted three times with 100 ml portions of 1 N NaOH. The aqueous solutions were combined, extracted three times with 100 ml of hexane, filtered, acidified to pH 1 and

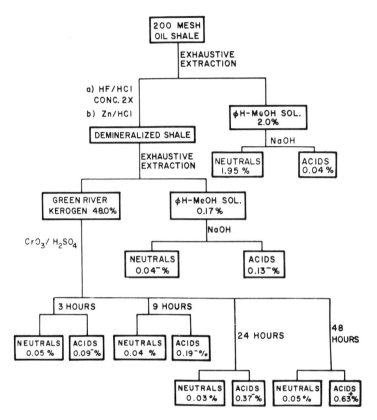

Fig. 1. Experimental flowsheet for the isolation of the various acid fractions from the Green River Formation oil shale

extracted with three 50 ml volumes of hexane. A total of 0.28 g of acidic material was obtained in this way. Acids were separated from phenols by extraction with a saturated solution of $NaHCO_3$ of half of this acidic material in 10 ml of hexane. The acids thus obtained were treated with BF_3/MeOH reagent and refluxed for one hour. Esters were analyzed by gas chromatography without further fractionation. Esters collected from one g.l.c. run (5 % SE-30, on 80–100 mesh Aeropak 30, 10' x 1/4" column, Helium carrier gas, flow rate of 50 ml/minute, programmed from 50°– 280° at 2°/minute) were analyzed by mass spectrometry without further purification. From a second separation on the same column (programmed at 4°/minute) collected fractions were rechromatographed [6' x 1/4" column, 3 % HIEPF 8 BP on 80/100 mesh Gaschrom Q (Applied Science), flow rate of 50 ml/minute, programmed at 6°/minute] and subsequently analyzed by mass spectrometry. Fractions from a third gas chromatogram (using the SE-30 column, conditions as for the first case) were analyzed by high resolution mass spectrometry. Identifications are based on the data from these three analyses. A typical gas chromatogram of the total ester mixture is shown in Figure 2 (10' x 1/16" column, of 3 % SE-30 on 80/100 mesh Aeropak 30, flow rate 30 ml/minute, programmed from 50° to 280° at 2°/minute).

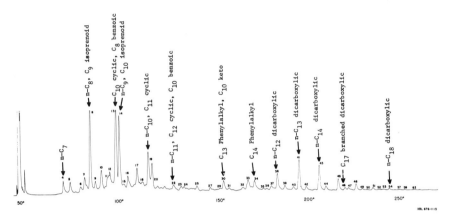

Fig. 2. Gas chromatogram of the total acid esters isolated from the first extract. Column conditions: 10 ft. x 1/16 in.; 3 percent SE-30 on 80/100 mesh Aeropak 30; 30 ml/minute helium; programmed from 50 °C to 280 °C at 2 °C/minute

A sample of the extracted oil shale described above was further extracted by the following procedure. After sieving the sample through 200 mesh it was Soxhlet extracted for one week with 3:1 benzene/methanol and then treated by ultrasonication with portions of the same solvent system until no more organics could be solubilized. All extracts were combined and the solvent evaporated under vacuum, yielding 440 mg organics per 100 g sample. The extract was dissolved in heptane and the acids were removed with 6 N NaOH. From the acidified aqueous solution 30 mg of acids were extracted with heptane and a subsequent diethyl ether extract yielded another 18 mg of more polar acids. Both fractions were esterified with BF_3/methanol and the heptane soluble acid ester fraction was clathrated with urea (Burlingame and Simoneit, 1968), yielding 1:1 normals/branched-cyclics. The total, normal and branched-cyclic fractions, were chromatographed on a 5 ft. x 1/8 in. column, packed with 3 % SE-30 on Chromosorb Q and programmed from 100° to 250° at 10°/minute with a flow rate of 40 ml/minute. The gas chromatograms of the heptane soluble acids are shown in Figure 3. The g.l.c. trace of the total ether soluble acids is shown in Figure 4. The labeled peaks were checked by coinjection of standards and identified from their retention times, low resolution mass spectra

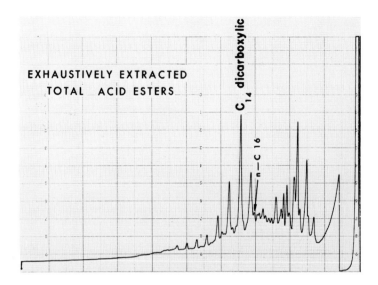

Fig. 3. Gas chromatogram of the total heptane soluble acid esters isolated from the second exhaustive extract. Column conditions: 5 ft. x 1/8 in.; 40 ml/minute helium; programmed 100 °C to 250 °C at 10 °C/minute

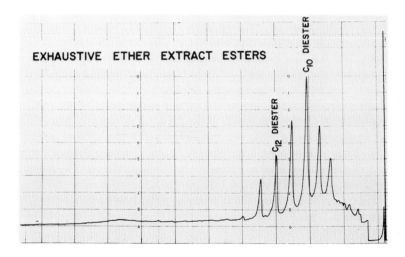

Fig. 4. Gas chromatogram of the total ether soluble acid esters isolated from the second, exhaustive extract. Column conditions as in Figure 3

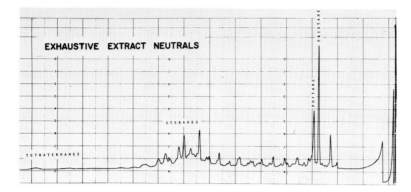

Fig. 5. Gas chromatogram of the neutral fraction isolated from the second, exhaustive extract. Column conditions as in Figure 3

and correlations with high resolution mass spectral data. For comparison the neutral and basic fraction from this extract was also analyzed by gas chromatography (Figure 5) and high resolution mass spectrometry (Figure 6).

All unit resolution mass spectra were obtained either on a modified G.E.C. − A.E.I. MS–902 or a C.E.C. 21–110B mass spectrometer using a direct insertion probe for sample introduction or an all glass introduction system for very volatile samples. The ion source temperature was kept as low as possible to achieve volatilization of samples, usually around $100° − 150°$. High resolution mass spectra were recorded *via* photoplate (C.E.C. 21–110B) (Burlingame, 1966) or *via* direct on-line computer data acquisition and processing (Burlingame, 1968; Burlingame, Smith, Merren and Olsen, 1968). High resolution mass spectral data are presented as heteroatomic plots (Burlingame and Smith, 1968).

Results

Data presented in this section are based on two sets of experiments. The first approach, as detailed in the experimental part, involved the extraction of relatively large quantities of rock and removal of acids from the total extract thus obtained. In order to insure more complete extraction of organic matter, the extracted rock powder from the large scale experiments was subjected to further exhaustive Soxhlet and ultrasonic extraction. In this section we combine the results from these two extractions, although methods of identification and experimental procedures differed somewhat.

The various homologous acid series found are listed in Table II and are discussed in the same order. The range of distribution and maxima indicated in this table are derived mainly from high resolution mass spectra of total mixtures. They are not *a priori* indicative of relative abundances of compounds and must be considered with

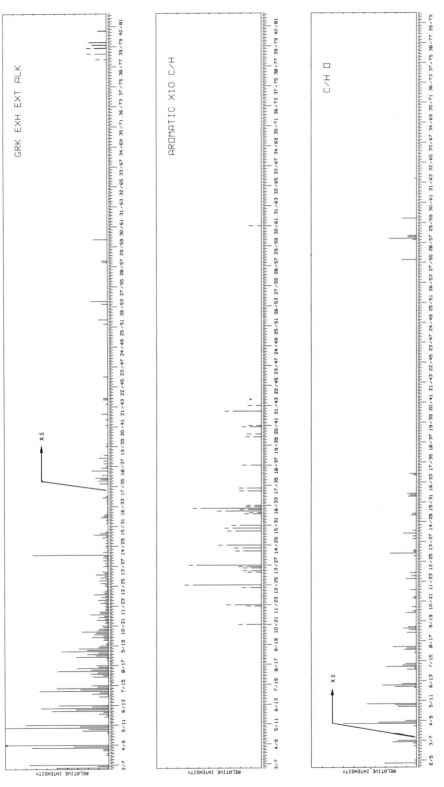

Fig. 6. High resolution mass spectral data for the neutral fraction isolated from the second, exhaustive extract

Table II. Organic acids from the exhaustive extracts of the Green River Formation oil shale (extracted with heptane and ether), listed as free acids.

	range	maximum concentration
1. Normal Acids		
first extract	C_7-C_{12}#+	C_8
exhaustive extract	C_5-C_{20}*	
2. Branched Acids		
first extract	C_9, C_{10}#+	C_9
exhaustive extract		
3. Dicarboxylic Acids		
first extract	$C_{12}-C_{18}$#+	C_{13}
exhaustive extract (heptane)	C_8-C_{15}*	
(ether)	C_8-C_{14}+	C_{10}
4. Ketoacids		
first extract	C_{11}, C_{14}#+	
exhaustive extract	C_5-C_{15}*	C_6
5. Cyclic Acids $(C_nH_{2n-2}O_2)$		
first extract	C_8-C_{12}#+	C_{10}
exhaustive extract	C_5-C_{16}*	
6. Aromatic Acids (phenyl $C_nH_{2n-8}O_2$)		
first extract	C_8-C_{14}#+	C_8
exhaustive extract	C_7-C_{17}*	C_8
7. Aromatic Acids (naphthyl $C_nH_{2n-14}O_2$)		
first extract	C_{12}, C_{13}#+	C_{12}
exhaustive extract	$C_{11}-C_{17}$*	C_{12}
8. Aromatic Acids $(C_nH_{2n-10}O_2)$		
first extract	$C_{13}-C_{15}$#+	C_{14}
exhaustive extract	$C_{10}-C_{17}$*	C_{10}

\# Determined by low resolution mass spectrometry of isolated samples
+ Determined from gas chromatogram
* Determined by high resolution mass spectrometry

some caution, since the relative abundances of molecular ions vary with compound type in addition to the non-linearity in photoplate response characteristics with ion beam intensity for high resolution mass spectrograms (Venkataraghavan, McLafferty and Amy, 1967). Relative ion beam intensity measurements are accurate to the 1–2 % level for the real-time high resolution data (Burlingame, Smith, Merren and Olsen, 1968). Figure 7 represents the high resolution mass spectrum of this fraction -- sorted according to heteroatomic content (i.e., C/H, C/H O, C/H O_2, etc. ions).

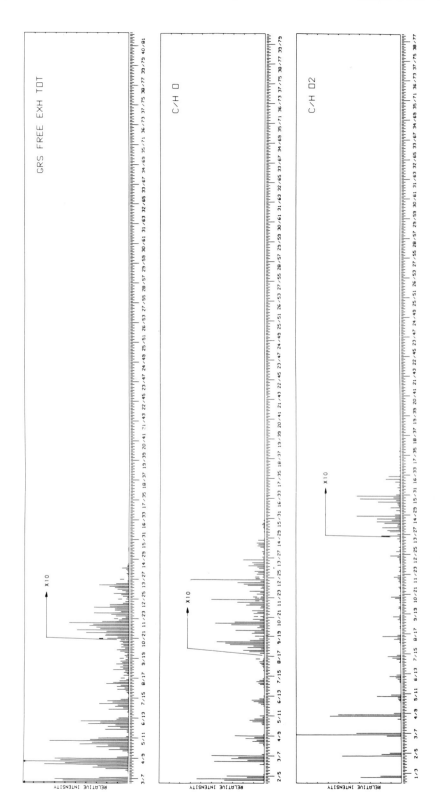

Part of Fig. 7

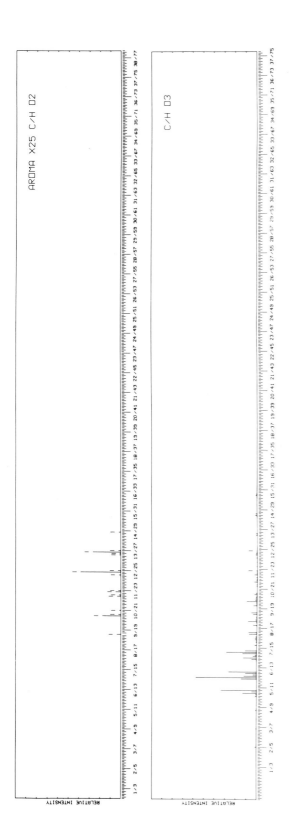

Fig. 7. High resolution mass spectral data for the total acid esters isolated from the second, exhaustive extract

The extraction experiments revealed a distribution of normal saturated acids ranging from C_5 up to C_{20}. From the first extraction five normal acids (C_7-C_{11}) were isolated and identified by mass spectrometry (present in peaks labelled 4, 8, 14, 19 and 22 in Figure 2). The high resolution mass spectrum of the total heptane soluble acid ester mixture (Figure 7) from the second exhaustive extraction exhibits molecular ions corresponding to saturated acids ranging from C_5 to C_{20}. For example, the molecular ion of the C_6 acid is found at $C_7H_{14}O_2$ (since the mass spectrum is that of the methyl ester mixture) in the C/H O_2 plot (Burlingame and Smith, 1968) of Figure 7. Higher homologues of this class are readily identifiable from this plot. The gas chromatogram of this ester mixture (Figure 3) shows some components above C_{10}, but our data indicate that the major acids obtained by direct extraction are relatively low molecular weight compounds. Only two branched acids, the C_9 and C_{10} isoprenoid acids, have been isolated from the extract. The g.l.c. pattern indicates that higher homologues are present, but no definite identifications were made. Results from the second extraction indicate that the branched acids represent only a very minor part of the total acid mixture. Pristanic and phytanic acids are certainly not major constituents of this mixture.

Seven saturated straight-chain α,ω-dicarboxylic acids (C_{12} to C_{18}, Haug, Schnoes and Burlingame, 1967) have been identified as constitutents of the first extract. In addition, the C_{13}, C_{15} and C_{16} dicarboxylic acids bearing one a-methyl substituent are present (Haug, Schnoes and Burlingame, 1967).

In the high resolution mass spectrum of the second exhaustive extract (Figure 7) a series of α,ω-dicarboxylic acids ranging from C_8 to C_{15} is apparent. The molecular ions are of very low abundance and are omitted from Figure 7 but the corresponding peaks resulting from losses of CH_3O and ketene (typical for this class of compounds) can be seen in the C/H O_3 and C/H O_2 plots respectively. The ether soluble acids from the second extraction (Figure 4) were shown to be a homologous series of saturated dicarboxylic acids (C_8 to C_{14}) by low resolution mass spectrometry. Thus a homologous series ranging from C_8 to C_{18} has been isolated from the shale by direct extraction. It is interesting to note that the ether-soluble acids exhibit a maximum at C_{10} (Figure 4) whereas the dicarboxylic acids obtained in the first extraction maximize at C_{13}, C_{14} (Figure 2, peaks 41, 43).

A series of ketoacids is indicated by the high resolution mass spectra of the total acid mixture. They appear to comprise all homologues from C_5 to C_{15}. As shown in Figure 7, the molecular ions of this series are found at positions $C_nH_{2n-2}O_3$ in the C/H O_3 plot and the peaks arising from elimination of CH_3O and C_3H_5O are prominently displayed in the C/H O_2 plot. Two of these were isolated from the acids of the first extraction and identified as the C_{11} and C_{14} methylketo acids (methyl 10-oxoundecanoate and methyl 13-oxotetradecanoate) by low and high resolution mass spectrometry (Haug, Schnoes and Burlingame, 1967).

Cyclic acids ranging in molecular weight from 150 to 212 (C_8 to C_{12}) have been isolated from the first extraction but no definite compounds have yet been identified. A similar series of cyclic and/or unsaturated acids is indicated by the high resolution mass spectrum (Figure 7) which shows peaks although of very low intensity corresponding to molecular ions of cyclic acid esters from C_5 to C_{16}.

There appears to be a relatively aboundant series of aromatic acids. The first extraction yielded a series ranging from C_8 to C_{14} among which methyl substituted benzoic acids (C_8 to C_{10}) are particularly prominent. Several (C_{11}, C_{12}, C_{13} and C_{14}) phenylalkanoic acids were also isolated. These acids could not be definitely identified, but the general structural type is readily recognized from the mass spectral fragmentation pattern. A similar distribution of aromatic acids in the heptane soluble mixture of the second extract is evident from the high resolution mass spectrum (Figure 7). Acids of composition $C_nH_{2n-8}O_2$ ranging from C_7 to C_{17} with an apparent maximum at C_8 were detected. Condensed aromatic systems are also present. From the high resolution mass spectrum a series of naphthyl carboxylic acids ranging from C_{11} (naphthoic acid) to C_{17} with a maximum at C_{12} are apparent.

Peaks corresponding to molecular ions of indane carboxylic acids (C_{10} to C_{17}) were observed. The C_{10} and C_{11} acids of this series appear to be major constituents. These data show that the bulk of these acid fractions obtained by direct extraction of whole shale material consists of low molecular weight normal and dicarboxylic acids. Cyclic acids appear to be important contributors to the acids below C_{12}, and keto and aromatic acids, while distributed over a wide mass range, are present in rather small amounts. The branched-chain acids represent a surprisingly small fraction of the total acids. In contrast to this the neutral and basic fraction of this extract included compounds up to C_{40} as evidenced by the high resolution mass spectrum (Figure 6). The presence of several C_{40} compounds, probably tetraterpenoidal hydrocarbons, is indicated by the peaks at $C_{40}H_{78}$ (corresponding to the molecular ion of perhydro-β-carotene, Murphy, McCormick and Eglinton, 1967), $C_{40}H_{70}$, $C_{40}H_{68}$, $C_{40}H_{66}$, $C_{40}H_{62}$, and $C_{40}H_{58}$ in the C/H plot. The peaks of composition $C_{30}H_{52}$ and $C_{29}H_{48}$ may be attributed to triterpanes. Particularly interesting are high mass ions in the C/H O plot, since their compositions, $C_{32}H_{52}O$, $C_{30}H_{48}O$ and $C_{29}H_{46}O$ and the corresponding M–CH$_3$ peaks suggest triterpenoidal ketones. This is a class of compounds not yet reported for this sediment, but now preliminary data suggest that a detailed search for them might be a promising undertaking.

Part II: Extract of Demineralized Shale

Experimental

The oil-shale exhaustively extracted as described in Part I was digested twice at room temperature for two days each with 1:1 concentrated hydrofluoric acid/hydrochloric acid. To remove sulfides and free sulfur, the residue was further treated with zinc dust in $6N$ hydrochloric acid at room temperature (Forsman and Hunt, 1958). By repeated ultrasonic extractions with 4:1 benzene/methanol, an extract weighing 190 mg was isolated upon evaporation of solvent from a 100 g sample. The exhaustively extracted residue, i.e., the kerogen concentrate, had a carbon-hydrogen analysis of 65.9 %C, 8.2 %H, 0.66 %N and 0.9 %S based on a mineral-free sample. The extract was dissolved in heptane and treated with $6N$ sodium hydroxide solution. The basic aqueous extract after back-extraction with heptane was acidified, and extracted first with heptane (3 x) and then diethyl ether (3 x). The heptane soluble acids amounted to 60 mg and the ether soluble acids to 1.5 mg. The acid fractions were esterified with BF_3/methanol and the heptane soluble acid esters were then clathrated with urea, yielding a normal and branched-cyclic fraction in the ratio of approximately 1:3. The three fractions were gas chromatographed under the same conditions as described above; the g.l.c. traces of the total normal and branched-cyclic fractions are illustrated in Figure 8. The ether soluble acid esters exhibit a g.l.c. pattern very similar to the gas chromatogram shown in Figure 3. Since the weight of this fraction was so low, it was not further studied. For correlation purposes the gas chromatogram of the neutral and basic fraction isolated from the demineralization is shown in Figure 9 (conditions as usual). An example of the high resolution mass spectral data for the total (heptane soluble) acid extract is shown in Figure 10 and for the neutral and basic fraction in Figure 11.

Results

Inspection of Table III shows that extraction of the demineralized shale yields essentially the same type of acids found in the exhaustive extraction of the shale described in Part I. However, significant differences in distribution and range of compounds are apparent. For example, the range of normal acids was found to extend up to C_{30} (by g.l.c. analysis, Figure 8) and C_{32} (by high resolution mass spectrometry, see Figure 10). The acids show maxima at C_{16} and C_{26}, whereby however, the high molecular weight acids clearly predominate (Figure 8). In the fraction containing branched acids, phytanic and norphytanic acid are major components. A homologous series of isoprenoidal acids from C_{15} to at least C_{21} is apparent from the gas chromatogram (Figure 8); a high resolution mass spectrum of this fraction shows peaks corresponding to molecular ions of saturated acids from C_8 to C_{22}, which, of course, may not necessarily all represent isoprenoidal acids.

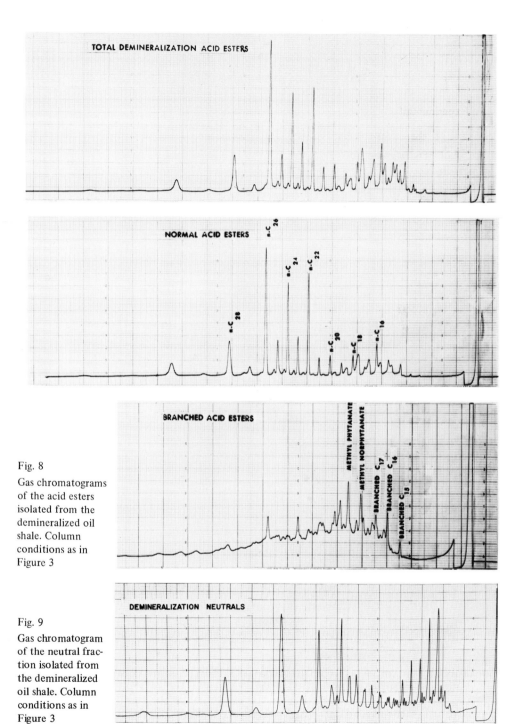

Fig. 8
Gas chromatograms
of the acid esters
isolated from the
demineralized oil
shale. Column
conditions as in
Figure 3

Fig. 9
Gas chromatogram
of the neutral frac-
tion isolated from
the demineralized
oil shale. Column
conditions as in
Figure 3

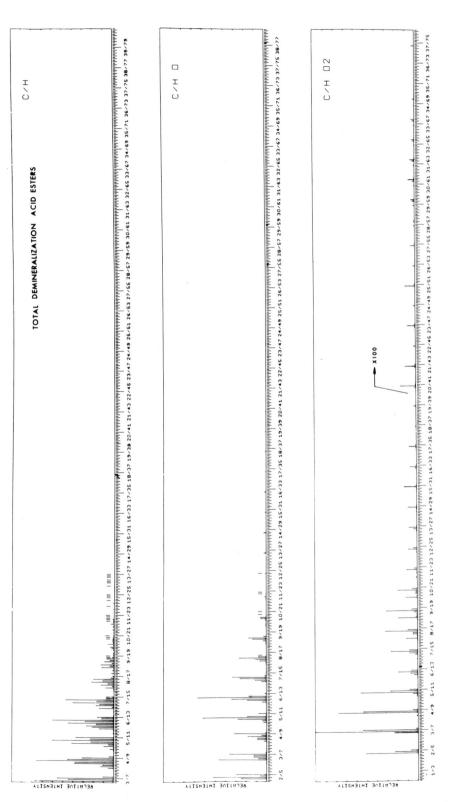

Part of Fig. 10

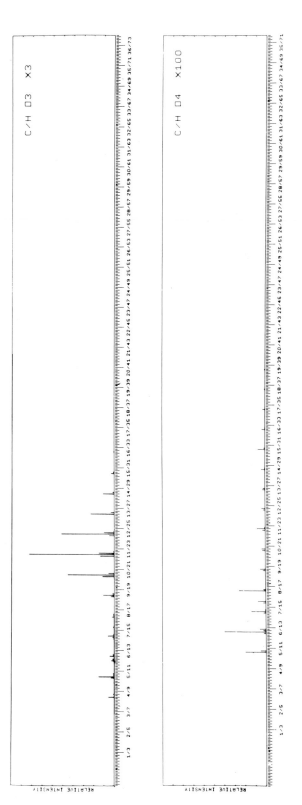

Fig. 10. High resolution mass spectral data for the total acid esters isolated from the demineralized oil shale

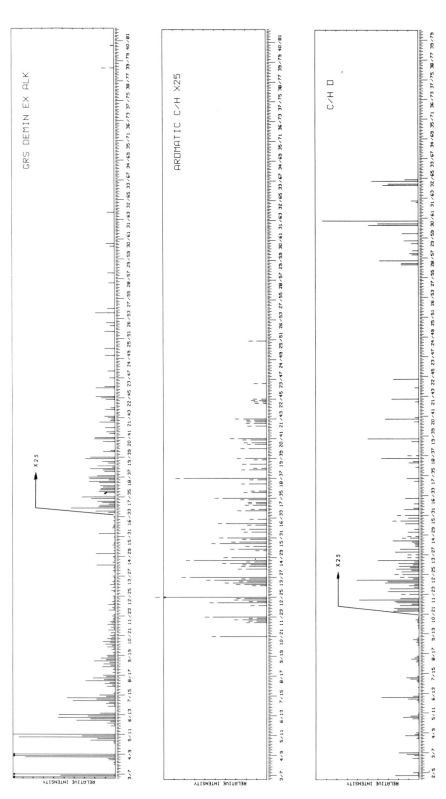

Part of Fig. 11

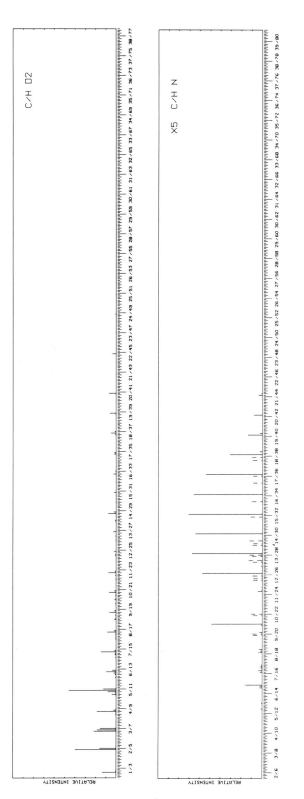

Fig. 11. High resolution mass spectral data for the neutral fraction isolated from the demineralized oil shale

Table III. Organic acids from the demineralized, exhaustively extracted oil shale of the Green River Formation, listed as free acids.

	range	maximum concentration
1. Normal Acids		
	C_5-C_{22}*	C_{16}, C_{24}
	C_8-C_{30}+	
2. Branched Acids		
	C_8-C_{22}*	C_{20}
	$C_{15}-C_{21}$+	
3. Dicarboxylic Acids		
	C_3-C_{18}*+	C_6
4. Methylketoacids		
	C_4-C_{16}*	C_{10}
5. Mono-unsaturated and Cyclic Acids ($C_nH_{2n-2}O_2$)		
	C_5-C_{18}*	C_6, C_{14}
6. Aromatic Acids (phenyl $C_nH_{2n-8}O_2$)		
	C_7-C_{15}*	C_9
7. Aromatic Acids (naphthyl $C_nH_{2n-14}O_2$)		
	$C_{11}-C_{14}$*	C_{11}
8. Aromatic Acids ($C_nH_{2n-10}O_2$)		
	$C_{10}-C_{15}$*	C_{11}
9. Aromatic Acids ($C_nH_{2n-12}O_2$)		
	$C_{10}-C_{13}$*	C_{10}
10. Pentacyclic Acids		
	$C_{28}-C_{34}$*	C_{30}

*   Determined by high resolution mass spectrometry
+   Determined from gas chromatograms

Dicarboxylic acids are represented by the series extending from about C_3 to C_{18}. The gas chromatogram shows a maximum at C_{14} for this series (the peak immediately preceding the C_{18} normal acid in the gas chromatogram of Figure 8 represents the C_{14} α,ω-dicarboxylic acid ester). Molecular ions of this series are apparent in the C/H O_4 plot of the high resolution mass spectrum (Figure 10). Peaks at $C_6H_{10}O_4$ and $C_8H_{14}O_4$ corresponding to C_4 and C_6 acids are particularly prominent, but these should not necessarily be taken as an accurate reflection of the relative abundance of these acids. Intense peaks in the C/H O_3 plot of Figure 10, provide further evidence for dicarboxylic acids. For example, the peaks at ($C_nH_{2n-3}O_3$) correspond to fragments resulting from loss of methoxyl radical from the molecular ion of dicarboxylic acids.

Indications of other classes of acids are based mainly on high resolution data. Thus, a series of ketoacids is apparent from the C/H O_3 plot of Figure 10, ranging apparently from C_4 to C_{16}. The peaks at $C_nH_{2n-2}O_3$ correspond to the molecular ions of these acids. Although at first sight these peaks must be regarded with some suspicion as definite indication of ketoacids since they might conceivably be explained as isotope and/or rearrangement ions, the results of the previous section and experiments to be mentioned later very clearly substantiate the occurrence of ketoacids in the sediment. A homologous series of apparently cyclic acids extends from about C_6 to C_{18}. Aromatic acids belonging to the phenyl ($C_nH_{2n-8}O_2$) series and naphthyl ($C_nH_{2n-14}O_2$) series are observed. The former appear to comprise the series from C_7 to C_{15}, the latter the group from C_{11} to C_{15}. Other groups, the homologues of the series $C_nH_{2n-10}O_2$ and $C_nH_{2n-12}O_2$, appear in various high resolution mass spectra. These occur, however, in fairly narrow distribution and low abundance, and might represent (at least partially) degradation products of other series. Special attention should be drawn however, to a series of apparently pentacyclic acids which are observed in the high resolution spectra of both the total and branched cyclic acids. Referring to the C/H O_2 plot of Figure 10, one notes, for example, the peaks of composition $C_{29}H_{48}O_2$ (m/e 428), $C_{30}H_{50}O_2$ (442), $C_{31}H_{52}O_2$ (456), $C_{32}H_{54}O_2$ (470), $C_{33}H_{56}O_2$ (484), $C_{34}H_{58}O_2$ (498) and $C_{35}H_{60}O_2$ (512). The series appears to maximize at C_{31} which would correspond to a C_{30} pentacyclic carboxylic acid. The suggestion of triterpenoidal acids appears obvious, but needs to be verified by more definitive experiments.

A comparison of the acids and the neutral and basic material from this extraction is provided by the gas chromatogram of Figure 9 and the high resolution mass spectrum of Figure 11. The C/H plot again shows some high mass ions such as $C_{40}H_{78}$ and $C_{40}H_{62}$ as well as polycyclic compounds in the region from C_{29} to C_{32}, some of which do not seem to represent triterpenoidal material, however. Prominent high mass C/H O peaks are observed which may represent ketonic material. The peaks $C_{30}H_{50}O$ and $C_{29}H_{48}O$ suggest the presence of triterpenoidal ketones. The corresponding peaks due to the loss of methyl radical from these molecular ions are also observed. The elemental compositions of most of the other ions, however, do not suggest triterpenoidal molecules. No more detailed interpretation can be advanced at this point.

Of interest also is the relative abundance of nitrogen compounds (C/H N plot of Figure 11), which was not observed in the neutral and basic fraction of the exhaustive extract. They appear to represent a homologous series of quinolines ranging in composition from $C_{13}H_{15}N$ to $C_{22}H_{33}N$.

Part III: Extraction of Oxidized Kerogen

Experimental

Twenty-five grams of kerogen concentrate from the demineralization was refluxed for 3 hours with 3 $\underline{M}$ chromic acid in sulfuric acid. The residue was filtered, washed with water and extracted three times, each first with heptane then diethyl ether, using ultrasonication to insure thorough extraction. The spent chromic acid solution was also extracted with heptane and then ether. The respective extracts were combined and the acids separated from the neutrals with 6 N sodium hydroxide solution. Esterification with BF_3/methanol yielded 0.034 g (0.13 percent of the kerogen concentrate) total esters from the heptane extract and 0.018 g (0.07 percent) total esters from the ether extract. In the case of the heptane soluble acid extract, the normal esters were separated from branched-chain esters by clathration with urea. Since it was found that the acids in the ether extract are of lower molecular weight and greater functionality than the acids of the heptane extracts, these ether extracts were not subjected to urea clathration, but were only esterified with BF_3/methanol. The yield of normal esters, which were again extracted with heptane, was 0.016 g (0.06 percent) and the branched-chain esters extracted from the adduct solution amounted to 0.010 g (0.04 percent). The residual kerogen was further oxidized for an additional 6 hours, the yield being 0.018 g (0.07 percent) acids extractable with heptane and 0.080 g (0.32 percent) acids extractable with ether. Esterification with BF_3/methanol and urea-clathration of the heptane extract gave 0.009 g (0.04 percent) of normal and 0.005 g (0.02 percent) of branched-chain ester fractions. The kerogen remaining from the 9 hour oxidation was oxidized for an additional 15 hours, resulting in 0.024 g (0.10 percent) acids extractable with heptane and 0.150 g (0.06 percent) acids extractable with ether. Esterification with BF_3/methanol and clathration of the heptane extract gave 0.021 g (0.05 percent) of normal and 0.008 g (0.03 percent) of branched-chain ester fractions. The residue from the previous oxidation, which still had a 14.7 percent carbon content, was subjected to 24 hours further oxidation. This resulted in 0.092 g (0.67 percent) acids extractable with heptane and 0.120 g (0.88 percent) acids extractable with ether. Esterification with BF_3/methanol and clathration of the heptane extract gave 0.021 g (0.05 percent) of normal and 0.008 g (0.03 percent) of branched-chain ester fractions. The residue from the previous oxidation, which still had a 14.7 percent carbon content, was subjected to 24 hours further oxidation. This resulted in 0.092 g (0.67 percent) acids extractable with heptane and 0.120 g (0.88 percent) acids extractable with ether. Esterification with BF_3/methanol and clathration of the heptane extract yielded 0.058 g (0.43 percent) of normal and 0.022 g (0.16 percent) of branched-chain ester fractions. It should be pointed out at this time that in working up reasonably concentrated fatty acid solutions in heptane (during washing of an extract before esterification, for example) the higher molecular weight acids tend to crystallize out. The low resolution mass spectrum of such a precipitate filtered off from the 48 hour oxidation extract is shown in Figure 12 and consists of normal acids ranging from C_{18} to C_{35}. The four oxidations, totalling 48 hours, removed all the organic carbon from the kerogen concentrate (elemental analysis of the final residue: 0.21 percent C, 0.41 percent H, 0.0 percent N, 0.05 percent S, and 97.1 percent residue).

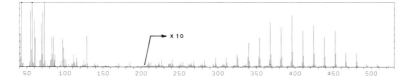

Fig. 12. Low resolution mass spectrum of the acid precipitate from the 48 hour oxidation

The total, normal and branched-chain ester fractions were chromatographed using the same conditions described earlier. The g.l.c. components were identified by their retention times, coinjection of standard compounds, low resolution mass spectra and then correlated to the high resolution mass spectra of the total mixtures. The g.l.c. patterns of the heptane soluble acid mixtures isolated from the 4 oxidations are virtually identical. There is an even/odd predominance in the normal acid fractions and the branched acids maximize at C_{16}. The 24 hour oxidation acid esters serve as illustration in Figure 13. The g.l.c. patterns of the ether soluble acid mixtures are also virtually identical and maximize at lower molecular weight acids. The ether extract acid esters from the 24 hour oxidation serve as illustration in Figure 14.

The high resolution mass spectral data of the total, branched and normal acid ester fractions and of the total ether extract ester fractions show that the various homologous acid series isolated from the 4 oxidations are the same and differ only in relative concentrations. Each fraction was subjected to increasing ion source temperatures (usually in the range $150°-270°$) while several mass spectra were taken to insure complete volatilization. The high resolution mass spectral data of the normal esters from the 3 hour oxidation are shown in Figure 15 and similar data for the branched-cyclic esters from the 24 hour oxidation are shown in Figure 16. The high resolution mass spectral data for the total ether extract esters from the 9 hour oxidation are shown in Figure 17. This is a representative example for the four ether extract fractions isolated from the respective oxidations.

For correlation purposes, the gas chromatogram of the 9 hour oxidation neutral and basic fraction is shown in Figure 18 and the high resolution mass spectral data are shown in Figure 19.

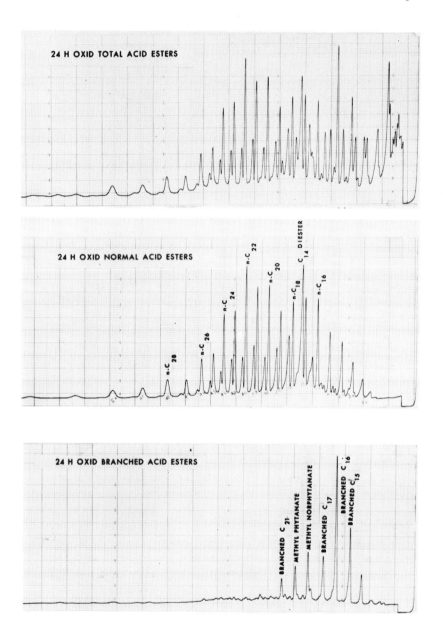

Fig. 13. Gas chromatogram of the heptane extract esters isolated from the 24 hour oxidation. Column conditions as in Figure 3

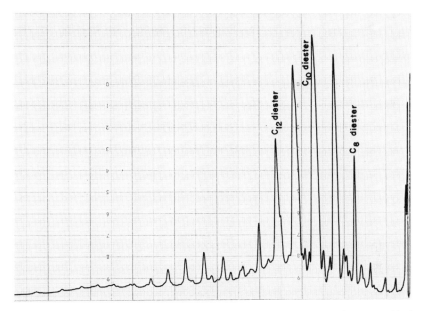

Fig. 14. Gas chromatogram of the ether extract esters isolated from the 24 hour oxidation. Column conditions as in Figure 3

Results

Each of the oxidation experiments yields the same type of acids, but differences are apparent in the relative abundance of the various classes of acids (Table IV). In Table I a summary of total amounts obtained in the 3, 9, 24 and 48 hour oxidations is presented. These data refer to successive oxidation steps on the same sample; after 48 hours of CrO_3/H_2SO_4 treatment all carbon is essentially removed from the "kerogen material". Both total organic matter and total heptane-extractable acids increase with successive oxidations; the tenfold increase in the amount of ether-extractable acids should be noted in particular, however. Another general trend evident from our data is the relative consistency of the range of acids within each series for the different oxidation experiments, and the decrease of branched acids relative to normal and dicarboxylic acids with extent of oxidation. Within each class of acids, the lower members of a homologous series tend to be concentrated in the ether extracts, the higher members are found in the heptane extracts.

Typical results for the 24 hour oxidation experiment are illustrated by the gas chromatograms of Figure 13. Normal, branched and dicarboxylic acids are major components in this mixture. The normals of the heptane extractable acids comprise

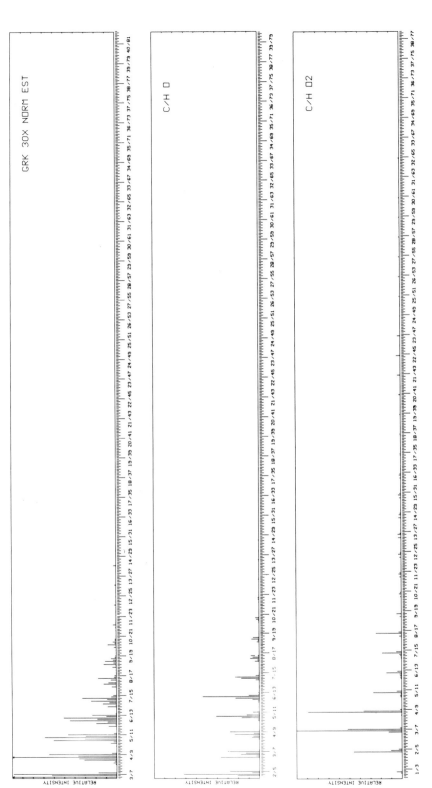

Part of Fig. 15

113

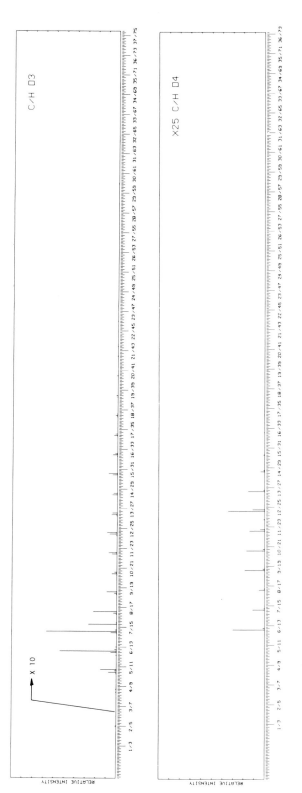

Fig. 15. High resolution mass spectral data for the normal acid esters from the 3 hour oxidation.

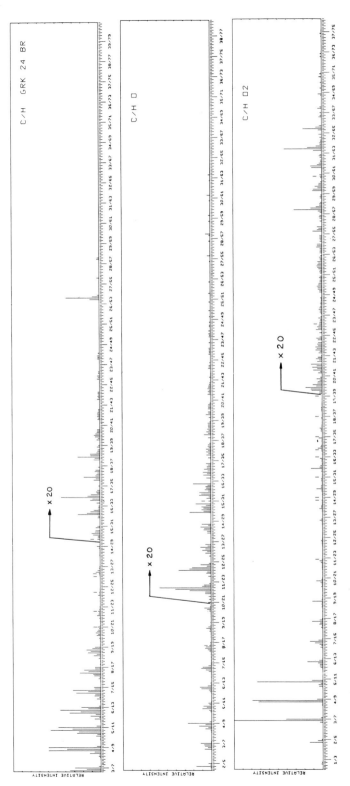

Part of Fig. 16

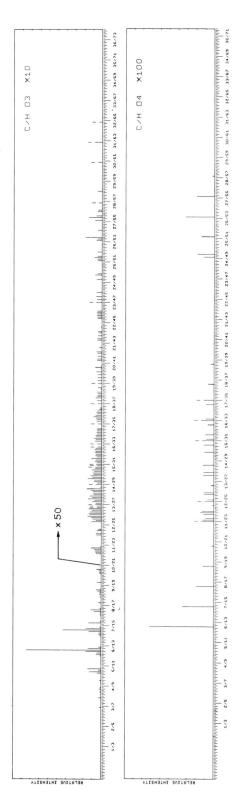

Fig. 16. High resolution mass spectral data for the branched acid esters from the 24 hour oxidation

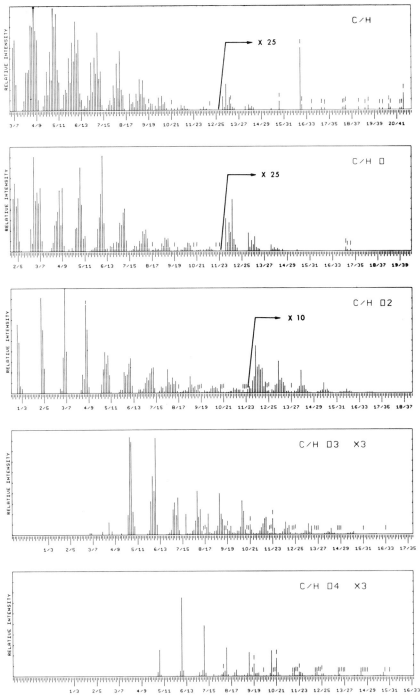

Part of Fig. 17

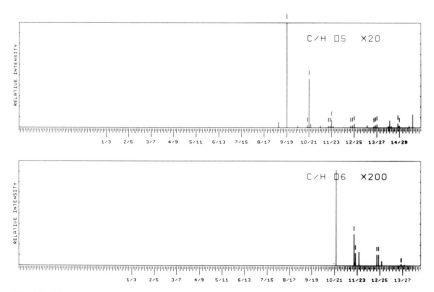

Fig. 17. High resolution mass spectral data for the total ether extract acid esters from the 9 hour oxidation

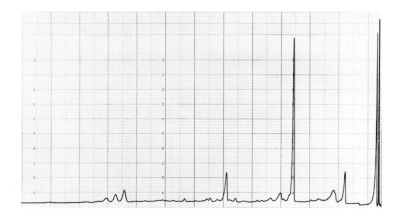

Fig. 18. Gas chromatogram of the neutral fraction isolated from the 9 hour oxidation. Column conditions as in Figure 3

the homologous series from C_8 to C_{30} with a maximum for the C_{22} acid. Phytanic and norphytanic acids were identified in the branched acid fraction but the range extends from C_{14} to C_{21}, maximizing at C_{16}. The remaining branched compounds are also isoprenoidal acids. Diacids are very prominent constituents; all normal dicarboxylic acids from C_{10} to C_{23} are present in the heptane-extractable mixture.

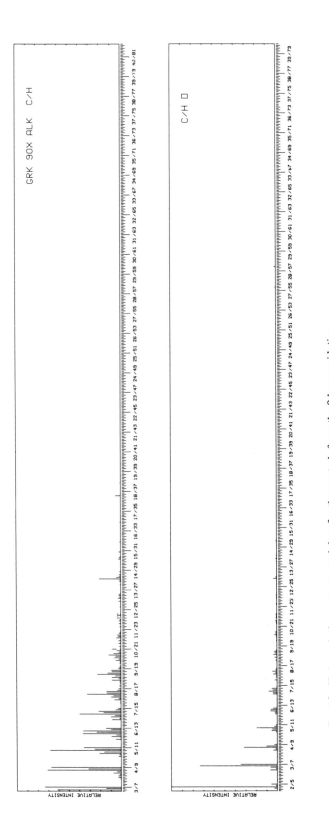

Fig. 19. High resolution mass spectral data for the neutrals from the 9 hour oxidation

Table IV. Organic acids from the stepwise oxidations of Green River Formation kerogen concentrate (listed as free acids), extracted with heptane and then ether.

		Range		Maximum Concentration	
		(Heptane)	(Ether)	(Heptane)	(Ether)
1.	**Normal Acids**				
	3 hour	$C_{10}-C_{30}+$ $C_5-C_{33}*$	C_5-C_8*	C_{22}	C_5
	9 hour	$C_9-C_{32}+$ $C_5-C_{34}*$	C_5-C_9*	C_{22}	C_5
	24 hour	$C_9-C_{32}+$ $C_5-C_{34}*$	C_5-C_8*	C_{22}	C_5
	48 hour	$C_{10}-C_{33}+$ $C_5-C_{36}*$	$C_5-C_{10}*$	C_{22}	C_6
2.	**Branched-chain Acids**				
	3 hour	$C_{14}-C_{22}+$ $C_5-C_{26}*$	- -	C_{16}	- -
	9 hour	$C_{14}-C_{22}+$ $C_5-C_{26}*$	- -	C_{16}	- -
	24 hour	$C_{14}-C_{22}+$ $C_5-C_{26}*$	- -	C_{16}	- -
	48 hour	$C_{14}-C_{22}+$ $C_5-C_{26}*$	- -	C_{16}	- -
3.	**Dicarboxylic Acids**				
	3 hour	$C_9-C_{22}+$ $C_6-C_{14}*$	$C_8-C_{12}+$ $C_3-C_{13}*$	$C_{12}+*$	$C_4* C_{10}+$
	9 hour	C_4-C_6* $C_{14}-C_{17}*$	$C_8-C_{12}+$ $C_3-C_{13}*$	$C_4\ C_{15}$	$C_4* C_{10}+$
	24 hour	$C_{10}-C_{23}+$ $C_4-C_{22}*$	$C_8-C_{12}+$ $C_3-C_{13}*$	$C_4* C_{14}+*$	$C_4* C_{10}+$
	48 hour	$C_{10}-C_{25}+$ $C_5-C_{25}*$	$C_6-C_{10}+$ $C_3-C_{12}*$	$C_{17}+*$	$C_4* C_8+$
4.	**Keto Acids**				
	3 hour	$C_4-C_{12}+$ $C_4-C_{16}*$	$C_5-C_{10}*$	$C_6+* C_{14}*$	C_6
	9 hour	$C_4-C_{16}*$	$C_5-C_{13}*$	$C_5\ C_{14}$	C_6
	24 hour	$C_4-C_{20}*$	$C_5-C_{13}*$	$C_6\ C_{14}$	C_6
	48 hour	$C_6-C_{17}*$	$C_5-C_{14}*$	$C_6\ C_{14}$	C_6

Table IV continued

	Range		Maximum Concentration	
	(Heptane)	(Ether)	(Heptane)	(Ether)
5.	**Cyclic Acids** (mono-unsaturated $C_nH_{2n-2}O_2$)			
3 hour	$C_5-C_{17}*$	$C_5-C_{12}*$	C_{12}	C_6
9 hour	$C_5-C_{23}*$	$C_5-C_{14}*$	C_{15}	C_6
24 hour	$C_5-C_{28}*$	$C_5-C_{14}*$	C_{17}	C_6
48 hour	$C_5-C_{17}*$	$C_5-C_{14}*$	C_{12}	C_6
6.	**Aromatic Acids** (phenyl $C_nH_{2n-8}O_2$) #			
3 hour	$C_7-C_{18}*$	$C_7-C_{13}*$	C_7	C_7
9 hour	$C_7-C_{18}*$	$C_7-C_{15}*$	$C_9\ C_{14}$	C_7
24 hour	$C_7-C_{18}*$	$C_7-C_{14}*$	$C_9\ C_{15}$	C_7
48 hour	$C_7-C_{18}*$	$C_7-C_{12}*$	C_{16}	C_7
7.	**Aromatic Acids** (naphthyl $C_nH_{2n-14}O_2$)			
3 hour	$C_{11}*$	$C_{11}*$	C_{11}	C_{11}
9 hour	$C_{11}, C_{12}*$	$C_{1i}, C_{12}*$	C_{11}	C_{11}
24 hour	$C_{11}*$	$C_{11}, C_{12}*$	C_{11}	C_{11}
48 hour	none	$C_{11}, C_{12}*$	- -	C_{11}
8.	**Aromatic Acids** ($C_nH_{2n-10}O_2$)			
3 hour	$C_{10}*$	$C_{10}-C_{12}*$	C_{10}	C_{10}
9 hour	$C_{10}-C_{18}*$	$C_{10}-C_{16}*$	C_{10}	C_{10}
24 hour	$C_{10}-C_{19}*$	$C_{10}-C_{15}*$	C_{10}	C_{10}
48 hour	$C_{10}-C_{19}*$	$C_{10}-C_{15}*$	C_{10}	C_{10}
9.	**Aromatic Acids** ($C_nH_{2n-12}O_2$)			
3 hour	none	$C_{10}-C_{12}*$	- -	C_{10}
9 hour	$C_{10}*$	$C_{10}-C_{13}*$	C_{10}	C_{10}
24 hour	$C_{10}*$	$C_{10}-C_{12}*$	C_{10}	C_{10}
48 hour	$C_{10}*$	$C_{10}-C_{12}*$	C_{10}	C_{10}
10.	**Pentacyclic Acids**			
3 hour	$C_{28}-C_{33}*$	none	C_{31}	- -
9 hour	$C_{28}-C_{33}*$	none	C_{30}	- -
24 hour	$C_{26}-C_{34}*$	none	C_{30}	- -
48 hour	$C_{29}-C_{32}*$	none	C_{30}	- -

Table IV continued

	Range		Maximum Concentration	
	(Heptane)	(Ether)	(Heptane)	(Ether)
11. Tetracyclic Acids ($C_nH_{2n-8}O_2$) #				
3 hour	$C_{18} - C_{20}$*	none	C_{18}	- -
9 hour	$C_{18} - C_{26}$*	none	C_{20}	- -
24 hour	$C_{18} - C_{32}$*	none	C_{30}	- -
48 hour	$C_{18} - C_{32}$*	none	C_{30}	- -
12. Dicarboxylic Aromatic Acids ($C_nH_{2n-10}O_4$)				
3 hour	none	$C_8 - C_{11}$*	- -	C_8
9 hour	none	$C_8 - C_{13}$*	- -	C_8
24 hour	none	$C_8 - C_{13}$*	- -	C_8
48 hour	none	$C_8 - C_{12}$*	- -	C_8
13. Tricarboxylic Aromatic Acids ($C_nH_{2n-12}O_6$)				
3 hour	none	$C_9 - C_{12}$*	- -	C_9
9 hour	none	$C_9 - C_{12}$*	- -	C_9
24 hour	none	$C_9 - C_{13}$*	- -	C_9
48 hour	none	$C_9 - C_{12}$*	- -	C_9

* Determined by high resolution mass spectrometry
+ Determined from gas chromatogram
# The aromatic acids are listed only to C_{18} since above C_{18} the data fit tetracyclic acids better.

The C_{14} component, dimethyl tetradecane-1,14-dioate is the major acid of this series (Figure 13). The lower dicarboxylic acids (C_8 to C_{12} in particular) are major constituents of the ether-extractable mixture (Figure 14). Small normal acids and/or branched-chain are present also (C_5 to C_8) but cannot be distinguished since the ether extract was not clathrated.

Essentially the same homologous series of these three acid types is present in all oxidation experiments (see Table IV for details). However, the amount of branched saturated acids markedly decreases relative to the normal and dicarboxylic acids with duration of oxidation (Table V). The presence of other classes of acids was

Table V. The relative percent abundance of isoprenoid acids *vs.* normal, dicarboxylic and ketoacids in the 4 oxidations.

Oxidation	Isoprenoids (percent of peak areas)	Others (percent of peak areas)
3 hour	60	40
9 hour	35	65
24 hour	16	84
48 hour	5	95

ascertained from the high resolution mass spectra. Referring back to the figures of the high resolution mass spectral data, a homologous series of normal acids up to $C_{32}H_{64}O_2$ is apparent from the C/H O_2 plot of Figure 15. Molecular ions of dicarboxylic acids can be seen in the C/H O_4 plot at $C_nH_{2n-2}O_4$. The M-CH$_3$O ions are found in the C/H O_3 plot; the last peak of the series $C_{21}H_{39}O_3$ would be derived from a C_{20} diacid ester. The isoprenoidal acids mentioned above appear in the C/H O_2 plot of Figure 16 at $C_nH_{2n}O_2$. Molecular ions for aliphatic oxoacids $C_nH_{2n-2}O_3$ are evident in the C/H O_3 plot of Figure 15. Peaks of composition $C_{11}H_{20}O_3$, $C_{12}H_{22}O_3$, $C_{13}H_{24}O_3$ etc., are major contributors, but the series appears to extend from about C_4 to C_{20} [1]). The ether extract of the 24 hour oxidation contains ketoacids comprising the lower homologous series from about C_5 to C_{13}.

Four series of aromatic acids are apparent from the high resolution mass spectra. In the heptane extract (Figure 16) the phenyl ($C_nH_{2n-8}O_2$) and naphthyl ($C_nH_{2n-14}O_2$) group appears to include homologues from n = 7 to 8 and n = 11, respectively. A distribution from n = 7 to 15 and n = 11 and 12 is found for the ether extractables. The other two aromatic series, $C_nH_{2n-10}O_2$ (indane carboxylic acids) and $C_nH_{2n-12}O_2$, occur in both the heptane and ether extracted mixtures. Table IV summarizes their distribution patterns, although these should be interpreted with some caution since the C/H O_2 plots of Figures 16 and 17 are quite complex.

The oxidation experiments yielded four new series of acids not obtained by extraction analyses; the high resolution spectrum of the branched fraction of the heptane soluble material gives definite indication of homologues of pentacyclic and tetracyclic acid constituents. For example, Figure 16 exhibits peaks of composition $C_{28}H_{46}O_2$, $C_{29}H_{48}O_2$, $C_{30}H_{50}O_2$, $C_{31}H_{52}O_2$, $C_{32}H_{54}O_2$, and $C_{33}H_{56}O_2$, which could be rationalized as molecular ions of perhaps triterpenoidal acids. Similarly, a series of compositions $C_nH_{2n-8}O_2$ (n = 18–20) can be noted. Both classes of compounds are absent in the ether-extractable acid mixture (see Figure 17). The ether extracts contain instead aromatic dicarboxylic and tricarboxylic acids. The ion of composition $C_{10}H_{10}O_4$ in Figure 17 corresponds to the molecular ion of a phthalic acid dimethyl ester. Higher homologues of this series are very minor constituents (Table IV). The most abundant compound of this class was identified

---

[1]) Confirmation that these compounds were indeed (ω - 1)-oxo-acids was provided by analysis of the real-time high resolution mass spectra on mixtures obtained in the following experiment: The normal acid ester fraction and the total ether fraction of the 24 hour oxidation acids were reduced with sodium borohydride and treated with silylating agent. Analysis of the real-time high resolution mass spectrum of these mixtures confirmed the presence of these ketoacids (W.J. Richter, B.R. Simoneit, D.H. Smith and A.L. Burlingame, unpublished results from this laboratory).

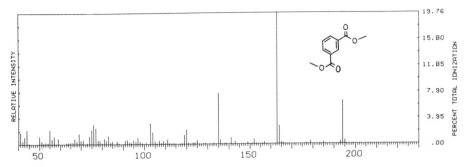

Fig. 20. Low resolution mass spectrum of dimethyl terephthalate isolated from the ether extract acids of the 24 hour oxidation

from its mass spectrum[1]) (Figure 20) as a phthalic acid ester, probably the *meta*-isomer. Tricarboxylic aromatic acids are indicated by the sequence $C_{12}H_{12}O_6$, $C_{13}H_{14}O_6$, $C_{14}H_{16}O_6$ in Figure 17. Again the lowest homologue is the most abundant species.

Monocyclic and/or mono-unsaturated acids of the general formula $C_nH_{2n-2}O_2$ were observed in all oxidation experiments. Table IV gives a summary of these results. For the 24 hour oxidation these acids appeared to comprise the series from C_5 to C_{28} in the heptane extract (Figure 16) and C_5 to C_{14} in the ether extract (Figure 17).

Part IV: Discussion of Results

Comparison of the data of Table I reveals the interesting fact that the amount of acids obtainable by various methods - - two extractions and demineralization follow-ed by extraction - - increases. The first extraction yielded only 8 mg of acids out of a total of 1300 mg hexane soluble extract, the exhaustive extraction and demine-ralization gave 38 and 60 mg of acids for 440 and 190 mg of total extract, respecti-vely. The low yield of acids from the first extract may well be due to incomplete removal of acidic material, since these experiments were conducted on a relatively large scale, making no attempt at quantitative removal of all acidic material from the total. However, the trend is too marked to be ignored. The differences between the first extract and the exhaustive extract can be ascribed to the more polar nature of the acidic materials, resulting in an artificial concentration of them in the exhaus-tive extract.

The high yield of acids relative to "neutral" organics from the demineralization experiment, however, suggests that the bulk of these acids are bound to the inorga-

---

[1]) Data was obtained *via* capillary g.l.c. – M.S. techniques using Apiezon L as liquid phase. Perkin Elmer, Model 900 gas chromatograph coupled to a G.E.C. – A.E.I. MS 902 mass spectrometer on-line to an S.D.S. Sigma 7 Computer.

nic matrix, perhaps as calcium salts. Part of them could also be derived by hydrolysis of the kerogen material. Not surprisingly, the yield of acids increases with
length of oxidation; particularly marked is the increase of the more polar (and probably more functionalized) acids; i.e., the ether extractable material (see Table I).
The branched-chain (isoprenoid) acids drastically decrease in concentration vs. the
normal, dicarboxylic and oxo-acids as the oxidation time increases. These results
are summarized in Table V and can also be discerned in Figure 21: The three-hour
oxidation yields a mixture in which isoprenoidal acids predominate (note in particular the abundance of the C_{16} branched acid), whereas the 48 hour oxidation yields
only minor amounts of branched acids (Figure 21).

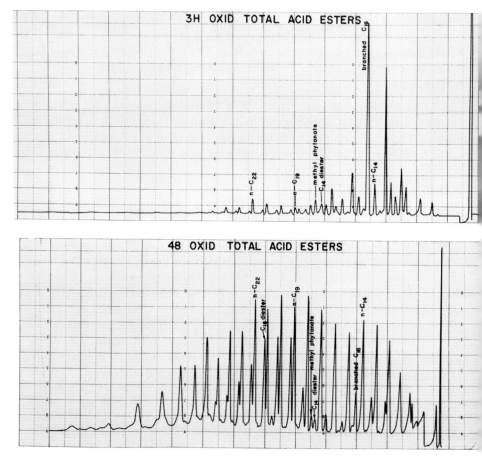

Fig. 21. Gas chromatograms of the total acid esters isolated from the 3 and 48 hour oxidations.
Column conditions as in Figure 3

More important than these observations are the differences in distribution of acids due to different extraction-isolation methods. The first extraction and exhaustive extraction not unexpectedly yield essentially the same mixtures. A notable characteristic of these extracts is the absence of any appreciable quantity of both the higher normal and branched (isoprenoidal) acids. Instead, saturated dicarboxylic acids are the major acid constituents of the higher weight material. By contrast, demineralization yields an acid mixture in which higher normal acids are very prominent, maximum about C_{22}, and which contains a series of isoprenoidal acids in the branched-cyclic fraction, with phytanic acid as the most abundant. However, the isoprenoidal acids are far less prominent in our extracts than in those of Eglinton et al. (1966) from a core sample of shale from Sulfur Creek which contained phytanic acid as the major single component of the total acid fraction. If these differences reflect the different shale samples, conclusions as to ancient geologies extrapolated for the entire shale but based on analysis of a single sample may well have to be advanced with some caution. Furthermore, our data appear to show that relative abundances of certain compound types may be a function of methods of isolation and therefore not necessarily indicate a specific source material.

The acids obtained by oxidation could arise by several processes;

(a) "loosening" of the kerogen matrix and removal of entrapped compounds which might subsequently be partially oxidized,

(b) hydrolysis of ester linkages to give acids and alcohols, the latter being oxidized to carboxylic acids, and

(c) oxidative cleavage of carbon-carbon bonds.

All three processes probably contribute and their relative importance is difficult to assess. However, some arguments may be advanced to support the view that a major portion of the acids is derived from carbon-carbon bond cleavage of side chains attached to the kerogen. Hydrolysis of kerogen in aqueous boiling base yields relatively small amounts of acidic and neutral material suggesting that hydrolyzable linkages are not predominant structural features of the kerogen material. If this process were to be an important one for the generation of acids, the assumption that oxidation makes hydrolyzable sites more accessible to solvent by partially rupturing the kerogen matrix would have to be made. The fact that branched acids are major constituents (relative to normals) in the 3 hour oxidation experiments would also suggest that carbon-carbon bond cleavage is a major process rather than simple hydrolysis or oxidation of entrapped compounds. The latter processes would be expected to yield an acid mixture rather similar to that obtained by extraction methods; whereas, carbon-carbon bond cleavages might be expected to occur at a greater rate for branched structures. The predominance of the C_{16} branched acid in these mixtures is perhaps a further indication of this process, for this acid would result from cleavage of the $C_{13}-C_{14}$ bond (next to tertary allylic carbon atom in phytol) in an isoprenoidal carbon chain. This would indicate polymer cross-linking at the allylic centers during kerogen formation. A suggested substituent structure of kerogen is illustrated in Figure 22, showing the various hydrolyzable side-chains and oxidation sites. The carbon-carbon bonded substitutents should dominate over the carbon-oxygen substituents.

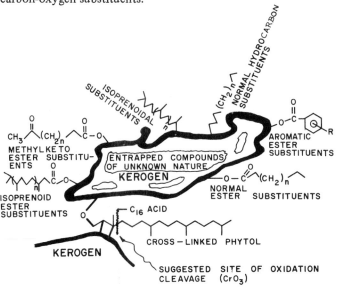

Fig. 22. The substituent structure suggested for kerogen

More extensive oxidation (9, 24 and 48 hours) leads not only to more acidic material in the total product mixture, but also to the predominant formation of normal acids and polyfunctional acids, in particular dicarboxylic acids. Our experiments do not yet point to any conclusion as to the structural attachments of the fragments obtained by oxidation. In particular, experiments with model compounds to determine the product distribution to be expected from these kinds of oxidation processes are needed. Data on the rate of oxidation of certain structural types also would be of interest.

Acknowledgements: We thank Mrs. Ellen Scott for technical assistance in Parts II and III, one of us (B.R.S.) for collection of the shale specimen, and Dr. D.H. Smith for assistance with the real-time high resolution data.

The work was supported by the U.S. National Aeronautics and Space Administration, Grants NGL 05-003-003, NGR 05-003-134 and NAS 9-7889.

References

Abelson, P.H. and Parker, P.L. (1961): Fatty Acids in Sedimentary Rocks, Carnegie Inst. Wash. Yearbook, 61, 181.

Baker, E.W., Yen, T.F., Dickie, J.P., Rhodes, R.E. and Clark, L.F. (1967): Mass Spectrometry of Porphyrins II. Characterization of Petro-Porphyrins, J.Am. Chem. Soc., 89, 3631.

Bendoraitis, J.G., Brown, B.L. and Hepner, L.S. (1962): Isoprenoid Hydrocarbons in Petroleum. Isolation of 2, 6, 10, 14-tetramethylpentadecane by High Temperature Gas Liquid Chromatography, Anal. Chem., 34, 49.

Bradley, W.H. (1966): Tropical Lakes, Copropel, and Oil Shale. Geol. Soc. Am. Bull., 77, 1333.

Burlingame, A.L. (1966): Application of High Resolution Mass Spectrometry in Molecular Structure Studies. In W.L. Mead, Ed., Advances in Mass Spectrometry, Vol. 3, Institute of Petroleum, London, p. 701.

Burlingame, A.L. (1968): Data Acquisition, Processing and Interpretation via Coupled High Speed Real-Time Digital Computer and High Resolution Mass Spectrometer Systems. International Mass Spectrometry Conference, Sept. 25–29, 1967, Berlin, in E. Kendrick, Ed., Advances in Mass Spectrometry, Vol. 4, The Institute of Petroleum, London, p. 15.

Burlingame, A.L., Haug, P., Belsky, T. and Calvin, M. (1965): Occurrence of Biogenic Steranes and Pentacyclic Triterpanes in an Eocene Shale (52 Million Years) and in an Early Precambrian Shale (2.7 Billion Years). A Preliminary Report. Proc. U. S. Nat. Acad. Sci., 54, 1406.

Burlingame, A.L. and Simoneit B.R. (1968): Isoprenoid Fatty Acids Isolated from the Kerogen Matrix of the Green River Formation (Eocene). Science, 160, 531.

Burlingame, A.L. and Simoneit, B.R. (1968): Analysis of the Mineral Entrapped Fatty Acids Isolated from the Green River Formation. Nature, 218, 252.

Burlingame, A.L. and Simoneit, B.R.: High Resolution Mass Spectrometry of Green River Formation Kerogen Oxidations, Nature, in press.

Burlingame, A.L. and Smith, D.H. (1968): Automated Heteroatomic Plotting as an Aid to the Presentation and Interpretation of High Resolution Mass Spectral Data, Tetrahedron, 24, 5749.

Burlingame, A.L., Smith, D.H., Merren, T.O. and Olsen, R.W.: Real-time High Resolution Mass Spectrometry, Proc. 16th Ann. Conf. on Mass Spectrometry and Allied Topics, May 12–17, 1968, Pittsburgh, Pa., p. 109.

Cummins, J.J. and Robinson, W.E. (1964): Normal and Isoprenoid Hydrocarbons Isolated from Oil Shale Bitumen, J. Chem. Eng. Data, 9, 304.

Douglas, A.G., Douraghi-Zadeh, K., Eglinton, G., Maxwell, J.R. and Ramsay, J.N.: Fatty Acids in Sediments including the Green River Shale (Eocene) and Scottish Torbanite (Carboniferous). In G.D. Hobson and G.C. Speers, Eds., Advances in Organic Geochemistry, Pergamon Press, London, in press.

Eglinton, G., Douglas, A.G., Maxwell, J.R., Ramsay, J.N. and Ställberg-Stenhagen, S. (1966): Occurrence of Isoprenoid Fatty Acids in the Green River Shale, Science, 153, 1133.

Eglinton, G., Scott, P.M., Belsky, T., Burlingame, A.L., Richter, W.J. and Calvin, M. (1964): Occurrence of Isoprenoid Alkanes in a Precambrian Sediment. In G.D. Hobson and M.C. Louis, Eds., Advances in Organic Geochemistry 1964, International Series of Monographs in Earth Sciences, Vol. 24, Pergamon Press, Oxford, 1966, pp. 41–74.

Forsman, J.P. and Hunt, J.M. (1958): In Habitat of Oil by L.G. Weeks, Ed., Am. Assoc. Petrol. Geol.

Haug, P.A. (1967): Applications of Mass Spectrometry to Organic Geochemistry. Ph.D. Thesis, University of California, Berkeley.

Haug, P., Schnoes, H.K. and Burlingame, A.L. (1967): Keto-Carboxylic Acids Isolated from the Colorado Green River Shale (Eocene). Chem. Comm. No. 21, 1130.

Haug, P., Schnoes, H.K. and Burlingame, A.L. (1967): Isoprenoid and Dicarboxylic Acids from the Colorado Green River Shale (Eocene). Science, 158, 772.

Haug, P., Schnoes, H.K. and Burlingame, A.L. (1968): Aromatic Carboxylic Acids Isolated from the Colorado Green River Formation (Eocene). Geochim. Cosmochim Acta., 32, 358–361.

Hills, J.R., Whitehead, E.V., Anders, D.E., Cummins, J.J. and Robinson, W.E. (1966): An Optically Active Triterpane, Gammacerane, in Green River, Colorado, Oil Shale Bitumen. Chem. Comm., 752.

Lawlor, D.L. and Robinson, W.E. (1965): Fatty Acids in Green River Formation Oil Shale. Paper presented at the Detroit Meeting, Amer. Chem. Soc., Div. Petrol. Chem., May 9, 1965.

Leo, R.F. and Parker, P.L. (1966): Branched Chain Fatty Acids in Sediments. Science, 152, 649.

Morandi, J.R. and Jensen, H.B. (1966): Comparison of Porphyrins from Shale Oil, Oil Shale, and Petroleum by Absorption and Mass Spectroscopy. J. Chem. Eng. Data, 11, 81.

Murphy, M.T.J., McCormick, A. and Eglinton, G (1967): Perhydro-β-carotene in the Green River Shale, Science, 157, 1040.

Robinson, W.E., Cummins, J.J. and Dinneen, G.U. (1965): Changes in Green River Oil Shale Paraffins with Depth. Geochim. Cosmochim. Acta, 29, 249.

Venkataraghaven, R., McLafferty, F.W. and Amy, J.W. (1967): Automatic Reduction of High Resolution Mass Spectral Data. Anal. Chem., 39, 178.

Discussion

W.G. Meinschein: You suggest that in demineralizing your samples with mineral acids you are saponifying some esters. Do you believe the release of fatty acids from their salts may also be an important source of the acids obtained after your demineralization procedure with HCl and HF?

A.L. Burlingame: Yes. c.f. Burlingame, A.L. and Simoneit, B.R., Nature, **218**, 252 (1968).

E.V. Whitehead: What do you regard as the effect of strong acids used in the separation or the possible polymerisation of naturally occurring unsaturated compounds liberated from the kerogen?

A.L. Burlingame: We do not have any evidence of olefinic substances liberated from this kerogen – with the possible exception of the C_{40} regions (c.f. perhydro-β-carotene and lower degrees of unsaturation (presumably rings – not double bonds of the olefinic variety).

Of course, we have evidence for the presence of tetra substituted double bonds in cyclic and polycyclic substances, e.g. Δ^8- in the lanosterol skeleton. We have developed an approach in determining the structures of enzymic steroid products by functionalisation of the hindered Δ^8-double bond with RuO_4 and subsequent high resolution mass spectral analysis, c.f. van Tamelen et al., J. Am. Chem. Soc. 89, 3284 (1968).

H. Kroepelin: Prof. Schmidt-Colerus, Denver[1]) has found in the methanol extract from Green River shale high molecular polymer acids (hydro-abietic and dehydro-abietic type). Have you observed these acids also?

A.L. Burlingame: We have not observed tricyclic aromatic acids of the resin variety occurring in nature (e.g. pine tree, etc.) in the Green River formation. We have evidence for their presence in the Tasmanites (see A.L. Burlingame, P.C. Wszolek and B.R. Simoneit; the fatty acid content of tasmanites, this conference).

On the other hand, we do have evidence for polycyclic acids in the C_{30} range, possibly the steroidal or triterpenoidal variety.

M. Louis: L'auteur a-t-il une idée de l'origine des acides benzène carboxyliques présents dans le schiste de Green River?

Est-ce que le milieu (lacustre) de dépôt de la matière organique peut être responsable de la formation d'une partie des composés oxygénés (phénols, ac. benzène carboxyliques)?

A.L. Burlingame: A suggestion regarding the possible biological precursors I for the phenyl alkanoic acids has been presented by us previously (Haug, P., Schnoes, H.K and Burlingame, A.L. Geochim. Cosmochim. Acta, **32**, 358–362 (1968)); whereas the lower homologs quite possibly are oxidation products of higher weight precursors.

I

---

[1]) Paper presented at the UN-Symposium "Utilisation of oil shale", Tallinn, September 1968.

The Fatty Acid Content of Tasmanites[1])

A. L. Burlingame, Patricia C. Wszolek and Bernd R. Simoneit

Space Sciences Laboratory, University of California
Berkeley, California, USA

Alaskan tasmanite, an organic-rich sedimentary rock of Late Jurassic to Early Cretaceous age (130 to 190 million years old), is made up almost entirely of compressed discs of *Tasmanites,* unicellular organisms thought to be fossil green algae with close biological affinities to the present day marine organisms, *Pachysphaera pelagica* Ostenfeld.

The investigation of the fatty acid content of the Alaskan tasmanite by means of gas chromatography and high and low resolution mass spectrometry reveals several interesting series of carboxylic acids. In addition to the straight chain saturated acids, several types of aromatic acids were detected by high resolution mass spectrometry; they contain one, two and three aromatic nuclei.

Five successive extraction procedures were used to isolate the tasmanite acids: ultrasonic solvent extraction, exhaustive Soxhlet extraction, ultrasonic extraction after demineralization, and saponification and oxidation of the kerogen. The five acid demineralization, and saponification and oxidation of the kerogen. The five acid ester distribution patterns vary, and the differences probably reflect the solubilities of the acids and the way they are bound in the sediment.

Tasmanian tasmanite (Permian, 220 to 275 million years old) is also made up of the remains of *Tasmanites,* but it has only half the organic content of the Alaskan sediment. The same extraction procedures were used to study the fatty acid content of the Tasmanian sample so that a direct comparison to the Alaskan fatty acids could be made.

Introduction

Two related ancient sediments have been under investigation in our laboratory. Alaskan tasmanite, an organic-rich rock of Late Jurassic to Early Cretaceous age (Tourtelot, Donnell and Tailleur, 1967) (130-190 million years old), is made up almost entirely of compressed discs of *Tasmanites* Newton 1875 (Tourtelot, Donnell and Tailleur, 1967; Newton, 1875). These unicellular organisms are thought to be fossil green algae with close biological affinities to the present day marine organisms *Pachysphaera pelagica* Ostenfeld 1899 and other species of *Pachysphaera* (Wall, 1962). Wall has suggested that *Tasmanites* should be classified in the order Chlorophyceae.

---

[1]) Paper XXVIII in the series High Resolution Mass Spectrometry in Molecular Structure Studies. For Part XXVII, see A. L. Burlingame, P. A. Haug, H. K. Schnoes and B. R. Simoneit, this Conference.

Tasmanian tasmanite (Permian, 220-275 million years old) is also composed of the remains of *Tasmanites,* although we are not certain that the species present in this sediment is identical to that of the Alaskan tasmanite. Figure 1, a photograph of the surface of Tasmanian tasmanite at a magnification of 65, clearly shows the individual discs of the microfossils. The Tasmanian tasmanite is only half as organic-rich as the Alaskan material. The latter is about 60 % carbon while the former is 30 % carbon (Table I).

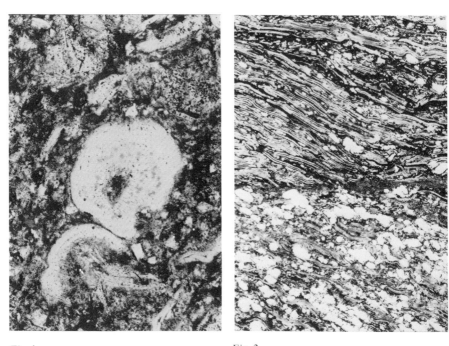

Fig. 1
The surface of Tasmanian
tasmanite (x 65)

Fig. 2
Alaskan tasmanite
thin-section (x 65)

Alaskan tasmanite has been more highly compressed than Tasmanian tasmanite. The Alaskan material is part of a complexly folded rock sequence (Tourtelot et al., 1967; Tourtelot et al., 1966; Donnell et al., 1966). Figures 2 and 3, photographs of thin sections of the two tasmanites (x65), are consistent with the known difference in the pressure histories of the sediments, as well as the different mineral contents. The number of discs per unit volume is greater in the Alaskan sample. Furthermore, the Tasmanian algal remains appear to be better preserved probably due in part to less severe pressure conditions.

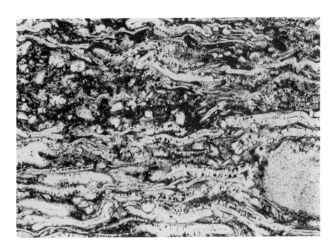

Fig. 3
Tasmanian tasmanite
thin-section (x 65)

The tasmanites are rare in that they have such a simple biological history. Apparently, they are derived from a single source and, hence, would be expected to yield simple mixtures of organic material which can be directly related to chemical components of the precursor organisms. We are aware of only one other ancient sedimentary rock, torbanite, which is derived so exclusively from a single defined organism. Torbanite consists of the remains of the green alga *Botryococcus braunii*. Scottish torbanite (Douglas et al., 1968; Ramsay, 1966; Maxwell, 1967) (250 million years old) is close in age to the tasmanites. It has roughly the same carbon content and oil yield as Alaskan tasmanite.

Here we report on the fatty acids isolated from the tasmanites with successive extractions. Saturated, straight-chain acids are the most abundant components found, especially in the Alaskan tasmanite acid mixtures. The minor components are largely aromatic in character, and several series of acids containing from one to three aromatic nuclei are observed in high resolution mass spectra. Keto acids and dicarboxylic acids are among the other minor components observed. Branched-chain acids have not been identified in the tasmanite acid mixtures. They appear to be absent from the Alaskan tasmanite mixtures, but there is some evidence that there are small quantities of low weight branched-chain acids in the Tasmanian sample.

Experimental

The Alaskan tasmanite studied (U.S. Geological Survey field number 65 ADL 8) was obtained at a location 68°37'30" N and 158°22'30" W in northern Alaska. The Tasmanian sample was collected in an abandoned shale mine on the Mersey River south of Latrobe, Tasmania, at a location 41°17' S and 146°28' E. After breaking, washing, and crushing, several extraction processes were used to successively free the organic material in the tasmanites. The same sample, or parts of the same sample, was used throughout these studies. Before extraction the tasmanite powders had the composition listed in Table I.

Table I. Elemental composition

| | Alaskan Tasmanite | | | Tasmanian Tasmanite | |
	whole rock	kerogen		whole rock	kerogen
C	61.9 %	84.1 %	C	29.0 %	63.2 %
H	8.39 %	11.1 %	H	4.02 %	7.65 %
N	0.59 %	1.04 %	N	0.25 %	0.76 %
S	1.20 %	1.09 %	S	3.03 %	5.32 %
Res.	26.4 %	—	Res.	26.9 %	16.5 %

For the Alaskan material the first extraction procedure was ultrasonic agitation of the powder three times in 3:1 benzene/methanol for 15 minutes. Exhaustive Soxhlet extraction of the residue with 4:1 benzene/methanol for one week followed. Then the residue was demineralized at room temperature by treating with (1) 2:1 HF/HC1 for one day and (2) HC1 and zinc dust for four days. The demineralized residue was agitated ultrasonically with solvent to remove any remaining organic solubles. The insoluble organic residue, i.e., the kerogen, makes up almost 70 % of the Alaskan sediment. Its elemental analysis is found in Table I. Some of the kerogen was then

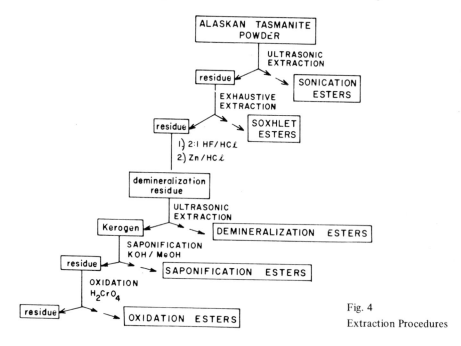

Fig. 4
Extraction Procedures

saponified with methanolic potassium hydroxide over a period of three days. Finally, the kerogen was subjected to chromic acid oxidation for six hours. The chromic acid reagent was made by saturating $6N$ sulfuric acid with potassium dichromate. The flowsheet, Figure 4, summarizes the various extractions.

The Tasmanian tasmanite was treated in a very similar manner. However, the initial ultrasonic extraction was omitted and only the Soxhlet extraction was employed before demineralization. The sample was subjected to two HF/HC1 treatments, one day each, for mineral removal.

The acids were removed from each of the extract solutions as their sodium salts with $1N$ sodium hydroxide in the case of the Alaskan tasmanite and with sodium carbonate [1) 3 %; 2) 1.5 %] for the Tasmanian tasmanite extracts. Treatment of the aqueous salt solutions with sulfuric acid or hydrochloric acid liberated the organic acids which were subsequently extracted with hexane and esterified with BF_3/methanol. Some of the ester mixtures were dried with magnesium sulfate before concentration under vacuum. Several of the tasmanite ester mixtures, especially those resulting from the Tasmanian sample, were adducted with urea. Hot methanol was saturated with three parts of recrystallized urea, and one part heptane containing 0.5 % decane was added. The mixture was cooled to a slurry before the esters were added in a minimum of solvent. After 24 hours the adduct was separated by filtration and rinsed with a small amount of benzene. The filtrate should contain only branched and cyclic esters. After destroying the adduct with water, the entrapped straight-chain acid esters were recovered by heptane extraction. Table II lists the quantitative data pertaining to the various extraction steps of the tasmanites.

Table II. Tasmanite extraction data

Extraction Procedure	Weight of Esters per 100g of Powder	
	Alaskan	Tasmanian
Ultrasonic	2.4 mg	
Exhaustive Soxhlet	0.9 mg	4.0 mg
Demineralization	< 0.1 mg	0.5 mg
Saponification	5.6 mg	12.0 mg
Oxidation	63.5 mg	20.0 mg

All analytical gas-liquid chromatography was carried out on an Aerograph Model 204B gas chromatograph using packed 5' x 1/8" columns of 3 % SE-30 on 100/120 mesh Gaschrom Q and Gaschrom Z. Temperature programming for the Alaskan tasmanite mixtures began at 50 °C. with a program rate of 5.5 °C./minute. For the Tasmanian tasmanite mixtures programming commenced at 100 °C. at a rate of

9 °C./minute. Helium flow through the columns was 30 ml/minute for the Alaskan
ester mixtures and 35 ml/minute for the Tasmanian. The detector and injector
temperatures were usually 250 °C. and 270 °C., respectively. Retention times and
coinjection of standard esters were used to identify straight-chain saturated components.

High resolution mass spectra of acid and ester mixtures were obtained with a
G.E.C.-A.E.I. MS-902 mass spectrometer and a C.E.C. 21-110B mass spectrometer coupled to an S.D.S. Sigma 7 computer (Burlingame, 1968), both equipped
with a direct introduction probe and a heated glass inlet system.

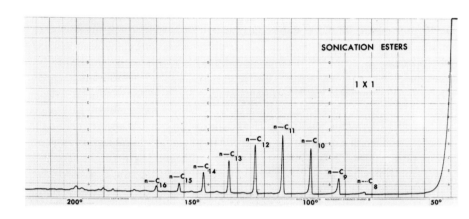

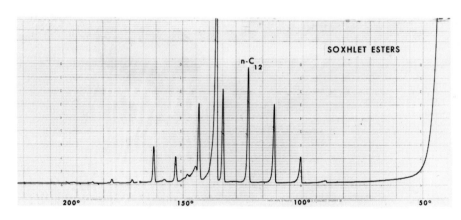

Fig. 5. Gas-liquid chromatograms of the fatty acid methyl esters isolated from Alaskan tasmanite I
solvent extraction

Results (Alaskan tasmanite)

The gas-liquid chromatogram of the methyl esters obtained from the first solvent extraction of the Alaskan tasmanite is shown in Figure 5, labeled sonication esters. The normal, saturated esters have a smooth distribution with a maximum at $n\text{-}C_{11}$; there is no predominance of even over odd acid esters.

The high resolution mass spectrum of the acid mixture (before esterification) shows several other series of acids to be present in the sonication extract. Figure 6a is the partial high resolution mass spectrum of the acids presented as heteroatomic plots (Burlingame and Smith, 1968). Series a in the $C/H\ O_2$ plot corresponds to the normal, saturated carboxylic acids, $C_nH_{2n}O_2$ (n = 8-15). Another prominent series, b[1]), includes ions of the composition $C_nH_{2n-20}O_2$ (n = 15-18). These acids probably have the phenanthrene or anthracene carbon skeleton. Series c consists of acids of the type $C_nH_{2n-8}O_2$ (n = 7-11, 13) to which phenylalkanoic acids can be assigned. Naphthyl alkanoic acids make up series d, which overlaps with series a and, thus, does not appear in the plot. These acids have the composition $C_nH_{2n-14}O_2$ (n = 14-16, 17). Ion e, $C_{18}H_{14}O_2$, probably has a cycloaromatic structure e.g.

The intense ions at the low mass end of the spectrum with the composition $C_nH_{2n-1}O_2$ are fragment ions due to cleavage along the straight-chain of the normal, saturated acids (series a).

Figure 6b represents the partial high resolution mass spectrum, after urea adduction, of the methyl esters corresponding to the acids in Figure 6a. The straight-chain esters were adducted by the urea and series a is no longer observed. For the same reason, the intense fragmentation at the low mass end is not present in this ester spectrum[2]).

Figures 6a and 6b are aligned such that the acid molecular ions and those of their corresponding esters fall under each other for ease of comparison of both patterns. Of course, each ester has one more methylene unit than its corresponding acid.

---

[1]) Many of these peaks have a tic mark above them, which indicates more than seven degress of unsaturation. Fragments of this kind are plotted below the next lower major saturated division, i.e., $C_{n-1}H_{2n-1}$. To convert the apparent composition of these ions as they appear on the plot to their actual composition, add one carbon and subtract twelve hydrogens.

[2]) This is evidence that there are little or no branched-chain acids present in the mixture. Branched-chain, saturated acids would give fragments with the same compositions as those resulting from straight-chain, saturated acids although their relative intensities would be different.

138   A. L. Burlingame et al.

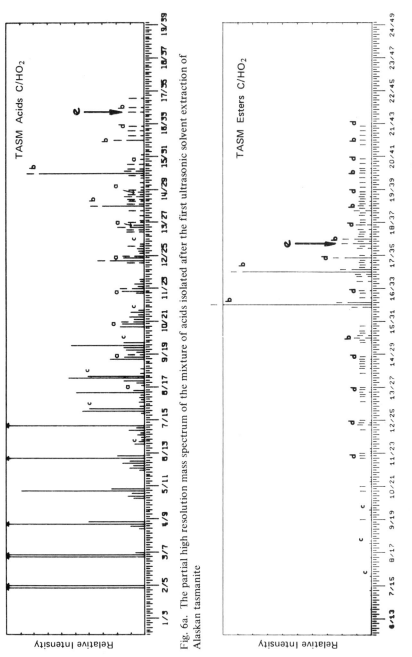

Fig. 6a. The partial high resolution mass spectrum of the mixture of acids isolated after the first ultrasonic solvent extraction of Alaskan tasmanite

Fig. 6b. The partial high resolution mass spectrum of the mixture of methyl esters derived from esterification of the acids (in Figure 6a above) and subsequent clathration. These esters were not included in the urea adduct.

Series b, c, and d are probably responsible for the small peaks in the chromatogram (Figure 5, sonication esters) which occur in between the labeled normal esters and beyond n-C_{16}. Although quantitatively these three series make up a small proportion of the mixture, their molecular ions are quite intense in the mass spectra (Figures 6a and 6b). This is not surprising since the stability of these aromatic molecular ions is greater than the stability of the molecular ions of the saturated series a.

The C/H O plot of the total sonication ester mixture has a series of ions with the composition $C_nH_{2n-18}O$ (n = 14–18). These could be phenols of the phenanthrene or anthracene skeleton.

Several series of dicarboxylic acids were also detected in the high resolution mass spectrum although in small quantities: $C_nH_{2n-2}O_4$ (n = 4, 5); $C_nH_{2n-10}O_4$ (n = 7, 8, 12, 13); $C_nH_{2n-16}O_4$ (n = 12, 14–16); and $C_nH_{2n-18}O_4$ (n = 13–16).

When the Alaskan tasmanite was exhaustively extracted in a Soxhlet, additional acids were obtained. The most abundant saturated acid is n-C_{12}, one carbon number higher than the maximum of the sonication acids. The outstanding feature of the Soxhlet ester mixture (see Figure 5) is the large peak eluted in between n-C_{13} and n-C_{14}. One peak also predominates in the high resolution mass spectrum of the mixture (in Figure 7). This ion occurs at m/e 184 and has the composition $C_{13}H_{12}O$. The compound must be a substituted naphthol or phenyl phenol to have been extracted with sodium hydroxide. Low solubility probably accounts for the increase in intensity of this compound over that observed in the sonication mixture.

Series b, c, and d and ion e described above are also observed in the high resolution mass spectrum of this Soxhlet ester mixture. However, they make up a smaller proportion of this mixture than of the sonication ester mixture. Small amounts of the phenanthrene or anthracene phenols are also observed as well as the various series of dicarboxylic acids noted above. Table III provides an outline of some of the most important features of the solvent extracted acid mixtures.

Demineralization of the Alaskan tasmanite yielded almost no fatty acids. The mineral content of the rock is only about 30 %, and apparently very little organic acid material is associated with the mineral matrix. Due to its low weight, this acid extract was not examined in any detail.

Reactions carried out on the Alaskan tasmanite kerogen, i.e., saponification and oxidation, yielded the largest amounts of fatty acids of all of the extractions. The most important components isolated from the kerogen are summarized in Table IV. The acids resulting from saponification (see Figure 8) are almost entirely normal acids from C_{10} to C_{24}. The maximum is at n-C_{12}, and there is little or no even/odd predominance. No aromatic acid esters of the series b, c, and d are observed in the high resolution mass spectrum. However, small amounts of $C_{14}H_{10}O$ and $C_{15}H_{12}O$ are present in the spectrum. These compounds are probably phenols of the phenanthrene or anthracene type. In addition, the mass spectrum indicates small amounts

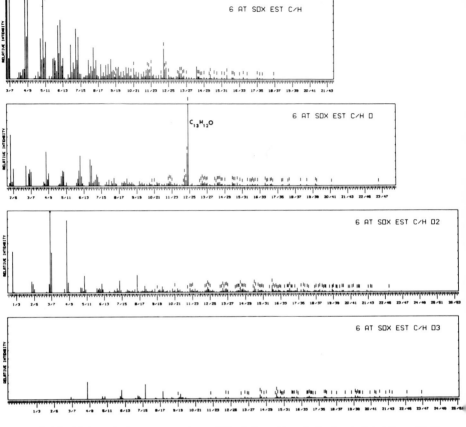

Fig. 7. The high resolution mass spectrum of the fatty acid methyl esters isolated from Alaskan tasmanite by Soxhlet extraction

of keto acids, $C_5H_8O_3$ and $C_6H_{10}O_3$, and small amounts of the dicarboxylic acids, $C_4H_6O_4$, $C_5H_8O_4$, $C_7H_4O_4$, and $C_8H_6O_4$.

When the saponification residue was oxidized, the largest yield of fatty acids was obtained. About 60 % of these acids remained in hexane solution, but the remainder precipitated as a waxy solid. The acids in solution gave a very smooth distribution (Figure 8) of normal, saturated acid esters from n-C_6 to n-C_{14} with a maximum at n-C_9. The high resolution mass spectrum indicates there are also small amounts of saturated acids from C_{15} to C_{22}. In addition, the mass spectrum contains ions corresponding to acids with the composition $C_nH_{2n-2}O_3$ (n = 5–7); these are likely to be keto acids. There are also small amounts of the dicarboxylic acids, $C_4H_6O_4$, $C_5H_8O_4$, $C_7H_4O_4$, and $C_8H_6O_4$.

Table III. Acids isolated from Alaskan tasmanite by solvent extraction

	Sonication		Soxhlet	
	range	maximum	range	maximum
1. Normal Acids	$C_8 - C_{16}+$	C_{11}	$C_9 - C_{18}+$	C_{12}
2. Aromatic Acids (phenyl, $C_nH_{2n-8}O_2$)	$C_7 - C_{11}, C_{13}*$	C_8, C_9	$C_7 - C_{12}*$	C_8
3. Aromatic Acids (naphthyl, $C_nH_{2n-14}O_2$)	$C_{14} - C_{16}, C_{17}*$	C_{17}	$C_{11} - C_{16}*$ $C_{18} - C_{20}*$	C_{13}
4. Aromatic Acids ($C_nH_{2n-20}O_2$)	$C_{15} - C_{18}*$	C_{16}	$C_{14} - C_{21}*$	C_{16}
5. Phenols ($C_nH_{2n-18}O$)	$C_{14} - C_{18}*$	C_{14}	$C_{13} - C_{15}*$ $C_{17} - C_{19}*$	C_{15}
6. Dicarboxylic Acids ($C_nH_{2n-2}O_4$)	C_4, C_5*		$C_4 - C_8*$ $C_{10}, C_{14}, C_{16}*$	C_6
7. Aromatic Dicarboxylic Acids ($C_nH_{2n-10}O_4$)	$C_7, C_8, C_{12}, C_{13}*$	C_7	$C_7 - C_9*$ $C_{11}, C_{13}, C_{15}, C_{16}*$	C_7
8. Aromatic Dicarboxylic Acids ($C_nH_{2n-16}O_4$)	$C_{12}, C_{14} - C_{16}*$	C_{15}	$C_{12}, C_{14}, C_{16}*$ $C_{18}*$	
9. Aromatic Dicarboxylic Acids ($C_nH_{2n-18}O_4$)	$C_{13} - C_{16}*$	C_{14}	$C_{13}, C_{15-17}*$	C_5

* Determined by high resolution mass spectrometry

+ Determined by gas chromatography

Table IV. Acids isolated from Alaskan tasmanite kerogen

	Saponification		Oxidation (solution)		Oxidation (precipitate)	
	range	maximum	range	maximum	range	maximum
1. Normal Acids	$C_{10} - C_{24}+$ $C_5 - C_{24}*$	C_{12}	$C_6 - C_{14}+$ $C_5 - C_{22}*$	C_9	$C_9 - C_{28}+$ $C_5 - C_{39}*$	C_{12}
2. Phenols ($C_nH_{2n-18}O$)	$C_{13} - C_{15}*$	C_{14}				
3. Keto Acids ($C_nH_{2n-2}O_3$)	C_5, C_6*		$C_5 - C_7*$		$C_5 - C_{14}*$	C_5
4. Dicarboxylic Acids ($C_nH_{2n-2}O_4$)	C_4, C_5*		C_4, C_5*		$C_4 - C_{11}*$ $C_{13}, C_{15} - C_{17}*$	C_4
5. Aromatic Dicarboxylic Acids ($C_nH_{2n-10}O_4$)	C_7, C_8*		C_7, C_8*		$C_7 - C_{10}*$	C_8
6. Aromatic Dicarboxylic Acids ($C_nH_{2n-12}O_4$)					$C_9 - C_{11}*$ $C_{14} - C_{16}*$ $C_{19}*$	C_{10}

* Determined by high resolution mass spectrometry

+ Determined by gas chromatography

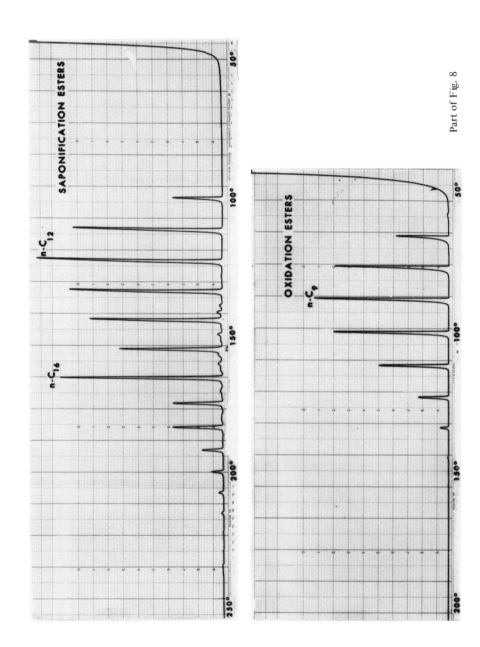

Part of Fig. 8

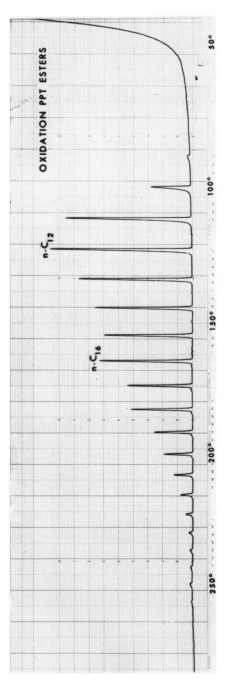

Fig. 8. Gas-liquid chromatograms of the fatty acid methyl esters isolated from Alaskan tasmanite kerogen

The waxy precipitate from oxidation is composed of saturated fatty acids up to C_{39} as indicated by the high resolution mass spectrum. Compared with the acids remaining in solution, there is a shift of the maximum to higher carbon number and the range is also extended. The gas chromatogram in Figure 8 shows that n-C_{12} is the maximum, and there is little or no even/odd predominance. Keto acids ($C_nH_{2n-2}O_3$) are again observed in the high resolution mass spectrum, but the series is extended (n = 5–14) to higher carbon numbers. Dicarboxylic acids with $C_nH_{2n-2}O_4$ (n = 4 – 11, 13, 15–17) are also present as well as aromatic dicarboxylic acids: $C_nH_{2n-10}O_4$ (n = 7–10) and $C_nH_{2n-12}O_4$ (n = 9–11, 14–16, 19).

Results (Tasmanian tasmanite)

The gas chromatogram of the total acid esters isolated from the exhaustive extract is shown in Figure 9. The high resolution mass spectral data for the total mixture is shown in Figure 10 and the various homologous acid series found are summarized in Table V. The saturated straight-chain acids ranged from C_{11} to C_{16} in the gas chromatograms, the maximum peak being the C_{14} acid. Branched-chain acids of only low molecular weight (C_5 to C_8) were indicated in the mass spectra of the branched fraction since the fragmentation ions due to the McLafferty rearrangement were of very low intensity and only the low mass molecular ions were observed (cf. Figure 6b). These acids could also be cross-contamination from incomplete urea adduction. This is strong evidence that pristanic and phytanic acids are

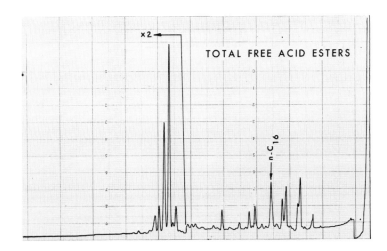

Fig. 9. Gas-liquid chromatogram of the fatty acid methyl esters isolated from Tasmanian tasmanite by exhaustive solvent extraction

Table V. Acids isolated from the exhaustive extract of Tasmanian tasmanite

	range	maximum
1. Normal Acids	$C_5 - C_{15}$* $C_{11} - C_{16}$+	C_{14}
2. Branched Acids	$C_5 - C_8$*	
3. Bicyclic Acids ($C_nH_{2n-4}O_2$)	$C_8 - C_{14}$*	C_{13}
4. Keto Acids ($C_nH_{2n-2}O_3$)	$C_{15} - C_{22}$*	C_{18}
5. Aromatic Acids (phenyl $C_nH_{2n-8}O_2$)	$C_8 - C_{11}$*	C_9
6. Aromatic Acids (naphthoic $C_nH_{2n-14}O_2$)	$C_{12} - C_{24}$*	C_{13}
7. Aromatic Tricyclic Acids ($C_nH_{2n-12}O_2$)	$C_{15} - C_{20}$*	C_{18}
8. Aromatic Tricyclic Acids ($C_nH_{2n-16}O_2$)	$C_{17} - C_{23}$*	C_{18}

* Determined by high resolution mass spectrometry
+ Determined by gas chromatography

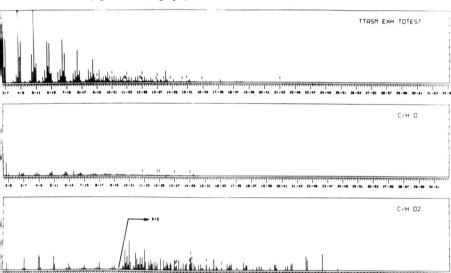

Fig. 10. The high resolution mass spectrum of the fatty acid methyl esters isolated from Tasmanian tasmanite by exhaustive solvent extraction

not present in this extract in any significant quantity. Bicyclic[1]) acids, $C_nH_{2n-4}O_2$ (n = 8–14, maximum 13), and tricyclic acids[1]), $C_nH_{2n-6}O_2$ (n = 15–22, maximum 18) were deduced from their molecular ions and respective $M-CH_3O$ peaks in the C/H O_2 and C/H O plots of Figure 10.

---

[1]) There is no evidence to rule out olefinic acids, but cyclic acids are more plausible in view of the two series with ranges of increasing carbon number. Cyclic acids would also be expected to be more stable under geologic conditions in this time frame.

There were several aromatic acid series found, and the naphthoic acids appear to be the most concentrated (quantitative assignments cannot be made based on relative ion intensities alone). A series of substituted phenyl alkanoic acids was indicated for $C_nH_{2n-8}O_2$ (n = 8–11) and a maximum at n = 9. The naphthoic acid series consisted of homologues of $C_nH_{2n-14}O_2$ where n = 12–24. Referring to Figure 10, the molecular ion of the C_{13} acid ester, which is the most abundant of the series, is at $C_{14}H_{14}O_2$ in the C/H O_2 plot. A homologous series of $C_nH_{2n-12}O_2$ (n = 15–20, C_{18} as maximum) and another of $C_nH_{2n-16}O_2$ for n = 17–23 (also C_{18} as maximum) were also found. The former series seems to fit a tricyclic aromatic skeleton as structure f and the latter series structure g.

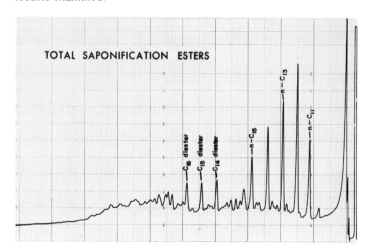

The exhaustively extracted sample was then demineralized, liberating a very small acid fraction (0.0005 percent of original sample). The gas chromatogram of the esters strongly resembled the gas chromatogram of the acid esters isolated from the subsequent saponification (Figure 11) of the tasmanite kerogen. It was assumed that the demineralization extract constituted a partial hydrolysis of saponifiable matter rather than acids associated with the mineral matrix and was therefore not further examined.

Fig. 11. Gas-liquid chromatogram of the fatty acid methyl esters isolated by saponification of Tasmanian tasmanite kerogen

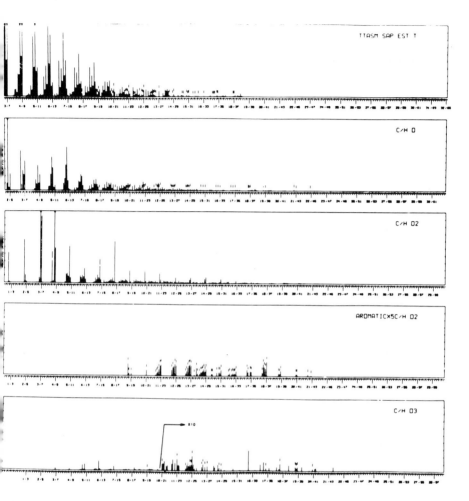

Fig. 12. The high resoluation mass spectrum of the fatty acid methyl esters isolated by saponification of Tasmanian tasmanite kerogen

The saponification extract acids consisted mainly of normals from C_{10} to C_{16} with the C_{12} acid most abundant and no even/odd predominance (Figure 11). In the high resolution mass spectral data (Figure 12) the range extended down to C_8. The high resolution mass spectrum of the branched-cyclic fraction was devoid of any extensive fragment ions due to alkanoic acid esters and molecular ions for only the $C_5 - C_8$ acids were observed. Keto acids, $C_nH_{2n-2}O_3$ (n = 4–9, with maximum at 5) were detected in small amounts by their molecular ions, as well as by the

M–CH$_3$O and M–C$_3$H$_5$O peaks found in the C/H O$_2$ plot of Figure 12. The same aromatic acid series as described for the exhaustive extract were found for this mixture with essentially the same distributions. There was no specific series which predominated. These series are probably indicated by the small peaks and elevated background in the gas chromatogram. Two homologous dicarboxylic acid series were found present in this fraction. The first consisted of dicarboxylic acids, C$_n$H$_{2n-2}$O$_4$, ranging from n = 9–17. The molecular ions were too small to be detected, but the series was established by the strong peaks due to M–CH$_3$O and due to the subsequent loss of ketene (Ryhage and Stenhagen, 1964; unpublished results of W.J. Richter, D.H. Smith and A.L. Burlingame). Referring to Figure 12, the C$_{15}$ acid has the M–CH$_3$O peak at C$_{16}$H$_{29}$O$_3$ in the C/H O$_3$ plot and the following loss of ketene results in the peak at C$_{14}$H$_{27}$O$_2$ in the C/H O$_2$ plot. This series is also visible in the gas chromatogram from C$_{14}$ to C$_{16}$ (Figure 11), established by coinjection of standards. The second series consisted of phenyl dicarboxylic acids, C$_n$H$_{2n-10}$O$_4$, ranging from n = 8–12 with the C$_8$ diacid as most abundant. This series was established from the strong M–CH$_3$O peaks as, for example, the C$_8$ acid has said peak at C$_9$H$_7$O$_3$ in the C/H O$_3$ plot of Figure 12. In the high resolution mass spectra of the branched-cyclic esters this series extended to the C$_{17}$ diacid and several molecular ions were indicated (in particular, C$_{10}$H$_{10}$O$_4$ as the most intense).

The gas chromatogram of the total acids isolated from the six hour chromic acid oxidation of the tasmanite kerogen is shown in Figure 13. An example of the high resolution mass spectral data for the total oxidation esters is presented in Figure 14, and the various homologous series found are summarized in Table VI. The major peaks of the gas chromatogram of the urea adducted fraction constituted a homolo-

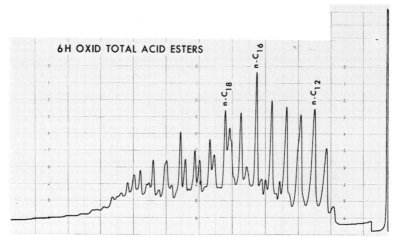

Fig. 13. Gas-liquid chromatogram of the fatty acid methyl esters isolated by 6 hour oxidation of Tasmanian tasmanite kerogen

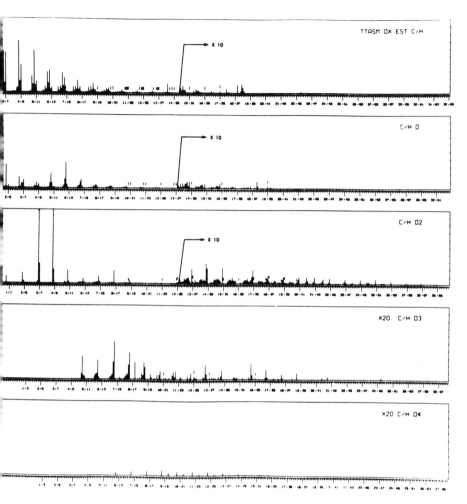

Fig. 14. The high resoluation mass spectrum of the fatty acid methyl esters isolated by 6 hour oxidation of Tasmanian tasmanite

gous series of normal fatty acids ranging from C_{10} to C_{27} (C_5 to C_{32} in the high resolution mass spectra) with C_{16} as largest and no even/odd predominance. The branched-chain acids ranged from C_5 to C_{13} in the high resolution mass spectral data. The dicarboxylic acids were found to have a wider range ($C_4 - C_{20}$ with C_7 maximum) and the ketoacids likewise ($C_5 - C_{17}$ with C_6 maximum). The phenyl dicarboxylic acid series, $C_nH_{2n-10}O_4$, was found present from C_8 to C_{13} with a phthalic acid $C_{10}H_{10}O_4$ in the C/H O_4 plot of Figure 14, as most abundant. The cyclic acids: $C_nH_{2n-4}O_2$ (n = 5–19) and $C_nH_{2n-6}O_2$ (n = 6–26) were present in rather low

Table VI. Acids isolated from the 6 hour oxidation of Tasmanian tasmanite kerogen

	range	maximum
1. Normal Acids	$C_5 - C_{32}$*	C_{16}
	$C_{10} - C_{27}$+	
2. Branched Acids	$C_5 - C_{13}$*	
3. Dicarboxylic Acids ($C_nH_{2n-2}O_4$)	$C_4 - C_{20}$*	C_7
4. Keto Acids ($C_nH_{2n-2}O_3$)	$C_5 - C_{17}$*	C_6
5. Aromatic Dicarboxylic Acids ($C_nH_{2n-10}O_4$)	$C_8 - C_{13}$*	C_8
6. Cyclic Acids $C_nH_{2n-4}O_2$	$C_5 - C_{19}$*	
$C_nH_{2n-6}O_2$	$C_6 - C_{26}$*	
7. Aromatic Acids phenyl − $C_nH_{2n-8}O_2$#	$C_8 - C_{18}$*	C_9
naphthyl − $C_nH_{2n-14}O_2$	C_{13}, C_{14}*	
$C_nH_{2n-10}O_2$	$C_{11} - C_{21}$*	C_{12}
$C_nH_{2n-12}O_2$	$C_{12} - C_{20}$*	
$C_nH_{2n-16}O_2$	$C_{17} - C_{19}$*	C_{18}
8. Tetracyclic Acids ($C_nH_{2n-8}O_2$)#	$C_{18} - C_{26}$*	C_{24}

* Determined by high resolution mass spectrometry

\+ Determined by gas chromatography

\# The aromatic acids are only listed to C_{18} since above C_{18} the data would be consistent with tetracyclic acids.

amounts, becoming more abundant towards greater carbon numbers (aside from the large peaks at low masses probably due to rearrangements). Various aromatic acid series were present. The phenyl alkanoic acids, $C_nH_{2n-8}O_2$ ranged from n = 8–18 with C_9 most intense. Only the C_{13} and C_{14} acids of the naphthyl series, $C_nH_{2n-14}O_2$ were indicated. The two series of tricyclics (structures f and g) were present as $C_nH_{2n-12}O_2$ with n = 12–20 and $C_nH_{2n-16}O_2$ with n = 17–19 (18 maximum). Another bicyclic series, $C_nH_{2n-10}O_2$ with n = 11–21 and C_{12} as largest was indicated by the molecular ions in the C/H O_2 plot of Figure 14 and can be thought of as indanoic acids. A tetracyclic acid series, $C_nH_{2n-8}O_2$ for n = 18–26 with C_{24} as maximum was present and was further substantiated by some ions corresponding to M−CH$_3$. These data tend to indicate steroidal acids of structure type h.

Discussion

The Alaskan tasmanite fatty acids are strikingly simple. Almost entirely straight-chain, saturated acids, they are concentrated at relatively low carbon numbers. Little or no even/odd predominance exists in any of the mixtures. The Tasmanian tasmanite fatty acids are somewhat more complex. The normal acids make up a much smaller proportion of the total Tasmanian acids. Nevertheless, the range of normal acids is about the same for the two sediments. The maxima of the normal acids is shifted to slightly higher carbon number for the Tasmanian sample, but again little or no even/odd predominance is evident.

Aromatic acids are common to both tasmanites although the distributions differ. The trinuclear aromatic species predominate in the Alaskan material, while the naphthoic acids appear to be the most abundant in the Tasmanian tasmanite. In general, the Alaskan tasmanite acids are more highly aromatized (more degrees of unsaturation) than the Tasmanian.

The presence of tricyclic and tetracyclic acids with varying degrees of aromatic character (e.g. series b, e, structure types f, g, and h,) in both sediments suggests a sterol origin for all of these species. The various compounds may represent different stages in the degradation of possible sterol precursors. Preliminary high resolution mass spectra of Alaskan tasmanite hydrocarbon fractions indicate that hydrocarbons analogous to acid series b and e are present as well as sterane-type molecules. Sterols have been isolated from representatives of all of the divisions of algae (Miller, 1962; Reitz and Hamilton, 1968), sitosterol being the most common sterol among the Chlorophyta (Miller, 1962).

We have found no branched-chain or isoprenoid acids in Alaskan tasmanite, and so far we have little evidence for their presence in Tasmanian tasmanite. Our results are consistent with the isolation of only very small amounts of branched-chain acids from present day blue-green algae (Parker et al., 1967; Leo and Parker, 1966; Oro et al., 1967). On the other hand, isoprenoid fatty acids have been isolated from the Green River Shale (Lawlor and Robinson, 1965; Haug et al., 1967; Burlingame, 1968; Eglinton et al., 1966; MacLean et al., 1968) and a California petroleum (Cason and Graham, 1965), and it is thought that these acids originate from the phytol side chain of chlorophyll. Thus, it is surprising that isoprenoid acids are not found in the tasmanites to any great extent since *Tasmanites* have been classified as green algae and should have contained chlorophylls a and b. Douglas et al. (1968) report the same result for Scottish torbanite held to have originated from the green alga *Botryococcus braunii*. Nevertheless, we have identified the C_{18} and C_{19} isoprenoid hydrocarbons from Alaskan tasmanite (A. L. Burlingame and P.C. Wszolek, unpub. results), and the C_{19} and C_{20} isoprenoid hydrocarbons were isolated from Scottish torbanite (Maxwell, 1967).

It appears to us that the fatty acids now isolated from the tasmanites do not represent clear evidence of the presumed algal origin of the sediments. Besides the lack of isoprenoid acids, the fatty acid content of the tasmanites, bears little resemblance to the acids of present-day algae and algal mats (Miller, 1962; Parker et al., 1967; Oró et al., 1967; Parker and Leo, 1965; Han et al., 1968). $n-C_{16}$ and $n-C_{18}$ are the most abundant normal acids isolated from living algae as well as from recent sediments derived from algae. Furthermore, algae contain large amounts of olefinic acids, chiefly those having one to three degrees of unsaturation. These olefinic acids are also concentrated at C_{16} and C_{18}. Only trace amounts of acids of odd carbon number are found in the algae.

Our findings for the tasmanites, particularly for the Alaskan material, indicate that there are several similarities to Scottish torbanite (Douglas, 1968). The range of normal acids is roughly the same, those isolated from torbanite extending from $C_{10}-C_{28}$ for the "free" fatty acids and from C_9-C_{27} for the total fatty acids. However, we do not observe the dominance of the $n-C_{16}$ and $n-C_{18}$ acids found in torbanite, and, in general, the tasmanite normal acids are concentrated at lower carbon number. Isoprenoid fatty acids are not present in the tasmanites and torbanite, at least not to any significant extent. All of these sediments contain dicarboxylic acids. A series of dicarboxylic acids from C_8 to C_{25} was isolated from the demineralized and saponified torbanite, and the tasmanite dicarboxylic acids were pointed out above.

Perhaps additional exhaustive oxidations of the tasmanite kerogens will shed more light on the nature of the sediments. The initial six-hour oxidations described above yielded acids which were predominantly aliphatic in nature, expecially for the Alaskan material. Once these simple oxidizable aliphatic chains have been removed, further oxidation may provide additional information. Certainly these kerogens are a rich storehouse of organic material as their carbon contents indicate. We are also proceeding with an extensive study of the tasmanite hydrocarbons and neutral fractions.

Acknowledgements: We wish to thank Mr. H.A. Tourtelot, U.S. Geol. Survey, Denver, for kindly providing us with the sample of Alaskan tasmanite; Mrs. E. Scott for technical assistance with the Tasmanian tasmanite; Dr. D. H. Smith for real-time high resolution mass spectra; Prof. H.K. Schnoes for discussions of these results; Mr. Donald Mikami for the microscopic examinations.

Financial support was provided by the U.S. National Aeronautics and Space Adm. Grants NGL 05-003-003 and NAS 9-7889.

References

Burlingame, A.L. (1968): Data Acquisition, Processing and Interpretation via Coupled High-Speed Real-time Digital Computer and High Resolution Mass Spectrometer Systems. In Adv. in Mass Spectrometry, Vol. **4**, E. Kendrick, Ed., Inst. of Petroleum, London, 1968, p. 15.

Burlingame, A.L. and Simoneit B.R. (1968): Isoprenoid Fatty Acids Isolated from the Kerogen Matrix of the Green River Formation (Eocene). Science, **160**, 531.

Burlingame, A.L. and Simoneit, B.R. (1968): Analysis of the Mineral Entrapped Fatty Acids Isolated from the Green River Formation. Nature, **218**, 252.

Burlingame, A.L. and Smith, D.H. (1968): Automated Heteroatomic Plotting as an Aid to the Presentation and Interpretation of High Resolution Mass Spectral Data. Tetrahedron, **24**, 5749.

Cason, J. and Graham, D.W. (1965): Isolation of Isoprenoid Acids from a California Petroleum. Tetrahedron, **21**, 471.

Donnell, J.R., Tailleur, I.L and Tourtelot, H.A. (1966): Northern Alaskan Oil Shale, presented at the 1966 Annual Meeting of the Geological Society of America, San Francisco, California, (Nov. 14–16).

Douglas, A.G., Douraghi-Zadeh, K., Eglinton, G., Maxwell, J.R. and Ramsay, J.N. (1968): Fatty Acids in Sediments including the Green River Shale (Eocene) and Scottish Torbanite (Carboniferous), Advances in Organic Geochemistry, 1966. G.D. Hobson, D. Speers, Eds., Pergamon Press, Oxford.

Eglinton, G., Douglas, A.G., Maxwell, J.R., Ramsay, J.N. and Ställberg-Stenhagen, S. (1966): Occurrence of Isoprenoid Fatty Acids in the Green River Shale. Science, **153**, 1133.

Han, J., McCarthy, E.D., Van Hoeven, W. and Calvin, M. (1968): Organic Geochemical Studies, II. A Preliminary Report on the Distribution of Aliphatic Hydrocarbons in Algae, in Bacteria, and in a Recent Lake Sediment. Proc. U.S. Nat. Acad. Sci., **59**, pp 29–33.

Haug, P., Schnoes, H.K. and Burlingame, A.L. (1967): Isoprenoid and Dicarboxylic Acids from the Colorado Green River Shale (Eocene). Science, **158**, 772.

Lawlor, D.L. and Robinson, W.E. (1965): Fatty Acids in Green River Formation Oil Shale. Paper presented at the Detroit Meeting, Amer. Chem. Soc., Div. Petrol. Chem., May 9.

Leo, R.F. and Parker, P.L. (1966): Branched Chain Fatty Acids in Sediments. Science, **152**, 649.

MacLean, I., Eglinton, G., Douraghi-Zadeh, K., Ackman, R.G. and Hooper, S.H. (1968): Correlation of Stereoisomerism in Present Day and Geologically Ancient Isoprenoid Fatty Acids. Nature, **218**, pp. 1019–1023.

Maxwell, J.R. (1967): Studies in Organic Geochemistry, Ph.D. Thesis, University of Glasgow.

Miller, J.D.A. (1962): Fats and Steroids. In Physiology and Biochemistry of Algae, Ralph A. Lewin, Ed., Academic Press, New York.

Newton, E.T. (1875): On "Tasmanite" and Australian "White Coal". Geol. Mag., **12**, pp. 337–342.

Oró, J., Tournabene, T.G., Nooner, D.W. and Gelpi, E. (1967): Aliphatic Hydrocarbons and fatty acids of some marine and fresh water microorganisms. J. Bacteriol. **93**, pp. 1811–1818

Parker, P.L. and Leo, R.F. (1965): Fatty Acids in Blue-Green Algal Mat Communities. Science, **148**, 373.

Ramsay, J.N. (1966): Organic Geochemistry of Fatty Acids, M. Sc. Thesis, University of Glasgow.

Ryhage, R. and Stenhagen, E. (1964): Mass Spectrometric Studies XI. On the Nature of the ions
    m/e 84 + n X14 (n = 0, 1, 2, ...) Present in Mass Spectra of Esters of Dibasic Acids. Arkiv
    Kemi, **23**, 167.

Tourtelot, H.A., Donnell, J.R. and Tailleur, I.L. (1967): Oil Yield and Chemical Composition of
    Shale from Northern Alaska, presented at the Seventh World Petroleum Congress, Mexico
    City, April 2–8.

Tourtelot, H.A., Tailleur, I.L. and Donnell, J.R. (1966): Tasmanite and Associated Organic-Rich
    Rocks, Brooks Range, Northern Alaska, presented at the 1966 Annual Meeting of the Geolo-
    gical Society of America, San Francisco, California, (Nov. 14–16).

Wall, D. (1962): Evidence from Recent Plankton Regarding the Biological Affinities of Tasma-
    nites Newton 1875 and Leiosphaeridia Eisenack 1958. Geol. Mag. Vol. **XCIX**, No. 4, pp.
    353–362.

Discussion

R. Byramjee: 1. The comparison of direct microscopic studies of organic matter and chemical analyses of the same is the main point of interest of the French Petroleum Co., and a paper on Saharan Tasmanites was given at the London Organic Geochemistry Meeting (Bordenave – Combaz – Giraud).

2. Any oxidation of kerogen must be clearly defined with respect to physical and chemical conditions, because the products obtained may vary considerably from one procedure to another.

P.C. Wszolek: At the moment we have no information regarding reproducibility of the mild chromic acid oxidation of tasmanite kerogen, either Alaskan or Tasmanian. However, during our studies of the Green River Formation kerogen, which were reported at this conference, we tried to get some feeling for the scope of this problem by repetitive oxidations of the kerogen with various reaction times. We realize that this type of experiment is exploratory in nature and aimed primarily at finding out the general nature of the kerogen that we are working with. More refined experiments are in progress which would be chemical transformations, more specific in nature than that of chromic acid treatment. We also have plans to define the nature of the oxygen incorporated during the chemical treatment by determining its location using stable isotopic labeling, which can, of course, be distingusihed from oxygen functionality indigenous to the kerogen.

M. Teichmüller: Die Dünnschliffbilder der beiden Tasmaniten haben gezeigt, daß der alaskische Tasmanit weit stärker metamorphosiert ist, als der australische, vorausgesetzt, daß beide wirklich vergleichbare Ausgangssubstanz („Tasmanites") enthalten. Der alaskische Tasmanit dürfte das Fettkohlen Stadium schon erreicht haben, da die Algen bereits rote Farbe im Durchlicht angenommen haben, während sie im australischen Tasmanit noch die goldgelbe Farbe schwach „inkohlter" Liptinite haben. Damit ist die Möglichkeit gegeben, mit geochemischen Methoden die diagenetischen Veränderungen der verschiedenen chemischen Verbindungen von Tasmaniten zu studieren. Andererseits sollte man die Unterschiede, die bei der Untersuchung der Fettsäuren in den beiden Tasmaniten gefunden wurden, durch den verschiedenen Metamorphose-Grad zu erklären versuchen.

P.C. Wszolek: Our comparison of the fatty acid compositions of the two tasmanites seems to be consistent with what you have said about the differences in diagenesis. The normal acids of the Alaskan tasmanite maximize at lower carbon numbers than those of Tasmanian tasmanite. The Alaskan sediment appears to contain a smaller proportion of acids with additional functional groups, e.g. dicarboxylic acids. The tricyclic and tetracyclic acids of Alaskan tasmanite have a higher degree of aromatic character than those of Tasmanian tasmanite. All of these observations probably indicate that the degradative processes are further advanced in the Alaskan sediment.

H.R. von Gaertner: Die Diskussion zeigt die Notwendigkeit gleichzeitig mikroskopische und chemische Studien zu integrieren. Die ausgezeichneten chemischen Studien sind Studien der Durchschnittszusammensetzung. Es wäre sehr wünschenswert, wenn man sehen könnte, was man wirklich gelöst hat. Hier könnte es Teil des Tasmaniten Fossils gewesen sein, es könnte von der nicht figurierten organischen Substanz stammen (z.B. durch mikrobiologische Vorgänge entstanden) oder von dem ganzen Fossil gleichmäßig kommen.

Gas Chromatographic — Mass Spectrometric Identification of Long Chain Hydroxy Acids in Plants and Sediments

Donald H. Hunneman [1]) and Geoffrey Eglinton

Organic Geochemistry Unit, School of Chemistry, University of Bristol
Bristol, England

Aliphatic hydroxy acids occur widely in the plant world as constituents of cutin, the polymerized hydroxy acid layer of the cuticle of the aerial parts of plants. Because of the chemical resistance of the cuticle a search has been made for these acids in geological samples.

A 5,000 year old freshwater lake sediment furnished, on hydrolysis, 0.6 % (based on dry weight) of aliphatic hydroxy acids including the expected acids from cutin and suberin (the cork layer of plants), i.e. ω-hydroxy C_{16}, C_{18}, C_{20}, C_{22}, C_{24}, and C_{26}, and the cutin acid 10,16-dihydroxyhexadecanoic. Also present were a wide range of α- and β-hydroxy acids, presumably oxidation products from the fatty acids found in the same sediment. Other geologically important specimens have also been examined.

Chemotaxonomy has made many advances in recent years. Useful taxonomic correlations have been found using such chemical products as hydrocarbons [1], fibrinopeptides [2] and cytochrome c [3]. However, the related field of paleochemotaxonomy has remained relatively undeveloped. While occasional efforts have been made to correlate the compounds found in a sediment with the organisms thought to have contributed to its composition [4], little work has been done on individual fossils.

The first example of a direct paleochemotaxonomic correlation has recently been published by Knoche and Ourisson [5]. The hydrocarbons extractable from fossil and fresh *Equisetum* showed an identical pattern.

However, the use of soluble and mobile compounds such as hydrocarbons as paleochemotaxonomic markers has a distinct disadvantage. Such compounds are readily transported and there is no way of proving that any such compounds found associated with a fossil are truly indigenous. Any products found may well have been transported from some other source, ancient or modern.

Fortunately, certain fossils are formed totally, or in part, of biopolymers, insoluble polymers originally deposited by the living specimen. One very striking example of a biopolymer is cutin, the non-cellular membrane comprising the principal component of the cuticle of the aerial parts of land plants (Figure 1) [6]. Cutin is composed of interesterified and polymerized hydroxy fatty acids, generally of C_{16} and C_{18} chain length (Figure 2) [7]. Suberin, the principal component of the cork layer of many plants, shows a similar composition to cutin.

---

[1]) Present address: Varian MAT GmbH, 28 Bremen 10, Postfach 4062, Germany

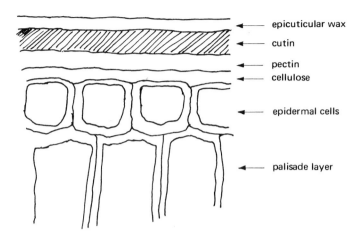

epicuticular wax

cutin

pectin

cellulose

epidermal cells

palisade layer

Fig. 1. Components of the cuticle of vascular plants

HO $(CH_2)_6$ CH $(CH_2)_8CO_2H$
                |
               OH

HO $(CH_2)_8$ CH $(CH_2)_8CO_2H$
                |
               OH

HO $(CH_2)_8$ CH CH $(CH_2)_7CO_2H$
                | |
               OH OH

HO_2C $(CH_2)_7$ CH CH $(CH_2)_7CO_2H$
                   | |
                  OH OH

HO $(CH_2)_{15}CO_2H$

HO $(CH_2)_{17}CO_2H$

HO $(CH_2)_8CH = CH$ $(CH_2)_7CO_2H$

HO $(CH_2)_5CH = CH CH_2CH = CH (CH_2)_7CO_2H$

Fig. 2
Typical cutin acids isolated from
cuticle of modern plants

We have developed a method of determining these hydroxy acids on the microgram scale (Figure 3) [8]. The sample is hydrolysed with methanolic KOH. The methanol is then evaporated, the residue acidified with HCl and the ether soluble acids extracted. The ether soluble acids are methylated with diazomethane and then thin layer chromatographed on silica gel in a mixture of hexane/ether/methanol (40:10:1). The R_f values of various hydroxy acids are given in Figure 3. The various fractions

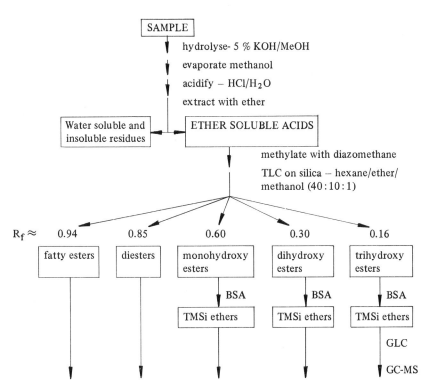

Fig. 3. Procedure for the analysis of hydroxy acids in modern plants and geological specimens

from the thin layer chromatogram are then eluted and converted into the trimethyl-silyl ethers (TMSi) with bis (trimethylsilyl) acetamide (BSA). The individual hydroxy ester, TMSi ethers are then determined by gas chromatography and combined gas chromatography – mass spectrometry.

The mass spectra of the TMSi ethers of hydroxy acid methyl esters are particularly easy to interpret (Figure 4) [9]. All the spectra are characterized by peaks at m/e 73 ($\overset{+}{\text{S}}$i(CH$_3$)$_3$), m/e 75 ((CH$_3$)$_2$ $\overset{+}{\text{S}}$i=O), M-15, M-31 and M-47. The peaks at m/e 146 and 147 are most useful. The peak at m/e 146 is a rearrangement fragment involving the methyl ester and the TMSi ether and is present in the spectra of mono TMSi, methyl esters; while m/e 147 is a fragment present in all the spectra of compounds containing more than one TMSi. In the case of vicinal di TMSi's a very strong fragmentation occurs between the two carbon atoms bearing the TMSi groups. With a mono TMSi in the middle of a chain, strong cleavage occurs on either side of the functionalized carbon.

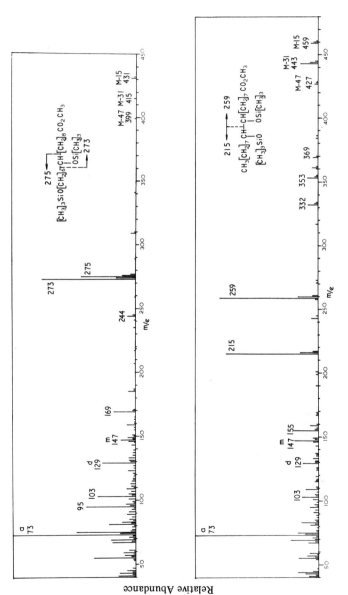

Part of Fig. 4

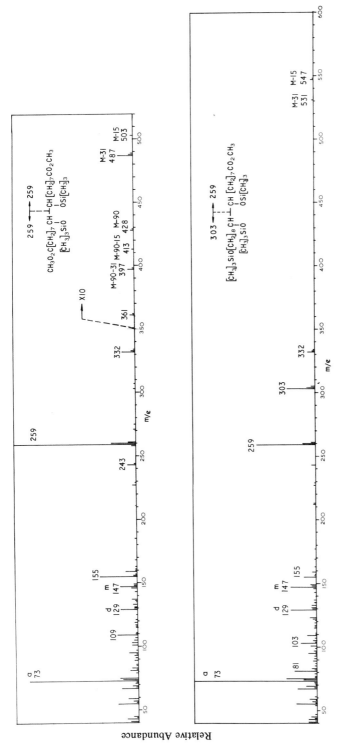

Fig. 4. Mass spectra of hydroxy acid, methyl esters, TMSi ethers

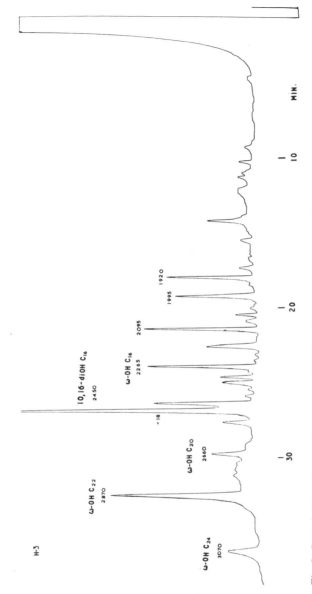

Fig. 5. Post glacial sediment – Esthwaite (∼ 5X10³ yrs). Gas chromatogram of hydrolysate hydroxy acid fraction as methyl esters TMSi ethers. GLC conditions: 10 ft x 1/16 in stainless steel column packed with 3 % SE · 30 on Gas Chrom Q. Programmed 100°–300° at 5°/min.

Compound	Relative percentage
α- and β-hydroxytetradecanoic	6.4 %
" " pentadecanoic	7.0
" " hexadecanoic	8.1
" " heptadecanoic	5.5
" " octadecanoic	2.4
ω-hydroxyhexadecanoic	8.3
" eicosanoic	2.9
" docosanoic	17.3
" tetracosanoic	6.4
" hexacosanoic	trace
10,16-dihydroxyhexadecanoic	18.8

Fig. 6. Principal hydroxy acids found in a 5000 year old lacustrine sediment

We have examined the hydroxy acids of a 5000 year old lacustrine sediment using the above outlined method [10]. The hydroxy acids comprised 0.6 % of the dry weight of the sediment. The compounds found are shown in Figure 5 and 6. As expected, the largest component is the ubiquitous cutin acid 10,16-dihydroxy-hexadecanoic. The longer chain ω-hydroxy acids are most probably derived from suberin, the substance related to cutin and occuring in the cork layer of many plants. Unexpectedly, a long series of α- and β-hydroxy acids were also found, paralleling in chain length distribution the fatty acids from the same sediment, suggesting that these acids are derived from the fatty acids.

The diacids from the same sediments paralleled in chain length distribution the ω-hydroxy acids and suggest that the ω-hydroxy acids may be precursors of the diacids. Diacids have been reported previously in sediments [11] and previously no satisfactory explanation of their origin has been suggested.

A number of aromatic acids were also isolated from the same sediment using a slightly modified extraction procedure. Among these was identified p-hydroxybenzoic acid. Such aromatic acids are well known as breakdown products of lignin.

The hydroxy acids of a much older sediment, the Brown "Current Wax" Coal from Czechoslovakia ($30 \cdot 10^6$ years old) were also determined. The fatty acids comprised approximately 0.28 % of the dry weight of the sediment and the hydroxy acids 0.6 %. The fatty acids were comprised principally of the $n-C_{26}$, $n-C_{28}$ and $n-C_{30}$ compounds. The monohydroxy acids (0.21 %) were composed of two series, one composed of the ω-hydroxy acids, $n-C_{24}$, $n-C_{26}$ and $n-C_{28}$ and one other as yet unidentified series. The ω-hydroxy acids may have two possible origins, as components of suberin or plant waxes. Their chain length is a bit too long for suberin acids, the usual principal ω-hydroxy acid in suberin being $n-C_{22}$. Further these acids are present in approximately the same amount as the fatty acids which undoubtedly derive from plant waxes.

Of the higher hydroxylated acids there were identified 10,16-dihydroxyhexadecanoic
9,10-dihydroxyoctadecan-1,18-dioic (phloionic) and 9,10,18-trihydroxyoctadecanoic
(phloionolic). The identity of these acids suggest that they are contributed both by
cutin and suberin.

Fossil cutin occasionally occurs in very extensive deposits resembling thin sheets of
brown paper tightly packed together. These are termed Paper Coals [12]. A large
percentage of the weight of these Paper Coals is composed of extractable humic
acids but the remaining insoluble residues appear very similar to modern cutin. We
have tried to determine the composition of these fossil cuticles. They are characterized by resistance to hydrolysis techniques which very rapidly break down modern
cutin, including such drastic techniques as refluxing 10 % KOH/EtOH. However,
oxidation with refluxing dilute nitric acid gave an 40 % yield of aliphatic diacids
from a Paper Coal from Indiana, USA. The identity of the diacids was confirmed
by GLC retention indices and GC-MS on the methyl esters. The GLC trace of the
diesters is shown in Figure 7.

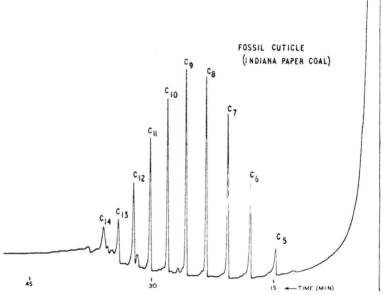

Fig. 7. GLC trace of aliphatic diacids (as dimethyl esters) obtained by nitric acid oxidation of
the Indiana Paper Coal. GLC conditions: 10 ft X 1/16 in o.d. stainless steel column packed
with 3 % OV-17 on GasChrom Q. Programmed 100°–300° at 5°/min.

Acknowledgement: This work was supported by NASA (NsG 101–61).

References

[1] G. Eglinton, R. J. Hamilton, R. A. Raphael and A. G. Gonzalez: Nature 193, 739 (1962).
[2] B. Blombäck, M. Blombäck, N. J. Gröndahl and E. Holmberg: Ark. Kemi 25, 411 (1966).
[3] T. Yamanaka: Nature 197, 1183 (1967).
[4] W. Henderson, V. Wollrab and G. Eglinton: Chem. Comm. 710 (1968).
[5] H. Knoche and G. Ourisson: Angew. Chem. (Internat. Ed.) 6, 1085 (1967).
[6] E. A. Baker and J. T. Martin: Nature 199, 1268 (1963).
[7] M. Matic: Biochem. J. 63, 168 (1956).
[8] G. Eglinton and D. H. Hunneman: Phytochemistry 7, 313 (1968).
[9] G. Eglinton, D. H. Hunneman and A. McCormick: Org. Mass.Spec. 1, 593 (1968).
[10] G. Eglinton, D. H. Hunneman and K. Douraghi-Zadeh: Tetrahedron, 24, 5929 (1968).
[11] A. G. Douglas, K. Douraghi-Zadeh, G. Eglinton, J. R. Maxwell and J. N. Ramsay: Advances in Organic Geochemistry (Ed. by Hobson and Speers) in press.
[12] R. C. Neavel and G. K. Guennel: J. Sed. Petrol. 30, 241 (1960).

Discussion

M. Teichmüller: Die Autoren haben Kutikulen aus verschiedenen Vorkommen untersucht. Es ist wahrscheinlich, daß der Metamorphose-Grad der untersuchten Sedimente verschieden ist und damit auch gewisse Unterschiede in der chemischen Zusammensetzung der Kutikulen erklärt werden können. Van Gijzel (Netherlands) hat eine elegante Methode ausgearbeitet, nach der man den Metamorphose-Grad von Liptiniten (zu denen auch die Kutinite gehören) durch Messung der Fluoreszenzintensität unter dem Mikroskop bestimmen kann. Die Strahlungsintensität nimmt mit zunehmender Metamorphose ab und verschwindet schließlich ganz im Fettkohlenstadium. Auch in diesem Falle empfehlen sich also gekoppelte chemische und mikroskopische Untersuchungen.

D. H. Hunneman: The only visual experiments we have attempted on these cuticles was to observe whether the conditions used had caused any visible breakdown. Our efforts have momentarily been directed to breaking down just one fossil cuticle and, of course, the consideration you mention must be kept in mind when we start any comparison between different cuticles.

H. Kroepelin: To the remark of Mrs. Teichmüller. The higher the aromatisation, the higher should be the amount of fluorescent compounds. But the observed fluorescence depends not only from this amount, but also from the abundance of compounds absorbing the exceting light or the fluorescence.

A. L. Burlingame: Have you varied the duration and oxidizing power in these experiments where you obtain a series of dicarboxylic acids − to get a feeling of how much you are chewing up the polymer?

D. H. Hunneman: Yes, we have oxidized the Indiana Paper Coal with 10 %, 30 % and 50 % HNO_3 for varying lengths of time. Although the yields of diacids from each treatment are different, the distributions of aliphatic diacids (from $C_5 - C_{16}$) are quite the same.

Carbohydrate Components of Paleozoic Plants

Frederick M. Swain, Judy M. Bratt, Samuel Kirkwood and Paul Tobback
University of Minnesota
Minneapolis, Minnesota and St. Paul, Minnesota, USA

The residual monosaccharide components in aqueous and acid extracts of 25 species of Devonian-Permian plant fossils range from traces to 420 micrograms per gram. The species are distributed as follows: Pteridophyta-Psilophytales (2 species), Pteriodophyta-Equisetales (4 species), Pteridophyta-Lycopodiales (9 species), Pteridospermatophyta (6 species), Gymnospermae-Cordaitales (4 species).

The Devonian psilophytes *Trimerophyton robustius* and *Rhynia gwynnevaughani* yielded by chromatographic and enzymatic analyses: galactose, glucose, mannose, xylose and perhaps arabinose. The former yielded somewhat more polymeric glucose than galactose, the latter has an excess of polymeric galactose and may have originally had predominantly galactans rather than cellulose as structural polysaccharides.

The Carboniferous Equisitales *(Calamites)* and some of the lycopods *(Lepidodendron, Sigillaria)* tend to have an excess of galactose over glucose suggesting structural galactans. Other Carboniferous lycopods, with predominant glucose, probably were evolving greater amounts of cellulose at that time.

The pteridosperms (*Annularia, Neuropteris,* etc.) have glucose predominant over galactose and mannose but the latter two are sufficiently abundant in the specimens analyzed to suggest that mannans and galactans were important structural polysaccharides in these plants.

In Devonian *Callixylon* galactose is the predominant sugar whereas glucose exceeds galactose in Pennsylvanian *Cordaites,* suggesting that an evolutionary change from galactan-rich algal type structural polysaccharides to cellulose may have occurred in the Cordaitales between Devonian and Upper Carboniferous time.

Aqueous extracts of Devonian *Rhynia* and of Pennsylvanian *Calamites duboisi* and *C. Suckowi* were dialyzed against distilled water to remove free monosaccharides and were then treated with α-amylase, β-amylase and cellulase preparations. Small amounts of maltose were produced by the α-enzymatic reaction which suggests that linear α-1$\rightarrow$4 linked glucopyranose (starch) is present in the fossils. Glucose was produced by the cellulase preparation in two species suggesting that linear β-1$\rightarrow$4 linked glucopyranose (cellulose) is present.

Preheating samples of a *Calamites* at 175 °C did not consistently give higher total carbohydrates yields, whereas such is the case in Devonian shale samples. Protective effects of associated mineral grains and a low rate of autoxidation of the carbohydrate residues in the shale is believed to account for this difference. Data are presented on thermal degradation studies of glucose alone and in the presence of mineral substances.

Introduction

Carbohydrate analyses of Precambrian rock and fossil samples indicate the presence of glucose, small amounts of galactose and arabinose and traces of unknown components (Swain et al., 1968 a; Swain, 1968). The organisms of Precambrian time were represented by Procaryotic types (including Bacteria and Blue-green Algae) and perhaps primitive Eucaryotic types. The structure of the polysaccharides has not been determined for these residues but the monosaccharides suggest that cellulose and starch and perhaps pectic substances may have occurred. It does not seem likely that cell-wall polysaccharides of the large marine algae (carrageenan, agar, etc.) were present in significant amounts on the basis of present data because of the low values of galactose.

It is of interest to examine the carbohydrates of early Paleozoic plant fossils and fossiliferous rocks to learn what developments may have occurred in plant carbohydrates that can be recognized by geochemical studies.

Procedures

The specimens studied were collected by the writers or were obtained from the U. S. National Museum or from the Department of Botany, University of Minnesota. The specimens were cleaned of weathered crusts and modern organic debris, dipped briefly in concentrated chromic acid solution, rinsed and dried. The cleaned specimens were separated from matrix, as much as possible, by hand chisels or a vibratool, powdered in a mortar or a ball mill, and stored in glass bottles or plastic bags. Before analysis the powdered samples were examined under the microscope for lint or other contamination particles.

Analyses for total carbohydrates were made in triplicate by a phenol sulfuric acid colorimetric method (DuBois et al., 1956). Absorption spectra of the colored products were measured to learn whether hexoses (abs $\lambda \sim 490$ mμ) or pentoses (abs $\lambda \sim 480$ mμ) were predominant.

Analyses for individual monosaccharides were made by treating the powdered samples with cold 72 % sulfuric acid followed by hydrolysis with boiling 1.0 N acid under refluxing conditions for 16 hours. After neutralization, desalting, and reduction to 1 ml final volume, the sugars were separated by paper chromatography using pyridine: ethyl acetate: water (11 : 45 : 6) as developer and ammoniacal silver nitrate as staining agent. The chromatograms are scanned in an integrating densitometer (Swain et al., 1968 a), and compared to standard mixtures.

Separation of some of the carbohydrate extracts was by means of gas chromatography of silyl ether preparations. Trimethylsilyl ethers were prepared by treating the glycose acid-hydrolyzates (1 ml) with anhydrous pyridine (1 ml), hexamethyldisilazane (0.2 ml) and trimethylchlorosilane (0.1 ml) for 5 minutes or longer at room temperature. The reaction mixture in 0.1 to 0.5 μl amounts was separated on a 5-foot × 1/8-inch gas chromatographic column (QF-1 on Aeropak 30), with a flame ionization detector.

Chloromethylsilyl ethers were prepared by treating the glycose acid-hydrolyzate (1 ml) with anhydrous pyridine (0.09 ml), dichloromethyltetramethyl-disilazane (0.03 ml) and chloromethyldimethylchlorosilane (0.01 ml) for 30 minutes at room temperature. The reaction mixture in 0.1 to 2.0 μl quantities was separated on the same column as in the preceding experiments, but an electron-capture detector was used. Both the TMS and CMDMS reagents were obtained from Applied Science Corp., State College, Pa.

Enzymatic analyses for monosaccharides were made for D-glucose and D-galactose using glucose-oxidase and galactose-oxidase preparations obtained from Worthington Biochemical Corp., Freehold, N. J.

Enzymatic analyses for α- and β-amylose and for cellulose were made with amylase and cellulase preparations supplied by the Department of Biochemistry, University of Minnesota. Prior to enzymatic analysis for polysaccharides, the powdered fossiliferous samples were dialyzed against distilled water for 24 hours to remove free sugars. The dialyzed samples were reacted with enzyme preparation and the resulting solution tested with glucose-oxidase preparation or were separated by paper chromatography for monosaccharide components.

For studies of thermal degradation of glucose, aqueous solutions of glucose alone and in presence of mineral substances (3.6 mg/ml) to which had been added uniformly C^{14} labelled glucose were heated in sealed Carius tubes under an atmosphere of He for periods of 10 of 180 minutes in the temperature range 180 °C to 250 °C. Total radioactivity in each tube at the start was 1.5 microcuries. After heating, the remaining glucose was determined:

(1) with a glucose-oxidase reagent (Worthington "glucostat");
(2) the remaining radioactivity was counted in a Nuclear-Chicago liquid scintillation counter;
(3) evaluation was made of peak areas on paper chromatograms of the residual solutions.

From these kinetic data the activation energies were calculated by application to the Arrhenius reaction rate equation. For study of glucose degradation in presence of minerals, 3 % wt/vol of powdered montmorillonite and of Devonian black shale (Marcellus Formation, Pennsylvania) were added to the glucose solution. In these cases, after heating, the suspensions were centrifuged and the remaining glucose determined on the supernatant fractions.

Previous Work in this Series

The individual sugar components of 10 species of Paleozoic plant fossils ranging from Lower Devonian to Lower Permian were found (Swain, Bratt and Kirkwood, 1967) to comprise mainly glucose, galactose, and xylose residues, together with smaller amounts of mannose, rhamnose, and arabinose. Cellulose, starch, galactans and xylans were suggested as making up the polysaccharides of the specimens analyzed. Glucose was the predominant sugar in most of the specimens but *Callixylon* sp. (Psilophytales) from the Upper Devonian has mostly galactose, which suggests that galactans were the principal cell-wall constituents in that plant.

The carbohydrates of eight additional species of Devonian to Pennsylvanian plants studied by Swain, Bratt, and Kirkwood (1968) showed that in fossil Psilophytales and Lycopodiales the general types and ratios of monosaccharides were similar to those of modern ferns. Fossil Equisatales *(Calamites)* on the other hand seem to have more galactose than their modern counterparts *(Equisetum)* suggesting that the fossil forms had more structural galactans in their cell material than their modern representatives in which cellulose is predominant. Similarly, a Devonian Cordaitales is suggested, on the basis of its high galactose content to have been rich in galactan-type structural polysaccharides.

In a further study of Upper Carboniferous plant carbohydrates from the Radstock area England (Swain, Bratt and Kirkwood, 1969), a smoothtrunked *Lepidodendron* with few leaf scars had an excess of galactose over glucose in its carbohydrate residues. Pectic polysaccharides or other galactans may have been relatively higher in this form than in other associated lycopods. The seed ferns analyzed, *Annularia* and *Alethopteris,* like the lycopods, contain enough galactose and mannose to suggest that galactans and perhaps mannans contributed to the cellwall polysaccharides in these extinct plants.

Free Sugar Components of Plant Fossils

The monosaccharides extracted with boiling water from several plant fossils, and Silurian limestone (Table 1) show a predominance of galactose over glucose in some specimens. Relatively large amounts of ribose and rhamnose in two species suggests a bacterial origin and probably represents contaminating material judging from the low amounts of these monosaccharides in most of the fossils studied. In the *Lepidophloios* for which the samples were treated with acid to separate polymeric sugars following water extraction of free sugars, the free sugars considerably exceed the acid-hydrolyzable sugars. Free sugars also predominate in *Calamites Suckowi* and *C. duboisi* but not in *Rhynia* where polymeric sugars are greatly in excess. Some of the sugars separated by water extraction may have been in polymeric form, but a part of this fraction may represent material introduced post-depositionally by circulating waters.

Table 1. Free sugars extracted with boiling water from fossil plants and rock specimens; a: chromatographic analyses; b: enzymatic analyses; n. d.: not determined; values are in micrograms per gram.

Species and sample number	age	gal	glu	man	ara	xyl	rib	rha	Σ
Rhynia gwynne-vaughani	Devonian	0 a / 0 b	0.03 a / 0.02 b		0.09 a	0.09 a	0 a	0 a	0.11 a
Calamites Suckowi	Pennsylvanian	1.26 a / 2.00 b	0.63 a / 0.17 b		0.48 a	0.56 a	8.11 a	6.95 a	17.99 a
Calamites Suckowi (different specimen)	Pennsylvanian	22.44 b	1.06 b	n.d.	n.d.	n.d.	n.d.	n.d.	
Calamites duboisi	Pennsylvanian	0 b	0.31 b	n.d.	n.d.	n.d.	n.d.	n.d.	
Lepidophloios laricinus	Pennsylvanian	2.11 a / 14.09 b	0.86 a / 0.43 b		0.68 a	1.42 a	13.34 a	8.89 a	25.30 a
Keyser Limestone	Silurian	2.66 b	0.07 b	n.d.	n.d.	n.d.	n.d.	n.d.	

Table 2. Acid hydrolyzable carbohydrate components of Paleozoic plant fossils and rock samples; a: Chromatographic analyses; b: enzymatic analyses, n.d.: not determined; values in micrograms per gram.

Species and sample number	age	gal	glu	man	ara	xyl	rib	rha	Σ
Sigillaria cf. *approximata*	Permian	2.65 - 5.35 a	1.14 - 5.96 a	0.61 - 11.22 a		0.4 a	0 a	0 a	4.80 - 22.93 a
Lepidophloios laricinus; (H_2SO_4 extr. of H_2O - extracted sample)	Pennsyl- vanian	0.55 a 0 b	3.48 a 3.15 b	1.14 a		0 a	0 a	0 a	5.17 a
Sigillaria brardi	Pennsyl- vanian	0.85 - 7.76 a ave. 3.42 0 b	4.25 - 15.15 a ave. 4.25 0 - 1.81 b ave.	2.33 - 8.71 a ave. 5.44	0.63 - 5.36 a ave. 2.56	1.06 - 11.35 a ave. 4.58	0 - 9.54 a ave. 3.18	0.87 a ave. 0.29	9.39 57.87 a ave. 23.72 a
Calamites Suckowi H_2SO_4 extract of H_2O extracted sample	Pennsyl- vanian	0 a 17.2 b	0 a 0.35 b	0 a	0 a	0 a	0 a	0 a	
Calamites duboisi H_2SO_4 extract of H_2O extracted sample	Pennsyl- vanian	0 a 1.69 b	1.97 a 0 b	0.69 a		0 a	0 a	0 a	2.66 a
Calamites sp. a (Radstock)	Pennsyl- vanian	0.50 a	0.90 a	0 a	0 a	0.14 a	0 a	0 a	1.54 a
Rhynia gwynne-vaughani (H_2SO_4 extr. of H_2O - extracted sample)	Devonian	1.18 a 0.17 b	? a 0.86 a	0.90 a		0 a	0 a	0 a	2.08 a; unknown yellow brown spot

Table 2 continued

	Period							
Drepanophycus spp.	Devonian	3.04 a / n.d. b	7.84 a / 0.34 b	4.90 a	3.32 a	6.44 a	0 a	
Taeniocradia dubia	Devonian	0.58 a / 0 b	8.80 a / 1.22 b	1.10 a	0 a	0 a	0 a	
Psilophyton sp.	Devonian	0.25 a / 0 b	2.75 a / 3.20 b	1.70 a	1.65 a	1.75 a	0 a	
Psilophyton princeps	Devonian	2.09 a / 0 b	5.60 a / 2.82 b	3.70 a	2.03 a	0.86 a	0 a	
Psilophyton princeps var. *ornatum*	Devonian	3.79 a / 0 b	16.07 a / 5.58 b	2.79 a	0 a	0 a	0 a	
Psilophyton princeps with long. striae	Devonian	0 a / 0 b	11.72 a / 37.43 b	0a	0a	0a	0a	
Psilophyton robustius	Devonian	0 a / 0 b	11.32 a / 0 b	0.65 a	0 a	0 a	0 a	
Loganophyton sp.	Devonian	0.54 a / 0 b	6.05 a / 3.23 b	4.39 a	1.79 a	0.57 a	0 a	
Hastinella sp.	Devonian	1.94 a / 0 b	3.39 a / 0 b	0 a	0 a	0 a	0 a	
Keyser Limestone	Silurian	0.67 a	0.71 a	0.14 a	0 a	0 a	0 a	1.52 a
Trenton Limestone	Ordovician	0 a	0.07 a	0.03 a	0.05 a	0.05 a	0 a	0.20 a
Virginia Argillite	Huronian (Precambrian)	0 a	0.05 a	0.05 a	0 a	0 a	0 a	0.10 a

Acid-hydrolyzable Sugars of Plant Fossils

The carbohydrates separated by partial chromatographic and enzymatic methods from sulfuric acid or hydrochloric acid hydrolyzates of fossil and rock samples are shown in Table 2. These supplement previous analyses (Swain, Bratt and Kirkwood, 1967, 1968, 1969) and show the widespread distribution of glucose in these primitive plants. In most instances where only glucose was determined by the glucose-oxidase method, the available sample was too small for other analyses.

Polysaccharide Components of Plant Fossils

Samples of three plant species, after dialysis against distilled water to remove free sugars, were treated with α-amylase and β-amylase enzymes for detection of possible starch components and with cellulase enzyme for detection of cellulose (Table 3). In the reaction of amylases on linear α-1→4 glucopyranose polysaccharides an intermediate product is maltose. Trace amounts of maltose were found in the α-amylase treatment of *Rhynia* and *Calamites duboisi*. Further fragmentation of the α-1→4–linked starch units and the β-1→4–linked cellulose units by the indicated enzymes yields glucose (Rogers, 1965).

The data strongly indicate the presence of both starch and cellulose among the carbohydrate residues of these primitive plants. Rogers (1965) had previously demonstrated the presence of a β-1→3 linked polysaccharide of laminaran type in Devonian black shale.

Table 3. Polysaccharide analyses of Paleozoic plant samples;
a: Chromatographic analyses for glucose following reaction with indicated enzyme;
b: enzymatic analyses for β-D–glucose.

Species and Sample Number	α-amylase (glu μg/g)	β-amylase (glu μg/g)	Cellulase (glu μg/g)	Polysaccharides indicated by enzymatic activity
Rhynia gwynne-vaughani	0 a 0 b Trace maltose a	0 a 0.89 b	0 a 0 b	Linear α-1→4 glucopyranose units (starch)
Calamites Suckowi	0.20 a[1]) 0.16 b	0.18 a[1]) 0 b	0.20 a[1]) 0.16 b	Linear α-1→4 glucopyranose units (starch); Linear β-1→4 glucopyranose (cellulose)
Calamites duboisi	0 a 0 b[2]) Trace maltose a	0 a 0 b[2])	0 a 0 b[2])	Linear α-1→4 glucopyranose units (starch) suggested by maltose

[1]) Small amounts of mannose, arabinose and ribose (∼0.1 – 0.2 μg/g) were present on chromatograms of extracts treated with indicated enzyme.

[2]) Small to moderate amounts of D-galactose (0.5 – 5.1 μg/g) detected by galactose-oxidase in extracts treated with indicated enzyme.

Effect of Heating and Oxidation on Carbohydrate Residues in Fossil Samples

Rogers (1965) found that preheating Devonian black shales up to 200 °C or more in air in some instances increased their yields of total carbohydrate residues when these were analyzed by a phenol-sulfuric acid test for furfurals. Increased yields were also obtained on Devonian shale by preheating under nitrogen up to 175 °C (Swain, Rogers, Evans and Wolfe, 1967).

In the present study powdered 10 g samples of specimens of *Calamites Suckowi* were heated at 175 ° C for 2 hours under nitrogen and the yields were compared to unheated samples extracted with acid in presence and absence of air (Table 4). The rather inconsistent results obtained indicate that there is no advantage to preheating these samples or eliminating oxygen as far as total carbohydrates yields are concerned. This may be due to the fact that oxidative degradation of the carbohydrates already occurred during fossilization to the extent that further mild oxidation is ineffective. The much greater yield of furfurals than of hydrolyzable sugars from this and other fossil specimens analyzed, by an order of magnitude or more, also shows the extent of this degradation.

Table 4. Total carbohydrate contents of three different samples of *Calamites Suckowi* from Radstock, England; values are in micrograms per gram of fossil sample containing about 8 % organic carbon; samples heated at 175 °C for 2 hours.

	5-Hydroxymethylfurfural (λ max 490 mμ)
Sample No. 1	
a, heated under N_2	31.8
b, unheated in air	33.4
Sample No. 2	
a, heated under N_2	39.3
b, unheated in air	41.2
Sample No. 3	
a, heated under N_2	30.6
b, heated in air	25.8

The Devonian shale samples referred to above appear to have the disseminated carbohydrates protected by mineral matter with the result that less degradation has occurred and pre-heating the samples is more effective in increasing carbohydrate yields.

Thermal Degradation of Glucose

The thermal decomposition of several oligosaccharides (cellobiose, maltose, dextrose) and a polysaccharide (potato starch) was studied by Puddington (1948). Cellobiose and dextrose degraded in two stages between temperatures of 210 °C and 240 °C; the first stage was principally that of dehydration with loss of two moles of water; the second stage was the production of CO and CO_2. The degradation of maltose was anomalous in that no dehydration step was noted. Starch decomposed in a manner like that of the second step of cellobiose.

The activation energy of degradation of cellobiose, following the first dehydration step which resulted in loss of about 15 % of the molecular water, was found to be about 40 Kcal/mole; that of maltose, in which water loss was more gradual, was about 35 Kcal/mole; and that of dextrose in which water loss was less than 5 % was about 29 Kcal/mole. The activation energy of degradation of potato starch was found to be reasonably constant at 29 Kcal/mole over the range of 1–4% of water given off.

Several workers have found that heating glucose in absence of, or in presence of, a catalyst produced dimer or polymer substances (Pictet and Castam, 1920; Cramer and Cox, 1922; Hurd and Edwards, 1949; O'Calla and Lee, 1956; Mora and Wood, 1952; O'Calla et al., 1962; and Sugisawa and Edo, 1964). According to Sugisawa and Edo (1964) heating glucose to a caramel without a catalyst resulted in the formation of 9 dimers and 2 trimer products. These authors made no attempt to formulate the activation energy of degradation of glucose.

For the present study Tobback heated samples of chemically pure glucose in aqueous solution, in sealed tubes in a helium atmosphere, first alone, and then in the presence of a montmorillonite, and of a Devonian black shale. Glucose alone was found to degrade with an activation energy of $\sim$ 22 Kcal/mole in the temperature range 180 °C to 250 °C (Fig. 1). Glucose in association with montmorillonite degraded with an activation energy of about 21 Kcal/mole (Fig. 2). Glucose in association with Devonian black shale degraded with an activation energy of about 25.4 Kcal/mole (Fig. 3).

Conclusion

The Paleozoic plants studied have yielded small but reasonably consistent carbohydrate residues by extraction and chromatographic and enzymatic analytical procedures. The results provide a basis for comparison with the carbohydrates of geologically younger representatives. Analyses of a few species for polysaccharide components indicate the presence of linear α- and β-1→4 linked glucopyranose units of the nature of starch and cellulose. Work on the polysaccharides in other fossils is being continued.

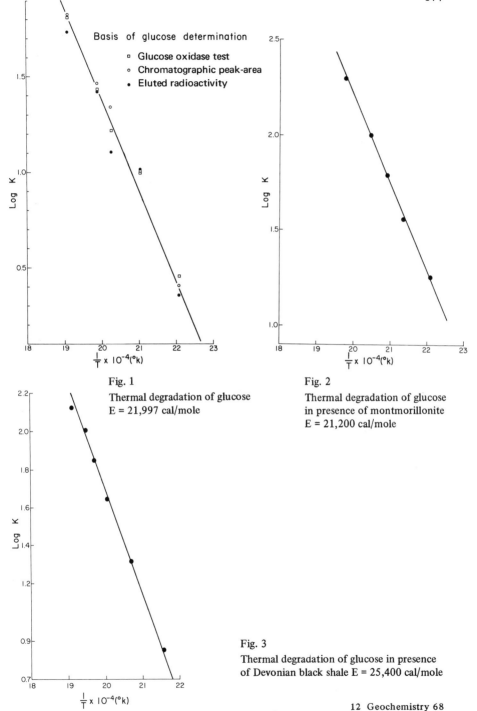

Fig. 1

Thermal degradation of glucose
E = 21,997 cal/mole

Fig. 2

Thermal degradation of glucose
in presence of montmorillonite
E = 21,200 cal/mole

Fig. 3

Thermal degradation of glucose in presence
of Devonian black shale E = 25,400 cal/mole

Preheating of samples of carbohydrate-bearing rock seems to increase yields of sugars owing to the disseminated and less-degraded character of the organic matter in the presence of protective mineral grains. The spotty results in carbohydrate yield on preheating large plant fossil specimens seems to be due to more complete aut-oxidative degradation of the organic matter in the absence of much protective mineral matter.

The activation energy of glucose in aqueous solution ranges from about 21.2 Kcal/ mole for glucose + montmorillonite to 25.4 Kcal/mole for glucose and Devonian black shale; the value for glucose alone is about 22 Kcal/mole. The observed activation energies are overall values for the possible polymer formation and other rearrangements believed to occur during the heating of glucose.

Acknowledgments: The support of National Aeronautics and Space Administration Grants NGR-24-005-054 and NGR-005-063 is gratefully acknowledged. Shirley A. Kraemer assisted with the analyses. Francis M. Hueber, Sergius H. Mamay and John W. Hall kindly provided specimens for analysis. Vernon de Ruyter, Frederick Boethling, Christian Engen and Charles Rhoades, students at the University of Minnesota, aided in preparation of specimens.

List of Samples

1. *Rhynia gwynne-vaughani* Kidston and Lang, Middle Devonian, near Rhynie, Aberdeenshire, Scotland; supplied by F. M. Hueber.

2. *Calamites Suckowi* Brongniart, Pennsylvanian, "Anthracite Series", near Pittston, Luzerne County, Pennsylvania; supplied by F. M. Hueber.

3. *Calamites Suckowi* Brongniart, Upper Coal Measures, Writhlington Mine, near Radstock, Somerset, England.

4. *Calamites duboisi* Artes, Pennsylvanian, "Anthracite Series", Olyphant, Lackawanna County, Pennsylvania; supplied by F. M. Hueber.

5. *Lepidophloios laricinus* Sternberg, Pennsylvanian, Pella, Iowa; supplied by J. W. Hall.

6. Keyser Limestone, Upper Silurian, Mt. Union, Huntingdon County, Pennsylvania.

7. *Sigillaria* cf. *approximata* Lesquereux, Greene Formation, Lower Permian, Vance, Greene County, Pennsylvania.

8. *Sigillaria brardi* Brongniart, Pennsylvanian, Pella. Iowa.

9. *Drepanophycus* sp. Lower Devonian, probably equivalent to Battery Point Formation, south side of Restigouche River, just west of Dalhousie Junction, Nova Scotia; supplied by F. M. Hueber.

10. *Taenocradia dubia* Krausel and Weyland *(nomen nudem)* Lower Devonian, Battery Point Formation, south side, Restigouche River, Dalhousie Nova Scotia, 175 yards west of first dirt road west of city playground; supplied by F. M. Hueber.

11. *Psilophyton* sp., same locality as No. 10.

12. *Psilophyton princeps* Dawson, same locality as No. 10.

13. *Psilophyton princeps* var. *ornatum* Dawson, same locality as No. 10.

14. *Psilophyton princeps* Dawson with prominent longitudinal striae, same locality as No. 10.

15. *Psilophyton robustius* Dawson, same locality as No. 10.

16. *Loganophyton* sp., same locality as No. 10.

17. *Hastinella* sp., same locality as No. 10.

18. Trenton Limestone, Middle Ordovician, south end of Kishacoquillas Valley, 1.5 miles south of Airydale, Mt. Union Quadrangle, Mifflin County, Pennsylvania.

19. Virginia Argillite, Animikie Group, Precambrian, Core hole at Biwabik, Minnesota; supplied by G. B. Morey.

References

Cramer, M. and Cox, E. H., 1922: Sur la constitution de la glucosene, Helv. Chem. Acta. **5**, 844.

Dubois, M., Gilles, K. A., Hamilton, J. K., Rebers, P. A. and Smith, F., 1956: Colorimetric method for determination of sugars and related substances, Anal. Chem., **28**, 350–356.

Hurd, C. D. and Edwards, O. E., 1949: Thermal degradation of sugars, J. Org. Chem. **14**, 680.

Mora, P. T. and Wood, J. W., 1958: Synthetic polysaccharides I. Polycondensation of glucose, J. Am. Chem. Soc. **80**, 685.

O'Calla, P. S. and Lee, E., 1956: Synthetic polysaccharides, Chem. and Ind. (London) **1956**, 522.

O'Calla, P. S., Lee, E. E. and McGrath, D., 1962: The action of cation-exchange resins on D-glucose, J. Am. Chem. Soc. **1962**, 2730.

Pictet, A. and Costam, P., 1920: Sur la glucosene, Helv. Chem. Acta., **3**, 645.

Puddington, I. E., 1948: The thermal decomposition of carbohydrates, Can. Jour. Res., **26 B**, 415–431.

Rogers, M. A., 1965: Organic geochemistry of some Devonian black shales from eastern North America: Carbohydrates (PhD thesis), Minneapolis, Minn. 246 p.

Swain, F. M., 1968: Chap. 13 in Eglinton, G. and Murphy, Sister M. T. J., Organic Geochemistry, Methods and Results, New York and Berlin, Springer-Verlag, in press.

Swain, F. M., Bratt, J. M. and Kirkwood, S., 1967: Carbohydrate components of some Paleozoic plant fossils, Jour. Paleontology, **41**, 1549–1554.

Swain, F. M., Bratt, J. M. and Kirkwood, S., 1968: Possible biochemical evolution of carbohydrates of some Paleozoic plants, Jour. Paleontology, **42**, 1018–1082.

Swain, F. M., Bratt, J. M. and Kirkwood, S., 1969: Carbohydrate components of Upper Carboniferous plant fossils from Radstock, England, Jour. Paleontology, **43**, in press (March issue).

Swain, F. M., Pakalns, G. V. and Bratt, J. M., 1968: Possible taxonomic interpretation of some Paleozoic and Precambrian carbohydrate residues, in Adv. in Org. Geochem. for 1966 G. D. Hobson ed., Oxford, Pergamon Press, in press.

Swain, F. M., Rogers, M. A., Evans, R. D. and Wolfe, R. W., 1967: Distribution of carbohydrate residues in some fossil specimens and associated sedimentary matrix and other geologic samples, Jour. Sed. Petrol. **37**, 12–24.

Sugisawa, H. and Edo, H., 1964: The thermal degradation of sugars I. Thermal polymerization of glucose. Chem. and Ind. (London) 892.

Watanabe, H. and Hase, S., 1956: Studies in dextrose III. Changes of properties of dextrose solution by heating, Rept. Food Res. Inst. Japan **11**, 49.

Zerban, F. W., 1947: The color problem in sucrose manufacture, Sugar Res. Found. Inc., Tech. Rept. **2**, 3.

Identification of Steranes and Triterpanes from a Geological Source by Capillary Gas Liquid Chromatography and Mass Spectrometry

William Henderson[1]), Vojtech Wollrab and Geoffrey Eglinton

Organic Geochemistry Unit, School of Chemistry, University of Bristol
Bristol, England

The hydrocarbon fraction from the soluble organic extract of the Green River shale (Eocene, about 50×10^6 years) has been investigated. After treatment with 5 Å molecular sieve a branched and cyclic alkane fraction containing steranes and triterpanes was obtained. Using capillary GLC on two liquid phases this alkane fraction has been compared with sterane and triterpane standards and the presence of 5 α-cholestane, 5 β-cholestane, stigmastane and gammacerane was established. By combined capillary GC-MS the presence of these compounds was confirmed and further data obtained which gave tentative evidence for the presence of ambreane, ergostane and hopane.

The present study shows that the branched and cyclic alkane fraction from this freshwater sediment is mainly composed of diterpanes, steranes, triterpanes and tetraterpanes. This indicates a biological origin and the low abundance of cholestane implies plant rather than animal sources. This paper also serves to demonstrate that these techniques provide identification of components in mixtures where only micro-quantities are available for analysis.

Organic geochemistry is concerned with the search for molecular carbonaceous remnants in sediments, petroleums and coals. It is now widely accepted that most of the organic compounds found in geological samples had a biological origin. These remnants are fossil natural products in the respect that the original compounds were synthesised by living systems and became incorporated in the geological environment by the normal sedimentary processes. The term biological marker was coined to indicate that the structure of a compound isolated from a geological source was identical to, or could be closely related to, a compound known to be produced by a living system. For biological markers to be of value, they should have good chemical stability to diagenesis and maturation, they should not be synthesised in significant quantities by abiogenic processes and they should possess a high degree of specificity in their skeletal features.

Of the commonly used biological markers, the normal alkanes [1–6], the 2- and 3-methyl alkanes [3], the isoprenoid alkanes e.g. farnesane, pristane and phytane [7–12], the steroids [13–19], the triterpenoids [15–27], and the tetraterpenoids [28], only the last three categories have been shown not to be synthesised by the Fischer-Tropsch process. Moreover they possess a high degree of specificity in their structures which make them ideal biological markers. The optical activity exhibited

---

[1]) Present address: Unilever Research Laboratory, Colworth House, Sharnbrook, Bedfordshire, England.

by many petroleums [32] has been associated with polycyclic alkanes and it was postulated that these may be steranes and triterpanes derived from naturally occurring steroids and triterpenoids [29, 30, 31]. The work of Hills and Whitehead [23, 24] and Danieli et al [22] has corroborated this theory. Tentative evidence for the presence of steranes and triterpanes in sediments has been afforded by the work of Burlingame et al [16] and Murphy et al [28]. Hills et al [21] and Henderson et al [17] provided the first conclusive identifications of steranes and triterpanes isolated from a shale.

Most tricyclic, tetracyclic and pentacyclic terpanes found in geological samples are present as saturated hydrocarbons, although some oxygenated compounds have been found, e.g. betulin, allobetulin, oxyallobetulin, friedelin and ursolic acid [18, 19, 25–27]. There is also some evidence for the presence of unsaturated hydrocarbon triterpenes in the Green River shale [33, 34]. The biosynthesis of steroids and triterpenoids has now been shown to follow the biogenetic isoprene rule via squalene epoxide [35–39]. However, no saturated hydrocarbon steroids or triterpenoids have been found in living organisms up to the present time. If the steranes and triterpanes found in geological samples had been formed by plants or animals, and not by the processes of diagenesis and maturation, a reductive enzyme system would have to be invoked. Since there would appear to be no evidence in support of the reductive enzyme theory, it would seem reasonable to assume that the steranes and triterpanes are fossil natural products which have been chemically altered to some extent. The various alteration processes which may occur are, thermal, catalytic, radioactive bombardment and bacterial activity [33, 34, 40]. By one, or more than one, of these processes it is possible that reduction of olefinic double bonds and oxygenated functions and decarboxylation by bacterial or thermal activity could take place. The diagenetic and maturation processes, while providing the facilities for reduction and decarboxylation may also cause skeletal rearrangements. Thus, not only do we have to isolate and identify reduced steroids and triterpenoids of known structure, but we also have to consider and look for new types of structures.

The distribution of steroids and triterpenoids in contemporary plants and animals may be briefly summarised as follows: steroid nuclei with no substituent in the C_{24} position in the sidechain occur widely in all types of organisms, but only to a small extent in plants; 24-methyl or methylene steroids occur in plants (mostly fungi and algae) as well as in some sea animals, e.g. oysters; 24-ethyl or ethylene steroids are mainly found in algae and higher plants; squalene occurs widely in plants and also in some animals (in large quantities in some fish liver oils); only tetracyclic triterpenes of the lanosterol and nor-lanosterol type are found in animals; the only pentacyclic triterpene found in animals so far is tetrahymanol in *Protozoan tetrahymena;* tetracyclic and pentacyclic triterpenes occur mostly in higher plants and to some extent in lower plants. This is only a broad generalisation of the distributions of steroids and triterpenoids in the plant and animal kingdoms. In order to establish chemotaxonomic and paleochemotaxonomic relationships, a much more detailed study of these distributions is required. A chemotaxonomic survey of these compounds is attempted in Table I. Since the compounds under examination in the laboratory are saturated hydrocarbons, Table I was constructed from that standpoint, i.e. the distributions of naturally occurring steroids and triterpenoids were examined and their structures are represented by the saturated hydrocarbon skeletons which might be derived from the biological material under the effects of diagenesis, bacteria, thermal alteration etc. in a geological environment. The structures shown in Figure 1 represent all the known biologically occurring steroids and triterpenoids as saturated hydrocarbons, i.e. steranes and triterpanes with the proposed conformation of squalene epoxide as precursor. This is only a preliminary survey, because, although many steroids and triterpenoids have been isolated and identified, it is by no means certain that those reported are the only structures

Table I. A preliminary chemotaxonomic survey of the occurrence of steroids and triterpenoids is attempted. The steroids and triterpenoids are represented as the cycloalkane compounds which could be derived from the former two classes of compounds.

Division	Class	Order	Cycloalkane distribution
Angiosperms	Monocotyledonae	Graminales [Herb, plants, rice, wheat, oats etc.]	Multiflorane (D:C-*friedo*-O) Taraxerane (D-*friedo*-O) Stigmastane
	Dicotyledonae	Sapindales	Oleanane
		Ebenales	Oleanane
		Primulales	Oleanane
		Saxifrageles	Oleanane
		Caryophyllales	Oleanane
		Meliales	Oleanane
		Personales	Oleanane
		Verbenales	Oleanane
		Ariales	Oleanane Ursane
		Myrtales	Oleanane Lupane
		Hamamelidales	Oleanane Lupane
		Cactales	Oleanane Lupane
		Rubiales	Oleanane Ursane
		Rosales	Oleanane Lupane
		Geraniales	Oleanane Ursane Lupane

Division	Class	Order	Cycloalkane distribution
		Euphorbiales	Oleanane
			Ursane
			Multiflorane (D:C-*friedo*-O)
			Bauerane (D:C-*friedo*-U)
			Elemane
			Dammarane
		Fagales	Oleanane
			3,4-*seco*-Oleanane
			Ursane
			Lupane
			Glutane (D:B-*friedo*-O)
			Friedelane (D:A-*friedo*-O)
		Loganiales	Oleanane
			3,4-seco-Oleanane
		Ericales	Oleanane
			Glutane (D:B-*friedo*-O)
			Friedelane (D:A-*friedo*-O)
		Celastrales	Friedelane (D:A-*friedo*-O)
		Utricales	Lupane
		Rhamnales	Lupane
			abeo-Lupane (Ceanothane)
		Asterales	Taraxerane (D-*friedo*-O)
			Taraxastane (rearr. lupane)
		Myricales	Taraxerane (D-*friedo*-O)
		Umbellales	Ursane
		Rutales	Ursane
			Arborane
		Leguminales	Oleanane
			Onocerane
			Ergostane
			Stigmastane
		Cruciales	Ergostane
		Chenopodiales	Stigmastane
Gymnosperms		Coniferales	Hopane
			Ursane
Pterophyta	True Ferns	Filicales	Fernane (E:C-*friedo*-Hopane)
			Hopane
			Adiantane (30-*nor*-Hopane)
Bryophyta	Musci (Mosses)	Sphagnidae	Ursane
			Taraxerane
			β-Sitostane
Chlorophyta (Green Algae)	Chlorophyceae		Ergostane
			Stigmastane
			Sitostane
Xanthophyta (Yellow-green Algae)	Xanthophyceae		Sitostane

Division	Class	Order	Cycloalkane distribution
Euglenophyta (Euglenids)	Euglenophyceae		Ergostane
Rhodophyta (Red Algae)	Rhodophyceae		Cholestane Stigmastane Sitostane
Phaeophyta (Brown Algae)	Phaeophyceae		Stigmastane
Chrysophyta (Golden Algae + Diatoms)	Chrysophyceae		Stigmastane

[N.B. Other steroids have been reported for the Algal Divisions, but too few algae examined to make generalisations. It is significant to note that all the algae contain carotenes (a, β, γ, and ϵ) in view of the high proportion of perhydro-carotene found in the Green River shale.]

Lichens			Taraxerane (D-*friedo*-O) Hopane
Eumycota (True Fungi)	Basidiomycetes		C_{31} Lanostane Lanostane Ergostane Cholestane
	Ascomycetes (Yeasts)		Lanostane Cholestane Ergostane

O = oleanane, U = ursane.

present in a particular family or order. It is entirely possible that they are the major constituents of the steroid and triterpenoid categories and that many of the minor constituents remain unidentified. Many of the investigations of the distribution of steroids and triterpenoids in plants were carried out without the aid of the sophisticated analytical techniques used today and as a result the published data may be incomplete. Nevertheless, some generalisations are possible.

In the Thallophyta, only steroids have been found. The algae have, at the present time, the longest authenticated history, dating from the Precambrian era (Figure 2). Higher plants are postulated to have evolved from algae and thus one would expect that the next stage of evolution in the plant kingdom would be characterised by a mixed distribution of steroids and triterpenoids, e.g. Eumycota, the Angiosperms Chenopodiales and Leguminales. Another interesting feature is the number of Angiosperm Orders which contain triterpenes only of the basic structures as defined by Halsall and Aplin [41], i.e. oleanane, ursane, lupane, hopane and arborane. The remainder contain one or more of the basic structures together with rearranged structures, or only rearranged structures. Two different evolutionary points of view may be taken of these statements. Firstly, that as plant evolution proceeded, the plants became more sophisticated and correspondingly their triterpenoid constituents became more complex, i.e. a biochemical evolution from the lupane,

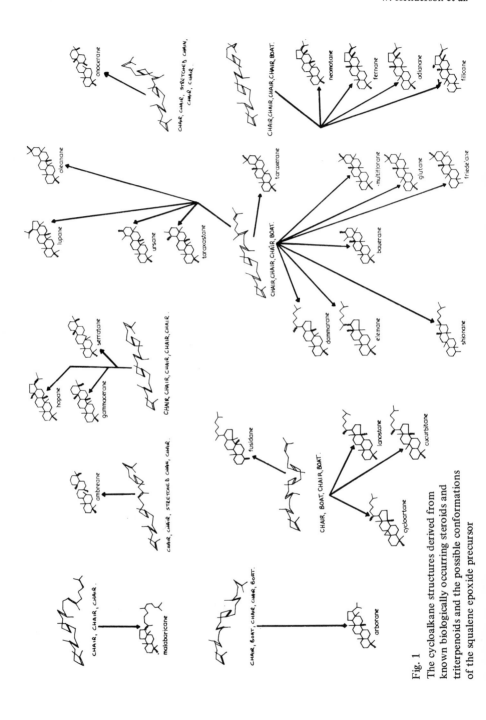

Fig. 1

The cycloalkane structures derived from known biologically occurring steroids and triterpenoids and the possible conformations of the squalene epoxide precursor

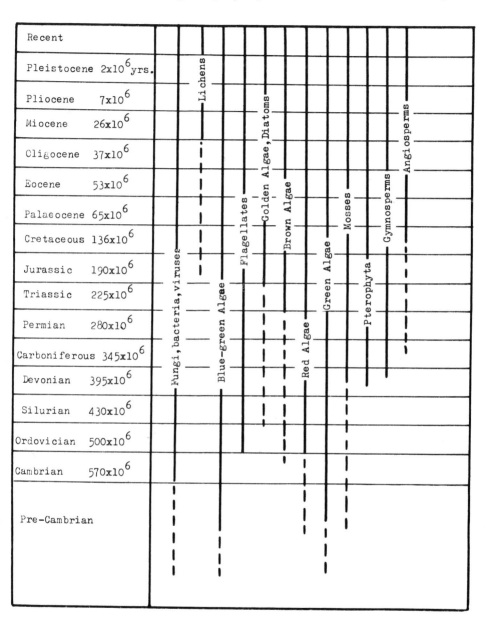

Fig. 2. The distribution of the plant divisions with reference to the geological periods of the Earth's history

ursane, oleanane hopane and arborane types to the *friedo* rearranged compounds, e.g. multiflorane, bauerane, friedelane, glutane, taraxastane and taraxerane types. Secondly, the reverse argument could be that as the plants evolved, the basic triterpane types became dominant. In the case of the plant sterols, considerable diversification is apparent in the higher plants. Cholesterol occurs in primitive invertebrates only as one member of complex mixtures of sterols, whereas at higher levels of evolution, animals and man, cholesterol has become essentially the only sterol present. If this were to hold for the triterpenoids, the second argument would be the more probable, i.e. that diversification of structural type occurred initially followed by the basic triterpenoid structures becoming dominant.

However this problem must remain unresolved at the present time, but it may be that by application of the techniques discussed in this paper, together with other analytical methods, that the problems of plant evolution will be elucidated by more thorough examination of steroid and triterpenoid distributions. In particular, chemotaxonomic studies could be usefully applied to algae, lower and higher plants with respect to steroids and triterpenoids, since these plants are probably the largest source of cycloalkanes in sediments and petroleums.

Before the biological origin of a particular fossil natural product can be postulated and compared with contemporary plants and animals, i.e. paleochemotaxonomy, it is important that the structure of the compound be conclusively identified. In fact, it is equally important to establish the absence of a particular type of sterane or triterpane as it is to prove its presence. The occurrence of these compounds may also provide information on the environment at the time of deposition of the sediment and on the past history of the sediment. For example, the presence of a particular compound may indicate that the maximum temperature experienced by the sediment has never reached, or exceeded, the decomposition point of the compound. On the other hand, the presence of a compound whose structure may be assumed to be altered from its original structure provides information on the conditions and environmental influences which may have caused these changes.

The techniques used for the analysis of the complex mixtures of steranes and triterpanes isolated from a sediment were open tubular capillary column gas liquid chromatography (GLC) and combined open tubular capillary column gas chromatography-mass spectrometry (GC-MS). By a detailed examination of the results obtained from these two techniques, several conclusive identifications of steranes and triterpanes were made and some tentative structures assigned in other cases.

Open tubular coated capillary columns have high efficiencies which allow the separation of closely related compounds. These separations result from the special properties of capillary columns. The carrier gas flow rate is not restricted as it passes through the column since the liquid phase is evenly distributed as a thin film on the walls of the capillary tubing. This results in a small pressure drop throughout the length of the column, enabling the use of long high performance columns with relatively short retention times. Since the molecular weight of steranes and triterpanes necessitates the use of high temperatures for GLC analysis, only the liquid phases of the highest thermal stability may be used. The hydrocarbon phase Apiezon L is generally the best phase to use for the analysis of saturated hydrocarbons. On the non-polar Apiezon L, the hydrocarbons are separated mainly according to their boiling points. More polar phases cause changes in retention times because of different interactions between the components and the phase due to slight differences in the polarities of the molecules. By the judicious use of polar and non-polar liquid phases coated on long capillary columns, satisfactory separations of sterane and triterpane mixtures can be accomplished. In the present work pretreated Apiezon L grease and 7-ring polyphenylether were the non-polar and polar phases used.

When high resolution capillary columns are combined directly with a mass spectrometer, detailed data and structural elucidations are obtained on individual components of a mixture. The sensitivity of the technique is such that identifications of discrete components are possible on the microgram level. Previous workers have used separatory methods on a much larger scale to isolate pure crystalline components of a mixture which are then subjected to detailed physical organic analysis, or they have used GLC conditions with inadequate resolution combined with a mass spectrometer thus getting spectra of mixtures. The present technique is important because it is not always possible to obtain sufficient material from a sediment, or perhaps an extraterrestrial sample, to allow the use of these other methods.

The steranes and triterpanes described in this paper were isolated from the Green River shale from Colorado, U.S.A. (Eocene, 50 x 10^6 years old). The geological history of this sediment has been well documented [42]. It seems to have suffered no major upheavals, igneous intrusions and therefore no greatly elevated temperatures throughout its history. It was deposited under a shallow inland lake covering several hundred square miles. The organic material found in the shale was probably derived predominantly from aquatic organisms, such as microscopic algae and protozoa, rather than land plants, pollens and spores. The temperature of the deposit has never exceeded 74 °C and therefore no excessive alteration of the organic material should have been effected.

Results

The branched and cyclic alkane fraction obtained from the shale by the methods described in the experimental section was analysed by capillary column GLC. The chromatographic records obtained on the two different liquid phases are shown in Figure 3. The retention data and Kovats indices [43] were calculated by coinjection

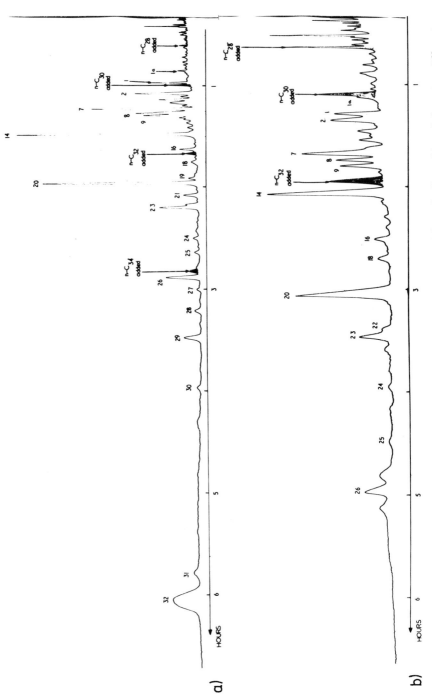

Fig. 3. The gas chromatographic records of the branched and cyclic alkane fraction isolated from the Green River shale on two different capillary columns: a) 200' x 0.01" stainless steel column coated with Apiezon L grease b) 150' x 0.01" stainless steel column coated with 7-ring polyphenylether

Table II. The carbon number retention data for the cycloalkanes present in the branched and cyclic alkane fraction of the Green River shale, compared with the carbon number data for the authentic steranes and triterpanes.

Peak no. (Fig. 3)	Abundance (%)	Carbon number (AP-L)	Carbon number (7-PPE)	Coinjected standards	Molecular[1]) formula
1a	0.7	29.58	30.07	5 β-cholestane	$C_{27}H_{48}$
1	2.3	29.90	30.49	5 α-cholestane	$C_{27}H_{48}$
2	5.1	30.30	30.73	–	$C_{28}H_{50}$ and $C_{30}H_{56}$
3	1.3	30.40	30.75	–	–
4	2.5	30.44	31.07	–	$C_{29}H_{52}$ and $C_{33}H_{64}$
5	2.7	30.61	31.15	–	–
6	1.3	30.72	31.36	–	–
7	6.6	30.82	31.42	–	$C_{28}H_{50}$
8	4.8	30.94	31.52	–	$C_{30}H_{56}$
9	3.7	31.00	31.62	–	$C_{29}H_{52}$
10	1.5	31.06	31.79	–	–
11	1.1	31.12	–	–	–
12	1.2	31.23	32.05	Onocerane III	$C_{30}H_{54}$
13	1.2	31.35	32.36	Onocerane II	$C_{30}H_{54}$
–	–	31.42	33.38	Lupane	$C_{30}H_{52}$
14	11.6	31.53	32.15	Stigmastane	$C_{29}H_{52}$
–	–	31.59	32.68	Onocerane I	$C_{30}H_{54}$
15	0.8	31.76	–	–	–
16	1.5	31.92	32.81	–	$C_{29}H_{50}$
–	–	31.98	33.81	Moretane	$C_{30}H_{52}$
–	–	32.05	32.50	Lanostane	$C_{30}H_{54}$
17	0.7	32.08	–	–	–
18	1.2	32.14	33.08	–	–
–	–	32.43	33.22	Adiantane	$C_{29}H_{50}$
19	1.1	32.44	33.25	–	–
20	11.2	32.60	33.51	–	$C_{30}H_{52}$
21	1.6	32.84	–	–	–
22	1.2	32.97	33.86	–	–
23	3.2	33.02	33.94	–	$C_{30}H_{52}$
24	0.9	33.52	34.41	–	$C_{31}H_{54}$
–	–	33.72	34.46	Friedelane	$C_{30}H_{52}$
25	1.0	33.74	35.10	–	$C_{31}H_{54}$
26	3.6	34.06	35.20	Gammacerane	$C_{30}H_{52}$
27	0.6	34.22	–	–	$C_{30}H_{52}$
28	1.1	34.46	–	–	–
29	2.4	34.76	–	–	–
30	1.0	35.27	–	–	–
31	3.4	36.66	–	–	–
32	16.0	36.82	–	β-Carotane	$C_{40}H_{78}$

[1]) From mass spectrometric data

of the mixture with a normal alkane mixture as reference (n-C_{28}, C_{30} and C_{32}). The authentic standard steranes and triterpanes also used for coinjection purposes were subjected to the same analytical procedure as the unknown mixture. The Kovats indices for the mixture and the authentic standards are shown in Table II. The percentage abundance of each peak in the chromatogram was calculated by measurement of the peak area from Figure 3. Where coinjection of an authentic compund produced peak enhancement on both liquid phases the standard compound was entered in Table II opposite the peak it enhanced. This was taken as one proof of identity. From Table II, it is immediately seen that the following peak enhancements occurred: 5β-cholestane and peak la: 5α-cholestane and peak 1; onocerane III and peak 12; onocerane II and peak 13; stigmastane and peak 14; gammacerane and peak 26.

The probable identifications made by GLC were limited by the number of authentic standards available for coinjection purposes. It is interesting at this point to examine the retention behaviour of some of the standards used. Figure 4 illustrates diagrammatically the retention characteristics of these standards. The column used in this case was $150'$ x $0.01''$ coated with 7-ring polyphenylether. The structures are shown so that the differences in retention behaviour may be more easily correlated with differences in structure. Adiantane, which has only 29 carbon

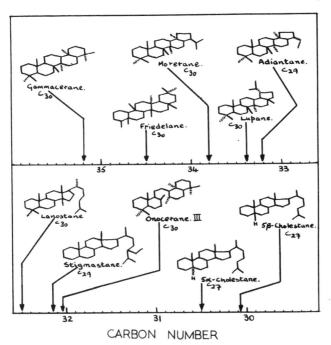

CARBON NUMBER

Fig. 4
The retention behaviour of some authentic steranes and triterpanes on a 7-ring polyphenyl-ether capillary column

atoms, has a longer retention time than lanostane and onocerane III (both are C_{30} compounds). It is apparent from the carbon number sequence that onocerane III, with an AB-DE fused tetracyclic system, has a shorter retention time than AB-CD fused tetracyclic systems with a steroid skeleton, followed by pentacyclic triterpanes with ring E being 5-membered and finally, pentacyclic triterpanes with only 6-membered rings. From these results the following relationships arise: for molecules with the same molecular weight the retention time increases with increasing numbers of fused rings; molecules with only 6-membered rings have longer retention times than those with one 5-membered ring; the shape and symmetry of a molecule may contribute to the retention time, e.g. gammacerane is a very symmetrical molecule but it has the longest retention time of all the standards used. However, before definite patterns of behaviour can be firmly established many more authentic compounds have to be examined.

In a similar way the mass spectral fragmentation patterns of many of these authentic compounds were thoroughly examined so that the mass spectral data from the branched and cyclic alkane fraction from the Green River shale should be more definitive. The individual fragmentations are not discussed in detail, but rather the differences are highlighted and by this means some general rules and some structural classifications become apparent. For the purposes of this discussion, the structures to be discussed may be broadly classified as follows:

(i)   pentacyclic with one 5-membered ring, e.g. lupane.

(ii)   tricyclic, tetracyclic and pentacyclic with only 6-membered rings e.g. gammacerane.

(iii)   tetracyclic with one 5-membered ring, e.g. lanostane and all the steranes.

Pentacyclic triterpanes are generally accepted to produce a major ion at m/e 191, attributed to one of the three species shown in Figure 5 B. However, not all pentacyclic triterpanes give rise to such fragments. Before examining the mass spectra of the authentic compounds, it is worth while discussing the possible reasons for bond cleavages to occur first of all, and secondly, what causes a fragment to give rise to an intense peak in a mass spectrum.

In cyclic systems, for fragmentation to occur, more than one carbon-to-carbon bond has to be broken. Normally, steroids and triterpenoids contain functional groups which give rise to high intensity ion fragments (e.g. McLafferty Rearrangement in ketotriterpenoids [44] and steroids [45]; Retro Diels-Alder decomposition in unsaturated steroids and triterpenoids [44]). Nevertheless, in cycloalkanes, some characteristic high intensity ion fragments are still formed and it is these which have to be examined. Since at least two bonds have to be broken to fragment a cyclic system, some stability is conferred on a cyclic molecule and therefore the molecular ion (caused by the loss of one electron) of a triterpane should always be at least reasonably intense, the abundance depending on the ease of fragmentation of the remainder of the molecule.

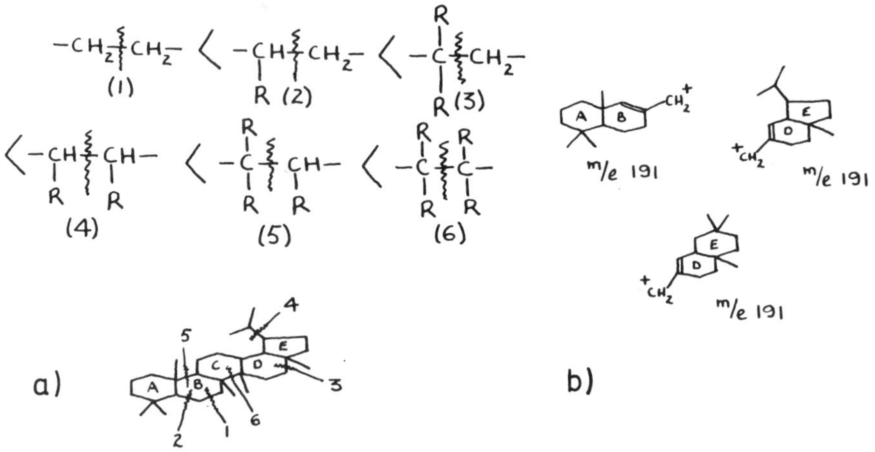

Fig. 5. a) The relative probabilities for carbon-carbon bond cleavages in cycloalkanes
b) The ion fragments attributed to the m/e 191 peak in the mass spectra of many triterpanes

The factors which govern the fragmentation of the positive molecular ions are the relative labilities of the bonds in the ion, the relative labilities of the potential fragment ions and the neutral fragments formed by competing fragmentation processes. The cleavage of bonds depends upon the activation energy of the bond and the stability of the positive ions and neutral fragments, which follow the same general rules as carbonium ion solution chemistry. The order of probability of cleavage is shown, and applied to a typical triterpane in Figure 5 A. Fragmentations (2) and (3) are possibly of the same probability. Obviously, fragmentations (4), (5) and (6) are the most likely to produce high intensity fragment ions because of both their carbon-carbon bond lability and the stability of the fragment ions produced. The structures and the mass spectral fragmentation patterns of the three broad categories of steranes and triterpanes are examined on the basis of the factors outlined above.

Figure 6 shows the mass spectral line diagrams of lupane, hopane and adiantane, all members of category (i) above. Lupane and hopane exhibit very similar fragmentation patterns with the characteristically intense m/e 191 peak caused by fragmentation (6) in Figure 5 A and 5 B. They also show a P-43 peak which is characteristic of compounds containing an isopropyl group. Adiantane is a C_{29} compound, but, like lupane and hopane, the same fragmentation occurs, i.e. fragmentation (6) giving rise to two equally intense peaks at m/e 191 and 177. On this basis it is possible to differentiate between the spectra of lupane and hopane and that of adiantane, but it is difficult to differentiate between lupane and hopane.

There are variations in their spectra, but mostly of small differences in intensity and these are not always reliable. However, these two compounds would be separated by open tubular capillary GLC and when the GLC effluent is led into a mass spectrometer ion source, mass spectra of the individual components would then be obtained. Thus, identifications could then be made on the basis of the combined data from GLC and mass spectrometry.

Figure 7 shows the mass spectral line diagrams of gammacerane, onocerane and friedelane, all members of category (ii) above. Gammacerane has a fragmentation pattern different from the other two, but similar to lupane and hopane with the main exception that gammacerane does not have a P-43 peak. Onocerane, being

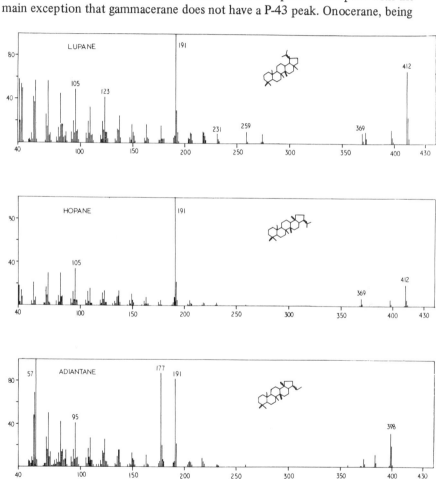

Fig. 6. The mass spectral line diagrams of authentic lupane, hopane and adiantane

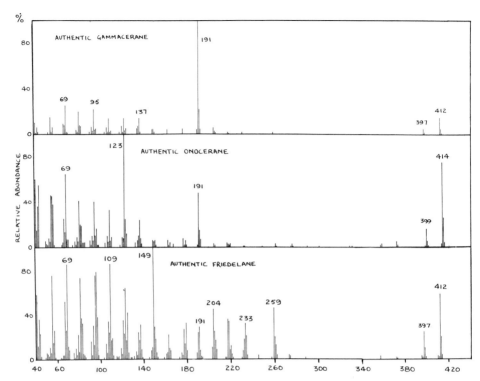

Fig. 7. The mass spectral line diagrams of authentic gammacerane, onocerane and friedelane

tetracyclic, has a molecular ion at m/e 414 instead of m/e 412 for gammacerane and friedelane. The m/e 191 peak is not nearly so intense as before and this may be attributed to fragmentation (2) shown in Figure 5 A which is less preferred than fragmentation (6). Onocerane has a characteristic peak at m/e 123 which may be attributed to fragmentation (5) which can occur between rings A and B and between rings D and E. Friedelane has a complex fragmentation pattern which should be typical of structures of this type which do not possess high probability sites for carbon-carbon bond cleavage.

Figure 8 shows the mass spectral line diagrams of 5 α-cholestane, stigmastane and lanostane, all members of category (iii) above. It is immediately obvious that the fragmentation pattern for lanostane is completely different from that of cholestane and stigmastane and indeed from any of the other spectra discussed so far. Lanostane has no adjacent quaternary carbon atoms which are likely cleavage points. It has a molecular ion at m/e 414 since it is tetracyclic and no really characteristic fragmentation. However, the steranes, cholestane and stigmastane, have characteristic molecular ions and also the characteristic fragment ion at m/e 217.

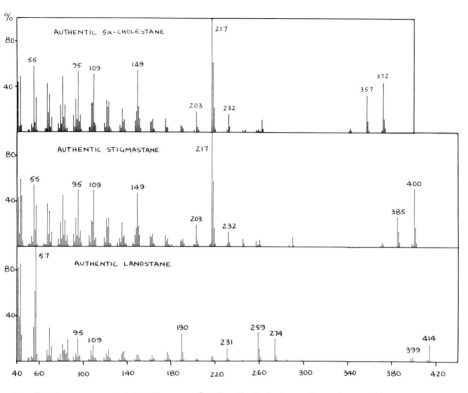

Fig. 8. The mass spectral line diagrams of anthentic cholestane, stigmastane and lanostane

The addition of an extra methyl group, or ethyl group is readily detected by the parent ion, i.e. m/e 372, 386 or 400 for cholestane, ergostane or stigmastane respectively. The position of any additional methyl may also be detected in general terms. If an additional methyl group is attached to the side chain, then the base peak, i.e. 100 % peak, will still be m/e 217. However, if the methyl group is attached to the cyclic nucleus, then the base peak will be m/e 231. In a similar way, loss of a methyl group will produce no change in the base peak if it was lost from the side chain, but if it was lost from the cyclic nucleus then the base peak would be m/e 203 and so on. The characteristic peak at m/e 217 allows easy differentiation between steranes and triterpanes in general.

In summary, mass spectrometry of steranes and triterpanes allows, at best, structural identification of a compound, or, at worst, assignment of the compound to a structural category. Combination of the data from high resolution GLC and from mass spectrometry from a combined GC-MS system allows positive structural identifications to be made, provided authentic compounds are available for comparison purposes [17, 33]. The technique is thus invaluable in analyses of complex mixtures of compounds which include structural and stereoisomers. It provides a rapid method for identification of components, thus circumventing the often tedious methods of separation and purification required by the more commonly used techniques of natural product organic chemistry.

The branched and cyclic alkane fraction isolated from the Green River shale was examined by combined capillary column GC-MS as described in the experimental section. Since the GLC conditions had to be modified to fulfil the mass spectrometric requirements, i.e. the concentration of each component reaching the ion source in the GLC effluent, the GLC analysis was seriously affected. This is illustrated in Figure 9 which shows the GLC record obtained from the GC-MS total ion current (TIC) using the AP-L capillary column (c.f. Figure 3). Two major effects are noticed, the first being that the region containing GLC peaks 1–9 has not been well resolved. Secondly, because of reduced sensitivity, the minor components observed in the GLC record (Figure 3), e.g. peaks 10, 11, 13, 18, 19, 24 and 25 are difficult to separate from the baseline noise. The baseline noise was caused by having to operate at the maximum TIC sensitivity setting and thus factors like column bleeding and fluctuations in the helium concentration in the ion source produce an unstable baseline which is not observed at the lower sensitivity settings. The mass spectrometric scan numbers with the corresponding GLC peak numbers in parentheses are also shown in Figure 9.

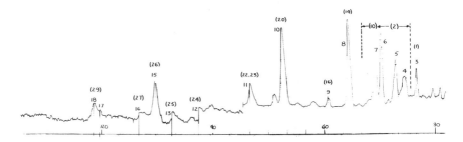

Fig. 9. The total ion current record obtained for the branched and cyclic alkane fraction isolated from the Green River shale, separated on a capillary column coated with Apiezon L grease, on the LKB 9000 GC-MS instrument. The mass spectrometric scan numbers are shown and the corresponding GC peak numbers are shown in parentheses

The parent ions, molecular formulae and compound type data obtained from these mass spectrometric scans are summarised in Table III. Comparison of the mass spectra of authentic compounds with the spectra obtained from the GC-MS analysis, together with the retention data shown in Table II, results in several definite structural identifications and other tentative identifications being made.

Table III. Mass Spectrometric Data for the Cycloalkanes from the Green River Shale and the Deduced Structure Types

G.l.c. peak no. (Fig. 3, 9) (AP-L)	G.c.-m.s. scan no. (Fig. 9) (AP-L)	Parent ion (m/e)	Molecular formula	Structure type
1	3	372	$C_{27}H_{48}$	Sterane (C_{27})
2	4	386	$C_{28}H_{50}$	Tetracyclic triterpane
		416	$C_{30}H_{56}$	Tricyclic triterpane
4	5	400	$C_{29}H_{52}$	Tetracyclic triterpane
5		460	$C_{33}H_{64}$	−
7		386	$C_{28}H_{50}$	Sterane (C_{28})
8	6	416	$C_{30}H_{56}$	Tricyclic triterpane
9		400	$C_{29}H_{52}$	Sterane (C_{29})
14	8	400	$C_{29}H_{52}$	Sterane (C_{29})
15	9	398	$C_{29}H_{50}$	Pentacyclic triterpane
20	10	412	$C_{30}H_{52}$	Pentacyclic triterpane
23	11	412	$C_{30}H_{52}$	Pentacyclic triterpane
24	12	426	$C_{31}H_{54}$	Pentacyclic triterpane
−	13	426	$C_{31}H_{54}$	Pentacyclic triterpane
26	15	412	$C_{30}H_{52}$	Pentacyclic triterpane
27	16	412	$C_{30}H_{52}$	Pentacyclic triterpane
28	17	476	$C_{34}H_{68}$	−
29	18	476	$C_{34}H_{68}$	−

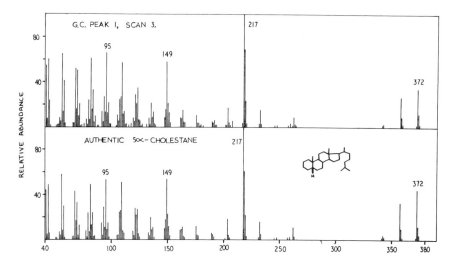

Fig. 10. The mass spectral line diagrams of GC peak (1), scan 3 and anthentic 5α-cholestane

The mass spectrum of scan 3, GLC peak (1) corresponds to that of authentic 5α-cholestane (Figure 10) and coinjection of the authentic compound produced enhancement of peak (1) on two different capillary columns, i.e. AP-L and 7-PPE. Thus peak (1) is 5α-cholestane. Peak (1a) was not observed in the GC-MS analysis, but on coinjection of authentic 5β-cholestane, enhancement of peak (1a) occurred on both liquid phases. Therefore peak (1a) may probably be assigned to 5β-cholestane.

Scans 4,5, and 6 produced mass spectra of simple mixtures, two components in each case. Scan 6 contained predominantly a sterane type fragmentation pattern and was probably due to ergostane. Scans 4 and 6 exhibited fragmentations of probably two isomeric tricyclic triterpanes of the ambreane, or possibly malabaricane types.

Figure 11 shows the mass spectra obtained from scans 7 and 8 and authentic stigmastane. The spectrum of scan 8 is weak from m/e 200 upwards because the scan was taken at a point when the maximum concentration of GC peak (14) had been

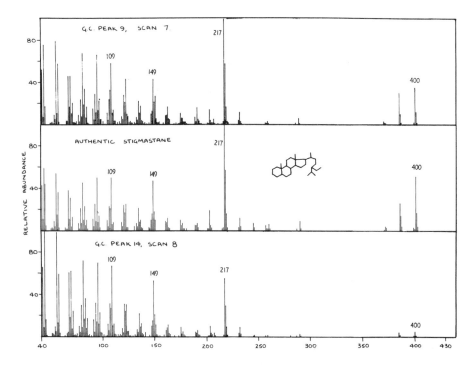

Fig. 11. The mass spectral line diagrams of GC peaks (9) and (14), scans 7 and 8, and authentic stigmastane

passed (the LKB 9000 magnet scans from low to high mass). Coinjection of authentic stigmastane enhanced peak (14) on both liquid phases (Table II). The fragmentation pattern of scan 7 is very similar to that of stigmastane. Similarly, the fragmentation pattern of scan 8 from m/e 200 downwards is almost identical to authentic stigmastane. Therefore, peak (14) is stigmastane and peak (9) is an isomer of stigmastane. The relative retention data for the steranes in Table II further substantiates the presence of isomers of stigmastane.

Figure 12 shows the mass spectra obtained from scans 10 and 11 and authentic lupane and hopane. At first sight, all four appear very similar and typical of pentacyclic triterpanes. However, on closer examination, it is apparent that scan 10 and

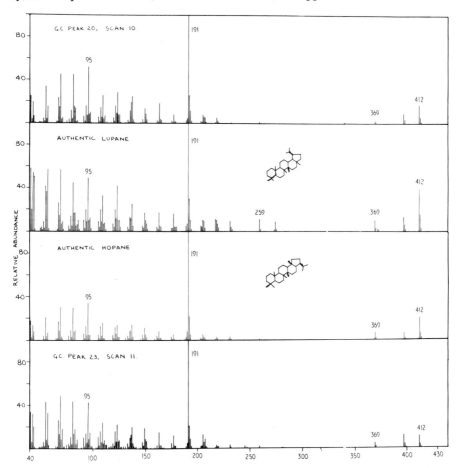

Fig. 12. The mass spectral line diagrams of GC peak (20), scan 10, and authentic lupane and hopane, and GC peak (23), scan 11

hopane are almost identical, whereas, lupane and scan 11 are slightly different from m/e 95 downwards. Coinjection of authentic lupane and moretane produced no peak enhancement on either liquid phase (Table II). The quantity of pure hopane available prohibited its use for GLC purposes. From this evidence it is almost certain that GC peak (20) is the pentacyclic triterpane hopane.

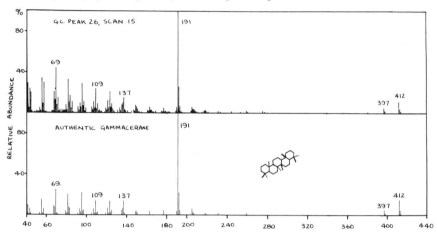

Fig. 13. The mass spectral line diagrams of GC peak (26), scan 15 and authentic gammacerane

Figure 13 shows the mass spectra of scan 15 and authentic gammacerane. The spectra are almost identical and are typical of pentacyclic triterpanes with only 6-membered rings. Coinjection of authentic gammacerane with the branched and cyclic alkane fraction produced enhancement of peak (26) on both liquid phases (Table II). Therefore peak (26) is gammacerane.

Thus, by a combination of GLC retention data and GC-MS data, 5α- and 5β-cholestane, ergostane, stigmastane, hopane and gammacerane were identified. Partial structures for several other peaks were postulated, but, at the present time, their identification is impossible because of inadequate reference data on authentic compounds.

Conclusions

The chemical information now available on the organic content of the Green River shale is extensive. The alkane fraction is particularly impressive, in that the branched and cyclic alkanes are predominant over the n-alkanes. The n-alkanes show a typical plant wax distribution, i.e. the C_{27}, C_{29} and C_{31} n-alkanes are dominant, but the distribution appears to be bimodal with another carbon number maximum at n-C_{17} alkane, typical of algal sources. The origin of the hydrocarbons in this sediment can be in no doubt when the branched and cyclic alkanes are considered.

The identifications of the isoprenoid alkanes farnesane, pristane and phytane and the impressive predominance of tricyclic, tetracyclic and pentacyclic cycloalkanes and perhydro-carotenes, must surely represent a biological origin. The presence of isomers of ergostane and stigmastane is compatible with a largely algal source for the organic material in the sediment. Table I provides substantial evidence that sterols are abundant in algae and that ergostane and stigmastane skeletons are dominant. The low concentration of the cholestanes points to a small contribution from animals. The high proportion of hopane found could be related to the known occurrence of hopane skeletons in the Pterophyta division which might be expected to thrive around the shores of an inland lake. The presence of gammacerane, derived from tetrahymanol the only pentacyclic triterpene found in animals *(Protozoan tetrahymena)*, is again compatible with the data.

Cycloalkanes have not been found in any of the present-day biological source materials investigated so far. It would seem reasonable to assume that they represent the products of diagenetic alteration of steroids and triterpenoids in sediments. As such, they are important fossil molecules, understanding of which could further illuminate the problem of biochemical and plant evolution and also increase our knowledge of petroleum genesis.

Experimental

Figure 14 describes the treatment and extraction procedures used to obtain the total soluble organic extract (0.35 g., 1.8 % by weight of rock). Figure 15 shows the separation and analytical procedures used to obtain a pure branched and cyclic alkane fraction from the total organic extract. The extract was chromatographed on neutral alumina (100 g) and eluted with n-hexane (150 ml) and benzene (600 ml). The combined eluates were evaporated and monitored by analytical $AgNO_3/SiO_2$ thin layer chromatography [46] and infra-red spectroscopy (0.100 g., 0.5 %). The alkane fraction was obtained by separation using preparative $AgNO_3/SiO_2$ TLC and the fraction monitored by infra-red and ultra-violet spectroscopy (0.055 g, 56 % by weight of the hydrocarbon fraction, 0.28 % by weight of rock). The alkane fraction was dissolved in iso-octane (20 ml) and heated under reflux with 5 Å molecular sieve (1/8″ pellets, 3.0 g) for 100hr. The sieve was washed thoroughly in an all-glass Soxhlet and the supernatant and the combined washings were evaporated to give the branched and cyclic alkane fraction (0.044 g., 80 % of the alkane fraction, 0.22 % by weight of rock).

All the GLC analyses were carried out on a Perkin-Elmer F.11 (mk. II), equipped with a flash heater and flame ionisation detector. The instrument was modified slightly to eliminate the temperature gradient between the column and the detector and the "dead-volume" decreased by modifying all the connections. The capillary columns used were: 200′ x 0.01″ coated with Apiezon L grease; 150′ x 0.01″

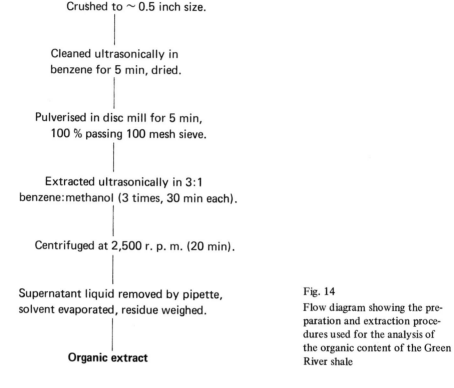

Crushed to ~ 0.5 inch size.

Cleaned ultrasonically in
benzene for 5 min, dried.

Pulverised in disc mill for 5 min,
100 % passing 100 mesh sieve.

Extracted ultrasonically in 3:1
benzene:methanol (3 times, 30 min each).

Centrifuged at 2,500 r. p. m. (20 min).

Supernatant liquid removed by pipette,
solvent evaporated, residue weighed.

Organic extract

Fig. 14
Flow diagram showing the preparation and extraction procedures used for the analysis of
the organic content of the Green
River shale

coated with 7-ring polyphenylether. The column efficiencies obtained were about
50,000 and 30,000 theoretical plates respectively. The carrier gas used was helium
at a flow rate of 2 ml/min. and a pre-column split ratio of 30/l. All analyses were
carried out isothermally at 250 °C. The efficiencies of the columns were monitored
throughout the analyses by measuring the plateages at 250 °C with 5α-cholestane.

The capillary GC-MS analyses were carried out using a modified LKB 9000 instrument. The modifications were as follows: the LKB 9000 oven was replaced with
the F. 11 oven; the effluent end of the capillary column was connected to the
Becker-Ryhage separator [47] assembly by a 0.01″ capillary tube about 18″ long
heated with resistance wire to a temperature of 275 °C; the first separator jet was
removed and the rotary pump isolated; when the system had been pumped down
to a satisfactory vacuum, i.e. 10^{-6} to 10^{-7} mm Hg, the oil diffusion and mercury
diffusion pumps were switched off and the vacuum maintained by the fore vacuum
pump alone; finally, the helium GLC inlet pressure was increased to 80 psi. This
system resulted in a higher proportion of the GLC effluent reaching the ion source

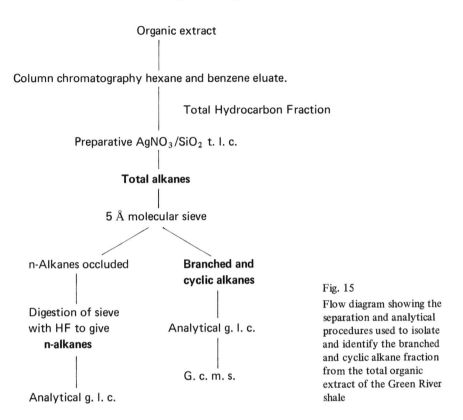

Organic extract

Column chromatography hexane and benzene eluate.

Total Hydrocarbon Fraction

Preparative AgNO$_3$/SiO$_2$ t. l. c.

Total alkanes

5 Å molecular sieve

n-Alkanes occluded

Digestion of sieve
with HF to give
n-alkanes

Analytical g. l. c.

**Branched and
cyclic alkanes**

Analytical g. l. c.

G. c. m. s.

Fig. 15
Flow diagram showing the
separation and analytical
procedures used to isolate
and identify the branched
and cyclic alkane fraction
from the total organic
extract of the Green River
shale

and thus greater sensitivity achieved. Mass spectra were recorded at 70 eV and
2 second scans used per mass decade. In order to check and facilitate the counting
of the mass spectra, perfluorokerosene was added to the GLC effluent at a constant rate and a second analysis of the branched and cyclic alkane fraction carried
out.

Acknowledgements: We thank Dr. C.J.W. Brooks for the use of the LKB 9000 GC-MS instrument at the Chemistry Department, University of Glasgow; the Natural Environment Research
Council for support and a visiting fellowship (V.W.); the Science Research Council for a
Research Studentship (W.H.); and the United States National Aeronautics and Space Administration for support (NSG 101–61).

References

[1]   G. Eglinton and R.J. Hamilton: in "Chemical Plant Taxonomy", ed. T. Swain, p. 187 (1963), Academic Press, London.

[2]   V. Wollrab, M. Streibl and F. Sorm: Coll. Czech. Chem. Comm., 28, 1904, 1963.

[3]   P. Jarolimck, V. Wollrab, M. Streibl and F. Sorm: Coll. Czech. Chem. Comm., 30, 880 1965.

[4]   W.G. Meinschein and G.S. Kenny: Anal. Chem., 29, 1153, 1957.

[5]   E.E. Bray and E.D. Evans: Geochim. Cosmochim. Acta, 22, 2, 1961.

[6]   W.E. Robinson and J.J. Cummins: J. Chem. Eng. Data, 5, 74, 1960.

[7]   R.A. Dean and E.V. Whitehead: Tetrahedron Let., 768, 1961.

[8a] G. Eglinton, P.M. Scott, T. Belsky, A.L. Burlingame and M. Calvin: Science, 145, 263, 1964; and in "Advances in Organic Geochemistry 1964", ed. G.D. Hobson and M.C. Louis, pp 41–74, 1966, Pergamon Press, London.

[8b] A.G. Douglas, K. Douraghi-Zadeh, G. Eglinton, J.R. Maxwell and J.N. Ramsay: in "Advances in Organic Geochemistry 1966", ed. G.D. Hobson and G.C. Speers, in press, Pergamon Press, London.

[9]   J.G. Bendoraitis, B.L. Brown and L.S. Hepner: Anal. Chem., 34, 49, 1962.

[10] J.G. Bendoraitis, B.L. Brown and L.S. Hepner: Sixth World Petroleum Congress, Frankfurt, June 1963.

[11] B.J. Mair, N.C. Krouskop and T.J. Mayer: J. Chem. Eng. Data, 7, 420, 1962.

[12] J.J. Cummins and W.E. Robinson: J. Chem. Eng. Data, 9, 304, 1964.

[13] W.G. Meinschein: Bull. Amer. Assoc. Petrol. Geol., 43, 925, 1955.

[14] M. Louis: Rev. Inst. Francais du Petrole, 19, 277, 1964.

[15] B.J. Mair and J.L. Martinez-Pico: Proc. Amer. Petrol. Inst, 42, 173, 1962.

[16] A.L. Burlingame, P.Haug, T. Belsky, and M. Calvin: Proc. Nat. Acad. Sciences, 54, 1706, 1965.

[17] W. Henderson, V. Wollrab and G. Eglinton: Chem. Comm., 710 1968.

[18] D.H.R. Barton, K.H. Overton and W. Carruthers: J. Chem. Soc., 788, 1956.

[19] W. Carruthers and J.W. Cook: J. Chem. Soc., 2047, 1954.

[20] I.R. Hills and E.V. Whitehead: Nature, 209, 977, 1966.

[21] I.R. Hills, E.V. Whitehead, D.E. Anders, J.J. Cummins and W.E. Robinson: Chem. Comm., 752, 1966.

[22] N. Danieli, E. Gil-Av and M. Louis: Nature, 217, 731, 1968.

[23] I.R. Hills and E.V. Whitehead: Summer meeting of the American Petroleum Institute's Research, Laramie, July 1966.

[24] I.R. Hills and E.V. Whitehead, in "Advances in Organic Geochemistry" 1966, ed. G.D. Hobson and G.C. Speers, in press, Pergamon Press, London.

[25] V. Jarolim, K. Hejno, M. Streibl, M. Horak and F. Sorm: Coll. Czech. Chem. Comm., 26, 451, 1961.

[26] V. Jarolim, K. Hejno, M. Streibl, M. Horak and F. Sorm: Coll. Czech. Chem. Comm., 26, 459, 1961.

[27] V. Jarolim, K. Hejno and F. Sorm: Coll. Czech. Chem. Comm., 28, 2318, 1963.
      V. Jarolim, K. Hejno and F. Sorm: Coll. Czech. Chem. Comm., 28, 2443, 1963.

[28]   Sister M.T.J. Murphy, A. McCormick and G. Eglinton: Science, 157, 1040, 1967.

[29]   M.R. Fenske, F.L. Carnahan, J.N. Breston, A.H. Caser and A.R. Rescorla: Ind. Eng. Chem., 34, 638, 1942.

[30]   F.L. Carnahan, R.E. Hersh, and M.R. Fenske: Ind. Eng. Chem., 36, 383, 1944.

[31]   W.D. Rosenfeld: J. Amer. Oil Chem. Soc., 44, 703, 1967.

[32]   T.S. Oakwood, D.S. Schriver, H.H. Fall, W.J. McAleer and P.R. Wunz: Ind. Eng. Chem., 44, 2568, 1952.

[33]   W. Henderson: Ph.D. Thesis, Glasgow, 1968.

[34]   A.G. Douglas, G. Eglinton and W. Henderson: in "Advances in Organic Geochemistry 1966", ed. G.D. Hobson and G.C. Speers, in press, Pergamon Press, London; and the references therein.

[35]   A. Eschenmoser, L. Ruzicka, O. Jeger and D. Arigoni: Helv. Chim. Acta, 38, 1890, 1955.

[36]   L. Ruzicka: Proc. Chem. Soc., 341, 1959.

[37]   R.B. Clayton: Quart. Reviews, 19, 168, 1965.

[38]   E.E. Van Tamelin, J.D. Willet, R.B. Clayton and K.E. Lord: J. Amer. Chem. Soc., 88, 4752, 1966.

[39]   W.S. Johnson: Accounts of Chem. Research, 1, 1, 1968.

[40]   W. Henderson, G. Eglinton, P. Simmonds and J.E. Lovelock: Nature, 219, 1012, 1968; and the references therein.

[41]   T.G. Halsall and R.T. Aplin: Fortschritte d. Chem. Org. Naturst., 22, 153, 1964.

[42]   W.H. Bradley: Geol. Soc. Amer. Bull., 77, 1333, 1966.

[43]   J. Jonas, J. Janak and M. Kratochvil: J. Gas Chrom., 332, 1966.

[44]   H. Budzikicuitz, J.M. Wilson and C. Djerassi: J. Amer. Chem. Soc., 85, 3688, 1963.

[45]   D.H. Williams, J.M. Wilson, H. Budzikicuitz and C. Djerassi: J. Amer. Chem. Soc., 85, 2091, 1963; and the references therein.

[46]   A.T. James and L.J. Morris: "New Biochemical Separations", Chap. 14, 1964, Van Nostrand, London.

[47]   R. Ryhage: Arkiv Kemi., 26, 305, 1967.

Investigations of the Early Precambrian Onverwacht Sedimentary Rocks in South Africa[1])

Bartholomew Nagy and Lois Anne Nagy

Department of Geochronology, The University of Arizona
Tucson, Arizona, USA

The Onverwacht Series is the oldest member of the Swaziland System, and it is well exposed in the Barberton-Badplaas region of the Eastern Transvaal in South Africa. The Swaziland System is a well preserved, oceanic to island arc and continental borderland sequence of volcanic and sedimentary rocks. The Onverwacht consist mainly of volcanic rocks with quite subordinate layers of tuffs, cherts and clastic sediements. These sediments appear to be the oldest known exposed sedimentary rocks on earth.

Spheroidal and cup-shaped microstructures as well as filamentous forms showing no distinguishing morphology were found in the Onverwacht sedimentary rocks, some of which are as much as 35,000–45,000 feet stratigraphically below the younger Fig Tree sediments from which similar "life-like" forms have been described as fossil algae and flagellates. Extreme caution is necessary in interpreting the origin of these microstructures because the lavas also contain rounded forms which are obviously nonbiological in origin but which show "double walls" and other remarkably cell-like morphologies. The organic content of the Onverwacht sediments studied to this date appears to be mainly in the form of kerogen which upon analysis consisting of ozonolysis, solvent extraction, esterification and combined capillary gas chromatography and mass spectrometry, appears to be basically aromatic in composition. It is interesting that the younger Fig Tree kerogen that was studied in this laboratory is basically aliphatic in nature. It has been often stated that aromatic structures in kerogen are derived from lignin; this explanation obviously is not applicable to the Onverwacht sediments which are more than 3×10^9 years old.

Introduction

The Onverwacht sedimentary rocks in South Africa are at present the oldest known sediments on earth. The authors and their co-workers found in these rocks what may be the oldest fossils (Nagy et al., 1967, Nagy and Urey, 1968, Nagy et al., 1968). Subsequently, additional information on these microstructures and on the Onverwacht geology was presented by Engel et al., 1968. The Onverwacht microstructures were found in sediments, some of which are 35,000–45,000 feet stratigraphically below the younger Fig Tree Series, from which similar microstructures have been described as fossil algae and flagellates, first by Pflug (1966) and then by Barghoorn and Schopf (1966), and Schopf and Barghoorn (1967).

---

[1]) Contribution No. 175, Program in Geochronology University of Arizona, Tucson

An Outline of the Geology of the Swaziland System

The Onverwacht Series is part of the Swaziland System, which is well exposed approximately 400 miles south-southeast of Bulawayo, in the Barberton-Badplaas region of the Eastern Transvaal, South Africa. This region is known as the Barberton Mountain Land, and it is geologically located in what is called the Rhodesian or South African Shield (Visser, 1956, Anhaeusser et al., 1967, Engel et al., 1968). Much of the Swaziland System is metamorphosed to the greenschist facies, although the marginal contacts with granitic intrusions consist of amphibolite rocks. The rocks are in part sheared and faulted; yet in some areas both the igneous and the sedimentary rock members escaped serious alterations from subsequent metamorphism. In the present investigation only the nonmetamorphosed Onverwacht sediments were studied.

The Swaziland System consists of three rock Series. The oldest is the Onverwacht Series which is overlain by the younger Fig Tree Series, which in turn is overlain by the Moodies Series. A good area for studying the Onverwacht is in and near the Komati River valley, 10 to 20 miles east of Badplaas, where many of the original sedimentary and volcanic structures and textures are well preserved. The Onverwacht Series at the type locality is 35,000 feet thick (Engel et al., 1968). It consists mainly of mafic, ultramafic and dacitic lavas, most of which were deposited in water as is shown by the pillow structures. The tuffs, cherts, carbonates and argillites, and other clastic sediments, are rare. Textural features such as crossbedding, laminations etc. show that the sediments were also deposited in water. Some of these Onverwacht sediments are charcoal-gray to black in color, caused by what appears to be a relatively high concentration of organic matter. These rocks appear to be more than 3 billion (3×10^9) years old.

The Onverwacht Series is overlain, in part unconformably, by the younger Fig Tree Series. The Fig Tree is approximately 12,000 feet thick and consists mainly of sedimentary rocks such as graywackes, arkoses, carbonaceous argillites, cherts and tuffs. In contrast to the Onverwacht, volcanic rocks are rare in the Fig Tree.

The youngest member of the Swaziland System is the Moodies Series which consists of arkosic sandstones, shales and thick layers of orthoquartzites. The Moodies Series lies unconformably over the Fig Tree and is approximately 12,000 feet thick. The Swaziland System and its three Series, the Onverwacht, Fig Tree and Moodies, represent a rather complete and well-preserved oceanic island arc and continental borderland sequence of rocks deposited in the early Precambrian sea (Engel et al., 1968).

Because the Onverwacht sediments are at present the oldest known sedimentary rocks on earth, a study of their organic content and of the microstructures which are enclosed in them may conceivably furnish some interesting information, either about the very early biological processes or about prebiological processes on earth. It may be prudent to emphasize at this early stage of the investigations that there is not yet any definite proof that life had already evolved in Onverwacht times; yet it is also possible that eventually the Onverwacht microstructures will prove to be fossils. However, in the authors' opinion this has not yet been demonstrated, and much detailed and careful analysis has still to be performed before one can ascertain the origin of the organic compounds and microstructures in the Onverwacht sediments.

Investigations of the Onverwacht Kerogen

The chemical composition of the organic substances in a black, argillaceous Onverwacht chert has been partially analyzed. The sample came from a location approximately 10,000 feet stratigraphically below the base of the Fig Tree Series. First, the exterior of the rock sample was drilled off with a portable drill to exclude surface contaminations. Next the sample was further cleaned in an ultrasonic cleaner and then pulverized in an acid-cleaned ball mill. The powdered sample was next Soxhlet extracted with 6:4 volume/volume benzene-methanol to remove soluble organic constituents. It was noted upon a careful study of petrographic thin sections that the sample had some porosity, and consequently the trace amounts of soluble organic substances might very well have been brought in much later by solutions which are, of course, well known to percolate through sedimentary rocks during geological time. It is most important to ascertain that organic matter brought in at a later age by percolating solutions not be mistaken for indigenous organic matter.

The extracted rock residue containing the insoluble kerogen was suspended in an aqueous KOH solution and ozonized with 2.8 % O_3 in a stream of oxygen for 18 hours. The ozonides were further oxidized with hydrogen peroxide and the oxidation products were fractionated by solvent extraction; this was followed by esterification of the products with diazomethane. The methyl esters were then analyzed by combined capillary gas chromatography-mass spectrometry using a 50 foot long carbowax capillary column.

The analysis of the kerogen ozonolysis products revealed a complex composition (Bitz and Nagy, 1968). The major components were aromatic compounds, dimethyl phthalate and the methyl ester of an alkyl substituted aromatic compound, the exact nature of which has not yet been determined. It should be emphasized that the sample and reagents never came in contact with plastic implements and that all glassware was acid-cleaned. Furthermore, blank runs never showed the presence of any organic compounds, including dimethyl phthalate. Consequently, it appears certain that this and other compounds are the oxidative degradation products of the Onverwacht kerogen. Minor components included dimethyl adipate, methyl palmitate, and what appear to be dicarboxylic acid methyl esters. Some of the other components have not yet been fully identified. The results of the mass spectrometric analysis showed that the Onverwacht kerogen is basically aromatic in nature, apparently consisting of relatively small, condensed aromatic nuclei connected by short aliphatic chains. Conceivably in suitable void spaces of this matrix, longer chains may be inserted and adsorbed.

It is interesting that the Onverwacht kerogen contains more aromatic components than the Fig Tree kerogen. It is commonly assumed that aromatic structures in coal and kerogen are derived from lignin. Yet lignin did not appear until much later in geological time, and it is difficult to account for a sufficiently high accumulation of the relatively rare aromatic biochemicals to produce this basically aromatic type Onverwacht kerogen. One must add that the geological field evidence indicates (Engel, 1967) a continuous low temperature environment; thus, postulating usual reactions leading to the synthesis of aromatic compounds is somewhat difficult. The aromatic nature of the earliest known kerogen emphasizes, in the authors' opinion, the need for considerably more work on this problem because obviously the present understanding is far from complete.

Microstructures

The Onverwacht microstructures pose an equal puzzle. Figure 1 shows an elongated microstructure, the elliptical section of which is 16 μ long, in a petrographic thin section from a carbonaceous chert in the lower Onverwacht. Note the lack of any distinguishing morphological features. Figure 2 shows a microstructure in a powdered preparation from a carbonaceous chert in the upper Onverwacht. Detailed microscopic examination shows that this particle has an opening or tear-mark in the center. It is 25 μ in diameter. Figure 3 shows another microstructure from another carbonaceous chert in the upper Onverwacht which is heavily mineralized and also has a central opening; note again the lack of well developed morphological features. It is 87 μ in diameter. Detailed microscopic studies have shown that the majority of the Onverwacht microstructures have a cup-shaped morphology.

One should add that the particles in the powdered preparation are believed to be as indigenous as those in the petrographic thin sections. Great care was taken to exclude contaminations; the surface of the rock samples was drilled off and then ultrasonically cleaned prior to pulverization. All microscopic samples were prepared in acid-cleaned glassware in a room ventilated by filtered air, and blank runs were constantly made to detect possible contaminations in the air. It appears, therefore, that these particles are not recent contaminations, but certainly they cannot yet be called microfossils because of their very poor morphology.

Great caution must be used in describing the nature of the early Precambrian microstructures. Morphology alone is not a sufficient criterion for designating these poorly-developed particles as microfossils. The nature of their chemical composition must be accurately established before one can reach a definite conclusion, and

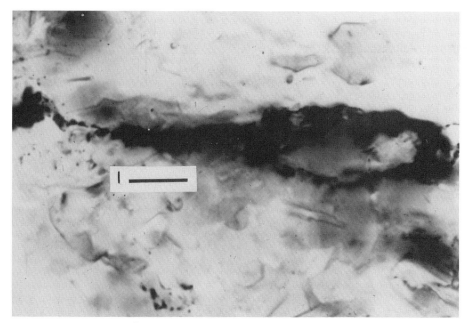

Fig. 1. Photomicrograph of a petrographic thin section a carbonaceous chert from the lower Onverwacht; horizontal line represents 5 μ

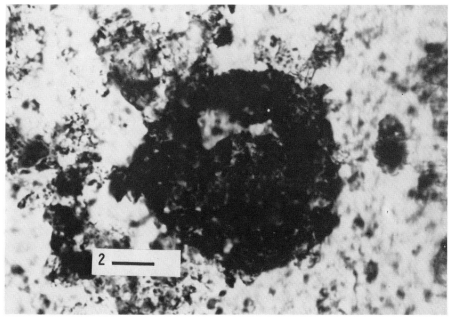

Fig. 2. Photomicrograph of a microstructure from a carbonaceous chert in the upper Onverwacht. Powdered preparations, which had been treated before mounting in Canada Balsam with O_3, KOH and H_2O_2. Horizontal line represents 5 μ

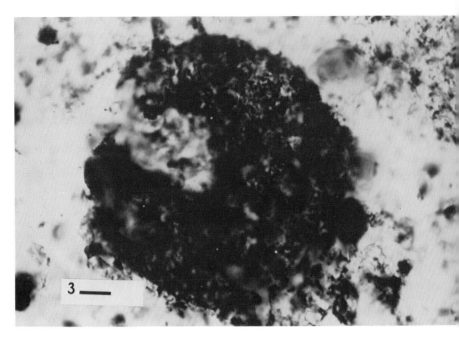

Fig. 3. Photomicrograph of a microstructure from another carbonaceous chert in the upper Onverwacht. Powdered preparation. Horizontal line represents 10 μ. All photomicrographs were taken with transmitted light under oil immersion

at present it is only known that these microstructures are not affected by hot 6N HCl, hot 48 % HF and O_3. The difficulties encountered in identifying the origin of these microstructures were illustrated by Nagy and Urey, (1968) and Engel et al., (1968). Round microstructures were found in petrographic thin sections of Onverwacht igneous rocks. These microstructures had double walls and center nucleus-like objects, and they looked remarkably biological; yet they are inorganic artifacts in an Onverwacht pillow lava, and are therefore unequivocally non-biological in origin. This again points out the great need for caution, patience and much more careful work in connection with early Precambrian life.

Acknowledgments: The rock samples were collected and the geological field relationships of the lithofacies worked out by Professor A.E.J. Engel of the University of California at San Diego, with the assistance of M.J. and R.P. Viljoen from the University of the Witwatersrand. The authors would also like to thank Professor Harold C. Urey of the University of California at San Diego and of the University of Arizona for his interest and advice. This investigation was supported by NASA grants NsG–541 and NGR–05-009-043.

References

Anhaeusser, C.R., Roering, C., Viljoen, M.J. and Viljoen, R.P.: Econ. Geol. Res. Unit Infor. Circ. 38, Univ. Witwatersrand, Johannesburg, South Africa (1967).

Barghoorn, E.S. and Schopf, J.W.: Science, 152, 758 (1966).

Bitz, M.C. and Nagy, B.: manuscript in preparation (1968).

Engel, A.E.J.: personal communication (1967).

Engel, A.E.J., Nagy, B., Nagy, L.A., Engel, C.G., Kremp, G.O.W. and Drew, C.M.: Science, 161, 1005 (September 1968).

Nagy, B., Nagy, L.A., Engel, C.G., Engel, A.E.J., Kremp, G.O.W. and Drew, C.M.: unpublished report (1967).

Nagy, B. and Urey, H.C.: 8th COSPAR Meeting, Preprint No. L. 2.6. (May 9–21, 1968).

Nagy, B., Nagy, L.A., Bitz, M.C., Engel, C.G. and Engel, A.E.J.: Abstracts, 4th International Meeting on Organic Geochemistry, p. 23 (August 1968).

Pflug, H.D.: Econ. Geol. Res. Unit Infor. Circ. 28, Univ. Witwatersrand, Johannesburg, South Africa (1966).

Schopf, J.W. and Barghoorn, E.S.: Science, 156, 508 (1967).

Visser, D.J.L.: South African Geological Survey, Spec. Paper, 15 (1956).

Enzyme aus bituminösen Schiefern, Braunkohlen und Torfen

Wolfgang Heller

Chirurgische Universitätsklinik
Tübingen, Germany

The investigations were made with pleistocene peats, miocene lignites and bituminous slates, jurassic bituminous slates (Posidonomya shales) and triassic (Anisienne/Ladinienne) bituminousslates. The bituminous slates are all black slates. The material for our investigationswas took from the quarry as sterile as possible. The bituminous slates as well as peats or the lignites were till this air tight closed. For the biochemical analysises the material must be groundas fine as possible. We did so with the Ultraturrax. After this procedure the so prpared materill was brought into bidestilled water (Amuwa). Some hours later we found that the temperature rosed in the calorimeter bottle. The temperature of the geological older material rose not so high than the geological younger. The bituminous slates shwoed only a trifling acsendance of temperature. But the ascendance of temperature is surely measurable and can only be related on the process of change of matter. We can this only show by bringing the material into bidestilled water.

The further investigations showed us that all sediments jet contain ATP. The quantity of ATP is dependent on the geological age of the sediment. (But it is astonishing that we can find on the whole ATP in the triassic and jurassic bituminous slates.)

The ascendance of temperature is surely caused by the reduction of ATP. This can be showed by measuring of it.

Besides ATPase we could show quantitatively the following enzymes: GLDH, GOT, G-6-PDH, GPT, ICDH, MDH, LAP and alpha-Amylase. This enzymes could only be found at small amounts in the sediments we investigated. The amounts of the enzymes in the bituminous slates are jet smaller.

Die Untersuchungen wurden vornehmlich an eiszeitlichen Torfen und tertiären Braunkohlen ausgeführt. Sie dehnten wir dann auf bituminöse Schiefer weiter aus und zwar insbesondere auf die jurassischen Posidonienschiefer und die triassichen bituminösen Schiefer vom Monte San Giorgio (Anis/Ladin).

Bringt man nach der steril erfolgten analysenfeinen Aufarbeitung das Untersuchungsgut in ein Kalorimetergefäß, so erfolgt nachdem man Wasser zugefügt hat eine Erwärmung, die je nach dem geologischen Alter des Materials unterschiedlich stark ist. Bei den bituminösen Schiefern ist der Temperaturanstieg nur geringfügig. Er ist aber noch deutlich meßbar und sicher auf Stoffwechselprozesse, die durch die Aufbereitung mit bidest. Wasser angeregt wurden, zurückzuführen.

Die weiteren Untersuchungen ergaben, daß je nach dem geologischen Alter des Sediments ein unterschiedlich hoher Gehalt an ATP feststellbar ist. Der Temperaturanstieg ist sicher weitgehend auf den ATP-Abbau zurückzuführen, wie diesbezügliche Messungen ergaben.

Die hier aufgeführten Enzyme sind z.T. nur in Spuren nachzuweisen. Das Enzymspektrum wurde diskutiert.

Einführung

Wohl nicht allein die Biochemie der rezenten Enzyme ist für die Untersuchung von
Reaktionsmechanismen dieser Stoffklasse von großem Interesse; wenn wir auch
hier bei weitem noch nicht vollständige Klarheit über alle uns interessierenden Vorgänge besitzen. Ich glaube vielmehr, daß wir bei der Aufklärung und Identifizierung
von fossilen Enzymen mit einen Beitrag leisten können, um einen Einblick und
auch Anregung zur weiteren Aufklärung von Mechanismen dieser selbständigen
Stoffklasse zu erlangen. Wir können natürlich nicht erwarten, daß wir noch die jeweiligen Enzyme aller uns heute bekannter Reaktionen finden, vielleicht aber die
Endprodukte oder auch das Substrat der enzymatischen Vorgänge.

Diese Untersuchungen dienen ferner dazu, um auf einem klar begrenzten Teilge-
biet einen Einblick in das biochemische Geschehen, das 150 Millionen Jahre und
weiter zurückliegt, zu erlangen. Wir haben uns die Aufgabe gestellt ein möglichst
weitgespanntes Enzymspektrum und die Substrate der jeweiligen Enzyme zu finden. Es muß daher schon eingangs darauf hingewiesen werden, daß es sich im
Grunde genommen um ausgesprochene Spurenanalysen handelt. Denn wenn wir
überhaupt etwas finden, so kann es sich höchstens um ganz geringe Mengen han-
deln, die an der Grenze der Nachweisbarkeit liegen.

Es stellte sich nun bei unseren Untersuchungen heraus, daß man sich bei der Be-
schäftigung mit fossilen Enzymen und deren Substrate, ausschließlich auf bituminöse Schichten oder Erdöle beschränken muß. Schon dadurch sind einem klare
Grenzen gesetzt. Für die genannte Fragestellung erweisen sich aber Erdöle als un-
interessant, da dafür nur die primäre Lagerstätte Bedeutung haben kann. Das ge-
förderte Erdöl befindet sich ja nicht im Muttergestein sondern durch die Migration
im Speichergestein. Zudem wäre eine sterile Entnahme der entsprechenden Proben unmöglich. Aus diesem Grunde beschränken sich meine Untersuchungen ausschließlich auf bituminöse Schiefer verschiedenen geologischen Alters und zwar
bis jetzt auf den Lias epsilon (Posidonienschiefer) mit Schwerpunkt Süddeutsch-
land und zu Vergleichszwecken auch aus Norddeutschland. Ferner bearbeiteten
wir Material triassischer (Anis/Ladin) bituminöser Schiefer vom Monte San Giorgio
(Tessin, Schweiz), sowie aus dem Tertiär von Messel (Hessen, BRD). Zu Parallel-
untersuchungen zogen wir noch tertiäre Braunkohle aus dem Geiseltal (DDR) und
pleistozäne Torfe Oberschwabens (BRD) heran. Somit liegen uns Proben verschiedenen geologischen Alters und verschiedener petrographischer Beschaffenheit,
jedoch allesamt bituminösen Charakters vor.

Über die Möglichkeit der selbsttätigen Erzeugung von biochemischen Umsetzungen im Untersuchungsgut

Ehe wir die Untersuchungen zum Nachweis von Enzymspuren in den genannten
bituminösen Schiefern ausführen, werden entsprechende Vorproben angestellt die

uns aber als ausgesprochen wichtig erscheinen. Das möglichst steril dem Aufschluß entnommene, bisher weitgehend luftdicht abgeschlossene Untersuchungsgut wird zur biochemischen Bearbeitung zuvor analysenfein gemahlen. Der genaue Aufarbeitungsvorgang soll noch geschildert werden. Bringt man die Proben anschließend in aqua bidest. steril (Ampuwa), so ist je nach dem geologischen Alter des Materials eine unterschiedliche deutlich meßbare Erwärmung im Kalorimetergefäß feststellbar. Bei den bituminösen Schiefern ist der Temperaturanstieg allerdings nur geringfügig. Bei Torfen und Braunkohlen ist er jedoch erheblich und beträgt je nach Probe mehrere Grad. Aber auch der geringfügige Temperaturanstieg bei den bituminösen Schieferproben ist mit hinreichender Sicherheit auf Stoffwechselprozesse, die durch die Aufbereitung mit aqua bidest angeregt wurden, zurückzuführen.

Die weiteren Untersuchungen ergaben nämlich, daß je nach dem geologischen Alter des Sediments ein unterschiedlich hoher Gehalt an ATP feststellbar ist. Dieser steht in ursächlichem Zusammenhang mit dem Gehalt an organischer Substanz im Sediment. M. E. ist es überhaupt erstaunlich, daß in den triassischen bituminösen Sedimenten noch ATP nachweisbar ist. Der Temperaturanstieg im Kalorimetergefäß ist sicher weitgehend auf den ATP-Abbau zurückzuführen, wie diesbezügliche von uns angestellte Messungen ergaben. Inwieweit dabei auch andere enzymatische Vorgänge beteiligt sind, können wir nicht mit Sicherheit sagen.

Der Gehalt an organischer Substanz im Sediment

Da der Schwerpunkt der Untersuchungen allgemein auf den bituminösen Schiefern liegt, wobei wir besonders eingehend, wie schon eingangs angedeutet, den Posidonienschiefer Schwabens untersucht haben, seien hier für ihn von uns im Zusammenhang früherer Untersuchungen ermittelte Einzelwerte besonders charakteristischer Fundpunkte aufgeführt. Unser zweiter Untersuchungsschwerpunkt betrifft die triassischen bituminösen Schiefer vom Monte San Giorgio und die tertiären bituminösen Schiefer von Messel. Diese beiden anderen bituminösen Schiefer zeigen durchschnittlich den doppelt so hohen Gehalt an organischer Substanz wie die Höchstwerte, die wir im Posidonienschiefer Schwabens finden. Es zeigte sich, daß für die Enzymuntersuchungen im Lias epsilon die beiden Fundpunkte Holzmaden bei Göppingen und Dotternhausen bei Balingen besonders geeignet sind. Finden wir doch hier auch die höchsten Werte an organischer Substanz in den bituminösen Mergelschiefern. Holzmaden ist bekannt durch die Ichthyosaurierfunde die B. Hauff bearbeitete. Im Aufschluß Dotternhausen konnte ich selbst ein relativ gut erhaltenes Ichthyosaurierskelett in einer ca. 30–50 cm mächtigen Asphaltlage ausgraben. Gerade im Bereich von Ichthyosaurierfunden konnten wir bisher die besten Ergebnisse im Posidonienschiefer erzielen. Und zwar einmal in den durch B. Hauff berühmt gewordenen Aufschlüssen von Holzmaden und andererseits in dem von Dotternhausen; hier insbesondere im Bereich von dem von mir ausgegrabenen Ichthyosaurier.

Die Aufarbeitung des Schiefermaterials zu Enzymuntersuchungen

Das steril dem jeweiligen Aufschluß entnommene Gestein, sowohl die Posidonienschiefer als auch die bituminösen Schiefer vom Monte San Giorgio oder von Messel,
wird mit einer sterilen Zange zuerst grob zerkleinert. So vorbereitet bringt man
dann anschließend das Gesteinsmaterial in die Mahlbecher der Kugelmühle, wo es
analysenfein gemahlen wird. Schon der Mahlvorgang bedeutet die erste Schwierigkeit. Denn die eventuell zu erwartenden Enzyme würden durch die dabei freiwer-
dende Wärme zerstört werden. Um eine zu starke Erwärmung zu vermeiden, wird
der Mahlbecher einem Kohlensäureschneestrom ausgesetzt. Auf diese Weise kann
es zu keiner Erwärmung der Mahlbecher, bzw. des Mahlguts kommen. Mit dem
Ultraturax homogenisieren wir dann das Analysenmaterial vollständig.

Auch der Vorgang des Homogenisierens wird in einem Gefäß durchgeführt, das
in Kohlensäureschnee eintaucht. Das Zerkleinern erfolgt also vollständig bei
Temperaturen die weit unter 0 °C liegen. Für Torfe und Braunkohle entfällt der
Mahlvorgang, sie können sofort nach dem groben Zerkleinern mit Ampuwa auf-
geschlämmt werden und anschließend mit dem Ultraturax unter den schon angegebenen Bedingungen homogenisiert werden. Das so aufgearbeitete Untersuchungsgut, Schiefermaterial bzw. Torfe oder Braunkohle sind nun zur Extraktion fertig.

Der nun folgende Extraktionsvorgang muß gleichfalls im Kühlraum oder in einer
geräumigen Kühltruhe erfolgen. Wir haben die Extraktion in der Tiefkühltruhe
durchgeführt. Das homogenisierte Probengut bringen wir in Kjeldahlkolben ein
und schlämmen es mit Ampuwa zu einem dünnflüssigen Brei auf. Die Kolben werden darauf in eine hochtourige Schüttelmaschine eingespannt die in der Tiefkühltruhe läuft. Die langhalsigen Kjeldahlkolben erweisen sich als besonders geeignet
für ein intensives Durchmischen des Probenguts. Der Schüttelvorgang geht über
24 Stunden. Das so intensiv extrahierte Probengut kann anschließend abgenutscht
werden. Da zum Extrahieren von 1 kg Schiefermaterial große Mengen steriles aqua
bidest. erforderlich ist, wird natürlich ein sehr starker Verdünnungsprozeß mit den
ohnehin nur in Spuren zuerwartenden Enzymen durchgeführt. Wir würden uns somit unter der Grenze der Nachweisbarkeit der Enzyme in den Extrakten bewegen.
Dasselbe gilt auch für die Braunkohlen und die Torfe. Zu einer aliquoten Menge
Braunkohle oder Torf wird bei der Extraktion noch mehr Wasser benötigt. Der
Verdünnungsprozeß ist jedoch nur scheinbar höher, da dieses Untersuchungsgut
eine größere Menge des jeweiligen Enzyms enthält als z.B. die Posidonienschiefer,
die bituminösen Schiefer vom Monte San Giorgio oder diejenigen von Messel.

Durch Gefriertrocknung wird nun das Extraktionsgut auf ein Minimum eingeengt.
Aus technischen Gründen, d.n. wegen der großen Flüssigkeitsmenge ist eine mehr-
malige Gefriertrocknung erforderlich. Nach der ersten Einengung nimmt man das
Extraktionsgut mit einer geringen Menge Ampuwa auf und setzt es dann einer

erneuten Gefriertrocknung aus. Nach der letzten Einengung kann das Extraktionsgut nun mit der für die einzelnen Nachweise nötigen Menge Ampuwa versetzt werden. In der Kälte ist der Extrakt haltbar.

Es hat sich gezeigt, daß wir auf diese Weise mit Hilfe der wässrigen Extraktion in der Kälte eine optimale Ausbeute dieses nur in geringer Menge in den bituminösen Schiefern verschiedenen geologischen Alters enthaltenen Untersuchungsgut erzielen können. Dasselbe gilt natürlich auch für Torfe und die Braunkohlen. Alle andere Wege der Extraktion, die von uns noch versucht wurden, erwiesen sich als untauglich.

Ehe die so vorbereiteten Extrakte zur Untersuchung auf Enzyme verwendet werden können, muß ein wesentlicher Faktor beachtet werden. Die bituminösen Schiefer verschiedenen geologischen Alters enthalten neben $CaCO_3, MgCO_3$ sowie den Tonmineralien Kaolinit, Illit und Montmorilonit noch geringe Mengen von Schwermetallen, wobei das Eisen an der Spitze steht (in Gestalt von FeS_2 und Fe_2O_3). Ferner findet sich auch noch in Spuren V, Cu und Ti. Alle diese Metalle sind natürlich ausgeprägte Fermentgifte und würden jeden Nachweis unmöglich machen. Um dies zu verhindern, fügen wir den Extrakten eine 5 molare EDTA-Lösung zu. So vorbereitet sind dann die Nachweisreaktionen mit den Extrakten aus den bituminösen Schiefern möglich. Auch die Extrakte aus den Braunkohlen und den Torfen bedürfen derselben Vorbereitung.

Die Auswertung des Extraktionsguts

a) Allgemeiner Teil

Schon die Vorversuche zeigten uns, daß nur bituminöse Schichten für diese Untersuchungen geeignet sind. Diese eingangs gemachten Feststellungen wurden durch die Hauptversuche nicht erschüttert. Wir stellten auch Versuche mit nicht bituminösem Material an, ohne entsprechende Erfolge erzielen zu können. Weiterhin zeigte sich auch, daß nicht allein das geologische Alter für die Erhaltung von Enzymspuren in solchen bituminösen Schichten ausschlaggebend ist. Vielmehr ist dafür ein wesentlicher Faktor entscheidend, der in solchen Schichten auftretende Gesamtgehalt an organischer Substanz. Als treffendes Beispiel seien die jurassischen Schiefer und die triassischen vom Monte San Giorgio angeführt, die wesentlich älter sind als die Posidonienschiefer. Letztere weisen annähernd den doppelt so hohen Gehalt an organischer Substanz auf als die Schiefer des Lias epsilon. Sie enthalten auch erheblich größere Spuren der einzelnen Enzyme als der Posidonienschiefer. Allerdings sind die Enzymwerte nicht doppelt so hoch.

Eine Sonderstellung nehmen natürlich die jüngeren tertiären Braunkohlen bzw. die pleistozänen Torfe ein. Auf Grund des höheren Gehalts an organischer Substanz sind auch höhere Enzymwerte zu erwarten. Die tertiäre Braunkohle und die tertiären bituminösen Schiefer lassen sich allerdings nicht miteinander vergleichen, da es sich um verschiedenartige Sedimente handelt. Als besonders günstig erwiesen sich die Braunkohlen aus dem Geiseltal. Durch ein besonderes Entgegenkommen ist es mir gelungen Untersuchungsmaterial von der berühmten Fossilfundstelle zu bekommen. Bekanntlich finden sich hier Amphibien in Hauterhaltung, desgleichen Blattreste Früchte ganze Baumstämme und sogar Chlorophylle. Es ist verständlich, daß sich dieses Material besonders für unsere Untersuchungen eignet.

b) Methodischer Teil

Bei der Bestimmung der einzelnen Enzyme haben wir uns auf die bei Bergmeyer (Methoden der enzymatischen Analyse 1965) aufgeführten Methoden gestützt. Die Werte der einzelnen Enzyme werden in Internationalen Einheiten (IU) angegeben.

c) Ergebnisse

Folgende Enzyme konnten wir bis jetzt in den bituminösen Schichten finden: GLDH, GOT, G-(-PDH, GPT, MDH, LAP, α-Amylase. Generell konnten wir feststellen, daß sich für solche Untersuchungen nur bituminöse Schichten relativ hohen Gehalts an organischer Substanz eignen. In nicht bituminösen Schichten treten keinerlei Enzymspuren auf. Die günstigsten Ergebnisse zeigen die jungen eiszeitlichen Torfe. Verhätnismäßig hohe Werte treten auch in den tertiären Braunkohlen des Geiseltals auf.

Tabelle 1

Enzym	Einh./kg	Substanz	(Mittelwerte)		
	1	2	3	4	5
Aldolase	7,1	3,2	6,4	12,5	25,3
α-Amylase	140,3	111,5	260,4	350,6	701,4
CPK	1	8,2	9,1	10,2	-
GLDH	60,5	40,3	70,6	100,1	150,3
GOT	175,3	160,5	180,2	460,5	500,4
G-6-PDH	26,8	14,3	34,5	50,4	96,3
GPT	180,2	130,1	140,5	180,9	800,2
JCDH	14,2	7,6	15,8	25,3	30,4
MDH	46,5	14,2	33,5	40,7	66,2
LAP	160,3	60,4	150,25	180,3	260,5
Trypsin	70,2	43,5	81,2	160,7	240,3

Als zweite Gruppe hinsichtlich der Ausbildung des Sediments müssen die bituminösen Schiefer angesehen werden. Hier zeigt sich, daß nicht das geologische Alter für die Höhe der Enzymwerte ausschlaggebend ist, sondern der Gesamtgehalt an organischer Substanz. Der Posidonienschiefer Schwabens, der als Untersuchungsschwerpunkt anzusehen ist, weist allgemein geringere Werte als die älteren triassischen bituminösen Schiefer vom Monte San Giorgio und die tertiären bituminösen Schiefer von Messel auf. Den höchsten Gehalt an organischer Substanz haben die bituminösen Schiefer vom Monte San Giorgio und die Schiefer von Messel.

d) Spezielle Ergebnisse aus den Posidonienschiefern Schwabens

Wie schon erwähnt stellt der Posidonienschiefer Schwabens das Hauptuntersuchungsmaterial für uns dar. Wir konnten allgemeine Ergebnisse in einer Vielzahl von Aufschlüssen erzielen. Ausgezeichnete Ergebnisse boten allerdings nur die Fundpunkte Holzmaden im Bereich von Ichthyosauriern und Dotternhausen an der Stelle, wo ich den Ichthyosaurier ausgraben konnte. Gerade im Bereich ehemaliger Tierkadaver findet sich ein erheblich höherer Gehalt an organischer Substanz. Hier werden Werte bis zu 40 % erreicht. Aber nicht allein der wesentlich höhere Gehalt an organischer Substanz im Sediment erscheint mir ausschlaggebend für die höheren Enzymwerte, sondern überhaupt, daß hier Tierkadaver mit ihren Abbauprodukten vorliegen. In deren Bereich hat sich natürlich ein stark vermehrter Bakterienstoffwechsel abgespielt. Ich glaube daher, daß gerade die Enzyme die aus diesem vermehrten Bakterienstoffwechsel stammen, im wesentlichen dazu beitragen, daß hier höhere Enzymwerte als im übrigen Sediment auftreten. Es handelt sich sicher nicht um solche dieser Tiere. Auch im Bereich fossiler Hölzer konnten wir im Posidonienschiefer Schwabens etwas erhöhte Enzymwerte feststellen. Sie erreichen aber bei weitem nicht diejenigen, die im Bereich von Ichthyosaurierskeletten oder auch von Fischen festgestellt werden konnten. Abschließend sei noch bemerkt, daß wir neben den Enzymen auch die entsprechenden Substrate nachweisen konnten.

Literatur

Abelson, P. H. und W. E. Hanson: Geochemistry of organic substances. In: Researches in Geochemistry. Edited by P. H. Abelson. New York – London 1959.

Bergmeyer, H.-U.: Methoden der enzymatischen Analyse. Weinheim 1962.

Beurlen, K.: Bemerkungen zur Sedimentation in den Posidonienschiefern Holzmadens. Iber. Mitt. oberrh. geol. Ver. 1925, 198/302.

Blumer, M.: Zur Geochemie der Sedimentgesteine. Theoretische Untersuchungen sowie Spurenanalysen schweizerischer Gesteine. Helv. chim. Acta 1950, Nr. 33.

Brockamp, B.: Zur Paläogeographie und Bitumenführung des Posidonienschiefers im deutschen Lias. Arch. Lagerstättenforsch., Heft 77. Berlin 1944.

Criddle, D. W. und R. L. Le Tourneau: Fluorescent indicator adsorption. Method for Hydrocarbon-Type Analysis. Analytic. Chem. 23, 1620/24 (1951).

Degens, E. T. und M. Bajor: Die Verteilung von Aminosäuren in bituminösen Sedimenten und ihre Bedeutung für die Kohlen- und Erdölgeologie. Glückauf 96, 1525/34 (1960).

Eggstein, M. und F. H. Kreutz: Eine neue Bestimmung der Neutralfette im Blutserum und Gewebe. Klin. Wschr. 44, 262/73 (1966).

Einsele, G. und R. Mosebach: Zur Petrographie, Fossilerhaltung und Entstehung der Gesteine des Posidonienschiefers im Schwäbischen Jura. Neues Jb. Geol. Paläont., Abh., 101, Nr. 3 319/430 (1955).

Fraas, E.: Die Ichthyosaurier der süddeutschen Trias und Juraablagerungen. Tübingen 1891.

v. Gaertner, H.-R. und H. Kroepelin: Petrographische und chemische Untersuchungen am Posidonienschiefer Nordwestdeutschlands. Erdöl und Kohle 9, 588/92, 680/82 (1956).

v. Gaertner, H.-R.: Petrographische Untersuchungen am Nordwestdeutschen Posidonienschiefer. Geol. Rdsch. 43, 447/63 (1955).

Hauff, B.: Untersuchung der Fossilfundstätten von Holzmaden im Posidonienschiefer Schwabens. Paläontographica 64, 1/2 (1921).

Heller, W.: Organisch-chemische Untersuchungen im Posidonienschiefer Schwabens. Neues Jb. Geol. Paläont., Mh., 2, 65/68 (1965).

Heller, W.: Organisch-chemische Untersuchungen im Posidonienschiefer Schwabens. In: G. D. Hobson und M. C. Louis, Advances in Organic Geochemistry. London 1966.

Heller, W.: Tonmineralien bituminöser Schiefer als natürliche Systeme der Verteilungschromatographie. Erdöl Kohle – Erdgas – Petrochem. 19, 557/61 (1966).

Hennig, E.: Über Ptycholepis bollensis. Jh. Ver. vaterl. Naturk. Heft 74, 173/82 (1918).

Knight, H. S. und S. Groenings: Fluorescent indicator adsorption method for hydrocarbon type analysis. Analytic. Chem. 28, 1949/54 (1956).

Malins, D. C. und H. K. Mangold (1960: In: N. Zöllner und D. Eberhagen. Untersuchung und Bestimmung der Lipoide im Blut, S. 181/82. Berlin 1965.

Mangold, H. K. (1959, 1961): ib.

Micheel, F. und W. Schminke: Papierchromatographische Trennung einfacher aliphatischer Alkohole und kondensierter aromatischer Kohlenwasserstoffe. Angew. Chem. 69, 334/35 (1957).

Morris, L. J. (1962): In: N. Zöllner und D. Eberhagen, Untersuchung und Bestimmung der Lipoide im Blut, S. 182/83. Berlin 1965.

Neuberger, A.: Symposium on Protein Structure. New York 1958.

Sawicki, E., et al.: Separation and characterization of polynuclear aromatic hydrocarbons urban air borne particulates. Analytic. Chem. **32**, 810/15 (1960).

Sawicki, E., et al.: Simple sensitive Test, for compounds containing the cyclopentadiene CH_2 grouping. Analytic. Chem. **32**, 816/18 (1960).

Schmitz, H.-H. und H.-R. v. Gaertner: Die organische Substanz des Posidonienschiefers als Hinweis auf eine Restöllagerstätte. Erdöl Kohle – Erdgas – Petrochem. **16**, 478/82 (1963).

Wieland, Th. und W. Kracht: Papierchromatographie von mehrkernigen Aromaten. Angew. Chem. **69**, 172/74 (1957).

Discussion

M. Bajor: Die Menge an organischen C steigt ebenfalls mit dem geologischen Alter an wie auch ATP. Daher kann nicht unbedingt die Erwärmung der Proben mit destilliertem Wasser auf ATP zurückgeführt werden. Die ansteigende Temperatur mit jüngerem Alter könnten auch z. B. mit zusammennehmenden C_{org} oder durch anorganischen Reaktionen erklärt werden. Andererseits weckt die Linearität zwischen C_{org} und ATP (bzw. Enzym) den Eindruck das der Gehalt an Enzymen vom Alter der Proben geradezu unabhängig ist.

W. Heller: Die Menge ATP läßt sich messen, ebenso die Menge AMP am Ende der Reaktion. Dies ist ein exakter Maßstab für den Verlauf der Reaktion.

P. H. Given: Some workers have considered the possibility that rocks at considerable depth contain an indigenous microflora. As far as I know, such a microflora has never been proved conclusively. But it is possible that micro-organisms exist deep in the crust, since some of them can live at 100° and 1000 atms pressure. Perhaps living micro-organisms, indigenous to the rock and not contaminants are responsible for the enzymes you find.

W. Heller: Typsin und creatinphosphorkinase kommen nur bei höheren Organismen vor. CPK bei Muskelabbau. MDH und ICDH vornehmlich im Nerven- und Gehirnstoffwechsel. GOT und GPT im Leberstoffwechsel.

K. E. H. Göhring: Mit welcher Sicherheit können Sie rezente bakteriellen Verunreinigungen ausschließen?

W. Heller: Zwei Enzyme kommen bei Bakterien nicht vor GOT (und GPT) sowie Typsin. Sie können also von außen nicht hereingebracht worden sein. (CPK = Muskelstoffwechsel.) Bei GOT und GPT scheidet Bakterienstoffwechsel auch weitgehend aus. MDH und ICDH stammen hauptsächlich aus dem Gehirnstoffwechsel.

G. Eglinton: My query concerns the extent of the preservation of enzyme structure proposed by Dr. Heller. In view of the changes found in shale proteins and in the conversion of amino acids over even a few million years, it seems unlikely to me that any enzyme should remain complete with a full sequencing necessary for bilogical activity. It would be more reasonable if these enzymes, if they be present, originate in Recent or living organisms.

Application of Gas Chromatography and Mass Spectrometry to Porphyrin Microanalysis

A Study of Homologous Porphyrin Series in Ancient Biological Residues

David B. Boylan, Yousif I. Alturki and Geoffrey Eglinton

Organic Geochemistry Unit, School of Chemistry, University of Bristol
Bristol, England

Recent advances have concerned the conversion of porphyrin pigments to volatile bis (trimethylsiloxy) silicon complexes that can be gas chromatographed under normal conditions. These techniques have been applied to the analysis of homologous series of porphyrins such as is found in recent and ancient sediments and oils. Gas chromatographic and mass spectrometric analysis of GC fractions of the Boscan petroporphyrins will be discussed and compared with results obtained from a preliminary analysis of Green River shale porphyrins.

Introduction

The presence of several homologous series of porphyrins has been demonstrated in some shales, shale oils and petroleums [1]. The complexity of porphyrin content is demonstrated by analytical results such as the low voltage mass spectrum of the Boscan crude oil shown in Figure 1 [2]. An ionization voltage of 12 electron volts is

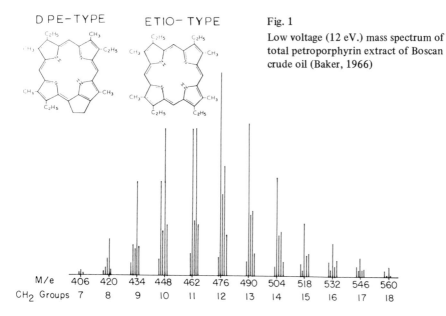

Fig. 1

Low voltage (12 eV.) mass spectrum of total petroporphyrin extract of Boscan crude oil (Baker, 1966)

used in order to suppress secondary fragmentations, rendering a less complex spectrum composed primarily of molecular ions (M^+). Thus, each line in the spectrum represents one or more isomeric molecular ions of a certain type of porphyrin molecule. Boscan petroporphyrins are composed mainly of two major types of molecules, an etio-type (I) thought to be related to hemin or perhaps chlorophyll via a diagenetic route, and a deoxophylloerythro-type (DPE-type) thought to be derived through a chlorophyll degradation scheme [3].

Closely related alkylporphyrin molecules of the same type are impossible to separate by conventional techniques such as thin-layer chromatography, zone melting, preferential crystallization and gel permeation chromatography [4]. Thus complex mixtures, such as those found in geological materials, would best be studied by application of more powerful separation techniques, such as gas chromatography and combined GC—MS. However, use of these microanalytical techniques has been limited by the relative involatility of these macrocyclic aromatic compounds.

Synthesis and Gas Chromatography of Volatile Silicon Complexes

Recent studies have shown that shielding of the macrocyclic nucleus with bulky trimethylsiloxy ligands attached to a central silicon ligand decreases intermolecular attractions, making a volatile complex that can be chromatographed at normal

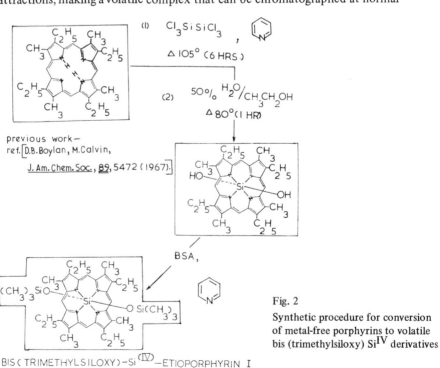

Fig. 2

Synthetic procedure for conversion of metal-free porphyrins to volatile bis (trimethylsiloxy) Si^{IV} derivatives

BIS (TRIMETHYLSILOXY)–Si$^{(IV)}$–ETIOPORPHYRIN I

temperatures and pressures [5]. Recent modifications in the synthetic procedures have led to excellent yields of bis (trimethylsiloxy) silicon derivatives (Figure 2). Hexachlorodisilane, pyridine and the metal free porphyrin (etioporphyrin I as standard) are heated, followed by hydrolysis in dilute hydrochloric acid and trimethylsilylation with bis (trimethylsilyl) acetamide to yield the volatile bis (trimethylsiloxy) derivatives (standard bis (trimethylsiloxy) silicon IV etioporphyrin I) – (sublimation 130 °C.–.05 mm Hg). Conversion of the metal free porphyrins to the silicon complex is accompanied by a fluorescence colour change from deep red to orange (under a 360 mμ lamp). Sublimation is employed as a convenient method for separating the volatile low molecular weight silicon porphyrin complexes from the less abundant high molecular weight pigments [4] that are not suitable for gas chromatographic analysis.

The mass spectra of the bis (trimethylsiloxy) silicon derivatives are rather simple, showing predominant ions at M^+ (m/e 682 for etioporphyrin I standard) and M^+-89 (m/e 593) resulting from loss of a trimethylsiloxy ligand group. Other less intense fragments correspond to cleavage of peripheral groups, which usually occur β to the macrocyclic ring (Figure 3). The application of gas chromatography to the analysis of homologous porphyrins is demonstrated in Figure 4. The bis (trimethylsiloxy) silicon IV derivatives of etioporphyrin I (M.Wt. 682), and a homologue con-

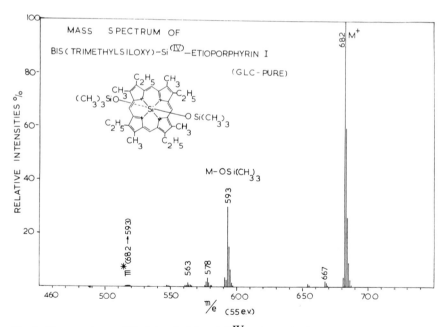

Fig. 3. Mass spectrum of bis (trimethylsiloxy) Si^{IV} aetioporphyrin I at ionization voltage 55 eV

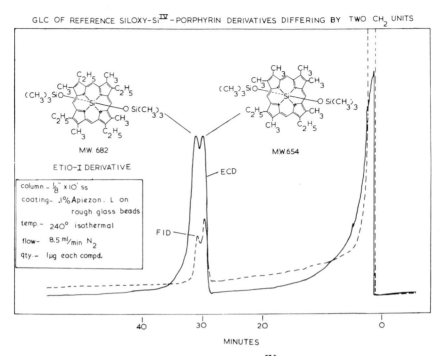

Fig. 4. Gas chromatography of bis (trimethylsiloxy) Si^{IV} derivatives of aetioporphyrin I (M. wt. 682) and homologue (M. wt. 654)

taining two less methylene units (M.Wt. 654) have been partially resolved on a $10' \cdot \frac{1}{8}''$ S.S. column containing 0.1 % Apiezon L coated rough glass beads. Both electron capture detector and flame ionization detector were used for sample detection. The sensitivity of the electron capture detector allows for porphyrin detection in the subnanogram region.

Geoporphyrin Analysis

Having demonstrated the feasibility of gas chromatographic separation of closely related porphyrims, the technique was applied to geoporphyrin analysis. Porphyrins from the Boscan crude oil (Cretaceous – $70 \rightarrow 135 \cdot 10^6$ yrs. old) were demetalated with methane sulphonic acid at 105 °C. for four hours [2] followed by concentration according to the scheme outlined in Figure 5. After further purification with thin-layer chromatography on alumina (benzene), the porphyrin residue was silylated using the previously described methods. After sublimation at 150° C. (.05 mm Hg), the product was analyzed by gas chromatography on two columns-glass beads coated with 0.1 % Apiezon L and with 0.1 % SE–30 (Figure 6). Again both electron capture and flame ionization detection was used.

ISOLATION PROCEDURE - BOSCAN PETROPORPHYRINS (CRETACEOUS, VENEZUELA)

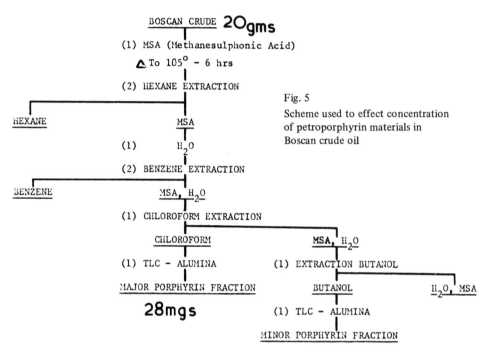

Fig. 5
Scheme used to effect concentration
of petroporphyrin materials in
Boscan crude oil

Apiezon L coating provided the best separations and was used in the further studies.
Each GC peak effluent from the Apiezon L coated column was collected by preparative techniques and surveyed by mass spectrometry (Figure 7). From this data
one can conclude that separations corresponding to porphyrin type as well as molecular weight have been effected. Thus peaks 2 and 3 contain mainly etiotype series
(molecular weight $310 + 14n$ where n is some integer) whereas GC fractions 4–7
contain a majority of DPE type porphyrins of the molecular weight range $322 + 14n$.
Fraction 8 contains an enriched quantity of previously undescribed homologous
porphyrins containing one more unsaturation equivalent than the DPE type, thus
indicating the presence of a portion of the series ($320 + 14n$). Within each porphyrin
type (i.e. DPE, etio etc.) as GC retention time increases, molecular weight also
increases.

Additional information has been gained through the use of a GC–MS combination
instrument. The situation is simplified by the use of fast scanning analysis of the gas
chromatographic effluent, making section analysis of each peak possible. However,
separator selectivity is a problem that we hope to overcome by experimenting with
several interfacial systems.

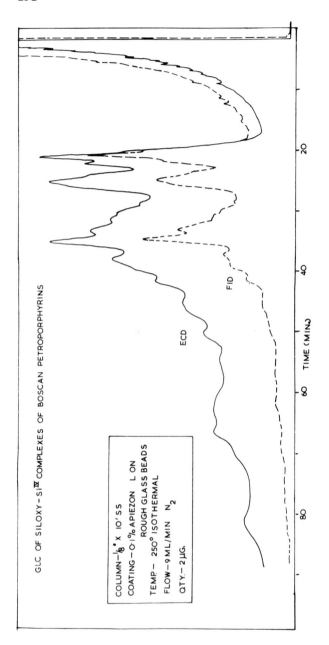

GLC OF SILOXY-Si^{IV} COMPLEXES OF BOSCAN PETROPORPHYRINS

COLUMN—$\frac{1}{8}$" × 10′ SS
COATING—0·1% APIEZON L ON
TEMP— 250° ISOTHERMAL ROUGH GLASS BEADS
FLOW—9 ML/MIN N$_2$
QTY.— 2 μG.

FID

ECD

TIME (MIN.)

(Part of Fig. 6)

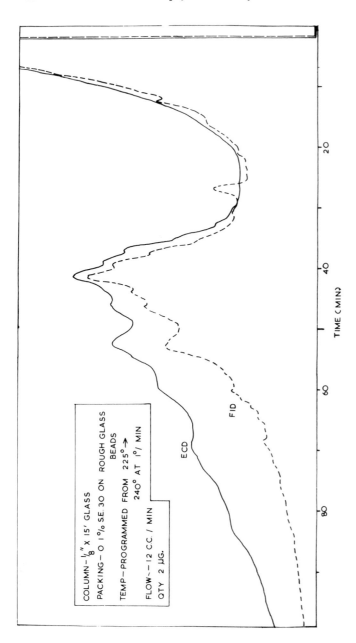

Fig. 6. Gas chromatography of Boscan petroporphyrins (Si derivatives) using two different phases. FID-flame ionization detector, and ECD-electron capture detector

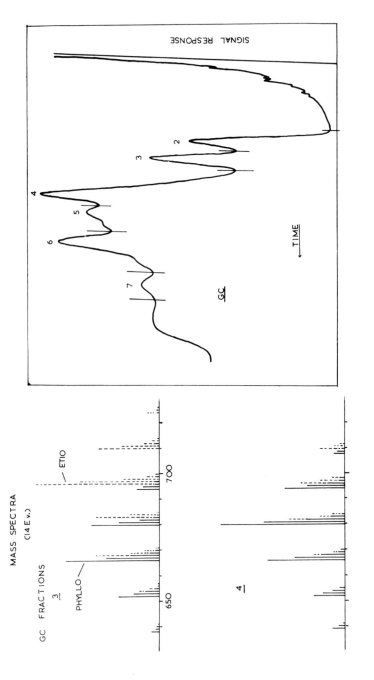

(Part of Fig. 7)

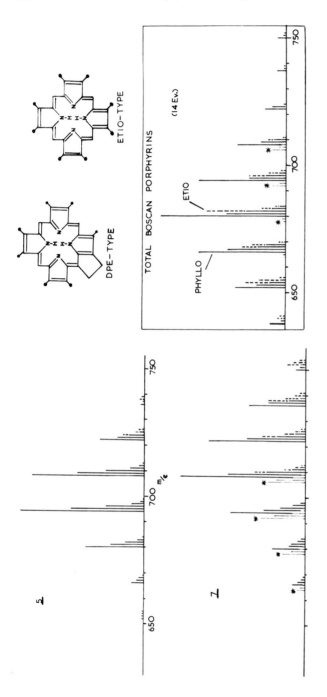

Fig. 7. Low voltage (14 eV.) mass spectra of GC fractions collected via preparative gas chromatography of Boscan petroporphyrins (Si derivatives)

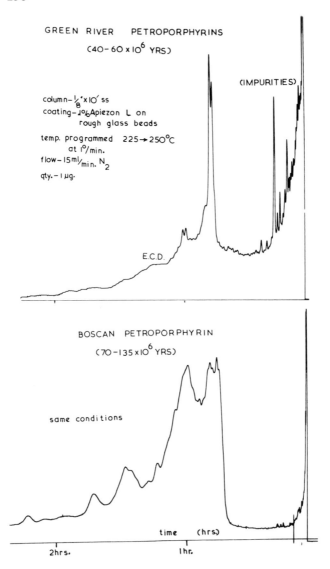

GREEN RIVER PETROPORPHYRINS

$(40-60 \times 10^6$ YRS)

column$-\frac{1}{8}" \times 10'$ ss
coating-1%Apiezon L on
rough glass beads

temp. programmed $225 \rightarrow 250°C$
at $1°$/min.
flow-15ml/min. N_2
qty.-1 µg.

(IMPURITIES)

E.C.D.

BOSCAN PETROPORPHYRIN

$(70-135 \times 10^6$ YRS)

same conditions

time (hrs)

2hrs. 1hr.

Fig. 8. Comparison of geoporphyrin distribution in Green River shale and Boscan petroleum by gas chromatography of Si derivatives

After proving our techniques using Boscan petroporphyrins (used because of their high content in the oil — 3,000 ppm) we sought to apply the methods to analysis of more recent shales whose organic content composition is expected to be less complex. Thus, the Green River Oil Shale from Colorado, USA ($50 \cdot 10^6$ years old) whose organics have been studied extensively [6] was chosen. The shale was found to contain only 20–30 ppm porphyrin which was isolated by initial extraction of the powdered rock by benzene/methanol extraction, followed by the same procedure that was described for the Boscan crude. A gas chromatographic analysis of the siloxy-silicon complexes indicates a simple bimodal distribution as opposed to the more complex Boscan distribution (Figure 8). These are preliminary results performed on extremely small quantities of extracted porphyrin and may not represent the complete porphyrin content. However, it is evident that analysis of the geoporphyrins will be possible by application of GC–MS techniques.

Experimental

All mass spectra were produced using an MS–9 fitted with direct inlet system and an ion source heated to 180 °C. The complex GC samples were analysed at 14 electron volts, whereas 70 electron volts were used for pure samples. All reported gas chromatography was done using a Pye 104 equipped with a nickel (63) electron capture detector, flame ionization detector and a modified Pye collection head for preparative GC analysis. Synthesis of silicon complexes is accomplished by heating the metal-free porphyrin (0.1–10 mg) with hexachlorodisilane (0.25 ml) and anhydrous pyridine (2 ml) in a screw cap glass vial at 100° C. for 5–10 hours. The excess reagent is blown off with nitrogen, and the residue is hydrolyzed in dilute hydrochloric acid (50 % ethanol/water) for fifteen minutes at 60 °C. The dihydroxy silicon complex is extracted into chloroform, concentrated in vacuum and thin-layer chromatographed on alumina using chloroform as a developer. The silicon complexes appear on the plate as bright orange bands (360 mμ light source). Yields of the silicon complex range from 80–90 %. The hydroxyls are then trimethylsilylated using an excess of bis (trimethylsilyl) acetamide in anhydrous pyridine and the product is sublimed at 150 °C. .05 mm Hg, prior to gas chromatographic analysis.

Of the many solid supports and coatings tested, only rough glass beads lightly coated with Apiezon L and SE–30 proved useful. The irreversible adsorption problem often associated with light coatings could only be overcome by injecting BSA and pyridine followed by repeated introduction of samples (10 μg) of standard etiporphyrin I silicon complex.

Conclusion

We have managed to develop a procedure for the analysis of micro amounts of complex porphyrin mixtures such as those found in geological materials. This analysis involves isolation and structural studies made possible by GC–MS combination instruments. Further refinement regarding the use of capillary glass columns for separation of complex closely related molecules is being studied. Methods are also being developed for detection of isomeric porphyrin materials that are impossible to differentiate using the conventional treatment. Geoporphyrin structures should provide a means by which ancient life can be traced and perhaps even provide information that will allow us to propose the biological precursors responsible for their deposition. The analogies will become much more meaningful when studies concerning contemporary biological sources, recent sediments, and fossil remnants from various ages provide information regarding the fate of porphyrin and chlorin pigments found in geological environments.

Acknowledgements: We thank Dr. W. E. Robinson (Bureau of Mines, Laramie, Wyo.), for the Green River Shale, Dr. P. A. Schenck (Koninklijke/Shell Exploratie in Produktie Laboratorium, Rijswijk, Holland) for the Boscan petroleum, and Prof. A. W. Johnson (Dept. of Chemistry, University of Nottingham, Nottingham, England) for supplying various porphyrin standards. We are also indebted to Dr. Melvin Calvin (Dept. of Chemistry, University of California, Berkeley, California) for useful discussions and to the National Aeronautics and Space Administration for their continued support of this project (NsG 101−61). One of us (Y.I.A.) is greatly indebted to the Saudi Arabian Government for support. We also thank Dr. R. L. Patterson for his kind offer of use of the GC−MS facilities at the Meat Research Institute in Langford, England.

References

[1]   E. W. Baker, T. F. Yen, J. P. Dickie, R. E. Rhodes and L. F. Clark (1967):
      Mass Spectrometry of Porphyrins. II. Characterization of Petroporphyrins: J. Am. Chem.
      Soc., 89, 3631.
[2]   E. W. Baker (1966): Mass Spectrometric Characterization of Petroporphyrins:
      J. Am. Chem. Soc., 88, 2311.
[3]   B. Nagy and U. Colombo (Ed.) (1967): "Fundamental Aspects of Petroleum
      Geochemistry", Elsevier Publishing Company, pp. 228–240.
[4]   M. Blumer and W. D. Snyder (1967): Porphyrins of High Molecular Weight in a Triassic
      Oil Shale: - Evidence by Gel Permeation Chromatography: Chem. Geol., 2, 35.
[5]   D. B. Boylan and M. Calvin (1967): Volatile Silicon Complexes of Etioporphyrin I:
      J. Am. Chem. Soc., 89, 5472.
[6]   Sister M. T. J. Murphy, A. McCormick, and G. Eglinton (1967): Perhydro-β-
      Carotene in the Green River Shale: Science, 157, 1040.

Discussion

W. G. Meinschein: Are you concerned about irreversible adsorption or exchange?

D. B. Boylan: We are concerned about the possibilities of exchange. This can and will be checked in the future as soon as we have solved some of the more immediate column problems. This phenomenon and concern may disappear as we go to glass capillary columns with higher phase loadings per surface area.

However, if this continues to be a problem then the use of a labeled porphyrin standard for initial active site coating may be neccessary.

A. L. Burlingame: Did I understand correctly that your column is conditioned using a standard silicon complex?

D. B. Boylan: Yes – Bis(trimethylsiloxy) Si^{IV} etioporphyrin I.

A. L. Burlingame: Do you know whether the silicon complex is decomposing on the column, thereby causing the adsorption (absorption)?

D. B. Boylan: The silicon complex is still intact, however the peripheral substituents or the trimethylsiloxy ligands may be altered by continuous heating at high temperature. Only the visible spectrum of the adsorbed material was checked, indicating that no major structural alteration of the silicon complex had taken place.

A. L. Burlingame: I would suggest attempting to run a mass spectrum putting the glass beads in the direct inlet to determine whether the silicon complex is intact.

D. B. Boylan: This could, and will be done!

A. L. Burlingame: Since the molecular ion distribution extends over homologous series of petroporphyrins, do you have any evidence which would rule out other functionality being present in these complex mixtures?

D. B. Boylan: No definite evidence. However, our synthetic procedure is selective for alkyl porphyrins. Thus, although porphyrins with carboxylic acid groups positioned around the macrocyclic ring periphery do form silicon complexes, the products do not seem to be volatile enough for gas chromatographic treatment. Studies are underway to determine the cause of and the chemical remedies for this unexpected result. We are also studying hydroxyl functionality to see if this leads to similar results.

Our immediate concern is to develop a method that can be applied to the separation and isolation of all expected geoporphyrins including oxygenated materials.

The functionality question will easily be answered when we can analyse individual porphyrins by high resolution mass spectrometry.

E. V. Whitehead: Do you have any data to show any selectivity of the methane sulphonic acid for a particular geoporphyrin.

D. B. Boylan: We do know that the etio-type porphyrin is quite resistant to the treatment used, however, the DPE type nucleus may not be as resistant and some artefacts may possibly form. However, evidence provided by Baker (personal communication) seems to indicate resistance of the DPE type molecule to degradation. I am not positive that this is the case and do intend to do reproducibility studies in the future.

W. Heller: What about metal complexes of porphyrins?

D. B. Boylan: We have not bothered to determine the metals present in the complexed fraction of total geoporphyrins. Since our aim was to develop techniques for separation and classification of the geoporphyrin materials, the total crude petroleum was treated with methane suphonic acid at 105 °C in order to effect demetalation.

However, I do think initial separation into metal complex fractions (i.e. each fraction containing the same metal complexing agent) followed by porphyrin distribution comparison of these fractions will be a worth while investigation.

Etude de la repartition dans un petrole brut des n-paraffines C par C de C_1 à C_{40} à l'aide des tamis moleculaires 5 Å et de la C. P. G.

Madeleine Fabre, Nicole J. Guichard-Loudet et Jeannine G. Roucache

Institut Francais du Pétrole
Rueil-Malmaison, France

The aim of this paper is to propose an analytic process for making a quantitative C-by-C analysis of the n-paraffins in a crude oil. Depending on the distillate cut examined, the analytic technique differs.

In the range from C_{10} to C_{16}, the n-paraffins are analyzed by G. P. C. in a capillary column (SE-30). A detailed description is given of the operating conditions which vary according to the carbon range considered. From nC_{10} to nC_{12} the analysis is done directly on the crude distillate cut. For cuts in the C_{12} to C_{14} and the C_{14} to C_{16} range, the analysis is done on saturated hydrocarbon fractions.

For cuts above C_{15} the n-paraffins are isolated from the narrow saturated-hydrocarbon fractions (C_{15} to C_{19}, C_{19} to C_{22}, C_{22} to C_{25} and C_{25} +) by being inserted in 5-Å molecular sieves, recovered after the sieves have been attacked by FH acid, and analyzed by G. P. C. with scaled temperatures.

The analysis is quantitative from nC_{15} to nC_{25}. Beyond this the vaporization of the sample is incomplete under the injection temperature conditions practiced (310 °C). The last identifiable peak is nC_{40}.

To conclude, the geochemical value of this analytic processes is demonstrated by applications to two crudes from the northern Sahara.

La présente communication a pour but de proposer un processus analytique permettant l'analyse quantitative dans un brut pétrolier, des n-paraffines C par C. Suivant la coupe de distillat étudiée, la technique analytique diffère.

Dans la gamme C_{10}- C_{16}, les n-paraffines sont analysées par C. P. G. sur colonne capillaire (SE-30). Nous décrivons en détail les conditions opératoires qui varient suivant la gamme de carbone considérée.

— de nC_{10} à nC_{12}, l'analyse est faite directement sur la coupe de distillat du brut;

— pour les coupes (C_{12} – C_{14}), (C_{14} – C_{16}), l'analyse est faite sur les fractions d'hydrocarbures saturés.

Dans la gamme $> C_{15}$, les n-paraffines sont isolées des fractions étroites d'hydro-carbures saturés (C_{15} – C_{19}, C_{19} – C_{22}, C_{22} – C_{25}, C_{25} +) par insertion dans des tamis moléculaires 5 Å, récupérées après attaque des tamis à l'acide HF, et analy-sées par C. P. G. avec programmation de température.

L'analyse est quantitative de nC_{15} à nC_{25}, au-delà, la vaporisation de l'échantillon est incomplète; dans les conditions de température d'injection pratiquées (310 °C), le dernier pic identifiable est nC_{40}.

En conclusion, pour montrer l'intérêt géochimique de ce processus analytique, nous l'appliquons à 2 bruts du Nord-Sahara.

I. Introduction

En vue de donner la répartition pondérale des n-paraffines carbone par carbone d'un brut pétrolier dans la gamme $C_{10} - C_{40}$, nous nous sommes proposé de comparer les différentes techniques qui permettent actuellement d'atteindre ce but, de mettre en relief les avantages et les inconvénients de chacune, de retenir le processus analytique qui nous semblera résoudre de la façon la plus satisfaisante ce problème analytique.

Nous avons choisi, d'une part comme limite inférieure n = 10, car on détermine facilement les n-paraffines de C_1 à C_{10} par C. P. G. et d'autre part, comme limite supérieure n = 40 correspondant à la limite d'investigation des techniques physiques actuelles.

Les techniques confrontées sont les suivantes:

— analyse directe des n-paraffines dans une fraction de distillat ou dans une fraction d'hydrocarbures saturés, par chromatographie en phase gazeuse sur colonne capillaire;

— analyse par chromatographie en phase gazeuse, des n-paraffines pures, isolées d'une fraction d'hydrocarbures saturés par insertion sur tamis moléculaires 5 Å.

Dans le présent travail nous décrivons les trois modes opératoires. Nous appliquons chacune des 3 techniques à l'analyse des n-paraffines carbone par carbone d'un brut pétrolier dans la gamme C_{10} +. Nous comparons les résultats obtenus, discutons de leur validité et nous proposons un processus analytique permettant d'analyser dans les meilleures conditions les n-paraffines de C_{10} à C_{40}, dans un brut pétrolier.

Nous montrons l'intérêt géochimique de cette technique en donnant la courbe de répartition des n-paraffines de deux bruts du Nord Sahara.

II. Analyse directe par C. P. G. des n-paraffines dans une coupe large de distillat ($C_{10} - C_{25}$) ou sur l'huile brute

Nous avons utilisé déjà en 1966 [1] les possibilités de séparation par chromatographie en phase gazeuse sur des huiles brutes, pour différencier des bruts d'origines diverses. Cette méthode nous amenait à grouper les prélèvements apparaissant identiques et à limiter ainsi le nombre de distillations (opérations longues et coûteuses).

Ces premiers essais faits sur des colonnes remplies (colonne de 1 m de long, 3 mm de φ int. remplissage: silicone SE 52 (15 % sur Firebrick) en programmation de température de 60 °C à 280 °C) avaient permis de localiser les n-paraffines jusqu'en C 30 ou 32. Nous avons amélioré la séparation en utilisant une colonne capillaire "Perkin Elmer" aux parois couvertes de silicone SE 30, le diviseur de flux à l'entrée de la colonne a été préalablement testé et ne montre aucune sélectivité décelable de C_6 à C_{20}.

Les conditions opératoires sont les suivantes:

Appareil	Chromatographe GIRDEL
Détecteur	Ionisation de flamme
Colonne	Col. capillaire Perkin Elmer
	(silicone SE 30). Long. 50 m.
	ϕ int 0,25 mm
Gaz porteur	Azote (pression en tête de colonne
	2 kg/cm^2)
Quantité introduite	0,5 μl
Diviseur d'entrée	1/10 environ
Température injecteur	280 °C
Température détecteur	280 °C

Programme de température du four: Isotherme 35 °C jusqu' à l'élution du n-octane (15 minutes environ)

Programmation à 2°/minute

T °C finale: 240 °C maintenue jusqu'à l'élution des derniers constituants.

Durée de l'élution jusqu'en nC 27 – 2 heures environ.

Calcul des teneurs en n-paraffines

Les chromatogrammes obtenus sont intégrés aussi soigneusement que possible: les n-paraffines sont repérées dans les cas douteux par addition de n-paraffines aux produits analysés (cas des premiers termes $<$ C 9 et aussi des isoprénoïdes au niveau des $C_{17} - C_{18} - C_{19}$).

Les surfaces sont rapportées à la surface totale ce qui donne les % en poids dans l'échantillon considéré, sauf pour le brut où il faut tenir compte du résidu non distillable.

Des étalonnages faits avec des mélanges de n-paraffines de C_6 à C_{20} ont donné des coefficients de réponse qui diffèrent au maximum de 10 %.

Le tableau 1 A montre qu'en programmation de température l'accord est meilleur qu'en opération isotherme.

Application

Nous avons appliqué cette technique à l'analyse des n-paraffines carbone par carbone:

1. dans un brut pétrolier – cf Figure 1
2. dans la coupe de distillat 100–410 °C (n $C_{10} - C_{25}$) de ce même brut – cf Figure 2
3. dans la coupe de distillat 100–336 °C (n $C_{10} - C_{19}$) cf Figure 3
4. dans la coupe de distillat 60–255 °C ($C_7 - C_{14}$) cf Figure 4.

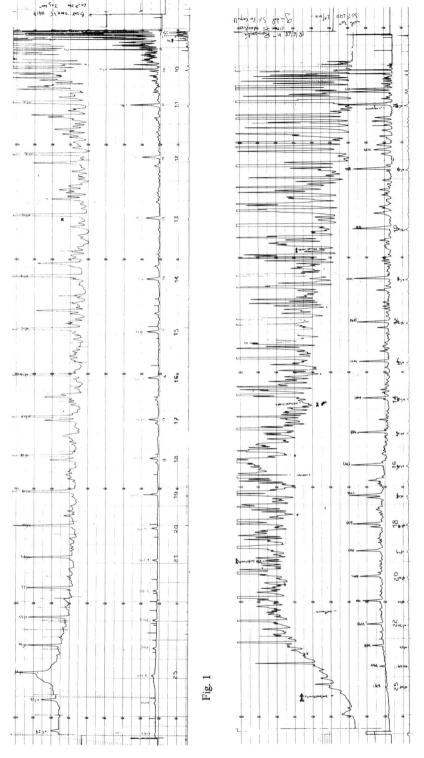

Fig. 1

Fig. 2

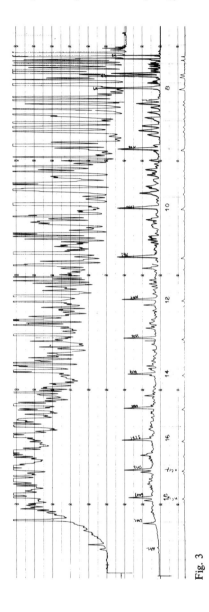

Fig. 3

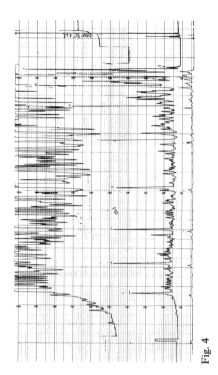

Fig. 4

Chromatogrammes de coupes plus ou moins larges de brut pétrolier (Brut du Nord-Sahara)

Analyse par C.P.G. capillaire

Fig. 1. Brut total
Fig. 2. Coupe 100–410 °C
Fig. 3. Coupe 100–336 °C
Fig. 4. Coupe de distillat 60–255 °C

Tableau 1 A. Correspondance % poids – % surface – analyse de n-paraffines dans des coupes plus ou moins larges de brut pétrolier.

n. p	% pds pesés	% surface isoth. 170 °C	% pds/% surface	% surface Programm	% pds/% surface
nC_6	14,4	12,1	1,16	14,5	1,00
nC_8	15,0	17,3	0,88	15,8	0,95
nC_{10}	15,9	17,1	0,94	16,5	0,96
nC_{12}	15,7	16,4	0,97	16,1	0,98
nC_{14}	16,7	16,8	0,99	16,7	1,00
nC_{16}	16,9	16,1	1,05	15,6	1,07
nC_{20}	5,4	4,3	1,25	4,9	1,10

Tableau 1 B. Correspondance % poids – % surface – analyse de coupes étroites d'hydrocarbures saturés.

T °C isotherme 100 °C	T °C isotherme 110 °C	T° programmée (1°,5/mn 110–160
nC_9 % pds/% surf. 1,02	nC_{11} % pds/% surf. 1,02	nC_{13} % pds/% surf. 1,07
nC_{10} % pds/% surf. 1,00	nC_{12} % pds/% surf. 1,04	nC_{14} % pds/% surf. 1,09
nC_{11} % pds/% surf. 1,02	nC_{13} % pds/% surf. 1,07	nC_{16} % pds/% surf. 1,12

Tableau 1 C. Reproductibilité et rendement des séparations des n-p par insertion sur tamis mol. 5 Å

Coupes	% iso + cyclo-paraffines		% n-paraffines		total récupéré	
	Essai 1	Essai 2	Essai 1	Essai 2	Essai 1	Essai 2
$C_{12}-C_{14}$	69,6	70,9	17,9	17,2	87,5	88,1
$C_{14}-C_{16}$	78,9	77,9	17,6	17,5	96,5	95,4
$C_{16}-C_{19}$	83,1	82,4	16,3	16,1	99,4	98,5
$C_{19}-C_{22}$	85,1	84,4	14,8	14,7	99,9	99,1
$C_{22}-C_{25}$	85,1	85,2	13,6	13,5	99,7	99,7
$C_{25}+$	90,5	90,0	9,0	9,6	99,5	99,6

La résolution obtenue est excellente jusqu'en C_{25}, puisque sur un même chromatogramme on a dénombré 300 pics séparés de C_6 à C_{25} (Fig. 2). De même au niveau de nC_{17} et nC_{18} on détecte la présence de 2 constituants importants qui sont vraisemblablement des isoprènoides dont le pristane (2–6–10–14 tétraméthyl pentadécane) [2].

L'exploitation quantitative des chromatogrammes (cf. Fig. 5) constitue un problème délicat pour lequel il n'y a pas de solutions réellement satisfaisantes.

L'approximation la plus couramment utilisée en chromatographie gazeuse est d'assimiler les % surfaces aux % poids des produits correspondants, cette méthode est entachée de 3 erreurs essentielles:

1. les % obtenus sont ceux des produits élués du chromatographe. Or il y a dans une huile brute ou une large fraction de distillation du brut, un résidu qui subira

Analyse des n-paraffines carbone par carbone dans un brut pétrolier résultats quantitatifs

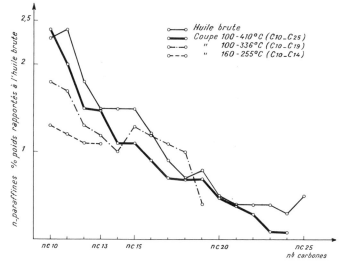

Fig. 5. Analyse par C.P.G. capillaire. Analyse directe sur des coupes plus ou moins larges de distillat

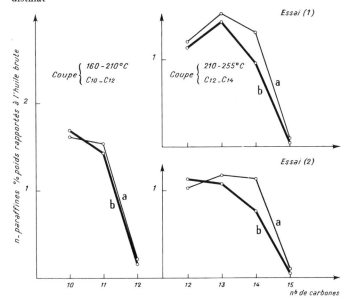

Fig. 6. Analyse par C.P.G. capillaire. Analyse sur des coupes étroites d'H. C. $<C_{16}$
Comparaison des résultats obtenus
a) sur la coupe de distillat total   o———o
b) sur la coupe désaromatisée   o———o

une vaporisation incomplète ou nulle dans les conditions de température d'injection déterminées précédemment.

2. même en employant un détecteur à ionisation de flamme (pour lequel l'approximation proposée est la moins fausse) le très large intervalle de nombre de carbones augmente les causes d'erreurs.

Si sur une coupe de 3 à 4 carbones on n'observe pas de variation sensible de réponse en masse, il n'en est pas de même sur une coupe de 15 carbones et plus [3].

3. la mesure des surfaces sur ces chromatogrammes complexes ne peut être réalisée que par intégration électronique. De plus les pics dessinés ne sont pas complètement séparés, ce qui rend imprécis tout type d'intégration.

III. Analyse par C. P. G. des fractions d'hydrocarbures saturés

Suivant une méthode déjà appliquée [4] nous avons d'abord fait des essais de dosages totaux des n—paraffines, par adsorption sur tamis moléculaires 5 Å en tête d'une colonne de chromatographie gazeuse; les résultats sont assez bons, mais on obtient difficilement une régénération du tamis sur place et l'étalonnage est à refaire pour chaque série d'analyses.

Nous avons remplacé ce dosage parfois délicat par un dosage purement chromato-graphique, en utilisant la séparation maximale offerte par la CPG. Nous avons utilisé le même appareillage que pour les coupes larges mais en température isother-me pour les coupes les plus légères ou avec des programmes courts pour les coupes moyennes et lourdes.

Conditions opératoires

Appareil GIRDEL à ionisation de flamme
Colonne capillaire SE 30 (50 m long, 0,25 ϕ mm int)
Gaz Porteur Azote
Division d'entrée 1/10 environ
Quantité introduite 0,5 μl
Intégrateur Infotronic CRS 11 HS B Magnetic tape Recorder.

Dans le tableau 2, sont rassemblés les paramètres caractéristiques de chaque coupe.

Des étalonnages faits sur des mélanges de n-paraffines 3 par 3 nous ont donné des variations de réponses très faibles (cf tableau 1 B). Aussi, ici encore, nous assimi-lons les % poids aux % surfaces des pics intégrés par un intégrateur électronique.

Pour obtenir une détermination précise, il est préférable dans les gammes de carbone $> C_{12}$, de travailler sur les coupes de distillation désaromatisées par une séparation sur silicagel type FIA [5].

Des essais comparés ont été faits sur des coupes $(C_{10} - C_{11})$ et $(C_{12} - C_{14})$ cf Figure 6. On observe de nettes interférences sur les n-paraffines de la coupe 210—255 °C en particulier pour nC_{13} et nC_{14}.

Tableau 2

Coupe de distillation	Température Injecteur Détecteur	Température de la colonne	Pression de gaz vecteur	Paraffines analysées
Fraction (160–210 °C) $C_{10}-C_{12}$	230 °C	isotherme 100 °C	0,9 kg/cm^2	nC_9 à nC_{13}
Fraction (210–255 °C) $C_{12}-C_{14}$	250 °C	isotherme 110 °C	0,9 kg/cm^2	nC_{11} à nC_{15}
Fraction (255–290 °C) $C_{14}-C_{16}$	280 °C	programmée de 110 °C à 160 °C à 1 °/minute	2,2 kg/cm^2	nC_{14} à nC_{17}
Fraction (290–330 °C) $C_{16}-C_{19}$	280 °C	programmée de 140 °C à 180 °C à 1 °/minute	2,2 kg/cm^2	nC_{16} à nC_{20}
Fraction (330–375 °C) $C_{19}-C_{22}$	300 °C	programmée de 160 °C à 190 °C	2,2 kg/cm^2	nC_{19} à nC_{23}

Application

Le brut précédemment étudié par CPG sur les coupes de distillat plus ou moins larges, fut fractionné en coupes étroites de 2 à 3 carbones et chaque coupe fut désaromatisée par chromatographie liquide sur silicagel [5]. Chaque fraction d'hydrocarbures saturés fut analysée par la technique chromatographique décrite précédemment (cf tableau 2).

Les figures 7, 8 et 9 montrent que l'on obtient une assez bonne résolution jusqu'au C_{16}, ce qui permet une analyse quantitative correcte des n-paraffines dans cette gamme; la figure 10 montre une bonne concordance des résultats dans la gamme $C_{10} - C_{13}$ entre l'analyse effectuée sur la coupe de distillat total et l'analyse effectuée sur les coupes d'hydrocarbures saturés. On remarque dans la coupe de distillat une interférence en C_{13} due aux aromatiques.

Au-delà des C_{15} (coupe 290–335 °C) l'analyse quantitative par C. P. G. n'est plus possible.

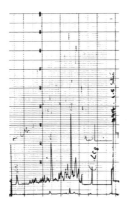

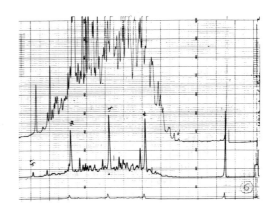

Fig. 7   Fig. 8

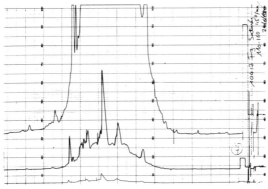

**Chromatogrammes
de coupes étroites
d'H. C. saturés**

Fig. 7
Coupe $C_{10} - C_{12}$
(160–210°C)

Fig. 8
Coupe $C_{12} - C_{14}$
(210--255 °C)

Fig. 9
Coupe $C_{14} - C_{16}$
(255–290 °C)

Fig. 9

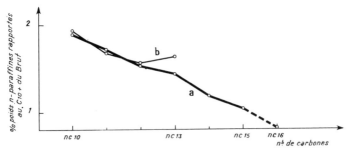

Analyse des n-paraffines carbone par carbone dans un brut pétrolier résultats quantitatifs

Fig. 10.   Analyse par C.P.G. capillaire. Analyse sur des coupes étroites d'H. C. $<C_{16}$
Comparaison des résultats obtenus
a) sur des coupes étroites d'H. C. saturés (gamme $C_{10} - C_{16}$) (160–290 °C)
b) sur la coupe de distillat total ($C_{10} - C_{14}$)

IV. Insertion sur tamis moléculaires 5 Å, récupération et analyse des normales paraffines, carbone par carbone dans la gamme C_{12} – C_{40}. Mode opératoire

Ce problème (séparation des n-paraffines) fut traité par de nombreux auteurs. Les méthodes classiques, cristallisation fractionnée, méthode à l'urée etc. . . n'ont pas retenu notre attention car ces techniques sont longues, les séparations se font par paliers successifs et les conditions opératoires varient suivant la gamme de nombre de carbone dans laquelle on opère. La séparation n-paraffines (iso + cyclo) n'est jamais parfaite et le bilan est toujours déficitaire.

De ce fait, nous avons retenu les techniques utilisant les propriétés des tamis moleculaires (propriétés rappelées par R. Petit et R. Pallaud) [6, 7] soit la possibilité d'insertion des n-paraffines dans les tamis moléculaires 5 Å; les gammes dans lesquelles les auteurs ont généralement travaillé sont:

— coupes très légères [8] C_5 – C_{11}, peu d'intérêt car par chromatographie en phase gazeuse, on obtient de très bons résultats.
— coupes légères C_{15} – C_{18} [9], C_{15} – C_{20} [10], C_{14} – C_{20} [11]
— fractions lourdes jusqu'à C_{31} [12, 13, 14].

Ce mode opératoire comprend deux phases:
— l'insertion des n-paraffines dans le tamis 5 Å,
— la récupération des n-paraffines insérées dans le tamis 5 Å.

Après avoir testé plusieurs méthodes d'insertion, nous avons retenu et modifié la méthode préconisée par "J. G. O'Connor, F. H. Burow, M. S. Norris" [14] (insertion à reflux avec l'iso-octane) avec laquelle nous avons obtenu les meilleurs résultats (insertion complète des n-paraffines).

De même, pour la récupération des normales – paraffines nous avons essayé plusieurs techniques et nous avons retenu celle décrite par "G. Eglinton, M.P. Scott, T. Belsky, A. L. Burlingame, W. Richter et M. Calvin" [10]. Le tamis 5 Å est attaqué à l'acide fluorhydrique en présence de $C_6 H_6$ à chaud. Il est nécessaire d'agiter. C'est la seule technique qui permette de récupérer avec un bon bilan toutes les n-paraffines insérées.

Insertion des normales paraffines

Dans un ballon à fond rond mettre 40 g de tamis moléculaire 5 Å. Suivant les coupes étudiées les proportions en poids à respecter entre la prise d'essai et le tamis 5 Å sont résumées dans le tableau 3 ci-après.

Tableau 3

Carbone	Produit	Tamis 5 Å	Solvant
C_{12} – C_{22}	1	10	iso-octane
C_{22} – C_{25}	1	10	Benzène
> C_{25}	1	100	Benzène

Activer le tamis sous vide pendant 4 heures à une température voisine de 400 °C, pression atmosphérique [(vide = 0,4 mm Hg; t °C = 170) conditions donnant le meilleur rendement à l'insertion].

Introduire le solvant sous vide, ainsi que la prise d'essai (4 grammes d'hydrocarbures saturés pesés exactement [1])).

Mettre à reflux 100 heures (temps permettant l'insertion d'un pourcentage maximum de n-paraffines). Pour éviter les pertes durant le reflux, l'emploi d'un réfrigérant à serpentin, de 50 cm de haut et d'un piège à H. C. léger à la sortie du réfrigérant, sont indispensables.

Filtrer la solution et mettre le tamis 5 Å dans un soxhlet.

Laver au même solvant pendant 4 heures.

Filtrer la solution et concentrer les 2 filtrats qui contiennent les iso + cyclo paraffines.

Sécher le tamis sous hotte à l'air libre.

Récupération des normales paraffines

Le tamis séché est attaqué à l'acide fluorhydrique à 24 % en présence de l'benzéne dans les proportions suivantes:

10,5 g de tamis; 70 cc HF à 24 %; 25 cc C_6H_6

Chauffer le tamis avec l'acide fluorhydrique dans un récipient en teflon au bain marie;

Agiter magnétiquement pendant 20 minutes;

Ajouter 100 cc de benzène (pour 40 g de tamis)

Continuer à chauffer au bain marie en agitant pendant une 1/2 heure.

Décanter à chaud dans une ampoule. La solution aqueuse est séparée de la solution benzénique par un voile grisâtre. Récupérer ce voile et le laver plusieurs fois au benzène (il faut recommencer plusieurs fois l'agitation magnétique de la solution aqueuse avec le benzène).

La solution benzénique contenant les normales paraffines est passée sur une colonne de carbonate de sodium préalablement lavée au C_6H_6.

Evaporer la solution. Les normales-paraffines sont légèrement jaunes.

Passer les normales paraffines sur silicagel activé pendant 4 heures à 140 °C afin d'obtenir des normales paraffines purifiées (blanches) (silicagel 100–200 mesh. : 10 g dans une colonne de 30 cm de hauteur et de 15 mm de diamètre).

---

[1] Les hydrocarbures saturés ont été séparés de la coupe de distillat par chromatographie liquide sur silicagel [5].

Dosage des normales paraffines par chromatographie en phase gazeuse. Conditions opératoires:

- chromatographe avec détecteur à ionisation de flamme type AEROGRAPH HFY 1200;
- gaz vecteur AZOTE, débit 20 ml/minute;
- débit de la pompe à air 300 ml/minute;
- température programmée de 100 °C à 300 °C à raison de 4°/mn
- température de l'injecteur: 250 °C − 260 °C; (pour C > 25 T °C ≃ 330)
- température du détecteur: 280 °C; (pour C > 25 T °C ≃ 300)
- colonne: longueur 5 feet ≅ (1,50 m)
    diamètre 1/8 inch
    support 10 % de SE 52 sur AEROPAK 30, 100/120, stabilisation
    12 heures à 350 °C avec un débit de gaz vecteur de 20 ml/minute.

Application

La méthode permet une insertion bien sélective des n-paraffines comme le montrent les figures 11, 12 et 13; en effet une analyse chromatographique (suivant le mode opératoire décrit chapitres II et III) montre que la fraction de n-paraffines isolée est pure, et que la coupe (iso + cycloparaffines) ne contient plus de n-paraffines (contrôle possible jusqu'en C_{30}).

- La reproductibilité de la séparation est très satisfaisante (cf tableau 1 C).
- Cette technique s'effectue avec un bon rendement dans la gamme > C 15 (cf tableau 1 C). Pour les fractions < C 15, le bilan est toujours déficitaire; on a intérêt, dans cette gamme à traîter des coupes assez larges. La figure 14 montre en effet que les pertes subies durant l'insertion de coupes très étroites d'hydro-carbures saturés (1 carbone) dont les points d'ébullition sont compris entre 210 et 294 °C (C 12 à C 16), sont plus importantes que lorsque l'on insère dans la même gamme des coupes de 2 à 3 carbones [1]).

- Cette séparation des hydrocabures saturés en une fraction de n-paraffines et une fraction d'iso et cycloparaffines, nous a permis de vérifier la valeur des renseigne-ments donnés par la spectrométrie de masse [15] lors de l'analyse d'une fraction d'hydrocarbures saturés totaux. Le tableau 4 compare les résultats de l'analyse par SM d'une fraction d'hydrocarbures saturés ($C_{20} − C_{25}$) et l'analyse de la fraction (iso + cycloparaffines) isolée de ces hydrocarbures saturés après insertion des n-paraffines. On constate que les résultats sont assez voisins.

---

[1]) Les pertes ont lieu durant l'attaque fluorhydrique à chaud, et l'évaporation des solvants.

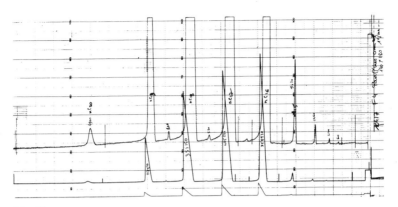

Fig. 11

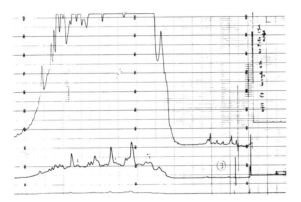

Fig. 12

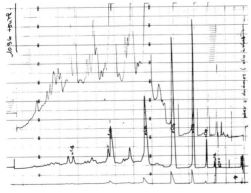

Fig. 13

Efficacit de la séparation des n-paraffines par insertion sur tamis 5 Å

Fig. 11
n-p isolées

Fig. 12
fraction (iso. + cyclo. p) + n-p pures

Fig. 13
fraction (iso. + cyclo. p) + n-p pures

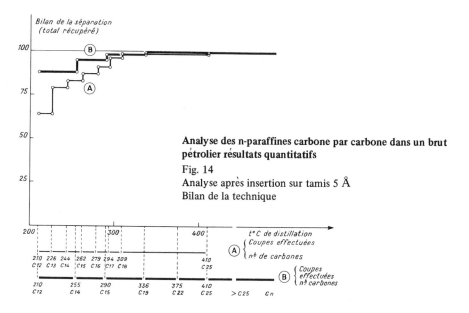

Analyse des n-paraffines carbone par carbone dans un brut pétrolier résultats quantitatifs

Fig. 14

Analyse après insertion sur tamis 5 Å
Bilan de la technique

Tableau 4. Analyse par spectrométrie de masse (S. M.)
1) des hydrocarbures saturés totaux.
2) des hydrocarbures saturés après insertion sur tamis 5 Å.

% volume		Coupe hydrocarbures saturés $C_{22}-C_{25}$	Coupe (iso + cyclop) $C_{22}-C_{25}$
Paraffines	à prédom-iso	47,01 n-p = 15,10 (ins. 5 Å)	
		isop = 31,91 (par diff)	30,72
Naphtènes	à 1 noyau	17,61	19,50
	à 2 noyaux	14,82	13,66
	à 3 noyaux	7,70	6,80
	à 4 noyaux	7,08	6,93
	à 5 noyaux	2,80	3,25
	à 6 noyaux	1,29	0,95
Monoaromatiques		1,68	2,06

En résumé

Ce mode opératoire s'applique à des coupes étroites (2 à 3 carbones) d'hydrocarbures saturés, vierges d'hydrocarbures aromatiques (ou teneurs en traces) dans une gamme allant des C_{16} aux C_{40}.

Dans l'intervalle $C_{16} - C_{25}$ on détermine:

— par C. P. G. la répartition C par C en n-paraffines (cf Fig. 15).
— par SM la composition détaillée de la coupe (iso + cyclo-paraffines) en isoparaffine
et naphtènes.

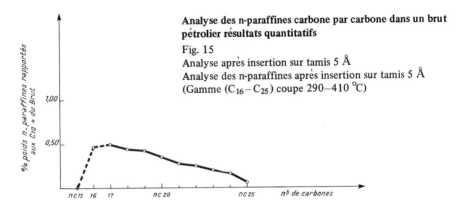

Analyse des n-paraffines carbone par carbone dans un brut pétrolier résultats quantitatifs

Fig. 15
Analyse après insertion sur tamis 5 Å
Analyse des n-paraffines après insertion sur tamis 5 Å
(Gamme $(C_{16} - C_{25})$ coupe 290–410 °C)

Dans l'intervalle $> C_{25}$ on peut montrer la répartition qualitative des n-paraffines
C par C de C_{25} à C_{40} (cf Figure 16).

Mais nous ne pensons pas que l'analyse quantitative soit possible. Dans cette gamme,
en effet, les méthodes physiques (C. P. G. – S. M.) ne permettent pas de vérifier
l'efficacité de la séparation, et nous ne savons pas si l'insertion des n-paraffines est
totale. Sur la figure 16 on constate que l'insertion d'une coupe d'hydrocarbures
saturés $> C_{25}$ (provenant du résidu de la distillation d'un brut jusqu'en C_{25}) fournit
une fraction de n-paraffines allant de C_{22} à C_{42} avec prédominance de C_{26} à C_{35}.
Après fractionnement de ces hydrocarbures saturés par distillation moléculaire en
5 coupes, et insertion des n-paraffines de chaque coupe, nous n'avons obtenu, là
encore, que des n-paraffines dans la gamme $C_{22} - C_{40}$. Ou bien la vaporisation de
la fraction à 300 °C n'est par totale lors de l'analyse par C. P. G., ou bien il y a une
limite d'insertion des n-paraffines pour $n > 40$.

V. Conclusion

Les essais analytiques précédents montrent:

1) que l'analyse directe des n-paraffines par C.P. G. capillaire dans un brut pétrolier
(soit sur le brut total, soit sur des coupes de distillat plus ou moins larges) ne permet
pas des résultats quantitatifs. Il y a d'une part une trop forte interférence des aromatiques et d'autre part, une vaporisation incomplète ou nulle du produit injecté
(c'est le cas des fractions à point d'ébullition > 290 °C). Seule la coupe légère
$C_{10} - C_{12}$ peut être analysée directement.

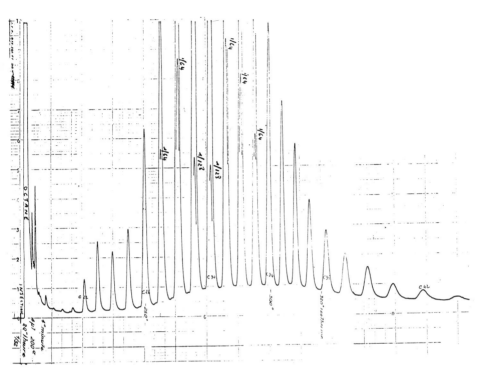

Fig. 16. N-paraffines d'un résidu > 410 °C

Echantillon: Paraffines C$_{20}$ –C$_{44}$

Origine: 338

Opérateur: L J   Date: 30-12-66

Aérograph. modèle: HYF 1 III 1200–1

Colonne: 5′ 1/8 inox (Super)

10 % SE S 2 Aeropak 30 100/120

T^0 colonne: 200–320   T^0 détecteur: 310°

T^0 injecteur: 320°   T^0 collecteur:

Programme de T^0: 4° minute

Gaz porteur: N$_2$ Débit: 30 ml/minute

Volume injecté: 4 μl

Enregisteur: Honeywell

Déroulement: 20″/heure

Sensibilité: 1/32–1/64 et 1/128 Hz 30 ml/minute

2) que l'analyse des n-paraffines par C. P. G. capillaire dans des fractions d'hydrocarbures saturés préparés à partir de coupes étroites de distillat désaromatisées par chromatographie liquide sur silicagel, permet une analyse quantitative dans la gamme C$_{10}$ – C$_{15}$ (150 °C–290 °C).

3) que l'analyse par C. P. G. des n-paraffines pures extraîtes des fractions d'hydrocarbures saturés après insertion dans des tamis moléculaires 5 Å, est possible avec un rendement de 100 % dans la gamme > C$_{15}$ (température d'ébullition > 290 °C).

De ce fait, le processus analytique qui permet l'analyse quantitative des n-paraffines dans un brut pétrolier est le suivant:

– de nC_{10} à nC_{12} (150 °C–210 °C) analyse par C. P. G. capillaire directement sur la fraction de distillat, dans les conditions opératoires décrites au chapitre 1.
– de nC_{12} à nC_{15} (210 °C–290 °C) analyse par C. P. G. capillaire de la fraction d'hydrocarbures saturés dans les conditions opératoires décrites au chapitre 2.
– dans la gamme $> C_{15}$, analyse par C. P. G. des n-paraffines pures isolées par insertion.

Pour montrer quel intérêt géochimique peut présenter ce processus analytique, nous l'avons appliqué à 2 bruts du Nord Sahara: le brut A d'origine dévonienne et gothlandienne, le brut B d'origine gothlandienne uniquement.

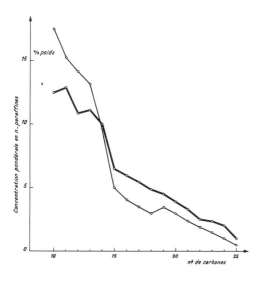

Fig. 17

Répartition pondérale des concentrations en n-paraffines de 2 bruts sahariens (Nord-Sahara)

Σ n-p $C_{10} - C_{25} = 100\ \%$

On constate (Fig. 17) que le brut A est moins riche en n-paraffines de C_{10} à C_{13} et plus riche de C_{13} à C_{20}. D'après les données géologiques, ceci peut-être dû:

– *soit à une évolution plus importante de la matière organique dans la roche mère* et à l'action catalytique des argiles de cette roche mère,
– *soit à l'influence du réservoir* lors de la migration secondaire (il y aurait eu une insertion préférentielle des n-paraffines à chaînes courtes dans le réservoir triasique plus argileux).

Remerciement: Nous remercions les Directions Exploration de la Compagnie française des Pétroles (Algérie) (C. F. P. A.) et de la Société nationale des Pétroles Algériens (S. N. REPAL) qui nous ont fourni les échantillons qui ont servi à la mise au point de cette technique.

Bibliographie

[1]   Guichard, N., août 1966: Différenciation des pétroles bruts par C. P. G. Rapport intérieur IFP n° 13 437, août 1966.

[2]   Bendoraitis, J. G., Brown, B. L., Hepner, L. S., 1962: Anal. Chem. 1962, 34 n°1, p. 49.

[3]   Dietz, W. A., 1967: Jof. G. C., 5, n°2, fev 1967, p. 68–70.

[4]   Whitham, B. T., 1962: Gas Chromatography, Academic Press, Ed. J. E. Callen et M. D. Weiss, New York 1962 p. 371.

[5]   Boulet, R., Guichard-Loudet, N., Henrion, P., Poulet, M., Raynal, M., Roucache, J., 1968: Analyse détaillée d'un brut par C. P. G., SM et RMN. Application aux problèmes géochimiques. Revue IFP, 23, n°3, mars 1968 p. 315.

[6]   Petit, R., Pallaud, R., 1964: Les tamis moléculaires: Application à la séparation des hydrocarbures. Chimie analytique, 49, 1964.

[7]   Petit, R., 1965: Les sacs moléculaires en chimie organique. Chimie analytique, 47, n°12, dec. 1965.

[8]   Eggersten, F. T., Groennings, S., 1961: Détermination of small amounts of n-paraffins by molecular sieve gas chromatography. Analytical chemistry, 33, n°9, august 1961.

[9]   Bendoraitis, J. B., Brown, B. L., Hepner, L. S., 1963: Isolation and identification of isofrenoids in petroleum Congrès Mondial du Pétrole. Francfort, juin 1963.

[10] Eglinton, G., Scott, M. P., Belsky, I., Burlingame, A. L., Richter, W., Calcin, M., 1964: Occurence of isoprenoid alkanes in a precambrien sediment Advances in organics geochimistry 1964.

[11] Dean, R. A., Whitehead, E. V., 1963: The composition of high boiling petroleum distillates and residue. Congres mondial du pétrole Francfort juin 1963.

[12] Welte, D. H., 1964: Nichtflüchtige Kohlenwasserstoffe in Keruproben des Devons und Karbons der Bohrung Münsterland 1. Geol. Rheinld. 12, dec. 1964.

[13] Bestouggef, 1963: Dosage des paraffines normales par tamis moléculaires (non publié).

[14] O'Connor, J. G., Burow, F. H., Norris, N. S.: Determination of normal-paraffins in C_{20} to C_{32} Paraffin waxes by molecular sieve adsorption. Analytical chemistry, 34, 1962.
      Molecular sieve adsorption, application to hydrocarbon type analysis. Analytical chemistry, 32, 701, 1960.

[15] Hood, A., O'Neal, M. J.: Statues of application of mass spectrometry to heavy oil analyses. Preprint congress IP university of London, Senate House, 24–26 sept. 1958. Pergamon Press.

Discussion

P. A. Schenck: You have told us that you concentrate the n-alkanes by means of molecular sieves. We have experienced that with very small samples, as is the case with e.g. rock extracts, no good separation between n-alkanes and iso-alkanes cyclanes from mixtures of saturated hydrocarbons occurs with molecular sieves. Do you have any experience with small samples?

J. Roucaché: La technique utilisée est applicable avec un tres bon rendement, une bonne efficacité, à des coupes étroites de HC saturés (coupes C_{14}–C_{15}; C_{15}–C_{19}; C_{19}–C_{22}; C_{22}–C_{25}; $C > C_{25}$). Lorsque la gamme de C est trop importante, il y a une insertion préférentielle de certaines n-paraffines, le tamis semble d'ailleurs agir différemment d'un essai à l'autre, mais la fraction de n-paraffines isolées est pure (il n'y a pas d'iso et cycloparaffines). Ces constatations ont été faites:

1) – sur un échantillon standard pesé,
2) – sur un Brut: Gamme C_{10}–C_{25} de HC saturés.

Je pense que dans le cas d'un extrait de roche, l'opération peut se faire en deux temps:

1) Insertion des n-paraffines après séparation des HC saturés,
2) Nouvelle insertion de la fraction (iso + cyclo paraffines) précédemment récupérée.

P. A. Schenck: Still one small direct question: What is the minimum amount of sample from which you isolated n-alkanes with molecular sieves?

J. Roucaché: Nous sommes toujours riches en échantillons et nous n'avons pas recherché à mettre au point une technique pour traiter de trés petites quantités notre échantillon le plus petit est environ 500 mg.

D. H. Welte: 1) The temperature of the injection point is very critical, because if the injection point is below a critical value (depending on the components that are analysed) some components may stay behind in the injection system.

2) The urea adduction technique seems to be superior over the molecular sieve technique especially for the very long chains of n-paraffins (above nC_{30}), because long chaing n-paraffins we had to desorb from the sieves.

J. Roucaché: 1) La température d'injection que nous avons utilisée est 300 °C. Pour T' = 300 °C nous n'avons pas trouvé sur le marché français, une qualité de septum qui résistait à ces températures. Pourriez vous me conseiller à ce sujet? Merci.

2) Je n'ai pas essayé les techniques à l'urée qui ne permettent pas d'isoler à 100 % toutes les n-paraffines d'une fraction de HC saturés.

The Predominance of the C_{22} n-Alkane in Rock Extracts

Pieter Alettinus Schenck [1])

Koninklijke/Shell Exploratie en Produktie Laboratorium,
Rijswijk, the Netherlands

In recent sediments, the odd-numbered n-alkanes predominate over the even-numbered ones in the range from C_{25} to C_{32}. Since this phenomenon has not been recorded in crude oils, the extracts showing this odd-predominance are not "crude-oil-like" and the sediments from which they are extracted are called "immature".

We found a predominance of the C_{22} n-alkane in extracts obtained from a large number of sediment samples ranging in age from Permian to Miocene. We think this predominance to be indicative of environmental conditions and/or the type of organisms originally present in the sediment.

To our knowledge, no such predominance has ever been observed in crude oils. This means that a n-C_{22} predominance should also be considered a criterion for "immaturity".

I. Introduction

Stevens, Bray and Evans (1956) were the first to report that, in extracts from recent sediments, odd-numbered high-molecular-weight n-alkanes predominate over the even-numbered ones. It has since become apparent that this odd predominance[2]) always occurs in the indigenous extracts of recent sediments.

Moreover, odd predominance has also been shown to be present in many living organisms, especially in terrestrial plants. Clark (1966) has given a comprehensive review of the literature data available on this subject up to the end of 1965.

No "odd predominance" higher than about 1.3 in crude oils has ever been recorded. It is now well established that in rock extracts odd predominance decreases with increasing depth, i.e. increasing temperature, and finally disappears. The composition of the extract, originally significantly different from that of a crude oil, becomes more and more "crude-oil-like" with increasing depth. Thus when the composition of an extract is not "crude-oil-like", as regards its n-alkane distribution the sediment from which it has been taken is termed "immature" (cf. Bray and Evans (1961), Philippi (1965, 1968)).

---

[1]) Present address: Delft University of Technology, Department of Chemistry, Delft, The Netherlands

[2]) "Odd-predominance" given as R-value, which is defined as $R_n = \dfrac{2 \times \% C_n}{\% C_{n-1} + \% C_{n+1}}$ with n = 27 or 29.

Now in work on oils and extracts specially concerned with these high-molecular-weight n-alkanes, our attention has been drawn to the fact that in many rock extracts n-C_{22} predominates over the neighbouring n-alkanes.

This phenomenon will be discussed below.

II. Experiments

Powdered rock samples were subjected to extraction with gasoline (boiling range 60–80 °C), diethyl ether or chloroform. The saturated hydrocarbons were isolated by adsorption chromatography on silica-alumina columns; the n-alkanes were preconcentrated by urea-adduction. The n-alkanes were analysed quantitatively by gas chromatography, the method used being either subtraction by molecular sieves (Schenck and Eisma (1964)) or dual-flame capillary GLC.

III. Results and Discussion

During the past ten years we have analysed several hundreds of rock extracts with special emphasis on the distribution of the high n-alkanes (range $C_{25} - C_{31}$). In the gas chromatograms of our "urea-adducts", we often observed a high peak with the retention time of n-C_{22}. Adsorption chromatography indicates that the compound giving rise to this peak belongs to the saturated hydrocarbons. Its behaviour in urea-adduction points to a straight-chain hydrocarbon. The latter was confirmed by infrared analysis of the compound, isolated by preparative scale gas chromatography. Its mass-spectrum leaves no doubt that its identity is that of n-C_{22}.

Contamination in the field by this particular compound n-C_{22}, in any case very improbable, can be fully excluded, since its predominance has been observed in samples taken by different geologists at different places at very different times.

Contamination in the laboratory can be excluded, too, because analyses by different operators on different apparatus with different charges of chemicals lead to reproducible results.

The presence of a n-C_{22} predominance[1]) has been mentioned implicitly in the literature (W.E. Robinson et al. (1965), Kvenvolden (1966)). No special attention was devoted to this phenomenon, however.

The following summarises the results we obtained after the analysis of some 450 rock extracts and some 250 crude oils.

1. A n-C_{22} predominance was found in extracts from samples of sediments ranging in age from Miocene to Permian. The occurrence is even rather frequent (see Fig. 1). The predominance, mostly showing values between 1.3 and 2.0, may

---

[1]) Expressed as $R_{22} = \dfrac{\% C_{22}}{\% C_{21} + \% C_{23}}$

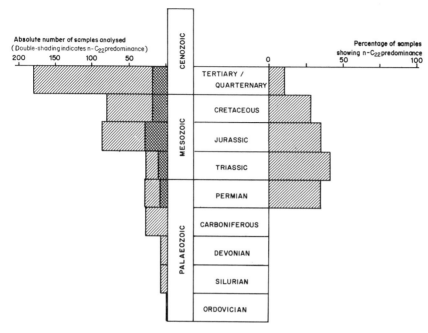

Fig. 1. Occurrence of n-C$_{22}$ Predominance in Rock extracts

Table 1. Examples of samples, the extracts of which show an "odd-predominance" and a "n-C$_{22}$-predominance"

Sample no.	Age	Country	depth in ft.	% C$_{org.}$ in extracted sample	% extract	R$_{27}$	R$_{29}$	R$_{22}$
Ni 214	Miocene or younger	Nigeria	6046–6195	1.21	0.071[1]	2.1	3.2	1.3
Ni 215	id	id	6999–7018	1.40	0.081[1]	2.6	2.7	1.4
Ni 216	id	id	8052–8090	1.78	0.068[1]	2.4	3.1	1.5
Ni 217	id	id	8903–8960	1.09	0.049[1]	1.4	2.1	1.7
Ni 218	id	id	9250–9297	1.60	0.085[1]	1.4	2.3	1.6
	Eocene (Green River)	USA	547–548	28.2	1.83[2]	2.9	4.3	1.3
	id	id	654–655	25.8	1.29[2]	4.0	4.0	1.3
Mou 1723	Cretaceous	France	Surface	1.30	0.01[3]	1.2	1.4	>1[4]

[1] extraction solvent : chloroform
[2] extraction solvent : diethyl ether
[3] extraction solvent : gasoline b.p. 60 °C–80 °C
[4] see footnote to table 2.

Table 2. Examples of samples, the extracts of which show a "n-C_{22}-predominance", but do not show an "odd-predominance"

Sample no.	Age	Country	depth in ft	% $C_{org.}$ in extracted sample	% extract	$R_{22} = \dfrac{\% \, C_{22}}{\% \, C_{21} + \% \, C_{23}}$
BIT 153	Lias δ/α	The Netherlands	8388	1.02	0.01[1]	$>$ 1[3]
SR 2059	Lias γ/δ	France	surface	0.96	0.01[1]	$>$ 1
BIT 204	Lias δ/ϵ	The Netherlands	1157–1164	0.33	0.01[1]	$>$ 1
SR 1409	Lias ϵ	Germany	surface	3.36	0.07[1]	$>$ 1
BIT 269	Lias ϵ	The Netherlands	5450	7.52	0.15[1]	$>$ 1
BIT 160	Lias ϵ/ζ	The Netherlands	3417	9.38	0.60[1]	$>$ 1
BIT 162	Lias ϵ/ζ	The Netherlands	3640	2.20	0.10[1]	$>$ 1
BIT 342	Triassic	Switzerland	surface	0.48	0.02[1]	3.5
BA 499	Triassic	Italy	surface	11.0	0.59[2]	1.5
BA 500B	Triassic	Italy	surface	31.6	0.95[2]	1.8
BA 502A	Triassic	Italy	surface	21.2	0.97[2]	1.8

[1] extraction solvent : gasoline b.p. 60 °C–80 °C

[2] extraction solvent : diethyl ether.

[3] the sign "$>$ 1" indicates that a n-C_{22}-predominance is distinctly present according to the gas chromatograms, but cannot be quantitatively expressed in a number owing to the method used

even rise to values as high as 16. It should be emphasised, however, that our samples were in no way statistically well distributed.

2. The n-C$_{22}$ predominance has never been encountered in crude oils.
3. The n-C$_{22}$ predominance may or may not occur simultaneously with an odd-predominance (see examples given in Tables 1 and 2). So extracts that are "crude-oil-like" as far as the absence of odd predominance in the range n-C$_{25}$ − n-C$_{31}$ is concerned, sometimes show this n-C$_{22}$ predominance.
4. Where series of samples from different depths have been analysed, the results do not point to a clear decrease in the n-C$_{22}$ predominance with increasing depth (temperature) (see table 1, Miocene, Nigeria). Nevertheless below a certain depth, it is to be expected that the predominance will disappear.

The results found can essentially be explained in two ways:

− this compound n-C$_{22}$ was deposited as such (as part of an organism) with the sediment;
− the compound was preferentially formed post-depositionally either by chemical or biochemical processes.

Considering the first explanation, it is interesting to note that Clark (1966), in his review mentioned before, gives examples showing that within the group of n-alkanes one n-alkane may be quantitatively outstanding (e.g. the odd-numbered C$_{11}$ − C$_{17}$ and C$_{27}$ − C$_{35}$ and even numbered C$_{16}$). The n-alkane C$_{22}$ is mentioned as slightly predominating in a very few cases of algae (Algae Cryptophyceae, Algae Skelotonema costalum and Algae Syracosphaera). This predominance is not pronounced enough to explain the predominance we have found in a number of rock extracts. These data suggest that organisms in which a strong predominance of n-C$_{22}$ occurs, may exist (or have existed).

Synsedimentation of a structurally closely related precursor − e.g. the n-C$_{22}$ alcohol − followed by a simple chemical process (reduction) is another possibility.

A post-depositional − non-biochemical − formation of n-alkanes through a kind of Kolbe-synthesis has been suggested by Sir Robert Robinson (1967). The C$_{22}$ n-alkane should then have been formed—according to this view − from the n-C$_{12}$-fatty acid. Since, however, the n-C$_{16}$ − and n-C$_{18}$ − fatty acids occur much more frequently in nature than the n-C$_{12}$ acid, a significant predominance of the n-alkanes n-C$_{30}$ and n-C$_{34}$ is rather to be expected, at least in a number of cases. Such significant predominances have never been found, however. We therefore consider it rather unlikely that the formation of the C$_{22}$ n-alkane follows such a path.

A biochemical formation in the early stage of sedimentation cannot be precluded on account of the data available at the moment. Both in this case, as well as in the case of synsedimentary origin, the n-C$_{22}$ predominance should be the result of a biochemical process.

In conclusion, this n-C_{22} predominance may be explained in assuming either
1. the deposition in the sediment of a specific organism (or group of organisms) containing a predominating amount of n-C_{22},

and/or

2. an environment favourable for the occurrence of an organism (group of organisms) which produces in the sediment
    a. this predominating amount of the n-C_{22} n-alkane or
    b. an immediately structurally related precursor such as the n-C_{22} alcohol.

As yet, we have not been able to correlate this n-C_{22}-predominance with the occurrence of a special group of identifiable organisms.

As mentioned in the introduction, the disappearance of the "odd predominance" with increasing depth (i.e. temperature) indicates that diagenetic processes influence the n-alkane distribution. The occurrence of the n-C_{22} predominance shows that the n-alkane distribution can be also indicative of environmental conditions and/or the type of organisms originally present in the sediment.

When comparing the compositions of extracts with those of crude oils, we have to keep in mind that we have never found this n-C_{22} predominance in crude oils. Consequently, extracts showing this n-C_{22} predominance are not "crude-oil-like" in this respect. This fact leads us to conclude that, like odd predominance, a n-C_{22} predominance should be considered a criterion for "immaturity".

Acknowledgement: The author wishes to thank the directors of Shell Research N.V., The Hague, for permission to publish this article.

References

Bray, E.E. and Evans, E.D.: Distribution of n-paraffins as a clue to recognition of source beds. Geochim. Cosmochim. Acta **22** (1961) 1–15.

Clark Jr., R.C.: Occurrence of normal paraffin hydrocarbons in nature. Woods Hole Oceanographic Institution, Technical Report, Ref. no. 66–34, July 1966.

Kvenvolden, K.A.: Evidence for transformations of normal fatty acids in sediments – Paper presented at the Third International Meeting on Organic Geochemistry – London – 26–28 September 1966, Pergamon Press, Oxford, to be published.

Philippi, G.T.: On the depth, time and mechanism of petroleum generation. Geochim. Cosmochim. Acta **29** (1965) 1021–1049.

Philippi, G.T.: Essentials of the petroleum formation process are organic source material and a subsurface temperature controlled reaction mechanism. Proceedings of the 4th Intern. Mtg. Organic Geochemistry – Amsterdam – 16–18 September 1968, Pergamon/Vieweg 1969, p. 25–46.

Robinson, Sir Robert: Origins of oil, a correction and further comment on the Brunnock even C-number predominance in certain higher alkanes of African crudes, and on the biogenesis of nonacosane. Nature **214** (1967) 263.

Robinson, W.E., Cummins, J.J. and Dinneen, G.U.: Changes in Green River oil-shale paraffins with depth. Geochim. Cosmochim. Acta **29** (1965) 249–258.

Schenck, P.A. and Eisma, E.: Quantitative determination of n-alkanes in crude oils and rock extracts by gas chromatography. In: Advances in Organic Geochemistry – Proceedings of the Intern. Mtg. in Milan, 1962, Pergamon Press, Oxford, 1964, p. 403–415.

Stevens, N.P., Bray, E.E. and Evans, E.D.: Hydrocarbons in sediments of Gulf of Mexico. Bull. Am. Ass. Petrol. Geol. **40** (1956) 975–983.

Discussion

D.H. Hunneman: You have only mentioned the C_{22} predominance, what is the predominance of the C_{24} and C_{26} hydrocarbons?

P.A. Schenck: In general, there is no predominance of n-C_{24} and n-C_{26} in those samples in which we find this n-C_{22} predominance.

In a very few cases we have found an occurrence of an "even predominance" of n-C_{24}, n-C_{26}, n-C_{28} and n-C_{30} in rock extracts. It is striking that in those cases also phytane is present more abundant than pristane, contrary to what we generally find.

G.S. Bayliss: Did you infer that in the cases you referred to in which the even n-alkanes predominated over the odd n-alkanes, that the phytane also predominated? If so this would appear to contradict tne findings for the Green River oil shale extract in which phytane predominates, yet the n-alkanes have the odd predominance.

P.A. Schenck: The finding of phytane being present more abundant than pristane occurred in those special cases I just mentioned, in which the even numbered n-alkanes of high molecular weight predominate over their neighbouring odd-ones. I agree that it occurs sometimes that phytane is more abundant than pristane; these cases are rather exceptional, however.

D.H. Welte: 1) The n-C_{22} predominance may partly be caused by the reduction of a C_{22}-alcohol which has been found very abundant in Green River shale for instance.

2) There are indeed oils which show an even predominance and then also a predominance of phytane over pristane.

E.V. Whitehead: One would expect there to be differences in the alkanes from rock extracts and those from petroleum which has undergone migration.

The thermal degradation may not be the entire explanation for the alkane patterns seen and their variation with depth. With increasing depth and hence geological age, so will the pattern of alkane contribution from the source plants change. Modern specialised plants possess wax alkane patterns which peak at C_{29} and possess pronounced odd predominance, whilst the more primitive aquatic plants possess n-alkane patterns which maximize in the region $C_{16} - C_{23}$. These changes in flora marine/terrestrial as well as in geological time, offer another partial explanation for these anomalous alkane patterns.

P.A. Schenck: Thank you; I thus understand that you fully agree with the suggestion that the presence of a specific type of organism may be the explanation of this n-C_{22} predominance.

K.E.H. Göhring: In micro-organisms a sulfolipid with a n-C_{22}-carbon chain seems to be generally occurring. Therefore, strong local bacterial activity during sedimentation may cause an enrichment of this lipid which later on may give rise to a n-C_{22} predominance.

Determination of C^{13}/C^{12} Isotope Ratios of Individual Higher n-Paraffins from Different Petroleums

Dietrich H. Welte

Chevron Oil Field Research Company
La Habra, California, USA

A method for collecting individual higher n-paraffins from petroleums for C^{13}/C^{12} isotope analysis has been developed. Quartz tubes filled with carbon-free molecular sieves type 5 A are attached directly to the exhaust port of a gas chromatograph and individual n-paraffins are collected in different tubes. The tube is then transferred to a combustion line. Carbon isotope ratios of the resulting CO_2 are determined in a mass spectrometer. In the three petroleums studied the individual n-paraffins $n-C_{17}$ to $n-C_{33}$ exhibited among themselves differences up to $1\%_0 \delta$ C^{13}/C^{12}. All three distribution curves of the isotope ratios show a minimum in the range from 27 to 31 C-atoms. These minima are tentatively interpreted to represent a higher concentration of biologically produced carbon skeletons in this particular molecular weight range.

Es wurde eine Methode entwickelt, die die Isolierung einzelner, höherer n-Paraffine für eine nachfolgende C^{13}/C^{12} Isotopenanalyse ermöglicht. Mittels Quarzröhrchen, die mit kohlenstofffreien Molekularsieben Typ 5 A gefüllt sind, werden die einzelnen n-Paraffine am Ausgang des Wärmeleitfähigkeitsdetektors eines Gaschromatographen aufgefangen. Die Quarzröhrchen werden danach in einen Verbrennungsofen übergeführt. Die Kohlenstoffisotopenverhältnisse werden mit einem Massenspektrometer bestimmt. Auf diese Weise wurden die einzelnen n-Paraffine mit 17 bis 33 C-Atomen von drei verschiedenen Erdölen auf ihre Isotopenzusammensetzung analysiert. Innerhalb der homologen Reihe der n-Paraffine eines Erdöls ergaben sich Unterschiede bis zu $1\%_0 \delta$ C^{13}/C^{12}. Die Isotopenverteilungskurven der drei Erdöle zeigen alle ein isotopes Minimum bei n-Paraffinen mit einer Kettenlänge von 27 bis 31 C-Atomen. Diese Minima werden mit Vorbehalt dahingehend gedeutet, daß sie diejenigen Molekularbereiche repräsentieren, die einen größeren Anteil ursprünglicher, biologisch gebildeter Kohlenstoffgerüste enthalten.

Introduction

One of the goals of organic geochemistry is the understanding of geochemical pathways and the recognition of those organic molecules in which the original, biologically produced carbon skeletons are preserved.

One possible approach for the solution of this problem is the identification and pursuit of typical biological molecular structures in geological environments.

Prominent among those molecular structures are components like isoprenoid isoparaffins and their corresponding acids (Blumer and Cooper, 1967), polycyclic components such as typical triterpanes (Burlingame, et al., 1965; Hills and Whitehead, 1966) or fossil pigments as represented by porphyrins (Hodgson, et al., 1967).

However, abiological, geochemical processes produce a large quantity of partially altered, or even completely anew synthesized organic molecules which obscure frequently the original biological pattern. This is especially true for molecules exhibiting less typical structures, as for instance the n- and iso-paraffins.

The breakdown of biologically produced organic material in geological environments after termination of microbial activity is mainly governed by the loss of functional groups, intramolecular rearrangements and a splitting of carbon-carbon bonds. Ultimately there is a tendency to form such components as CO_2, CH_4 and graphite. The local temperature conditions largely control the decomposition processes and there is general agreement that thermal cracking is a prominent subsurface geochemical reaction mechanism.

As pointed out by Silverman (1964; 1967) and Sackett (1968) the thermal degradation of petroleum compounds and of sedimentary organic material (kerogen) and the accompanying production of methane and other low molecular weight compounds result in an isotope fractionation. This is based on the fact that there is less energy required to break a $C^{12}-C^{12}$ bond than a $C^{13}-C^{12}$ bond. Hence in thermal cracking $C^{12}-C^{12}$ bonds repture about 8 % more frequently (Stevenson, et al., 1948; Brodskii, et al., 1959). Because of the production of isotopically light methane the source molecule is relatively enriched in the heavy C^{13} isotope. Furthermore, because of the realtive large hydrogen content of the methane molecule the source material is dehydrogenated, which necessarily results in unsaturation and the creation of more reactive double bonds. This in turn would lead to polymerization reactions of the residual molecules giving rise to components of even higher molecular weight. Following this line of thought, Silverman (1967, 1968) explained the observed carbon isotopic composition of narrow distillation fractions from crude oils. According to this principle a minimum in the carbon isotope distribution curve will be observed in the molecular weight region which contains the highest concentration of biologically produced carbon skeletons.

This general concept, we thought, would be even more meaningful if it were not only applied to narrow distillation fractions, which still contain a great number of components, but to individual members of homologous series of hydrocarbons.

Since the n-paraffins are very abundant in nature and especially in petroleum, and since their mechanism of formation is far from being understood, we conducted a study of the carbon isotope ratios of the individual higher n-paraffins in oils in order to gain a better understanding of their origin.

Analytical Procedure

A method suitable for such a measurement has been developed and the carbon isotopic composition of individual members of the homologous series of n-paraffins ranging from 17 to 33 carbon atoms isolated from a crude oil was determined.

n-Paraffin concentrates were prepared by urea adduction from different crude oils. The n-paraffin concentrate was injected into a gas chromatograph employing a packed column (180 cm x 0.45 cm; 10 % OV−1 on gaschrom R 80/100 mesh) and a thermal conductivity cell as detector. The exhaust port was modified in such a way that a specially designed collection tube could be attached by means of a heated adapter (Figure 1).

The quartz collection tubes (75 mm long; 5 mm internal diameter) were filled with pretreated carbon free molecular sieves type 5 A (Figure 2).

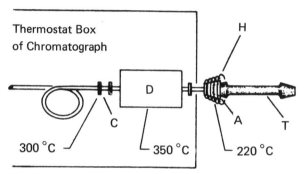

Fig. 1. Diagram of apparatus used for collection
C   Column
D   Detector (heat conductivity)
H   Heating tape
A   Adaptor
T   Tube for collection

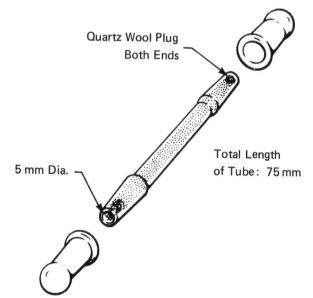

Fig. 2
Quartz collection tube filled
with molecular sieves

In successive gas chromatographic runs (10–15), the individual members of the
n-paraffin series were collected in different tubes till each tube showed a minimum
weight increase of 3 mg. Extreme care has to be applied in order to avoid contamination from even the laboratory air. After the collection procedure, the entire
quartz tube is transferred to a combustion line for conversion of the n-paraffins
into CO_2 for the carbon isotope measurement. (See flow chart in Figure 3.)

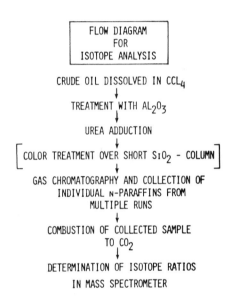

Fig. 3
Flow diagram for isotope analysis

Details of the sample preparation and analytical procedures for the isotope measurement are given by Silverman and Epstein (1958). The C^{13}/C^{12} ratios reported
here as δ-values are deviations, in parts per thousand (‰= per mil) of the C^{13}/C^{12}
ratios of the samples from the N.B.S. No. 22 petroleum standard

$$(\delta\text{‰} = \left(\frac{C^{13}/C^{12} \text{ sample}}{C^{13}/C^{12} \text{ standard}} - 1\right) \times 1000).$$

This petroleum standard is 29.4 ‰lower than the PDB standard originally used by
the University of Chicago. The precision of the reported analysis is ± 0.1‰. Utili-
zing this technique, a combination of nondestructive analytical gas chromatography
with high precision isotope ratio mass spectrometry, the C^{13}/C^{12} isotope ratios of
the higher n-paraffins $nC_{17}-nC_{33}$ have been determined. The data reported here
are the result of at least two independent runs. Analytical details will be reported
elsewhere.

Carbon Isotope Ratios of Individual n-Paraffins in Three Selected Petroleums

For determination of the carbon isotope ratios of the n-paraffin homologous series, three different crude oils have been selected:

(1) A non-marine oil of Tertiary age from Red Wash field, Utah;
(2) A marine oil of Cretaceous age from Locust Ridge field, Mississippi; and
(3) An oil from a deltaic environment of Tertiary age from Pennington field, Nigeria.

The C^{13}/C^{12} ratios of the individual higher n-paraffins and their relative abundance in the particular crude oil are presented in Figures 4, 5, and 6. In Figure 4, the spread of the isotope ratios is shown for two independent measurements on two different n-paraffin isolates for the same oil (Red Wash). The largest difference between two isotope measurements on two different concentrates of an individual n-paraffin from the same crude oil was 0.36‰, the average spread is better than 0.2‰.

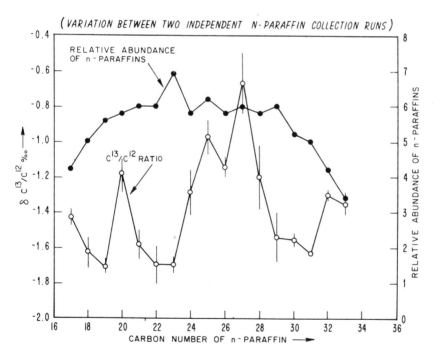

Fig. 4. Relation between the carbon isotopic composition of individual n-paraffins and their relative abundance in an oil, Red Wash Field Utah

18 Geochemistry 68

As shown in Figures 4–6, the isotope ratios of the individual n-paraffins from one oil show differences as high as 1.0‰. The one feature the three isotope ratio curves have in common is a minimum toward the end of the curve in the region from 27 to 31 carbon atoms, in the boiling range from 420 °C to 455 °C. It is interesting to note that this minimum is in the same boiling range where previously Silverman (1967) detected a minimum in C^{13}/C^{12} isotope ratios of narrow distillation fractions of crude oils and where Rosenfeld (1967) detected a maximum in the specific optical rotation.

The Red Wash isotope curve (Figure 4) appears to be the most complex one. There are minima around n-C_{19}, n-C_{22} to n-C_{23} and n-C_{29} to n-C_{31}, maxima in the C^{13}/C^{12} ratio occur at n-C_{20} and at n-C_{25} and n-C_{27}. The Locust Ridge isotope curve (Figure 5) shows a relatively smooth distribution with steadily increasing C^{13}/C^{12} ratios that reaches a maximum at n-C_{27} and from then on it drops down to a minimum at n-C_{31}.

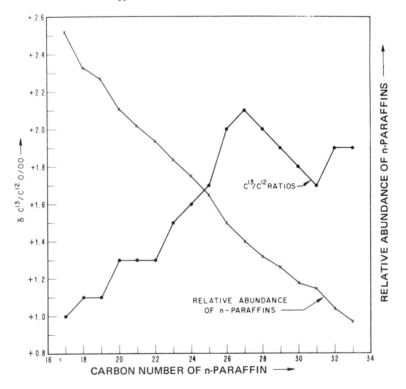

Fig. 5. Relation between the carbon isotopic composition of the n-paraffins and their relative abundance in locust Ridge, Miss. petroleum

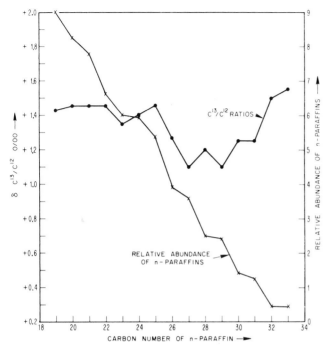

Fig. 6. Relations between the carbon isotopic composition of the n-paraffins and their relative abundance in a Nigerian petroleum

The isotope curve of the Nigerian Oil (Figure 6) shows only a variation in the order of about 0.5‰. It exhibits a maximum at n-C$_{25}$ and n-C$_{33}$ respectively. In the range from n-C$_{26}$ to n-C$_{33}$ the odd-numbered n-paraffins are isotopically slightly lighter relative to the n-paraffins having an even number of carbon atoms. This coincides with a relatively larger abundance of the odd-numbered n-paraffins in this particular crude oil.

Discussion of Results

The three different oils were selected in such a way that they represent three different types of environments; a non-marine oil from the Uinta basin (Red Wash), a marine oil from the Mississippi salt basin (Locust Ridge), and an oil from a typical deltaic environment (Pennington).

Therefore, the original organic source material from which those oils have been derived should also be different. The Locust Ridge oil, being very probably derived from a fine grained marine shale should have had a more uniform biological source facies than both the deltaic Nigerian oil and the non-marine Uinta Basin oil.

On the other hand, it is to be expected that the Nigerian oil is derived from a source rock which contains marine planktonic organisms and also a considerable amount of terrestrial organic debris, like fragments from higher plants. The most probable source for the Uinta Basin oil contains mainly fresh water organisms (algae) and only some land derived plant fragments.

The n-paraffin distribution curves, showing the relative abundance of the individual n-paraffins in the oils exhibit distinct differences.

The Locust Ridge oil being the oldest (Cretaceous) and deepest oil ($\sim 9000'$) has a rather smooth n-paraffin distribution curve with a continuous decrease in abundance from n-C_{17} to n-C_{33} (Figure 5). The n-paraffin distribution curve of the Nigerian oil ($\sim 5000'$) also shows a continuous decrease in abundance with increasing carbon number, however, there is a small but distinct odd-predominance to be noticed (Figure 6). In the Red Wash oil (Figure 4) the n-paraffins increase in relative abundance from n-C_{17} to n-C_{23} where there is a maximum. From n-C_{23} on there is a slight decrease in abundance and also a distinct odd-predominance.

The following interpretation of the C^{13}/C^{12} ratios of the individual n-paraffins in three different oils is only a tentative one, because these are the very first data available and certainly many more oils have to be investigated. However, in the light of the foregoing information the following tentative conclusions may be justified. Because of the preferential cleavage of $C^{12}-C^{12}$ bonds during the abiological thermal degradation of organic molecules, the pronounced minima in the carbon isotope curves represent those n-paraffins which contain the highest concentration of biologically produced carbon skeletons. Contrary to that, n-paraffins with a higher than average C^{13}/C^{12} ratio should be mainly of secondary origin.

The relatively simple isotope curve of the Locust Ridge oil may be evidence for the higher maturity of the oil and/or its more uniform source substances. The complexity of the Uinta Basin oil isotope curve on the other hand could be evidence for a wider variety of biological precursors.

The coincidence of the occurrence of an odd-predominance in the Nigerian oil with the fact that these odd numbered n-paraffins are isotopically lighter than their even numbered neighbors may be caused by the contribution of terrestrial organic matter to the source material. This is because higher plants are known to cause a strong odd-predominance among the higher n-paraffins and because they are also known to be isotopically considerably lighter than marine organic material.

Acknowledgement: I would like to express my sincere thanks to S.R. Silverman, Chevron Oil Field Research Company, La Habra, California, for many stimulating discussions.

References

Blumer, M., and W.J. Cooper: Isoprenoid Acids in Recent Sediments. Science 158, 1463 (1967).

Brodskii, A.M., R.A. Kalinenko, and K.P. Lavroskii: On the Kinetic Isotope Effect in Cracking. Intl. Jour. Applied Radiation and Isotopes 7, 118 (1959).

Burlingame, A., P. Haug, T. Belsky, and M. Calvin: Occurrence of Biogenic Steranes and Pentacyclic Triterpanes in an Eocene Shale (52 Million Years) and in an Early Precambrian Shale (2.7 Billion Years): A Preliminary Report. Proc. Nat. Acad. Sci. U.S. 54, 1406 (1965).

Hills, I.R., and E.V. Whitehead: Triterpanes in Optically Active Petroleum Distillates. Nature 209, 977 (1966).

Hodgson, G.W., B.L. Baker, and E. Peake: Geochemistry of Porphyrins. p. 177 in B. Nagy and U. Colombo: Fundamental Aspects of Petroleum Geochemistry. Amsterdam — London — New York: Elsevier 1967.

Rosenfeld, W.D.: Optical Rotation of Petroleums. J.Am. Oil Chem. Soc. 44, 703 (1967).

Sackett, W.M.: Carbon Isotope Composition of Natural Methane Occurrences. Am. Assoc. Petrol. Geol. Bull. 52, 853 (1968).

Silverman, S.R.: Investigation of Petroleum Origin and Evolution Mechanisms by Carbon Isotope Studies. p. 92 H. Craig, S.L. Miller, and G.J. Wasserburg: Isotopic and Cosmic Chemistry. Amsterdam: North Holland Pub. Company 1964.

Silverman, S.R.: Carbon Isotopic Evidence for the Role of Lipids in Petroleum. J. Am. Oil Chem. Soc. 44, 691 (1967).

Silverman, S.R.: Carbon Isotopic Evidence for the Origin and Transformation of Petroleum and Gas. All-Union Conf. on Origin of Oil and Gas, Moscow, U.S.S.R., Jan. 15—20, 1968.

Silverman, S.R., and S. Epstein: Carbon Isotopic Compositions of Petroleums and Sedimentary Organic Materials. Am. Assoc. Petrol. Geol. Bull. 42, 998 (1958)

Stevenson, D.P., C.D. Wagner, O. Beeck, and J.W. Otvos: Isotope Effect in the Thermal Cracking of Propane-1-C^{13}. J. Chem. Phys. 16, 993 (1948).

The General Scheme of Petroleum and Gas Formation, Alteration and Migration in the Earth's Chrust

Vasily A. Sokolov, Artem A. Geodekian and Ziya A. Buniat-Zade

IGIRGI, Scientific Council of Academy of Sciences USSR on the origin of petroleum
Moscow, USSR

The formation, alteration and migration of petroleum and gas are tightly connected with each other. The course of these processes depends upon chemical and physical conditions, thickness and structure of rocks and the history of their development.

In the original stage of sediments history the organic matter and partly high-molecular hydrocarbons are formed. Methane is also formed, but the greater part of methane has been dispersed, dissolving in water and migrating into the atmosphere. During the following stages, at the submersion of sedimentary rocks, owing to thermocatalytical processes the whole set of hydrocarbons and other components of petroleum and gas is formed. In the most submersed sedimentary rocks (6–7 km and deeper) methane is mainly formed.

The primal migration caused by breaks of gases, squeezing out the fluids, diffusion and the following lateral and vertical migration lead to definite distribution of petroleum and gas and their accumulation in traps. The gases, formed mainly in the lower part of the section, accumulate owing to differentiation at lateral migration in traps on border zones of basins and at the vertical migration in the upper part of the section.

In magmatic rocks the conditions for formation, migration and accumulation of petroleum and gas are not favourable. We may expect here only small concentrations of dispersed hydrocarbons. Meanwhile from the upper mantle through the disruptions are coming in the lower zones of the earth crust, in magmatic rocks, the gases consisting of H_2O, CO_2, H_2, SO_2, HCl, HF mixed with other substances.

In the paper on the base of newest data are considered the formation and migration of petroleum and gas in their connection and the general schemes of these processes are proposed for typical geological conditions.

The formation and further alteration of petroleum and gas, their migration and differentiation, accumulation and dissipation are intimately connected with one another. The intensity and directionality of all these processes, which take place in sedimentary rocks, are dependent on composition and properties of rocks, their structure and the history of their geological development.

That temperature, pressure and catalysis as the cause of petroleum formation from organic matter in sedimentary rocks and the cause of the further alteration of petroleum were already put forward in reports on the early investigations on this subject. The roles and the meanings of these factors were further studied in more detail.

V.A. Sokolov (1948) proposed that the formation and alteration of petroleum and gas were due to thermal and thermocatalytic transformation of initial organic matter and initially formed petroleum. The final products of these processes were considered to be carbon and methane. The velocity of transformation of organic matter and petroleum is dependent on temperature. With the aid of the Arrhenius equation it was calculated, that petroleum cannot be conserved at 200 °C during geological periods of time. In connection with this, zones of petroleum formation and alteration depending on depth were established. In the upper biochemical zone, the formation of initial organic matter takes place, deeper, in the thermocatalytic zone (from 0,5–1 to 6–7 km), petroleum and gas are formed and deeper still methane is mainly formed.

The schemes of formation and alteration of petroleum were described also by J.G. McNab and others (1952), N.B. Vassojevich (1955), R.D. McIver (1963), V.A. Sokolov (1964, 1965, 1966), G.T. Philippi (1965), D.H. Welte (1965), A.A. Geodekjan (1966, 1968) and others. In these papers, the formation and alteration of petroleum is also cinsidered as the thermal and catalytic transformation of complicated molecules of organic substances into simpler ones.

The formation and alteration of petroleum and gas is dependent on:
1. The composition of the initial organic matter
2. The action of temperature, pressure and catalysis, which change through the section of rocks.

Biochemical processes, which are active in recent sediments, play an important role in the transformation of plant and animal remains, on which depend the composition of the organic matter in sedimentary rocks.

However, the hydrocarbons $C_2 - C_{13}$ typical of petroleum and gas, are practically not formed in recent sediments, according to data acquired by the authors and other investigators. Only small traces of these hydrocarbons are observed, which cannot be the base for the formation of petroleum and gas deposits.

All the experiments concerning bacterial action on differenct organic substances established the formation of methane and also carbon dioxide, nitrogen, sometimes hydrogen sulfide, but more heavier gaseous and light liquid hydrocarbons practically were not discovered.

The biochemical methane of recent sediments is almost completely dissipated, dissolving in water and migrating into the atmosphere.

The formation of petroleum and gas hydrocarbons, as a result of thermal and catalytic transformations of different organic substances was confirmed by many experiments by heating (100–400 °C) of marine and fresh-water silts, shales, other sedimentary rocks, also fatty acids and other organic substances (V.A. Sokolov, 1956, J.M. Hunt, 1962, A.I. Bogomolov, 1967, A.A. Petrov, 1967, E. Eisma and J.W. Jurg, 1967, M.C. Louis and B.P. Tissot, 1967, T.V. Tichomolova, S.D. Pustilnikowa, A.A. Petrov, 1968 and other).

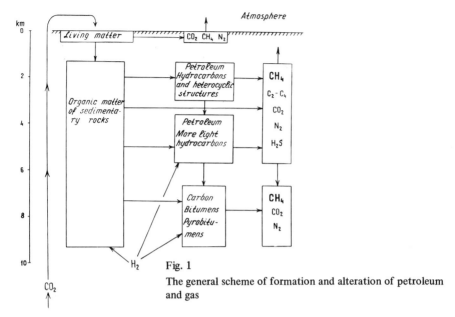

Fig. 1
The general scheme of formation and alteration of petroleum and gas

The general scheme of petroleum and gas formation and alteration is presented on Fig. 1. Carbon dioxide, which rises through volcanoes and disruptions from the upper mantle and lowest part of the earth's crust into the atmosphere, is assimilated by plants and is the cause of the formation of different organic substances in living organisms. All the carbon of organic matter in sedimentary rocks derives from the atmosphere. In recent sediments and the upper layers of sedimentary rocks the transformation of organic matter gives rise to CO_2, CH_4 (N_2 and small quantities of other gases), which disperse into the atmosphere. In recent sediments a small quantity of high-molecular hydrocarbons is formed. As these go deeper in sedimentary rocks (1 km and deeper) the petroleum and hydrocarbon gas are formed. The principal features of petroleum evolution are the following.

There are formed originally the different liquid and solid hydrocarbons with important content of polycyclic hydrocarbons and also heterocyclic compounds. The lipid fraction of organic matter plays an important role in hydrocarbon formation. The further alteration of petroleum is the result of degradation and other transformation of complicated molecules. Under this the petroleum is enriched by light hydrocarbon fractions. Methane and other gaseous hydrocarbons also are formed. However, the main supplier of methane and other hydrocarbon gases is the organic matter of sedimentary rocks. its humic and carbonic substances. With depth the temperature becomes higher and the role of hydrogen cracking is increased, which is favourable for the formation of hydrocarbon gases and light fractions of petroleum.

The next stage, caused by prolonged exposure to elevated temperature, is more complete degradation of hydrocarbons and heterocyclic compounds of petroleum. During these processes, the rocks become enriched with the remains of petroleum, such as carbon, the most stable polycyclic hydrocarbon compounds and bitumens.

In the thermocatalytic zone (1–6 km) methane and other gaseous hydrocarbons, C_2-C_4, are formed. At greater depth, the part consisting of hydrocarbons C_2-C_4 decreases and mainly methane is conserved.

The achievement of any stage of this evolution is dependent on:

1. Temperature, which in turn is dependent on depth and geothermal gradient.
2. Time of existence of petroleum and gas at this temperature, which is connected with the depth of the rocks and the history of their geological development (subsidence and re-emergence).
3. Catalytic properties of rocks, taking into account that these properties are not the same in all rocks.

The distribution of petroleum and gas deposits through the section, their composition and properties are dependent not only on processes of formation and alteration, but also on petroleum and gas migration and differentiation.

The migration and differentiation of petroleum and gas, their accumulation and dissipation are a complex of physical and physico-chemical processes. That is the filtration, the squeezing and transfer of water with dissolved and free hydrocarbons, the buoyancy of gas and petroleum, diffusion. The directionality of these processes enables one to distinguish among primary lateral and vertical migration. The part played by each of these processes, the possibility of accumulation of petroleum and gas, and their dissipation are dependent on the properties and structure of rocks, temperature and pressure.

According experiments carried out long ago for investigations on gas surveying and gas-logging, the differentiation of these hydrocarbons takes place during the migration of hydrocarbon mixture through rocks (sand, sandstone). We then observe a chromatographic effect – methane passes first, then a mixture rich in ethane and propane and finally heavier hydrocarbons (V.A. Sokolov, 1948, 1958, 1965). The chromatographic distribution of hydrocarbons during migration has also been considered by B. Nagy (1960). The scheme of migration of petroleum and gas was described by S.R. Silverman (1964).

The alteration of isotopic composition during the migration of hydrocarbons was established by U. Colombo et al. (1964), S.R. Silverman (1964), P. Muller (1967).

The proposed scheme of migration of petroleum and gas is presented in Fig. 2. The primary migration from clay into sand and other rocks arises through the expulsion of water with dissolved hydrocarbons, the percolation of petroleum and gas through the clay, and diffusion. The petroleum coming from clayey rocks is rich in light fractions. This petroleum, once in sand and carbonate rocks, formed the mixture with hydrocarbons and heterocyclic compounds which had formed in these rocks. Furthermore, petroleum and gas, together with the water, migrate laterally through the sand and carbonate rocks from the most deeply buried part of a basin to its periphery, depending on hydrogeological conditions. During this migration the differentiation of hydrocarbon mixtures takes place. The gaseous hydrocarbons migrate more rapidly than the oil, especially the high-molecular substances in the oil. Methane reaches the highest parts of rocks on the periphery of the basin first. If there are traps in the parth of the laterally migrating petroleum and gas, deposits may be formed in them. The gas deposit may be held in the trap only if the cap rock over the gas deposit has a very low permeability. The nitrogen migrates more quickly than methane, therefore in some cases the gas that has migrated over a large distance may be rich in nitrogen. At great depth, the traps may contain the compressed gas with dissolved liquid hydrocarbons. Further lateral migration of this compressed gas leads to the appearance of petroleum and gas-condensate (Fig. 2).

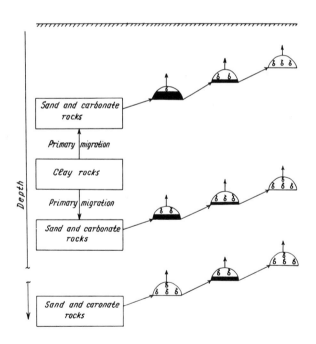

Fig. 2. The general scheme of migration of petroleum and gas δ Gas, – Petroleum,⤳ Lateral migration, ↟ Vertical migration, ⌒ Traps

From every trap containing petroleum and gas vertical migration takes place. If the cap rock has a very low permeability the vertical migration is only by diffusion. Only diffusion of gas is important, the loss of which during the long periods of geological time may be important. The loss of petroleum owing to diffusion is insignificant. As a result of disruptions vertical migration takes place by filtration, buoyancy and other processes. As a result of this vertical migration, petroleum and gas deposits may be formed, in other, shallower traps. If this migration reaches the earth's surface an important or almost complete loss of gas may happen.

Considering together the processes of petroleum and gas formation and migration as a function of geological and geochemical conditions, we must note that the formation of methane (with admixture of other gaseous hydrocarbons) takes place mainly in the deepest parts of the basin. Meanwhile, the gas in comparison with petroleum migrates mainly in the upper part of the section. During the migration the light fractions of petroleum also outstrip the high-molecular components. The distribution and the composition of petroleum and gas deposits over the section will depend on which of these processes predominates. If the intensity of migration is insignificant, the content of gas and light fractions in petroleum will increase with depth. If the intensity of migration is important, another situation is possible: the content of heavy fractions in petroleum will increase with the depth. The course of these processes and the scale of petroleum and gas formation and migration also depend on the dimension of the basin and the thickness of sedimentary rocks. If the volume of rocks in the methane zone (deeper than 6–7 km) is small and the intensity of migration is important, the reserves of gas in the lower part of the basin may be insignificant. If the volume of rocks in the methane zone is large, it may conserve an immense reserve of methane in the lower part of the basin. An example of this is the South-Caspian basin, where the thickness of sedimentary rocks, according to seismic data, in some parts reaches 20–25 km. At present powerful eruptions of gas (methane with admixture of other gases) take place from the mud volcanoes, which is evidence of immense reserves of methane in the deepest part of the basin.

Magmatic rocks does not contain the organic matter that is present in sedimentary rocks and is the source of petroleum and gas. In magmatic rocks small concentrations of dispersed carbon and high-molecular heterocyclic compounds are present. In the presence of hydrogen we may expect the hydrogenisation of these substances and formation of small quantities of hydrocarbons. At the high temperature in the lower part of the earth's crust only traces of methane are formed. The question arises of the possibility of synthesis of hydrocarbons from hydrogen and carbon oxide or dioxide. However, the role of this synthesis in rocks under natural conditions is unimportant, as we can see from the composition of volcanic gases at different temperatures. As the temperature becomes lower the content of CO_2 in gases increases and the content of other gases decreases. We do not, however, observe the formation of methane and other hydrocarbons. In Fig. 3 we show the alteration of the mean content of volcanic gas components as a function of temperature. The content of methane is of the order of some tenth part of one per cent.

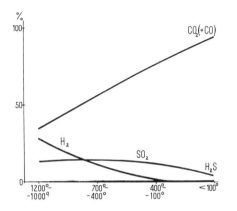

Fig. 3
The average composition of volcanic gases. The contents of HCl, HF and others components are not represented

The traces of this methane and other hydrocarbons are present in magmatic rocks in dispersed state. However, the negligible content of hydrocarbons and negligible porosity and permeability of magmatic rocks prevents the formation of any considerable accumulations of these hydrocarbons in magmatic rocks.

We may point out the following principal types of petroleum and gas evolution, applying to definite geological conditions.

1. The basins in which the thickness of sedimentary rocks does not surpass 1 km. The formation of petroleum and gas in important quantities does not take place.

2. The basins and platforms in which the thickness of sedimentary rocks is more than 1 km and reaches 3–7 km. Here the formation of petroleum and gas takes place in such quantities, that may secure the formation of big deposits. The greater the dimension of the basin and the greater the volume of rocks in the thermocatalytic zone, the more petroleum and gas may be formed. However, the distribution and the dimension of deposits, the composition and properties of petroleum and gas are also dependent on the distribution and the dimension of traps. If on the periphery of the basin there are good traps, gas deposits may be formed here, as a result of lateral migration. In the central part of the basin, as a result of intensive vertical migration, in the traps of the upper part of the section also gas and petroleum deposits may be formed.

The intensity of lateral and vertical migration also influences the composition and properties of the petroleums through the section.

Some influence on the composition of petroleum, mainly in the upper part of the section, may be exerted by the processes of oxidation and sulfuration.

3. The basins with large thickness of sedimentary rocks — 7–10 km and more. In the lower part of the section of such basins the formation of important quantities of methane takes place. The scale of methane formation depends on the volume of sedimentary rocks in the methane zone. The continued formation of methane may be the cause of abnormally high pressures of gas, its tearing through the rocks and eruption from the mud volcanoes.

All the depths mentioned above in this paper are approximate mean values. Depending on the geothermal gradient, catalytic properties of rocks and the continued influence of all the factors concerned, actual values may deviate from these mean values either upwards or downwards.

4. In the magmatic rocks of the earth's crust the conditions for formation, migration and accumulation of petroleum and gas are unfabourable. We may expect here only very small concentrations of hydrocarbons. From the upper mantle, as a result of deep disruptions, gases, consisting mainly of H_2O, CO_2, H_2, SO_2, H_2S, HCl, HF with admixture of other components, reach the magmatic rocks in the deeper zones of the earth's crust.

References

Bogomolov, A. 1967: Geochemical reactions and experiments on their modeling. Origin of petroleum and gas. Nedra, Moscow.

Colombo, U.; Gazzarini, F.; Sironi, G.; Confiantini, R. and Tongiorgi, E. 1964: Isotopic measurements of C^{13}/C^{12} ratio on Italian natural gases and their geochemical interpretation. Intern. Geochem. Meeting, Paris.

Eisma, E.; Jurg, J.W. 1967: Fundamental aspects of the diagenesis of organic matter and the formation of petroleum. 7. World Petroleum Congress. Mexico.

Geodekjan, A.A. 1966: On the formation of petroleum and gas in South-Caspian basin. Geology of petroleum and gas. N 5.

Geodekjan, A.A. 1968: The scales of formation of petroleum and gas in South-Caspian basin. Origin of petroleum and gas. Nauka, Moscow.

Louis, M.C. et Tissot, B.P. 1967: Influence de la température et de la pression sur la formation des hydrocarbures dans les argiles à kerogéne. 7. World Petroleum Congress. Mexico.

McIver, R.D. 1967: Composition of kerogen-clue to its role in the origin of Petroleum. 7. World Petroleum Congress. Mexico.

McNab, J.G.; Smith, P.V. and Betts, R.L. 1952: The evolution of Petroleum. Ind. Eng. Chem. 44, 2556–2563.

Müller, P.; Wienholz, R. 1967: Bestimmung der natürlichen Variationen der Kohlenstoff-isotope in Erdöl und Erdgaskomponenten und ihre Beziehung zur Genese. V. Intern. Geochem. Konferenz, Magdeburg.

Nagy, B. 1960: Review of the chromatographic "plate" theory with reference to fluid flow in rocks and sediments. Geochim. Cosmochim. Acta, 19, 383–396.

Petrov, A.A. 1967: The structure of petroleum hydrocarbons and the probleme of origin of petroleum. Origin of petroleum and gas. Nedra, Moscow.

Philippi, G.T. 1965: On the depth, time and mechanism of petroleum generation. Bull. Am. Assoc. Petrol. Geol., 43.

Silverman, S.R. and Epstein, S. 1958: Carbon isotopic composition of petroleums and other sedimentary organic materials. Bull. Am. Assoc. Petrol. Geologists. 42, 998–1012.

Silvermann, S.R. 1964: The migration and segregation of oil and gas. Geol. Fluids Symp. Midland, Texas.

Sokolov, V.A. 1948: Outlines of the origin of petroleum. Gostoptechizdat, Moscow.

Sokolov, V.A. 1956: Migration of gas and petroleum. Ed. Academy of Science USSR. Moscow.

Sokolov, V.A. 1958: Scientific foundation of the geochemical prospecting of petroleum and gas. Conference on the geochemical prospecting methods. Ed. Academy of Science USSR, 1959, Moscow.

Sokolov, V.A. 1964: The modern ideas on the origin and migration of petroleum and gas. New investigations on the origin of petroleum and gas. Zniteneftegas, Moscow.

Sokolov, V.A. 1965: The processes of petroleum and gas formation. Nedra. Moscow.

Sokolov, V.A. 1966: Geochemistry of the gases of the earth crust and atmosphere. Nedra, Moscow.

Tichomolova, T.V.; Pustilnikova, S.D.; Petrov, A.A. 1968: On the composition of benzines received at the thermocatalysis of fatty acids. Origin of petroleum and gas. Nauka, Moscow.

Vassojevich, N.B. 1955: On the origin of petroleum. VNIGRI, geol. coll. M 83. Gostoptechizdat, Moscow.

Welte, D.H. 1965. Relation between Petroleum and Source Rocks. Bull. Am. Accos. Petrol. Geolog, N 12.

Some Aspects of the Chemistry of Crude Oil Metamorphism

Wlodzimierz Kisielow and Anna Marzec

Department of Petroleum and Liquid Fuel Technology, Technological University
Gliwice, Poland

A definition of the degree of crude oil metamorphism has been proposed. According to it, the degree of metamorphism should be expressed by such values of the property of syngenetic component which are monotonic function of time. Criteria, which make possible the estimation whether a component of crude oil is a syngenetic one and whether the values of a property form monotonic function of time, have been proposed.

Some problems of the chemistry of crude oil metamorphism have been worked out on the basis of analysis of 99 Polish crude oils from 56 oil fields of the Carpathians and Carpathian Foreland. All hadrocarbons (except n-paraffins) having boiling point higher than 200°C were isolated from each crude oil separately. These hydrocarbon parts of crude oils (called "oils") were present in amounts 30 % – 65 % in crude oils. The contents of hydrogen (% H) and aromatic carbon atoms (X) in oils were determined. Oils were separated by means of chromatography into two parts: saturated and aromatic hydrocarbons. The amounts of saturated hydrocarbons in oils (Y) were determined. Aromatic hydrocarbons were examined using Infra-Red, Ultra-Violet and Nuclear Magnetic Resonance. The existance of the relationships among % H, X and Y was stated and expressed as linear functions calculated using least squares method:

$$Y = - 2,25 \quad X + 105 \tag{1}$$
$$X = - 8,65 \% H + 128 \tag{2}$$

The following processes:
- intra- and intermolecular disproportionation of hydrogen,
- cleavage of saturated structural groups,
- hydrogenation

were considered as the reasons of the existence of function 1. On the basis of IR, UV and NMR data and function 2, hydrogenation of aromatic hydrocarbons as the main geochemical process, and cleavage of saturated elements as the secondary geochemical process, were estimated. No evidence of the activity of hydrogen disproportionation reactions has been found.

In conformity with the definition and analytical data, Y values have been accepted as the degree of crude oil metamorphism. Some regularity in the geological locality of crude oils having low degree of metamorphism has been stated, and an attempt of their source rock localisation has been made.

The paper represents an attempt to explain some problems of the chemistry of crude oil metamorphism, which is based on analytical data of 99 crude oils from 56 oil fields of the Carpathians and Carpathian Foreland, occurring in mesozoic and cenozoic formations. General data regarding the classification, the composition of Polis crude oils and the geography and geology of their deposits as well, were published earlier [1]. This paper is concerning mainly with the oily part of crude oils.

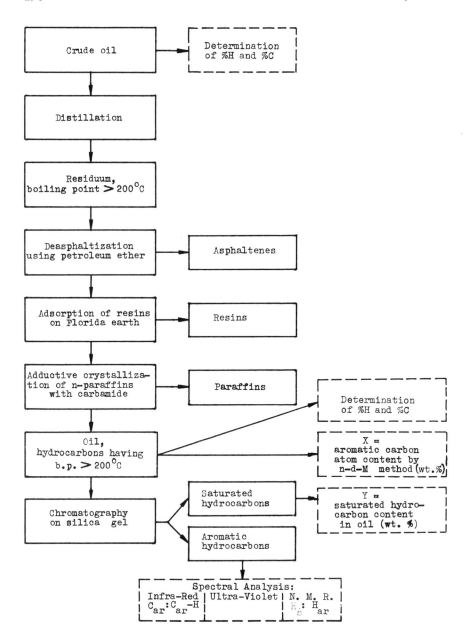

Fig. 1. Crude oil analysis

According to the scheme of crude oil analysis (Figure 1) all hydrocarbons boiling above 200° C were isolated from each crude oil separately. These hydrocarbon parts, except for n-paraffins, are present in crude oils in amounts 30–65 w. %. The content of aromatic carbon atoms – designated as X – by means of the n-d-M method [2] and the content of hydrogen – H % – were determined in the oils. Then the oils were separated using column chromatography, into two parts: saturated and aromatic hydrocarbons. The amounts of saturated hydrocarbons in weight percent of the oils were determined and designated as Y. The UV, IR and NMR spectra of aromatic hydrocarbons were taken.

The existence of a linear relationship between X and Y values was established, the function was calculated using least squares method:

$$Y = -2.25 X + 105$$

The high correlation coeficient r = 0.885 is characteristic for the equation. The results of the determination of the X and Y values for 99 crude oils are illustrated in Figure 2.

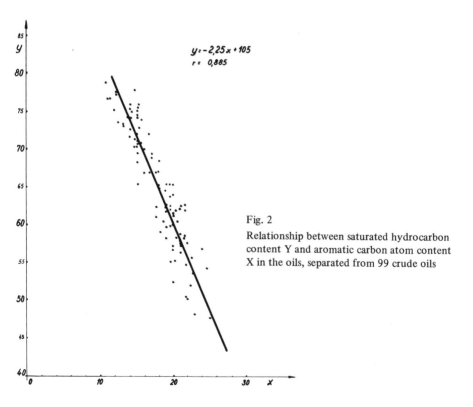

Fig. 2

Relationship between saturated hydrocarbon content Y and aromatic carbon atom content X in the oils, separated from 99 crude oils

The X + Y sums vary within the range 72–92%. X and Y are the properties of the group component, commonly present in crude oils, consisting of all aromatic and isoparaffinic/cycloparaffinic hydrocarbons, having boiling points higher then 200° C.

The Interpretation of the Y = – 2.25 X + 105 Function

In the first place it should be explained whether some physical processes leading to the supply or outflow of aromatic or saturated hydrocarbons to or from the system "oil" could be the reason of the existence of the above mentioned function. If so, there will have to exist a relationship between oil content in the residua and saturated and/or aromatic hydrocarbon content in the oils.

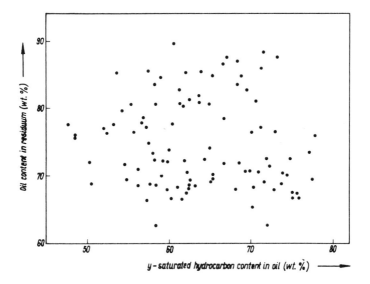

Fig. 3. Saturated hydrocarbon content in oil and oil content in residuum

The data shown in Figure 3 prove the lack of any relation between these values. It suggests that the internal transformations within the system "oil" are responsible for the experimentally estabilished function.

The following processes ought to be taken into account:
— hydrogenation
— intermolecular disproportionation of hydrogen
— intramolecular disproportionation of hydrogen
— cleavage of saturated elements present within the aromatic molecules.

These processes are shown schematicly in Figure 4 as the functions expressed in X, Y coordinates.

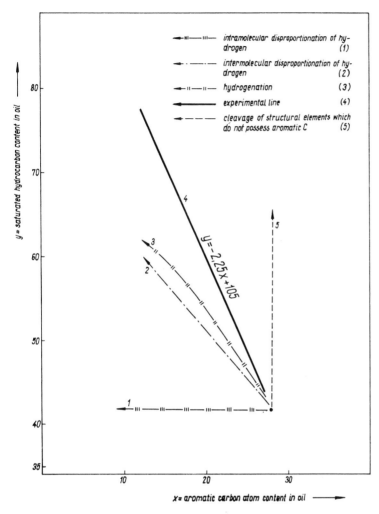

Fig. 4. Mutual transformations of aromatic and saturated hydrocarbons expressed in x, y system

Line 1 represents the intramolecular disproportionation of hydrogen; line 2 represents the intermolecular disproportionation of hydrogen, both within the aromatic molecules. Dobrianski [3] postulated a process of hydrogen disproportionation of saturated hydrocarbons leading to the aromatic hydrocarbons and more "hydrogenated" saturated hydrocarbons according to the scheme:

$$4\,C_nH_{2n} = C_nH_{2n-6} \ddagger 3\,C_nH_{2n+2} \quad \text{etc.}$$

We established however, that the hydrogen content in the saturated portion of the oil did not increase and that the ring content did not decrease when the amount of saturated hydrocarbons in oils decreased. These data negate the existence of such a process and therefore it has not been considered within the framework of interpretation of the experimental function $Y = f/X/$.

Line 3 illustrates the hydrogenation process, line 4 the experimental function $Y = f/X/$, and line 5 the process of cleavage.

The contribution of these processes in formation of the experimental function was estimated on the ground of spectral analyses of aromatic hydrocarbons isolated from the oils.

Disproportionation of Hydrogen from the Point of View of Infra-Red Spectra

The intra- and intermolecular disproportionation of hydrogen which leads to the change of hydrogen atom position in aromatic molecules may be expressed as follows:

$$C_{ar} - H + C_{ar} - H = C_{ar} - + CH_2$$
$$2C_{ar} - H + - C_{ar} = 2 - C_{ar} + CH_2$$

As is appears from the scheme the disproportionation is effecting the decrease of the content of aromatic carbon atoms bonded to protons $C_{ar}-H$, parallel to the increase of the content of aromatic carbon atoms devoid of hydrogen $-C_{ar}$. In other words, the disproportionation results in an increase of the ratio $C_{ar}/C_{ar}-H$ which means an increase of condensation of aromatic rings. Such a change should be observable by means of Infra-Red spectra of aromatic hydrocarbons.

The Infra-Red spectra of aromatic hydrocarbons separated from the oils, were made. On the ground of planimetration of absorption bands (Figure 5) corresponding to aromatic $C = C$ skeletal vibrations ($1480-1660$ cm^{-1}) and aromatic $C-H$ stretching vibrations ($3000-3165$ cm^{-1}), it was established that the ratio of the areas was slightly differing (within the range $0.65-0.84$) but that it was equal to 0.7 for 70% of the investigated crude oils. Moreover, the spectra of aromatic hydrocarbons following within the wide range $680-330$ cm^{-1} (Figure 6) are similar as well.

These data lead to the conclusion that the inter- and intramolecular disproportionation of hydrogen ought not to be taken into consideration.

Disproportionation of Hydrogen from the Point of View of Ultra-Violet Spectra

The differences in condensation of aromatic molecules induced by disproportionation of hydrogen should be easily visible through UV-spectra.

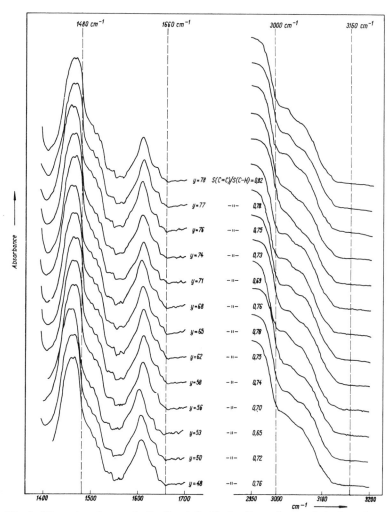

Fig. 5. IR-spectra of aromatic C = C and C – H vibrations of aromatic hydrocarbons separated from various crude oils

(considering the similarity of all spectra only these ones are presented in this Figure which concern aromatic hydrocarbons isolated from the oils containing considerably different amounts of saturated hydrocarbons)

The UV-spectra of aromatic hydrocarbons separated from the oils, were made in cyclohexane solutions (Figure 7).

The similarity of the spectra, especially the lack of considerable change of relative intensities of absorption bands, leads to the same conclusion as for the IR-data: there is no reason to take the disproportionation of hydrogen into consideration.

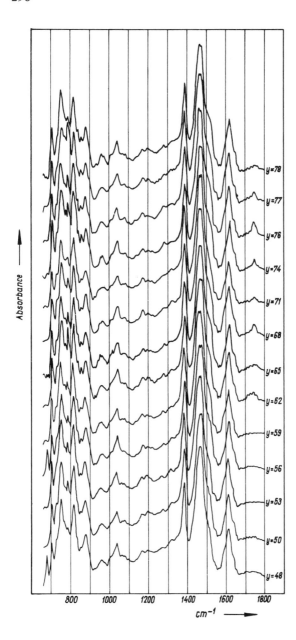

Fig. 6. IR-spectra of aromatic hydrocarbons separated from various crude oils (selection of the spectra as indicated in Figure 5).

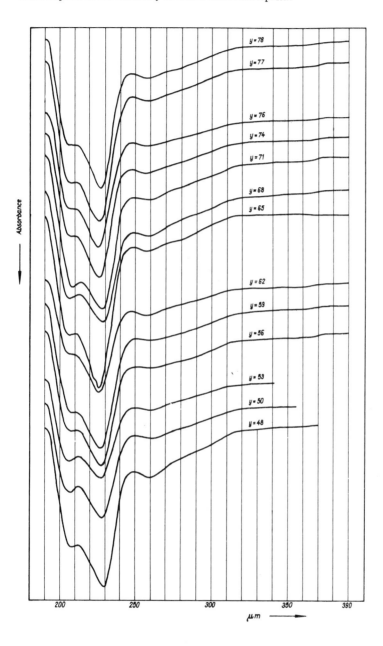

Fig. 7. UV-spectra of aromatic hydrocarbons separated from various crude oils (selection of the spectra as indicated in Figure 5)

The Cleavage Process of saturated Elements from the Point of View of NMR-Data

The clevage process leading to the increase of the content of saturated hydrocarbons may be detected using NMR-spectra since it must change the ratio of saturated and aromatic elements in aromatic fractions.

The NMR-spectra of aromatic hydrocarbons isolated from 55 crude oils separately, were made in CCl_4 solution. One of them is presented in Figure 8.

The ratios of the content of protons bound to saturated carbon atoms and the content of protons bonded with aromatic carbon atoms — H_s/H_{ar} were determined on the ground of integration curves. Putting the case that two protons H_s are bonded with one $C_{sp}3$ atom and one proton H_{ar} — with one aromatic $C_{sp}2$ atom, the ratios C_{sat}/C_{ar}—H were calculated.

The mean value of C_{sat}/C_{ar}—H for the crude oils having Y values lower than 57 is equal to 3.6 and the mean value of C_{sat}/C_{ar}—H for the crude oils having Y values higher than 71 is equal 3.2. These data indicate that the total increase (30w.%) of saturated hydrocarbons (see Figure 2) cannot be induced by the cleavage process exclusively.

The NMR-data, however, provide evidence of participation of cleavage process in the chemical transformation of crude oils.

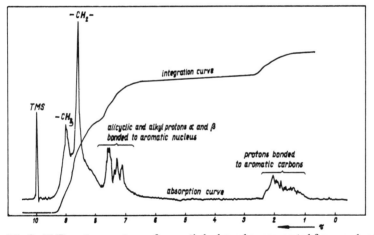

Fig. 8. NMR proton spectrum of aromatic hydrocarbons separated from crude oil

Hydrogenation Process from the Point of View of elementary Analysis

The content of aromatic carbon atoms in the oils varies from 12% to 25% (Figure 2). The only processes which could cause this variation are: disproportionation of hydrogen and hydrogenation. The first process cannot produce any change of hydrogen content in the oils. If the latter is occurring however, it will alter the hydrogen content inevitably. In fact, a relationship was found to exist between hydrogen content $- \%H$ and aromatic carbon atom content $- X$. The relationship has been expressed as a linear equation having high a correlation coefficient, both calculated using least square method:

$$X = -8.65 \%H + 128 \qquad r = 0.922$$

The equation indicates that the hydrogenation process is the cause of the aromatic carbon atom decrease and the saturated hydrocarbon increase as well.

Reconsidering the results of the investigation of 99 crude oils we may say: a hydrogenation process seems to be the basic geochemical process effecting the change in the hydrocarbon part of the crude oils, boiling above 200° C and making up 30–65 % of crude oils. The cleavage process seems to have secondary influence on the composition of the high molecular part of crude oils. No evidence that disproportionation processes are active, has been found.

The present views on the chemistry of crude oil metamorphism particularly on the participation of hydrogenation process are rather controversial. Colombo [4], co-author of the book presenting opinions of numerous geochemists, does not mention hydrogenation process in the chapter "The Geochemical Evolution of Petroleum". Sokolow [5] sees the hydrogen source in radiolytic decomposition of water. According to Dobrianski [3, 6] some components of crude oils are producing hydrogen which is used in the hydrogenation of other components, afterwards. In our opinion, hydrogen comes from outside crude oils since it has been stated that the hydrogen content of total crude oils and the hydrogen content of the "oils" increase parallelly (see Table 1), so crude oil itself cannot be a source of hydrogen.

Moreover, the data presented (Table 1, column d) prove that high-molecular aromatic hydrocarbons are not the only crude oil component being hydrogenated; some other components of the non-boily part of crude oil are hydrogenated as well.

Degree of Crude Oil Metamorphism

A new definition of the degree of crude oil metamorphism is proposed since it is closely connected with the problem of chemistry of crude oil metamorphism.

According to the definition being proposed, the degree of crude oil metamorphism should be expressed by such values of a property of crude oils which fulfil the following conditions:

- the property concerns the component which may be regarded as a syngenetic component of crude oil,
- the values of the property form a monotonic function of time,
- the variation in the property should be explicable from the point of view of chemistry of metamorphism.

Table 1

Y − saturated hydrocarbon content in "oils" w.%	"Oil" content in crude oils w.%:100	Hydrogen content		
		in "oils" w.%	in crude oils w.%	in nonoily part of crude oils, calculated as: $d = \dfrac{c - ab}{1 - a}$
	a	b	c	d
47.6	0.45	12.0	12.0	12.0
50.0	0.41	12.2	12.5	12.7
52.0	0.35	12.2	12.2	12.2
54.2	0.53	—	12.6	—
56.2	0.36	12.4	12.9	13.1
58.2	0.45	12.4	12.6	12.7
60.0	0.52	12.4	12.9	13.5
62.3	0.48	13.1	13.0	12.9
65.0	0.62	12.7	13.1	15.7
68.0	0.48	13.2	13.3	13.5
68.8	0.52	12.7	13.5	14.4
69.7	0.56	13.2	13.6	14.1
71.5	0.55	12.4	14.3	15.3
71.8	0.54	13.2	14.0	15.2
72.0	0.45	13.0	13.2	13.3
73.5	0.57	13.2	13.8	14.7
74.0	0.48	13.0	14.2	15.4
74.0	0.56	13.3	13.6	14.1
74.8	0.46	13.3	13.9	14.4
74.9	0.49	13.4	14.0	14.5
75.7	0.59	13.2	13.8	14.6
76.3	0.60	13.3	13.9	14.8
76.5	0.57	13.5	14.0	14.7
76.5	0.57	13.5	14.0	14.7
77.1	0.47	13.1	14.3	15.3
77.4	0.53	13.3	14.0	14.8
77.7	0.62	13.1	14.1	15.8

The criterion of syngenetic nature should be applied to a component which is present in all crude oils. The criterion seems to be too strong but it is difficult bo find any better one at present knowledge on crude oil metamorphism.

It is difficult as well, to ascertain whether the values of a property form a monotonic function of time. It is evident however, that one should look for such a property among the properties which are mutually related in simple functions, for the following reasons:
if the values of a property A and the values of a property B are a monotonic function of time, then the function A = f/B/ will be a monotonic function as well. The

existance of monotonic function $A = f/B/$ will have to be regarded as a condition sine qua non if one wants to propose the values of a property as a measure of the degree of transformation.

Present knowledge on crude oil metamorphism should form the third criterion. It should be emphasized, that up to date proposals of determination of degree of crude oil metamorphims [3, 7, 8] have only taken into account the third condition, formulated within the presently proposed definition.

The content of saturated hydrocarbons in the oils, i.e. Y-values and the content of aromatic carbon atoms, i.e. X-values fulfil, in our opinion, the above mentioned conditions. Y and X values concern properties of the "oil" which is the component present in all crude oils in considerable amounts and it should therefore be regarded as a syngenetic component. The second condition formulated within the definition is fulfiled by existance of the relationship $Y = -2.25 X + 105$.

The variation in Y and X was explained in the first part of the work as the result of hydrogenation and cleavage processes.

Y values have been accepted as the measure of degree of transformation since determination of X needs more work.

The degree of crude oil metamorphism of Carpathian oil fields were determined and confronted with geological and geographical data [9]. The concept of localization of source rocks on the basis of locality of oil fields having crude oils with the same degree of metamorphism, has been proposed [9].

References

[1]   W. Kisielow: Proceedings of the 7th World Petroleum Congress, vol. 2, p. 533, 1967.

[2]   K. van Nes, H. A. van Westen: Aspects of the Constitution of Mineral Oils. Elsevier, 1951.

[3]   A. F. Dobrianski: Geochimia niefti. Gostoptiechizdat, 1948.

[4]   B. Nagy, U. Colombo: Fundamental Aspects of Petroleum Geochemistry. Elsevier, 1967.

[5]   W. A. Sokolow: Geochimia gazow ziemnoj kory i atmosfiery. Niedra, Moskwa, 1966.

[6]   P. F. Andrejew, A. I. Bogomolow, A. F. Dobrianski, A. A. Karcew: Priewraszczenija niefti w prirodie. Gostoptiechizdat, 1958.

[7]   G. P. Kurbskij: Nieftiechimija; Izd. AN Turkmenskiej Rep., 1963.

[8]   S. R. Sergiejenko: Wysokomolekularnyje sojedinienija niefti. Gostoptiechizdat, 1959.

[9]   W. Kisielow, A. Marzec, H. Kozikowski: Nafta, 24, 33, 1968.

Discussion

A. Hood: Dobrianski (1959, 1961) has emphasized the importance of hydrogen disproportionation reactions in what he calls "transformation of crude oils". Bogomolov (verbal communication) has emphasized that this applies not only to *oils* but also to *any* organic matter (oils, coals, organic-rich rocks) in the subsurface as it is buried to greater depths and temperatures.

The lack of evidence of hydrogen-disproportionation activity in the change of composition of the oils as described in this paper suggests (if Dobrianski and Bogomolov are correct) that these oils may not have undergone any thermal transformation after expulsion from their source formations. Variations in compositions may therefore result from non-thermal transformations of the oil. Such changes in oil composition could occur as an oil migrates from its original depth in a generally upward direction; this is a logical consequence of Philippi's (1965) evidence for deep, high-temperature generation and expulsion of oil, which suggests the deep paraffinic oils may be primary instead of thermally transformed oils.

W. Kisielow and *A. Marzec:* We are aquainted with Dobrianski's theory of petroleum transformation. We knew him personally and appreciate him as an outstanding geochemist. He really emphasized the disproportionation of hydrogen as the main process of petroleum transformation. The similarity of Infra-Red and Ultra-Violet spectra of aromatic hydrocarbons must be however taken into account, as it means that the predominant aromatic hydrocarbons in various crude oils do not show any significant differences of their structure. The disproportionation of hydrogen would have to result in such a difference if it were the main process of crude oil metamorphism.

In other words, we cannot believe in disproportionation of hydrogen if we do not find the evidence of such a process by means of present analytical methods.

Regarding your question as to the part of thermal and non-thermal processes in forming of variations of oil composition which have been stated by us, our opinion is as follows:
what you understand by "non-thermal processes" we call them "physical processes", particularly – the supply or outflow of aromatic (or saturated) hydrocarbons to (or from) the system "oil". If such processes were the reason of any composition variations there would have to exist a relation between oil content in the residua of petroleums (or in the petroleums) and saturated hydrocarbon content in oily part of petroleums. As we can see in the Figure 3, there is no relation between these values. So we are forced to take into account the internal, chemical processes between aromatic and saturated hydrocarbons as the reason of the variations and we cannot load physical processes with the responsibility of these variations.

Interpretation des variations de composition chimique presentees par les bruts des horizons productifs du gisement de Tiguentourine (Algerie)

Michel Correia [1]), Jean Lacaze [2]), Michel Poulet [1]) et Jeannine Roucaché [1])

[1]) Institut Français du Pétrole
   Rueil-Malmaison, France
[2]) Entreprise de Recherches et d'Activités Pétrolières
   Paris, France

This paper contains the results of the chemical analyses made on crudes from the Tiguentourine field in the Polignac Basin, Algeria. These crudes were taken from 5 reservoirs in formations from different periods: The Lower Devonian F_6 and F_4, the Upper Devonian F_2, and the Lower Carboniferous D_4 and D_2. The results were interpreted on the basis of data relating to the oilfield.

The crudes were analyzed in detail in the $C_{10} - C_{25}$ fraction. Mass spectrometry was used to determine what the composition of these crudes was in paraffins, naphthenes with 1 to 6 rings, and aromatic and naphtheno-aromatic families with the formula C_nH_{2n-p} (with n varying from 10 to 25, and p from 6 to 18). Gas chromatography was then used to determine the carbon-by-carbon distribution of normal paraffins.

The crudes from the F_6, F_4 and F_2 reservoirs proved to have differences in content and in distribution of saturated hydrocarbons and aromatics in the different cuts. These variations are interpreted as being due to the different evolution of the crudes depending on their depth of burial. The most highly evolved crudes are richer in saturated hydrocarbons and have a higher ratio of paraffins to naphthenes. The also contain a larger proportion of light aromatics (C_nH_{2n-6}, C_nH_{2n-8}) and a smaller proportion of di- and tri-aromatics (C_nH_{2n-12} to C_nH_{2n-18}).

On the other hand, the crudes from D_4 and D_2 are identical to each other and to the crude from F_2.

On the basis of these results and on that of geological data, we can assume that:

1. The crudes from F_6 and F_4 (Lower Devonian) as well as from F_2 (Upper Devonian) have a common origin and probably accumulated before the Hercynian orogeny.

2. The crudes in the Carboniferous layers (D_4 and D_2) dysmigrated from F_2 via the faults connecting the different reservoirs.

Cette étude présente les résultats des analyses chimiques effectuées sur des bruts provenant du gisement de Tiguentourine (Bassin de Polignac, Algérie) et prélevés dans cinq réservoirs d'âge différent: F_6 F_4 Dévonien inférieur, F_2 Dévonien supérieur, D_4 D_2 Carbonifère inférieur. Ces résultats sont interprétés en fonction des données relatives au gisement.

Les bruts ont été analysés en détail dans la fraction $C_{10} - C_{25}$; par spectrométrie de masse on détermine la composition des bruts en paraffines, en naphtènes de 1 à 6 noyaux, en familles d'hydrocarbures aromatiques et naphténo-aromatiques de formule C_nH_{2n-p} (n variant de 10 à 25, p de 6 à 18). Par chromatographie en phase gazeuse on détermine la répartition des normales paraffines carbone par carbone.

Les bruts du F_6 F_4 F_2 montrent des différences de teneur et de répartition dans les diverses coupes pour les hydrocarbures saturés et aromatiques. Les variations sont interprétées comme dues à une évolution différente des bruts liée à un enfouissement plus ou moins poussé. Les bruts les plus évolués sont plus riches en hydrocarbures saturés, le rapport paraffine sur naphtène étant plus élevé. Ils ont également une teneur plus forte en aromatiques légers (C_nH_{2n-6}, C_nH_{2n-8}) et moins forte en di et tri-aromatiques (C_nH_{2n-14}, C_nH_{2n-16}, C_nH_{2n-18}).

Par contre les bruts du D_4 et du D_2 sont identiques entre eux et au brut du F_2. A partir de ces résultats et des données géologiques, on peut envisager que:

les bruts du $F_4 - F_2$ (Dévonien inférieur) et F_2 (Dévonien supérieur) ont peut-être une origine voisine mais ont subi une évolution différente.

les bruts des niveaux carbonifères ($D_4 - D_2$) proviennent du F_2 par dysmigration de long des failles mettant en relation les différents réservoirs.

I. Introduction

Cette étude a pour objet la présentation des résultats des analyses de composition chimique de bruts provenant des divers niveaux productifs du gisement de Tiguentourine et l'interprétation des variations de composition observées en fonction des données géologiques.

On étudiera d'abord les données géologiques relatives au gisement et les caractéristiques des niveaux réservoirs. Puis on formulera des hypothèses sur la genèse, la mise en place et l'évolution des bruts dans la structure.

Les résultats des analyses chimiques effectuées sur ces bruts seront étudiés et confrontés aux hypothèses géologiques.

On espère ainsi mettre en évidence l'influence des différents facteurs (genèse et évolution) sur les divers constituants du brut.

II. Donnees geologiques et hypotheses sur les caracteristiques des bruts

Le gisement de Tiguentourine est constitué par un anticlinal faillé d'axe Nord-Sud ouvert dans les argiles du Carbonifère supérieur. Des hydrocarbures sont présents dans certains niveaux gréseux ou argilo-gréseux du Carbonifère ($B_{11} - D_0 - D_2 - D_4$) et du Dévonien ($F_2 - F_4 - F_6$). On a prélevé, analysé et étudié les bruts provenant des réservoirs $D_2 - D_4 - F_2 - F_4$ et F_6 (Fig. 1−2).

II. 1. Caractéristiques des réservoirs

L'étude des différents réservoirs montre que le D_2 est le plus poreux et le plus perméable, alors que les caractéristiques des réservoirs D_4, F_2 et F_6 sont médiocres.

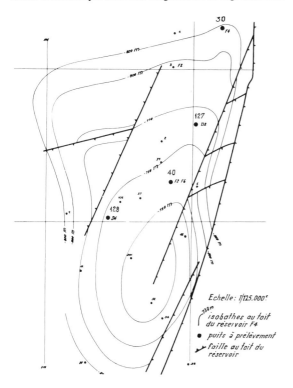

Fig. 1

Gisement de Tiguentourine –
Emplacement des puits à
prélèvement

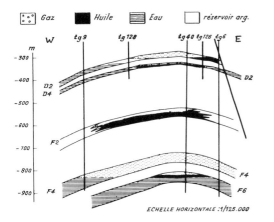

Fig. 2

Coupe schématique ouest-est
du gisement de Tiguentourine

Les fluides sont répartis inégalement, en effet le réservoir F_4 présente une hauteur
en hydrocarbures de 140 m alors que les autres ont une hauteur en hydrocarbures
plus faible (D_2 = 40 m; D_4 = 57 m; F_2 = 65 m; F_6 = 40 m). La plupart d'entre

eux ont une hauteur imprégnée en huile supérieure ou égale à celle en gaz, sauf le réservoir F_4 où le gaz prédomine (rapport hauteur gaz/hauteur huile = 3,3). Les eaux de formation des réservoirs F_2, D_4 et D_2 présentent des salinités moyennes plus fortes que celles du F_6 et du F_4 dont les eaux sont plutôt douces. L'hydro-dynamisme est par contre plus fort pour les réservoirs du Dévonien inférieur $F_6 - F_4$ dont on remarque l'inclinaison des plans huile eau vers le Nord.

Des relations existent entre les différents réservoirs (Fig. 2); c'est ainsi qu'entre le F_6 et le F_4 le contact gaz huile étant à la même cote ($- 830$ m et $- 832$ m) des communications peuvent se faire, il en est de même pour les réservoirs D_2 et D_4 où le contact huile eau est identique ($- 392$ m). Ces relations sont dues aux failles qui peuvent mettre en contact les différents réservoirs (F_6 et F_4, D_2 et D_4) ou favoriser des dysmigrations (cas du F_2 en surpression hydrostatique par rapport aux autres réservoirs).

II. 2. Formation et mise en place des hydrocarbures dans les différents réservoirs

On suppose que la Matière Organique qui fournit les hydrocarbures aux différents réservoirs est localisée dans les formations argileuses encaissant ces horizons. L'évo-lution de la Matière Organique en brut dépend de l'histoire thermique de la roche-mère, de l'enfouissement dans des régions considérées comme des zones d'apport subsidentes (C.D.E.) par rapport à la structure (Fig. 3). L'histoire géologique du bassin de Polignac dans lequel se situe le gisement de Tiguentourine est marquée par deux cycles sédimentaires l'un paléozoique, l'autre mésozoique séparés par la phase d'érosion hercynienne. C'est pourquoi on distinguera deux époques pour l'enfouissement.

La température et par conséquent la profondeur à partir de laquelle la Matière Or-ganique se transforme en hydrocarbures n'est pas connue avec précision (M. Correia 1967, Mc. Louis, B. Tissot 1968) On a retenu comme profondeur critique 1500 m. Les éventuelles roches mères des réservoirs F_6 et F_4 (Fig. 4) atteignent cet enfouis-sement pendant le Paléozoïque, on peut donc envisager une production d'hydrocar-bures au Paléozoïque et au Mésozoïque. Pour le réservoir F_2 (Fig. 4) les 1500 m sont atteints à la fin du Paléozoïque c'est donc surtout au Mésozoïque que le brut alimentant le réservoir F_2 sera produit. Enfin, pour les réservoirs D_4 et D_2, cette profondeur est à peine atteinte au Mésozoïque la production d'hydrocarbures sera par conséquent faible.

Les bruts ainsi produits dans les zones subsidentes vont se déplacer vers la zone haute de Tiguentourine. Ce déplacement étant identique pour chacun des bruts les modifications de composition chimique (M. Poulet 1968) imputables à la migra-tion seront homogènes. La mise en place du brut ne peut intervenir que si la ferme-ture est suffisante or à Tiguentourine celle-ci est déjà favorable au Paléozoïque pour

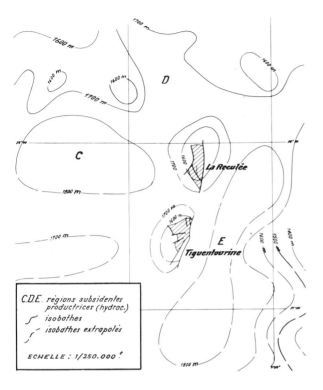

Fig. 3. Bassin de Polignac – Région de Tiguentourine la Reculée. Isobathes du réservoir F6 à la discordance hercynienne

emmagasiner les hydrocarbures produits (Fig. 3). Une fois le brut mis en place comme le gisement varie de profondeur au cours des temps géologiques, il va être influencé par l'histoire thermique du réservoir.

II. 3. Hypothèses géologiques sur les caractéristiques des bruts

En fonction des données géologiques précédemment énoncées on peut tenter de définir les caractéristiques des bruts étudiés.

Les bruts des réservoirs du Dévonien inférieur (F_6 et F_4) seront semblables par leur origine, par leur évolution et parce qu'ils peuvent communiquer entre eux; les légères différences constatées seraient dues à une influence de la température plus faible pour le F_4 et à des caractéristiques lithologiques différentes.

Le réservoir du Dévonien supérieur (F_2) possède un brut différent des précédents par son origine (roche-mère du Dévonien supérieur) et par son état d'évolution moins marqué.

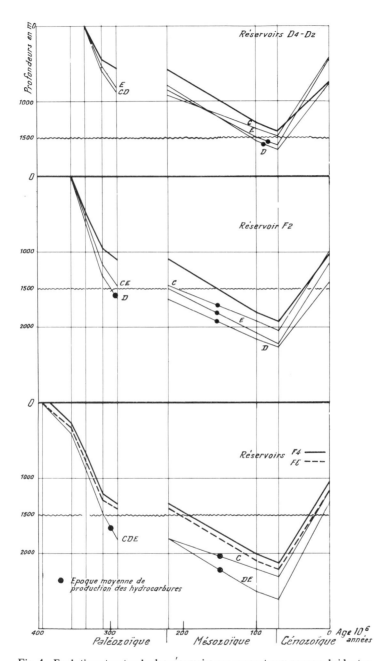

Fig. 4. Evolution structurale des réservoirs par rapport aux zones subsidentes

Les réservoirs du Carbonifère inférieur (D_4 et D_2) doivent avoir des bruts semblables car ils sont en communication. Par rapport aux bruts précédents $F_6 - F_4 - F_2$ ont peut envisager deux possibilités suivant l'hypothèse géologique adoptée: ou bien les bruts du Carbonifère D_4 et D_2 sont moins évolués que les trois bruts dévoniens ou bien des dysmigrations le long des failles sont possibles du réservoir F_2 vers les réservoirs carbonifères et en conséquence les bruts F_2, D_4 et D_2 auront une composition chimique voisine.

Les analyses chimiques effectuées sur ces bruts et les résultats obtenus nous permettront de confirmer ou d'infirmer ces hypothèses.

III. Composition chimique des bruts et interpretation geochimique

III. 1. Introduction

Les bruts étudiés ont été prélevés à pression atmosphérique en tête de puits. C'est la fraction $C_{10} +$ qui a été analysée suivant la méthode décrite dans une précédente communication (R. Boulet, N. Guichard, etc. ... 1967) il a été démontré par ailleurs qu'elle représente bien le brut in situ (M. Poulet, J. Rouchache, 1966).

Les données globales nous renseignent sur les pourcentages de distillat d'hydrocarbures saturés et aromatiques dans les différentes fractions.

Les analyses détaillées effectuées sur la gamme (C_{10} C_{25}) par spectrométrie de masse permettent de déterminer la composition des bruts en paraffines, en cyclo-paraffines, en familles d'hydrocarbures aromatiques et naphténo-aromatiques.

Pour des raisons analytiques les hydrocarbures saturés sont analysés par coupes étroites de 2 à 3 carbones, et les résultats sont donnés en % volumiques. Pour éliminer les interférences coupe à coupe dues à la distillation du brut, on compare la répartition des pourcentages cumulés des paraffines et des naphtènes. Pour s'affranchir de l'influence du mode de prélèvement on considère les rapports des familles d'hydrocarbures saturés entre elles. Les familles d'hydrocarbures aromatiques de formule générale $C_n H_{2n-p}$ sont analysées carbone par carbone en fonction de n et p. On donne pour chaque brut la répartition pondérale de chaque famille par rapport aux $C_{10} +$, la répartition molaire de la fraction aromatique $C_{10} - C_{25}$ considérée égale à 100 moles, et la répartition molaire de chaque famille $C_n H_{2n-p}$ considérée comme égale à 100 moles.

III. 2. Comparaison entre bruts des réservoirs F_6 et F_4 et F_2

On étudiera successivement les résultats des données globales puis ceux des analyses détaillées sur la fraction $C_{10} - C_{25}$ des trois bruts: F_6 F_4 F_2.

III. 2.1. Analyses globales: composition pondérale des C_{10}+

Les teneurs totales en hydrocarbures saturés décroissent du F_6 au F_2 (F_6 = 82,4; F_4 = 77,6; F_2 = 72,0).

Cependant leur concentration dans les deux fractions $C_{10}-C_{25}$ (71,4 à 73,3) et C_{25}+ (26,7 à 28,6) est voisine pour tous les bruts, la fraction $C_{10}-C_{25}$ étant plus riche.

Les teneurs totales en hydrocarbures aromatiques et en résines varient en sens inverse: elles augmentent du F_6 au F_2 (F_6 = 17,6; F_4 = 22,0; F_2 = 27,0). En outre, les concentrations varient: dans la fraction $C_{10}-C_{25}$ elles décroissent du F_6 au F_2. Le rapport des concentrations en hydrocarbures aromatiques dans les 2 fractions $C_{10}-C_{25}$ et C_{25}+ est voisin de 1.

III. 2.2. Analyse détaillée de la fraction $C_{10}-C_{25}$

Hydrocarbures saturés: le brut F_6 est plus riche en paraffines (F_6 = 39,1 %; F_2 = 32,0 %).

Dans la gamme $C_{10}-C_{25}$: on a dans l'ordre décroissant $F_6 > F_4 > F_2$. Par contre les trois bruts ont des teneurs voisines en naphtènes. De ce fait la répartition des concentrations des deux familles est la suivante: paraffines : $F_6 > F_4 > F_2$; naphtènes : $F_6 < F_4 < F_2$.

La répartition volumique coupe par coupe des paraffines montre que la différence observée entre F_6 et F_4-F_2 se situe dans la gamme $C_{10}-C_{19}$ (Fig. 5). La répartition des naphtènes est voisine pour les trois bruts.

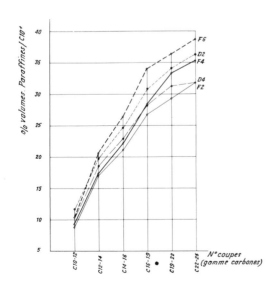

Fig. 5

Répartition des paraffines en pourcentages cumulés coupe par coupe

Les rapports paraffines/naphtènes (Fig. 6) montrent que l'on a pour toutes les coupes l'ordre suivant : F_6, F_4, F_2, les différences entre le F_6 et le F_4 étant plus faibles.

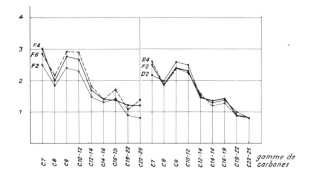

Fig. 6

Rapport Σ paraffines sur Σ naphtènes

Hydrocarbures aromatiques et naphténo-aromatiques:

Répartition en familles C_nH_{2n-p} (p = 6 à 18): la répartition pondérale (Fig. 7) montre que pour chaque famille on a l'ordre suivant $F_6 \simeq F_4 < F_2$; la répartition des concentrations (C_nH_{2n-p} = 100 %) (Fig. 8) montre les variations suivantes:

C_nH_{2n-6}, C_nH_{2n-8} : $F_6 > F_4 > F_2$

C_nH_{2n-10}, C_nH_{2n-12} : $F_6 = F_4 = F_2$

C_nH_{2n-14}, C_nH_{2n-16}, C_nH_{2n-18} : $F_6 < F_4 < F_2$

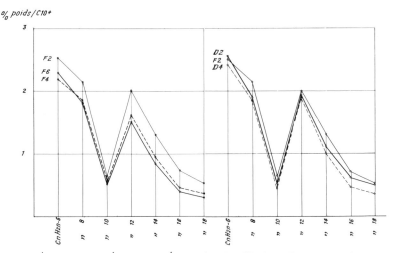

Fig. 7. Répartition pondérale des différentes familles d'hydrocarbures aromatiques

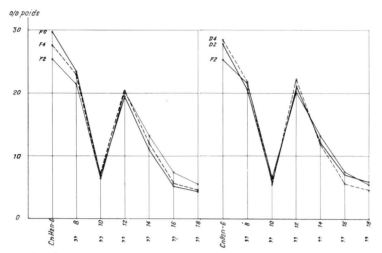

Fig. 8. Répartition des concentrations en poids de chaque famille d'hydrocarbures aromatiques (Σ familles: 100 % en poids Gamme $C_{10} - C_{25}$)

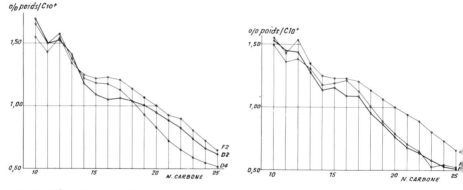

Fig. 9. Répartition pondérale des hydrocarbures aromatiques en fonction de leur rang n quelque soit p (Gamme $C_{10} - C_{25}$)

Répartition en fonction de n quel que soit p (n = 10 à 25): la répartition pondérale (Fig. 9) montre que le brut du F_2 est plus riche dans toute la gamme de carbone particulièrement pour n = 17, les bruts du F_6 et du F_4 étant voisins. On notera cependant une inversion au niveau du carbone de rang 12; la répartition des concentrations (Fig. 10) montre:

de C_{10} à C_{12} $F_6 > F_4 > F_2$

de C_{13} à C_{17} $F_4 > F_6 > F_2$

de C_{17} à C_{25} $F_6 \simeq F_4 < F_2$

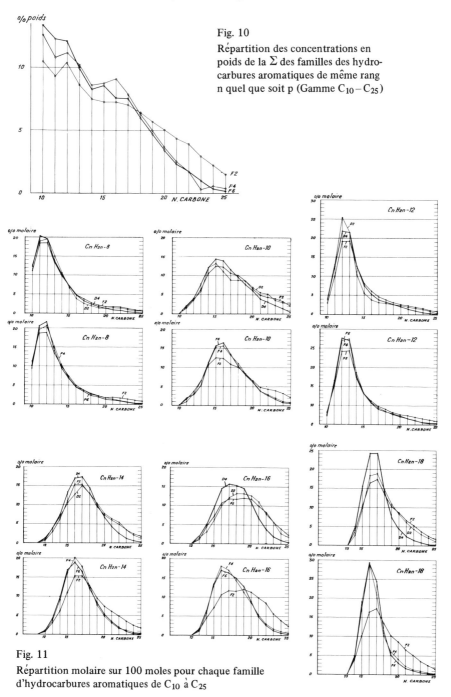

Fig. 10

Répartition des concentrations en poids de la Σ des familles des hydrocarbures aromatiques de même rang n quel que soit p (Gamme $C_{10} - C_{25}$)

Fig. 11

Répartition molaire sur 100 moles pour chaque famille d'hydrocarbures aromatiques de C_{10} à C_{25}

Répartition des concentrations molaires de chaque famille (C_nH_{2n-p} = 100 moles) (Fig. 11): on n'a pas pris en considération la famille C_nH_{2n-6} incomplète. On contate que les bruts du F_6 et du F_4 sont très voisins: cependant quelques différences apparaissent dans les maxima de chaque famille. Ces maxima correspondent au constituant ayant 3 à 4 carbones substitués.

Par rapport aux bruts F_6 F_4, le F_2 présente une répartition différente: dans toutes les familles et principalement pour C_nH_{2n-14}, C_nH_{2n-16}, C_nH_{2n-18}, il est moins riche dans la gamme $C_{10}-C_{18}$ et plus riche dans la gamme $C_{18}-C_{25}$.

III. 2.3. Interprétation

Les hypothèses géologiques précédemment formulées (cf. II. 3) permettent d'interpréter les variations constatées comme dues à une évolution différente des trois bruts. Le brut F_2 serait moins évolué que les bruts F_6 et F_4 car il a été produit plus récemment et à une profondeur moindre, en outre depuis sa mise en place dans le gisement, il a été soumis à une température plus faible (dénivelée de 200 m entre F_2 et F_4).

Le brut F_6 apparait comme un peu plus évolué que le F_4. Le peu d'amplitude des différences observées s'explique par la mise en place contemporaine aux deux bruts, la faible dénivelée entre les deux niveaux (100 m) et la possibilité de communication entre les réservoirs.

III. 3. Comparaison des bruts des réservoirs $F_2-D_4-D_2$

La comparaison des bruts $F_6-F_4-F_2$ a permis de faire apparaitre un certain nombre de variations interprétées comme dues à une évolution différente des trois bruts. En comparant les bruts D_2 D_4 au brut F_2 on doit:

– ou bien retrouver les mêmes variations que celles observées entre F_2 et F_6, F_4, les bruts D_2 D_4 étant moins évolués que le brut F_2 ;

– ou bien trouver des variations différentes qui seraient elles liées à une alimentation par dysmigration à partir du F_2.

III. 3.1. Analyses globales – composition pondérale des $C_{10}+$

Les teneurs totales en hydrocarbures saturés et aromatiques et en résines sont voisines pour les trois bruts.

Hydrocarbures saturés: F_2 = 73,0; D_4 = 73,3; D_2= 75,4
Hydrocarbures aromatiques: F_2 = 27,0; D_4 = 26,7; D_2 = 24,5

Le brut D_2 se différencie des deux autres bruts par une concentration plus élevée en saturés et en aromatiques dans la fraction $C_{10}-C_{25}$.

Hydrocarbures saturés: F_2 = 73,0; D_4 = 70,6; D_2 = 76,8
Hydrocarbures aromatiques: F_2 = 46,0; D_4 = 44,3; D_2 = 52,6

III. 3.2. Analyse détaillée de la fraction $C_{10} - C_{25}$

Hydrocarbures saturés: le brut D_2 est un peu plus riche en paraffines que les deux autres qui ont des teneurs identiques. Les trois bruts présentent des teneurs en naphtènes très voisines.

% paraffines: $F_2 = 32{,}0$; $D_4 = 32{,}0$; $D_2 = 36{,}3$
% naphtènes: $F_2 = 22{,}0$; $D_4 = 20{,}7$; $D_2 = 22{,}9$

La répartition des concentrations des diverses familles est la même pour les trois bruts.

La répartition volumique coupe par coupe des paraffines (Fig. 5) montre que les bruts F_2 et D_4 sont très voisins et que le brut D_2 est légèrement plus riche dans chaque coupe.

Les rapports paraffines/naphtènes (Fig. 6) confirment l'analogie étroite de F_2 et D_4, eux-mêmes peu différents du brut D_2.

Hydrocarbures aromatiques et naphténoaromatiques:

Répartition en familles C_nH_{2n-p} (p = 6 à 18): la répartition pondérale (Fig. 7) montre que les trois bruts sont très voisins. On a cependant pour toutes les familles, les différences étant faibles, $D_4 < D_2 < F_2$. La répartition des concentrations (Fig. 8) confirme cette analogie. Les seules différences concernent:

C_nH_{2n-6} $F_2 < D_2 = D_4$

C_nH_{2n-16}; C_nH_{2n-18} $D_4 < F_2 = D_2$

Répartition en fonction de n quel que soit p (n = 10 à 25): la répartition pondérale et celle des concentrations (Fig. 9) montrent les faits suivants:

de C_{10} à C_{14} : $D_2 \simeq D_4 \simeq F_2$

de C_{14} à C_{18} : $F_2 = D_4 > D_2$

de C_{18} à C_{25} : $F_2 = D_2 > D_4$

Répartition des concentrations molaires dans chaque famille: les trois bruts sont identiques pour les C_nH_{2n-8}, C_nH_{2n-10}, C_nH_{2n-12} (Fig. 11). Pour les autres familles (Fig. 11) on a une analogie étroite entre D_2 et F_2, D_4 se différenciant par une concentration plus forte dans la gamme $C_{10} - C_{19}$, associée à une concentration plus faible dans la gamme $C_{19} - C_{25}$.

III. 3.3. Interprétation

Dans l'ensemble les variations constatées entre les bruts F_2, D_2, D_4, sont plus faibles que celles observées pour les bruts F_2, F_4, F_6. En outre, elles sont beaucoup moins cohérentes.

On avait en effet entre le F_2 et le F_4 des différences similaires à celles existant entre le F_4 et le F_6 mais plus importantes. Ici tantôt les trois bruts sont identiques, tantôt F_2 est identique à D_2 (analyses globales et analyse détaillée des saturés), tantôt F_2 est identique à D_4 (répartition molaire des aromatiques C_nH_{2n-16} et C_nH_{2n-18}).

Dans le cas de variations liées à l'évolution on aurait dû retrouver pour l'ensemble des bruts l'ordre suivant: F_6, F_4, F_2, D_4, D_2, (D_4 et D_2 étant très voisins). On peut donc interpréter les faibles variations observées entre les trois bruts D_2, D_4, F_2, comme dues à une dysmigration du brut F_2 dans les réservoirs D_2 et D_4 à la faveur de failles. Cette dysmigration a été assez récente pour que la différence de température liée à la dénivelée existant entre F_2 et D_2 D_4 n'ait pu jouer. Cette interprétation est confirmée par le fait que dans les gisements du bassin de Polignac les niveaux carbonifères ne sont productifs que lorsque le réservoir F_2 renferme du brut et que la structure est faillée.

IV. Conclusions

Les observations statistiques faites sur des bruts (Tissot, B., 1966) ou les études sur modèles naturels (Louis, M., Tissot, B., 1967; Philippi, G.T. 1966) indiquent que l'évolution du brut en fonction de la profondeur se traduit par une augmentation de la teneur en saturés et en paraffines, une diminution de la teneur en aromatiques et naphténo-aromatiques et une condensation de leur structure.

On retrouve ces mêmes variations sur les bruts des réservoirs F_6 F_4 F_2 malgré les faibles différences de profondeur (300 m entre F_2 et F_6), en outre des faits nouveaux apparaissent.

L'évolution plus poussée se traduit en effet:
- *sur la fraction* $C_{10}+$: par une augmentation de la teneur totale en saturés et une décroissance de la teneur en résines et en aromatiques;

  par une augmentation de la concentration en aromatiques dans la fraction $C_{10}-C_{25}$.
- *sur la fraction* $C_{10}-C_{25}$; pour les saturés: par une augmentation de la teneur en paraffines (en particulier de C_{10} à C_{19}), le rapport paraffines/naphtènes croissant dans toutes les coupes de distillation;

  pour les aromatiques: par une diminution de la teneur dans toutes les familles de C_nH_{2n-6} à C_nH_{2n-18}, par une concentration plus forte en familles mono-aromatiques C_nH_{2n-6} et C_nH_{2n-8}) et une concentration plus faible en di et tri-aromatiques (C_nH_{2n-14}, C_nH_{2n-16}, C_nH_{2n-18}), dans chaque famille d'hydrocabures aromatiques de C_nH_{2n-8} à C_nH_{2n-18} par une concentration plus forte en aromatiques peu substitués $n < 18$ et plus forte en aromatiques très substitués.

Les variations de composition chimique subies par un brut lors de sa dysmigration sont mal connues (Poulet, M. 1968). On pense qu'elles sont de même nature mais moins importantes que celles causées par l'évolution. Dans le cas particulier de

Tiguentourine les variations observées entre F_2 (brut d'origine) et D_2 D_4 (bruts dysmigrés) sont faibles et inférieures à celles constatées entre les bruts des deux réservoirs D_2, D_4 distants de 40 m et vraisemblablement en communication. On peut donc penser que dans ce cas la dysmigration a introduit des variations de composition chimique trop faibles pour être considérées comme caractéristiques du phénomène.

Remerciements: Nous remercions l'Entreprise de Recherches et d'Activités Pétrolières qui a bien voulu nous autoriser à publier ces résultats.

Bibliographie

Boulet, R., Guichard-Loudet, N., Henrion, P., Poulet, M., Raynal, M., Roucaché, J. (I.F.P.) 1968, Cornu, A., Ulriche, J. (C.E.N.G.) 1968: Analyse détaillée d'un brut par chromatographie en phase gazeuse, spectrométrie de masse et RMN-Application aux problèmes géochimiques. Revue de l'Institut Français du Pétrole, **XXIII** n° 3, mars 1968.

Correia, M., 1967: Relations possibles entre l'état de conservation des éléments figurés de la matière organique (microfossiles palynaplanctonologiques) et l'existence de gisements d'hydrocarbures. Revue de l'institut Français du Pétrole, **XXI** n° 9, septembre 1967.

Correia, M., Lacaze, J., Poulet, M., 1968: Rapport I.F.P./E.R.A.P., réf. 15.455 (a & b), janvier 1968.

Correia, M., Lacaze, J., Poulet, M., 1968: Rapport I.F.P./E.R.A.P., réf. 15.512, janvier 1968.

Louis, MC., Tissot, B., 1967: Influence de la température et de la pression sur la formation des hydrocarbures dans les argiles à kérogène. Publication au VII° Congrès Mondial du Pétrole, Mexico 2 au 9 avril 1967.

Philippi, G.T., 1956: On the depth time and mechanism of petroleum generation. Geochimica Cosmichimica Acta **29**.

Poulet, M., Roucaché, J., 1966: Influence du mode d'échantillonnage sur la composition chimique des fractions légères d'une huile brute. (à paraître). 3° symposium international de Géochimie Organique de Londres, 1966.

Poulet, M., 1968: Problèmes posés par la migration secondaire du Pétrole et sa mise en place dans les gisements. Revue de l'Institut Français du Pétrole, **XXIII** n° 2, février 1968.

Roucaché, J., 1968: Rapport I.F.P., réf. 15.510.

Smith, G., Wilcock, B., 1964: The Phanerozoic Time Scale. A symposium dedicated Pr. A. Holmes edit. by W. B. Horland. Suppl. Quaterly Journ. Geol. Soc. London, **1205**.

Tissot, B., 1966: Problèmes géochimiques de la genèse et de la Migration du Pétrole. Revue de l'Institut Francais du Pétrole, **XXI** n° 11, novembre 1966.

Discussion

R.J. Murris: 1) Has any attempt been made to correlate source bed extracts with crude properties.
2) What has been the influence of the influx of fresh water on the crude properties of Tiguentourine?

M. Correia: 1) Pour l'instant il n'y a pas eu de corrélation entre les extraits des éventuelles roches-mères et les propriétés des bruts.
2) Nous pensons que l'influence des eaux météoriques récentes, si influence il y a, a pu évidemment se manifester sur les bruts des réservoirs F_4 et F_6. Cependant un certain nombre de résultats d'analyse concordent avec ceux signalés dans la bibliographie comme conséquences de l'évolution.

E.V. Whitehead: In view of the similarity of the mass spectrometric analyses that have been reported, will the authors elaborate:
a) Was the method based on a matrix analysis;
b) Which was the time interval between analyses of individual samples;
c) Was the method standardised to overcome variations in mass spectrometre source sensivity.

J. Roucaché: Nous avons traité ce problème dans une communication présentée au Congrès de Géochimie de Londres par M. Poulet et J. Roucaché: "Influence du mode de prélèvement sur la composition chimique d'un brut "
Je signalerai seulement qu'une analyse faite sur Atlas CH_4 au Centre d'Etudes Nucléaires de Grenoble, et ensuite sur MS 12 à l'Institut Français du Pétrole nous ont donné des résultats identiques.

K.E.H. Göhring: You did not mention the crudes from the shallowest reservoir in Tiguentourine, the B 11 reservoir, in your paper. These crudes from the B-reservoir differ as far as I know not from the other crudes, especially in the light aromatic content. Do you have any reason not to mention these crudes or did you not analyse these oils.

M. Correia: Nous n'avons pas analysé les bruts du réservoir B 11 car ces bruts ne nous ont pas été fournis.

Geochemical Interpretation of Libyan and North-Saharan Crude oil Analyses

Rustum Byramjee and Lionel Vasse

Compagnie Francaise des Pétroles
Paris, France

Compagnie Francaise de Raffinage
Harfleur, France

A study of North-Western Libyan crudes (concessions 23-61) was carried out to find out their relationship and give reasonable assumptions on their origin and migration paths. A comparison was made with North-Saharan crudes previously analysed with similar techniques.

The samples from Libya all come from the palaeozoic "Acacus" formation which apparently contains both source rocks and reservoir rocks. Two types of accumulations were located:

a) Structural traps towards the centre of the basin (Southwards);
b) Bevel traps below the palaeozoic unconformity (Northwards).

The analytical results show that all crudes are of the same family, i.e. of the same origin, and that the minor differences found, especially in the aromatic profiles, could account for a regional migration from the SW to the NE. In addition to their chemical composition, geological considerations and source-rock studies show that these oils are palaeozoic. This last point is confirmed by comparing the Acacus oil with the North-Saharan palaeozoic crudes, especially on the basis of aromatic profiles and isoprenoid distributions. The Acacus oil is similar to the Saharan type II oil, i.e. Hassi-Messaoud type, but is less matured. Besides, some of the differences found reflect directly respective differences in the facies of origin.

Introduction

A study of North Western palaeozoic Libyan crudes was carried out to find out their similarities and give reasonable assumptions on their origin and migration paths. On a scientific standpoint, these crudes are of particular interest because of the fact that the same geological formation presumably contains both the source rocks and the reservoir rocks. In the same line it was thought desirable to establish a comparison with North-Saharan palaezoic crudes previously analysed with similar techniques, essentially on the basis of origin and maturation.

Geological Environment

On Figure 1 is shown the *geographic location* of the main North-Saharan fields, the Tunisian El Borma field and the area of small North-Libyan pools.

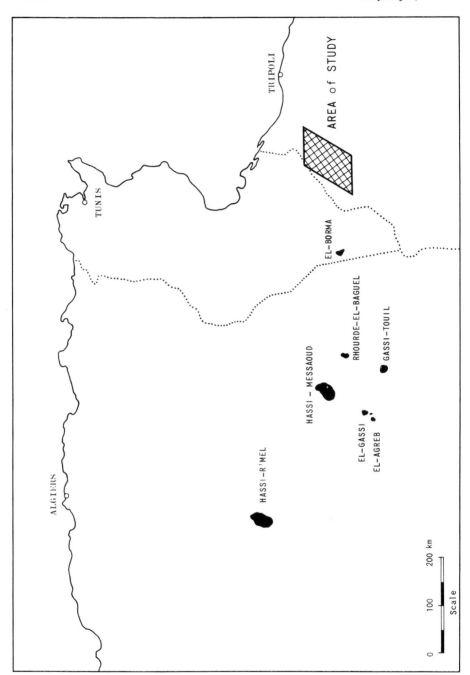

Fig. 1. Geographic location of the main North-Saharan fields and North-Libyan pools

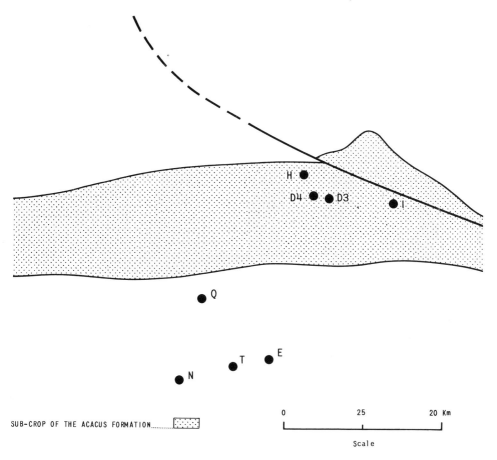

Fig. 2. Location map of the area of study with the sub-crop limits of the Acacus formation

Figure 2 shows the area of study which is situated in the *North-Western part of Libya.* On this figure is represented the *sub-crop limits* of the palaeozoic formation called Acacus in which are located the oil pools. The age of the Acacus formation ranges from upper Silurian to lower Devonian. The regional dip is southwards.

Each dot on Figure 2 corresponds to an oil pool, samples of which were analyzed. There are two different types of traps:

– In the South, *structural traps* (Hamada) (wells Q, N, T, E)
– In the North, *stratigraphic traps* (Djeffara) (wells, H, D_3, D_4, I) in beds truncated by the palaeozoic unconformity surface, and covered by permian red shales.

These two types of traps can be better seen on Figure 3, which is a North-South section that gives a schematic image of the geological conditions.

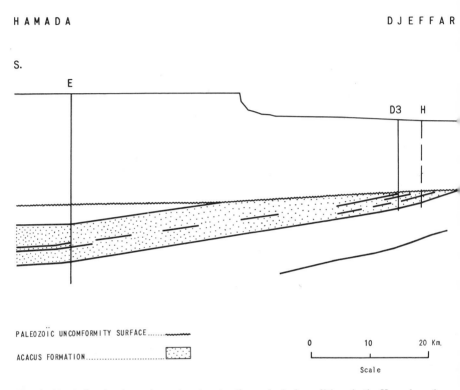

Fig. 3. North-South schematic section showing the geological conditions in the Hamada and Djeffara areas

The *Acacus formation* consists of mainly shales, with sandy intervals. The sandstone layers are more or less lenticular, but at least some of them seem to be continuous throughout the whole area.

This section also points out the differences in depth of burial from the stratigraphic traps to the structural traps.

Regarding *the origin of oil,* it is obvious that the stratigraphic traps could not have existed before the deposition of the permo-triassic beds which seal them. On the other hand the permian red shales are by no means source rocks. So the Acacus oil must be of palaeozoic origin. This is supported by previous geochemical studies which have demonstrated that some of the Acacus and underlying shales are good source rocks for oil.

This situation is somewhat *similar* to that of the *North-Sahara* where some oil fields are sealed by lower Triassic red shales, and where the source rocks must be seeked in the Silurian and Devonian black shales.

In both cases, much of the oil generated must have been lost at the time of the pre-Triassic erosion.

Crude Analyses

The samples were all taken on site at standard surface conditions. They were analyzed at the Research Laboratory of the Compagnie Française de Raffinage.

Only conventionnal analyses were made, the essential of them being as follows:

- U. S. Bureau of Mines standard distillation;
- Distribution of normal paraffins from C_3 to C_{22}, (by means of gas chromatography and molecular sieves);
- Aromatic percentages for B. O. M. fractions 3 to 10 (mass spectrometry);
- Isoprenoids pristane and phytane (gas chromatography).

Interpretation of Analytical Results

From the general characteristics, the B. O. M. fractions and the n-paraffins distribution, it appears immediately that all the crudes analyzed belong to the same family.

The correlation index curves are given on Figure 4. One can see that all the curves fit in the paraffino-naphtenic category of H. M. Smith. There are slight differences from one crude to another but practically no regional variation from South to North: the curves are rather intermingled.

The aromatic profiles (Figure 5) are more significant for they show greater differences that correspond to regional variations: the Hamada crudes are more aromatic in the light fractions than the Djeffara crudes.

The saturated hydrocarbons/aromatics ratio versus depth (Figure 6):

- first illustrates the fact that the Hamada pools are all deeper than the Djeffara ones,
- second, that the Hamada oils are the poorest in saturated hydrocarbons, which is what might be expected after Figure 5.

On Figure 7 have been plotted the average percentages in *phytane and pristane* for the Hamada and the Djeffara crudes. The pristane/phytane ratio is almost identical [1, 4] and so are the N–C_{17}/pristane and N–C_{18}/phytane ratios.

So the only difference appears to be a statistical increase in isoprenoids from the Hamada area to the Djeffara area.

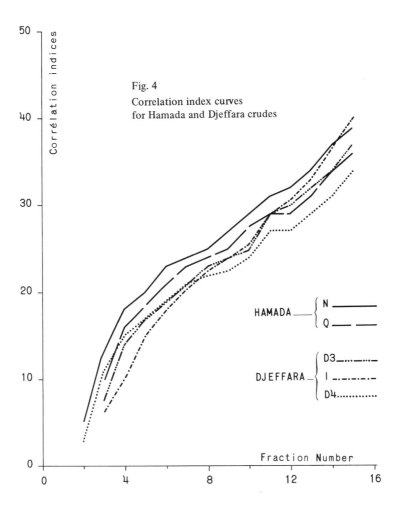

Fig. 4
Correlation index curves
for Hamada and Djeffara crudes

Summarizing the analytical results of the Hamada and Djeffara crudes, we have:
— *as similarities:*
— same B. O. M. type
— similar general characteristics
— same pristane/phytane ratio
— *as differences* (actually regional differences), when one proceeds from South to North one cane observe:
— a decrease in aromatics in fractions 3 to 10
— an increase of the saturated/aromatics ratio
— an increase of the isoprenoid content

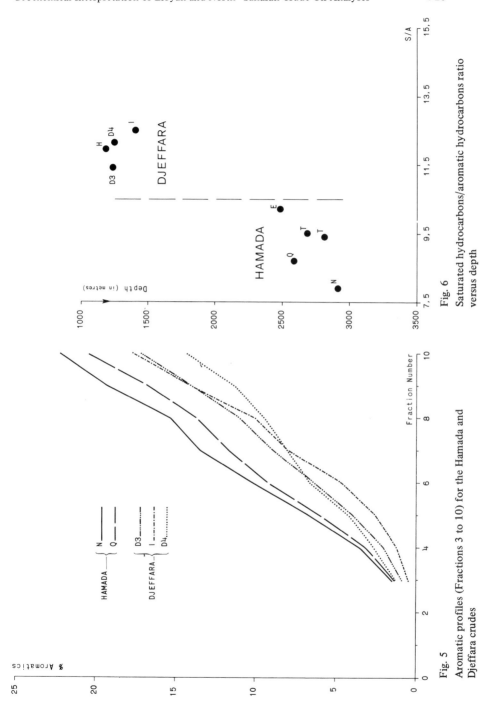

Fig. 6
Saturated hydrocarbons/aromatic hydrocarbons ratio versus depth

Fig. 5
Aromatic profiles (Fractions 3 to 10) for the Hamada and Djeffara crudes

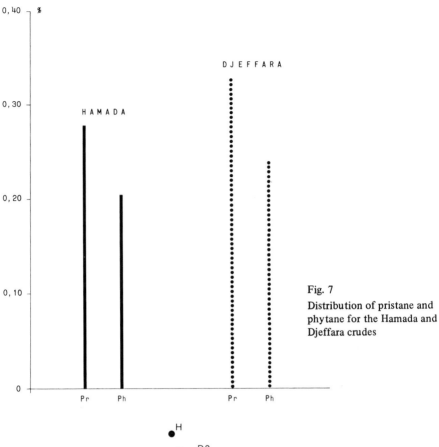

Fig. 7

Distribution of pristane and
phytane for the Hamada and
Djeffara crudes

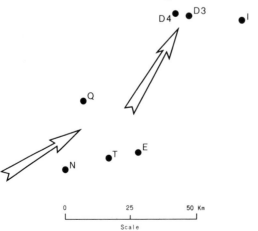

Fig. 8

Regional migration path in North-
West Libya

A variation in oil properties, similar but weaker than that observed from *South to North, can also be seen from West to East.*

These results are consistant with the differences in geological conditions, i.e. greater burial and higher temperatures in the Hamada zone.

Thus we came to the conclusion that the latest *regional migration path must have been from the SW to the NNE,* as shown by the arrows on Figure 8. (This also definitely rules out the hypothesis of a Triassic source.)

Comparison with the North-Saharan Crudes

The North-Saharan crudes are accumulated in palaeozoic or lower triassic reservoirs. But it has been demonstrated that they all are of palaeozoic origin.

They can be divided in two main types on the *aromatic profiles* (fractions 3 to 10) (Figure 9):
— Type I shows a very low aromaticity,
— Type II has a much higher aromatic content.

After their *correlation index curves,*
— Type I is highly paraffinic,
— Type II is naphteno-paraffinic. This second type includes the Hassi-Messaoud oil.

A simple way of comparing North-Saharan and West Libyan crudes by means of their major constituants is to plot the corresponding values on *a triangular diagram, Paraffins, Aromatics, Napthenes.* One can see on Figure 10 that Libya Hamada and Libya Djeffara are very close to one another, and also close to Sahara II, whilst Sahara I is distinctly more paraffinic.

But regarding *isoprenoid* contents, Sahara I and II are very similar, and strikingly different from Libyan types (Figure 11). These differences remain unchanged when one considers the $N–C_{17}$/pristane and $N–C_{18}$/phytane ratios instead of the absolute percentages of phytane and pristane. Moreover, the pristane/phytane ratio is lower for Sahara II than for Libya.

According to different authors, the isoprenoid content is interpreted as an indicator of evolution of crude oils and the distribution of isoprenoids is somewhat related to the original organic matter.

Thus it seems that our *Libyan crudes have a similar origin than the North-Saharan ones but are less matured. This is in accordance with the geological history of North Africa:* The North-Saharan crudes were buried much deeper than the North-West

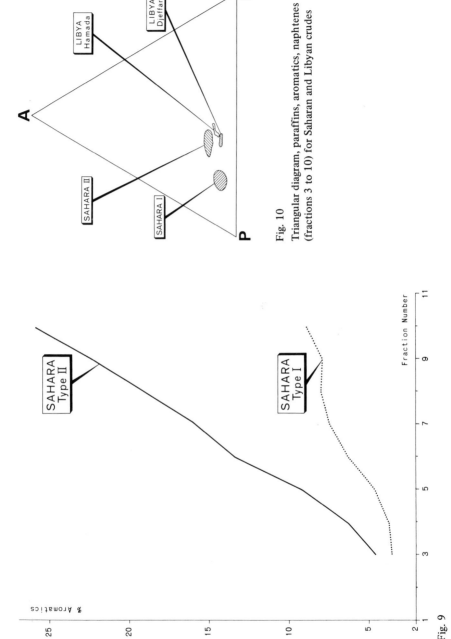

Fig. 10

Triangular diagram, paraffins, aromatics, naphtenes
(fractions 3 to 10) for Saharan and Libyan crudes

Fig. 9

Aromatic profiles (fractions 3 to 10) typical of the two categories of

Libyan crudes and as a consequence submitted to high temperature. On the other hand the source rocks appear to be in both cases essentially restricted in upper Silurian (Glothlandian) and lower or middle Devonian black shales. The regional facies changes fròm West of East would account for variations in the pristane/phytane ratio.

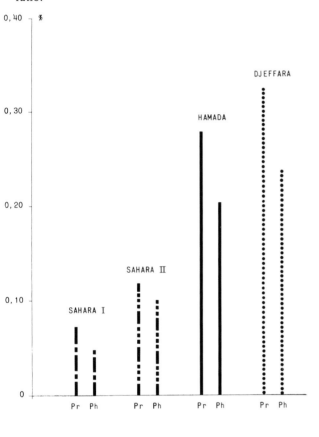

Fig. 11
Distribution of isoprenoids, pristane and phytane for Saharan and Libyan crudes

Concluding Remarks

It should be emphasized that the results and ideas discussed in this paper are based on simple analytical procedures that any oil company can set up. They also concern a geologically well known area, so that our work essentially consisted in *integrating geological and geochemical data.*

Geochemical studies, both on source rocks and on crude oils, permit to find some of the factors controlling oil and gas accumulation, which has not been sufficiently considered so far, and which can be added to other geological factors for prospect evaluation.

References

[1]   Barbat, William, N.: Crude-oil correlations and their role in exploration. Bull. Amer. Assoc. Petrol. Geol. **V**, 51, N°7 (July 1967), pp. 1255–1292, 29 Figs., 1 table.

[2]   Jones, T. S. and Smith, H. M.: Relationships of oil composition and stratigraphy in the permian basin of West Texas and New Mexico – Fluids in subsurface environments. Amer. Assoc. Petrol. Geol. Memoir n°4, 1965.

[3]   Welte, Dietrich, H.: Correlation problems among crude oils. Third international meeting on organic geochemistry London 1966.

Discussion

K. E. H. Göhring: Did you also compare these Northwestern Libyan crudes with other Libyan crudes, for example from the geologically younger reservoirs in the Syrte basin?

R. Byramjee: No, but I know that the Syrte crudes are entirely different and of younger origin.

D. H. Welte: In your interesting paper you discussed the pristane/phytane ratio as a possible means of crude oil correlation. I very much agree with this as long as the oils are not too different in terms of their geological history. But I also like to mention that the other isoprenoid hydrocarbons should be checked as well, because the pristane/phytane ratio may be similar but other specific hydrocarbons with specific biological molecular structures may be different.

R. Byramjee: I entirely agree with this remark, especially as we had planned to determine the other members of the isoprenoid series such as the Farnesane. Unfortunately this was not done because of lack of time.

Classification et caractérisation des pétroles bruts soufrés

Application à Certains Gisements du Moyen-Orient

Michel Bestougeff [1]), Rustum Byramjee [1]) et Lionel Vasse [2])

[1]) Compagnie Française des Pétroles
Paris, France

[2]) Compagnie Française de Raffinage
Harfleur, France

The authors have undertaken a study of certain Middle-East crudes with the object of a better understanding of their origin and migration processes.

The presence of sulphur compounds in crudes raises specific problems for their differentiation and classification. In particular, the standard "Bureau of Mines" nomenclature is inadequate in most cases. On the other hand, the presence of sulphur may be one more element for the distinction of different crudes in a basin, especially as sulphur compounds are many and their relative proportions may vary from one crude to another.

The authors applied various techniques to determine the different forms of suphur compounds, in particular the non-thiophenic functions, both in total crudes and in their B. O. M. fractions. Besides there appears to be a certain constancy of the considered characteristics through the fractions up to the residue.

These methods applied to about ten Middle-East crudes allowed to distinguish at least two oil types. Besides other characteristics (aromatic content, trace elements, etc.) join in to confirm these distinctions.

The investigation of the geological environment of the area of study had already led to suspect the existence of at least two types of oil that would have different origins. The confirmation brought by the chemical analyses allow, in addition, to make assumptions on migration paths.

Therefore the studies carried out bring a contribution to the problems of origin and evolution, and also elements for a classification of high-sulphur crudes.

Nous avons entrpris une étude de certains bruts du Moyen-Orient dans le but de mieux comprendre leur origine et les phénomènes de migration.

La présence de composés soufrés dans les bruts pose des problèmes spécifiques pour leur différentiation et leur classification. En particulier, la nomenclature classique type "Bureau of Mines" est inopérante dans la plupart des cas. Par contre, la présence du soufre peut être un élément de plus pour distinguer les différents bruts d'un bassin, d'autant plus que les composés soufrés sont multiples et que leurs proportions relatives peuvent varier d'un brut à l'autre.

Les auteurs ont appliqué diverses méthodes permettant de déterminer differentes formes de composés soufrés, en particulier les fonctions non thiophéniques, aussi bien dans les bruts en l'état que dans leurs fractions B. O. M. On observe d'ailleurs une certaine constance des caractères à travers les fractions jusqu'au résidu.

Ces méthodes appliquées à une dizaine de bruts du Moyen-Orient ont permis de
distinguer au moins deux types de pétroles. D'autres caractéristiques (teneurs en
aromatiques, contaminants, etc.) permettent d'ailleurs de confirmer ces distinctions.

L'examen des conditions géologiques de la région étudiée avait déjà conduit à
soupçonner l'existence d'au moins deux types d'huiles dont les origines seraient
différentes. La confirmation apportée par les analyses chimiques permet en outre
de formuler des hypothèses sur les trajets de migration.

Les études effectuées apportent donc une contribution aux problèmes d'origine
et d'évolution ainsi que des éléments de classification des bruts sourfrés.

Introduction

L'étude des pétroles soufrés pose des problèmes qui leur sont propres. La présence
même du soufre oblitère certains caractères usuels et ne permet pas en particulier
d'utiliser les classifications conventionnelles telles celles de H. M. Smith (US Bureau
of Mines). Par contre, l'existence de composés soufrés constitue un paramètre
supplémentaire et nouveau pour la caractérisation des pétroles.

En se basant sur les analyses d'un certain nombre de bruts du Moyen-Orient, l'un
de nous (M. Bestougeff) a été conduit à présenter, dans une première partie, un
nouveau schéma de classification des pétroles soufrés, reposant en particulier sur
la quantité de soufre total dans les bruts. Dans une seconde partie, les auteurs ont
examiné de plus la qualité des composés soufrés: outre les déterminations classiques, il a été utilisé une nouvelle méthode permettant de doser la forme non thiophénique du soufre dans le brut total et dans les fractions. De telles méthodes
permettent de définir des marqueurs qui peuvent être très utiles pour repérer des
pétroles soufrés d'origine différente.

Une application a été tentée dans la région d'Abu Dhabi, où les données analytiques intégrées aux conditions géologiques ont permis des distinctions intéressantes.

I. Essai de classification des pétroles bruts soufrés

1. Caractéristiques générales des pétroles bruts soufrés

Le soufre est réparti très inégalement dans les pétroles bruts [10, 3].

Les fractions distillant avant 250 °C, composées sourtout de constituants saturés,
contiennent le plus souvent de très faibles quantités de produits soufrés; en effet,
le soufre est surtout lié aux structures aromatiques et polycycliques. Pour cette
raison, les teneurs en soufre des pétroles bruts légers, sont en général plus basses
que celles des bruts lourds. Les fractions moyennes de 250 à 350° renferment des
quantités plus importantes de constituants soufrés.

Enfin, les résidus de distillation au-dessus de 350 °C riches en constituants poly-aromatiques renferment d'ailleurs habituellement de 65 à 90 % de la totalité du soufre, que les pétroles bruts soient très soufrés ou non [1,3, 8].

On peut appeler comme degré de sulfuration d'un pétrole brut donné le taux de la saturation par le soufre des composés aromatiques et polycycliques présents dans ce pétrole.

Ainsi, la teneur en soufre d'un pétrole brut n'exprime pas à elle seule le degré de sa sulfuration et doit être complétée, dans la mesure du possible, par détermination du taux de soufre des constituants aromatiques et polycycliques.

Les considérations générales que nous venons d'exposer permettent d'envisager l'existence d'une certaine corrélation entre la densité (masse volumique) et la teneur en soufre des pétroles bruts (voir Figure 1). Ce graphique, qui donne une vue d'ensemble des pétroles bruts soufrés et non soufrés, constitue l'amorce de notre schéma de classement.

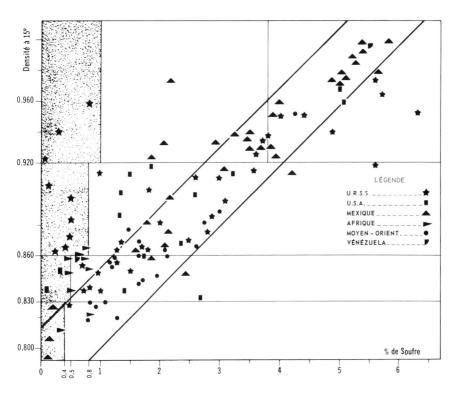

Fig. 1. Corrélation densité – Teneur en soufre des pétroles bruts

2. Examen des différents modes de classification des bruts

Les schémas de classification des pétroles bruts proposés jusqu'à ce jour n'ont pas pu intégrer convenablement les pétroles soufrés.

En particulier, la nomenclature classique du " Bureau of Mines " (correlation index) comprend deux systèmes: un pour les pétroles bruts non soufrés et l'autre pour les soufrés. Dans la plupart des cas, ce dernier système est d'ailleurs assez inopérant, les indices de corrélations des différents types de pétroles bruts soufrés se trouvant confondus (9, Fig. 1, Crude Oil Variety) [10].

Un autre classement plus récent dit " Carpatica de Creanga " tient compte lui aussi du facteur soufre; il permet de distinguer deux catégories de pétrole brut soufré et non soufré, mais là encore les pétroles soufrés ne forment qu'un seul groupe [4].

Les progrès réalisés dans l'étude de la constitution chimique des bruts avec la possibilité de déterminer même approximativement leur composition chimique globale justifie une nouvelle tentative de classification plus rationnelle.

Le classement que nous mettons au point devrait permettre de:

1°) Répondre à la fois à des exigences pratiques et théoriques.

2°) Refléter la constitution chimique des bruts aussi complètement que possible.

3°) Réaliser la distinction entre les différents types de pétroles bruts soufrés.

Nous travaillons actuellement sur un schéma de classement basé sur les critères suivants:

1°) Classification des bruts tout d'abord par masses volumiques croissantes.

2°) Ensuite par sous-groupes, d'après leurs teneurs en soufre et en asphaltènes (comparer tableaux I et Figure 1), et

3°) Enfin, par subdivisions tenant compte de leur constitution chimique (paraffines − naphtènes − aromatiques).

Le tableau I illustre le principe de ce classement.

Les caractéristiques de base:

1°) **La masse volumique** (densité) permet de faire un tri grossier des bruts. Nous avons formé ainsi quatre catégories de pétroles bruts: léger, moyen, lourd et trés lourd, en précisant les limites pour chaque catégorie.

2°) **La teneur en soufre** permet d'établir plusieurs sous-groupes de bruts: pétroles bruts non soufrés, soufrés et très soufrés.

Il est intéressant de noter que les huiles *très* soufrées ne sont compatibles qu' avec la catégorie des pétroles lourds: les pétroles bruts ne peuvent pas être en même temps très soufrés et légers.

3°) **Teneur en asphaltènes.** Cette caractéristique est intéressante pour suivre les constituants hétéroatomiques d'un pétrole brut.

Elle permet de réaliser des subdivisions dans les classes de pétroles bruts soufrés et non soufrés.

4°) **Constitution chimique** [2]. On se base sur les rapports pris deux à deux des trois groupes d'hydrocarbures: paraffines (normales et iso), naphtènes et aromatiques − en excluant les autres constituants contenant les hétéroatomes. Notre classification diffère aussi des anciens classements chimiques, en distinguant autant que possible les constituants proprement aromatiques des composés naphténo-aromatiques et thioaromatiques.

Il est nécessaire de noter que la caractérisation plus détaillée (impossible dans l'état actuel de nos connaissances) des constituants hétéroatomiques et surtout soufrés, reste à faire au fur et à mesure du progrès des recherches.

Il est possible actuellement de distinguer et de quantifier les différents pétroles bruts non seulement selon leur richesse relative en composés soufrés, mais également ment selon l'aspect chimique de leurs constituants hydrocarbonés.

II. Applications du nouveau classement à certains gisements du Moyen-Orient

1. Etude et classification des pétroles bruts de l'Abu Dhabi

Tout nouveau système de classification doit être éprouvé méthodiquement, sur un grand nombre d'exemples, afin d'en vérifier la validité.

Pour tester le schéma décrit précédemment, les auteurs se sont proposés de l'appliquer à certains gisements du Moyen-Orient, en l'occurence à divers bruts de la région d'Abu Dhabi (Terrestre et Marine). Ainsi un certain nombre de pétroles bruts ont été analysés et quelques uns d'entre eux ont été positionnés dans le tableau I selon les critères retenus:

− densité
− teneur en soufre
− teneur en asphaltènes
− constitution chimique

Un rapide examen du classement obtenu fait apparaître des positions assez différentes, bien que ces bruts fassent partie d'un périmètre géographique assez restreint.

Une investigation plus poussée sur chacun des bruts cités a donc été réalisée; elle comporte les déterminations classiques suivantes:

− caractéristiques physico-chimiques générales suivant les standard ASTM
− distillation et analyse US Bureau des Mines (BOM)
− analyses PONA sur les fractions BOM 3 à 10

Tableau I. Schéma d'essai de classification des petroles bruts

Corrélation Générale			Legers < 0,830				Moyens 0,831–0,860			
			n. s. < 0,4 %	S. 0,4 à 1,5 %			n. s. < 0,6 %		S. 0,6 à 2,8 %	
			n. As. < 0,5 %	n.As. < 0,6 %	As. > 0,6 %		n. As. < 0,6 %	As. > 0,6 %	n. As. < 0,7 %	
Corrélation chimique										
Rapport P/N	Rapport Ar/N	Symbole								
> 1	< 0,25	P	El Roble Ponca-city	Asab Murban	Qatar			Dolina		
0,7–1	< 0,25	PN	Hassi-Messaoud	Zakum			Rhourde el-Bagel	Grosny	Um Shaif Zakum (Z-2)	
0,5–0,7	–	NP					Mulata Surachany			
< 0,4	0,25 0,35	NPA								
< 0,4	< 0,25	N								
< 0,4	> 0,35	NA								

Observations et légende du Tableau I

1 °C) Observations

Les teneurs (les limites) en soufre et en asphaltènes pour différents groupes de pétroles bruts ont été fixées statistiquement en nous basant sur plusieurs centaines d'analyses disponibles actuellement. (Principales sources: publications du Bureau of Mines, de l'Institut Français du Pétrole, des Instituts de Recherches soviétiques, etc.)

Pour définir et quantifier les différents types chimiques de pétroles, nous avons utilisé conjointement les résultats d'analyses "PONA", d'analyses chromatographiques sur colonne pour les fractions lourdes et résidus, les déterminations "n-d-M" et d'autres corrélations.

La composition chimique "globale" [2] peut être évaluée d'après ces données avec une précision suffisante pour le but de classification, étant donné la faible proportion de constituants "mixtes" principalement naphténo-aromatiques dans le bilan général après soustraction des constituants saturés soufrés, asphalténiques et aromatiques "purs".

Ainsi, nous avons constaté que le type chimique d'un pétrole brut se détermine déjà assez nettement suivant la composition des premiers 50 % de distillats.

Lourds 0,861–0,920					Tres Lourds > 0,920					
n. s. < 0,8 %	S. 0,8 à 4,0 %				n. s. < 1,0 %		S. 1,0 à 4,5 %		T. S. > 4,5 %	
As. > 0,7 %	n. As. < 0,7 %	As. > 0,7 %	n. As. < 0,7 %	As. > 0,7 %	n. As. < 0,8 %	As. > 0,8 %	n. As. < 0,8 %	As. > 0,8 %	n. As. < 2,0 %	As. > 2,0 %
Irak Zubair										
Tuimasy Kuweit		Bitrov	Wilming-ton	Romash-kino						
Agha-Jari			Oman (Natih et Fahud)	Gach-Saran Shah						
	Prioser-Noe		Lagome-dio	Darius Bahrein				Francita		Gela Cyrus
	Dossor	Balacha-ny			Kalugski Calcutta	Catebo		Lagunil-las		Panuco
	Sugar Land	Kamenskoe		Safani-ya	Romenskoe Valeny			Cerro-Azul		Boscan Ebano

2°C) Légende

Symboles

P   Paraffinique
PN   Paraffino-Naphténique
NPA   Naphténo-Paraffino-Aromatique
N   Naphténique
NA   Naphténo-Aromatique
NP   Naphténo-Paraffinique
n. s.   non-soufrés
T. s.   Très soufrés
s.   soufrés
n. As.   non-Asphaltiques
As.   Asphaltiques

Les résultats obtenus apparaissent dans le tableau II. Ces compléments d'analyse joints aux indications fournies par le mode de classement, conduisent aux remarques suivantes:

1°) Les pétroles de la région d'Abu Dhabi et Abu Dhabi Marine sont classés parmi les bruts les moins soufrés et les plus légers du Moyen-Orient. Ils se distinguent également par une teneur en aromatiques relativement faible surtout dans les légers; la teneur en asphaltènes est faible.

2°) D'après la classification (tableau I) ces pétroles se répartissent en deux types: léger et moyen, les plus légers étant ceux de Zakum, Murban et Abu Jidu qui sont paraffiniques: 39 à 40 % d'hydrocarbures paraffiniques. Les gisements de Shah et de Fateh sont naphténo-paraffiniques.

Tableau II. Analyses des quelques pétroles bruts du golfe persique

	Méthode	Qatar	Zakum P–1 Zone 5	Murban Bu-Hasa P–19	Murban Bab P–17	ABU – JIDU Asab	ABU – JIDU Shah
Resevoir		Jura.	Crétacé Super.	Crétacé	Crétacé	Crétacé Infér.	Crétacé Super.
Densité 15 °C	AFNOR	0,818	0,827	0,827	0,829	0,816	0,877
Soufre % poids	ASTM	1,3	0,95	0,82	0,71	0,77	1,47
Rapp. $\frac{\text{S-thioph}}{\text{S-total}}$	LCPC	0,84	0,80	0,70	0,70	0,86	0,63
Paraff. à-30 °C % poids	CFR	5,9	7,0	8,6	9,5	8,0	5,6
Asph. % poids	AFNOR	0,9	0,05	0,25	0,25	<0,05	1,3
Res. Conradson % poids	AFNOR	5,9	1,3	1,6	1,7	1,2	4,2
Acidité mg K OH/g	AFNOR	0,1	0,1	0,05	0,05	0,10	0,15
Composition fractionnée % en volume (Distillation BOM)							
Fract. (jusqu'à 150 °C)	BOM	24,0	22,0	19,55	21,67	23,55	12,44
Fract. 150–250 °C	BOM	23,6	23,5	23,9	24,79	24,87	17,30
Resid. s/vide	BOM	19,2	21,0	22,3	21,8	19,0	35,0
Densité 15 °C du résidu	BOM	0,957	0,945	0,940	0,934	0,943	0,973
Composition chimique des fractions BOM de 3 à 10							
Rendement % volume des fractions 3 à 10 par rapport P. B		48,4	46,2	46,8	47,0	50,4	33,9
Analyse PONA							
— Paraffines % vol.	PONA	72,1	63,5	60,5	59,4	61,1	47,0
— Naphtènes	PONA	14,9	18,7	19,8	20,7	19,3	41,6
— Aromatiques	PONA	13,0	17,8	19,7	19,9	16,6	11,4

3°) Dans la région d'Abu Dhabi, nous remarquons que le pétrole de Shah se distingue de tous les gisements voisins: ce pétrole, d'une part possède la teneur la plus élevée en hydrocarbures naphténiques, et d'autre part, se distingue par sa teneur assez élevée en asphaltènes (Figures 2, 3).

Pour préciser davantage cette position particulière du brut d'Abu Jidu Shah, divers critères ont été examinés, en particulier la répartition du soufre.

Les auteurs ont appliqué une nouvelle technique analytique [7] qui permet de doser dans les bruts et leurs fractions *la forme non thiophénique du soufre*. La méthode a été pratiquée sur les bruts en l'état ainsi que sur les coupes BOM sous vide.

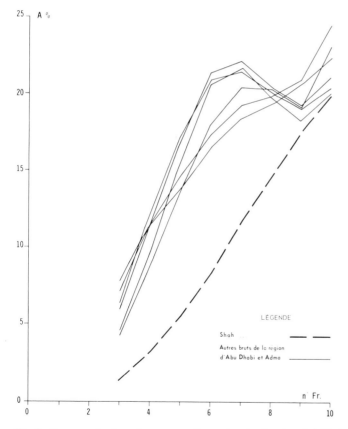

Fig. 2. Teneur en hydrocarbures aromatiques dans les fractions 3 à 10 de différents pétroles bruts du Moyen-Orient

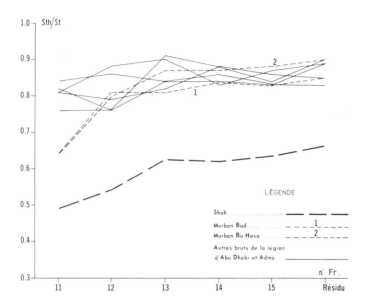

Fig. 3. Rapport soufre thiophénique/soufre total dans les fractions de différents bruts du Moyen-Orient

Les résultats, indiqués dans le tableau III, et sur la **Figure 3** semblent montrer une certaine constance du rapport S thiophénique/S total à travers les fractions, de sorte qu'il paraîtrait plus judicieux de se contenter, dans la plupart des cas, de définir ce rapport sur le brut global.

Néanmoins, il n'est pas exclu qu'un fractionnement plus efficace (type T. B. P.) ne fasse apparaitre quelques variations, d'autant plus que notre expérience nous a déjà montré que les profils de teneur en soufre peuvent différer d'un brut à l'autre.

Quoiqu'il en soit nous considérons que *le rapport soufre thiophénique/soufre total semble pouvoir être utilisé comme marqueur* pour les pétroles soufrés. Par ailleurs, on constate aisément que là encore le pétrole brut d'Abu Jidu Shah prend une position privilégiée: en effet la proportion des composés soufrés non thiophéniques est particulièrement élevée de sorte que le rapport soufre thiophénique/ soufre total est de 0,63 ce qui est faible par rapport aux valeurs trouvées pour les autres gisements d'Abu Dhabi lesquels sont voisins de 0,80 (Figure 3).

Ce bref examen des pétroles d'Abu Dhabi montre qu'ils ne sont donc pas tous semblables mais possèdent au contraire des particularités probablement dues à leur environnement géologique et géochimique.

Tableau III. Rapport entre le soufre thiophénique et le soufre total dans les pétroles bruts

Gisement	Région	Formation	S. Total	$\dfrac{\text{S. Thiophénique}}{\text{S. Total}}$
Safanya	Arabie	Crétacé	3,10	0,89
Abu-Jidu (Asab)	Abu-Dhabi	Crétacé	0,77	0,86
Dukhan	Qatar	Jurassique	1,30	0,84
Zakum 1 (Zone 2)	Abu-Dhabi Marine	Crétacé	0,95	0,80
Burgan	Kuweit	Crétacé	2,20	0,77
Zubair	N. Irak	Crétacé	1,95	0,77
Agha Jari	Iran	Tertiaire et Crétacé	1,40	0,76
Kirkuk	N. Irak	Tertiaire et Crétacé	2,00	0,75
Murban (Bu-Hasa)	Abu-Dhabi	Crétacé	0,79	0,72
Murban (Bab)	Abu-Dhabi	Crétacé	0,82	0,70
Gash Saran	Iran	Tertiaire et Crétacé	1,65	0,64
Abu-Jidu (Shah)	Abu-Dhabi	Crétacé	1,47	0,63
Santa Maria	Californie	Tertiaire	5,12	0,60
Wilmington	Californie	Tertiaire	1,49	0,46

III. Corrélations entre les propriétes physico-chimiques des pétroles soufrés d'Abu Dhabi et l'environnement géologique

Pour pourvoir utiliser les données analytiques sur le soufre (et composés soufrés) pour les corrélations géologiques, il ne faut pas oublier que la teneur en composés soufrés des pétroles bruts n'est généralement subordonnée ni à des formations géologiques déterminées (sauf les très anciennes) ni aux situations géographiques.

On trouve les pétroles soufrés et très soufrés dans différentes régions du monde, répartis dans des formations allant du Quaternaire jusqu'au Primaire (Dévonien).

Cependant, pour les régions assez limitées et les formations géologiques assez restreintes, on constate une certaine constance dans la teneur et la nature des composés soufrés caractéristiques pour un type de pétrole brut ou pour une formation (faciès) déterminée.

En ce qui concerne la région d'Abu Dhabi, nous avons vu précédemment que le gisement de Shah avait des caractéristiques géochimiques tout à fait différentes de celles des gisements voisins (Murban-Bab Dome, Murban-Bu Hasa, Abu-Jidu-Asab) (Figure A). Or, ces différences chimiques sont en accord avec les hypothèses géologiques que l'on peut faire et selon lesquelles le pétrole de Shah serait de source différente.

Legende:

M.M :	Maydam Mazam
I el S :	Idd el Shargi
S :	Sassan
U. Sh :	Umm Shaif
ZK :	Zakum
F :	Fateh

Fig. A
Situation des principaux champs de la région d'Abu Dhabi

Rappelons que les champs de Bab, Bu Hasa et Asab sont productifs dans le Thamama (Crétacé inférieur), alors que la structure de Shah est productive dans l'Aruma (Crétacé supérieur).

Dans ces conditions, on avait avancé l'hypothèse que les roches-mères du pétrole de Shah seraient différentes de celles des autres gisements d'Abu Dhabi, et pourraient être constituées par les argiles du Crétacé moyen localisées dans le synclinal Nord-Ouest de Shah.

L'étude géochimique indique effectivement que l'huile de Shah ne provient pas du gisement d'Asab et a une origine différente; de plus, elle apparaît mois évoluée en ce qui concerne le soufre. Ces faits ne sont pas opposés à l'hypothèse d'une huile plus jeune.

IV. Conclusions

a) Une nouvelle classification des pétroles bruts est proposée permettant de tenir compte des particularités des pétroles bruts soufrés. Cette classification devrait permettre un progrès sur les anciens classements, en particulier sur ceux basés seulement sur les courbes d'indices de corrélation.

b) On a montré que les P. B. du Moyen-Orient ne sont pas semblables, mais diffèrent sensiblement même pour les régions assez restreintes comme par exemple pour la région d'Abu Dhabi.

c) Les déterminations systématiques du rapport soufre thiophénique/soufre total, effectuées pour les pétroles bruts soufrés et leurs fractions de la région d'Abu Dhabi montrent que ce rapport peut être utilisé comme marqueur géochimique. Il a permis en particulier de mieux individualiser le gisement de Shah, en accord avec les hypothèses géologiques.

Remerciements: Nous remercions M. M. Dubois [1]) et Thiault [1]) qui ont effectué les analyses de soufre non thiophénique.

Bibliographie

[1] Bestougeff, M. A.: Proc. 5th World Petrol. Congress. New York 1959 (sect. V) 143–164- Constitution des composés sulfurés cycliques du pétrole: leur séparation et identification.

[2] Bestougeff, M. A.: Advances in Organic Geochemistry. Proc. Internat. Meeting in Paris. 1964. Pergamon Press 1966. London, pages 197–211.

[3] Bestougeff, M. A.: Proc. 7th World Petrol. Congress. Pan disc. 23, pap. 5, 69–116. Mexico 1967.

[4] Creanga, C.: Chemical classification of crude oils. Carpatica classification. Acad. Rep. Populare Romine, Studii Cercetari Chim., 9, 93–108, 1961.

[5] Dunnington, H. V.: Stratigraphical distribution of oilfields in the Irak-Iran-Arabia basin. J. of Insti. of Petroleum 53, 130–161, 1967.

[6] Drushel, H. V. and Miller, J. F.: Spectrometric determination of aliphetic sulfides in crude petroleum oils and their chromatographic fractions. Analyt. chem. 27, 498–1955.

[7] Lamathe, J. Mme.: Dosage potentiométrique des fonctions soufrées non thiophéniques. Application aux produits d'origine pétrolière. Chimie Analyt. 49, 119–126, 1967.

[8] Martin, R. L. and Grant, J. A.: Determination of thiophenic compounds by types in petroleum samples. Analyt. Chem. 37, 649–657, 1965.

[9] Smith, H. M.: Some significant facts concerning the composition of petroleum. Geochemistry conference. Budapest Oct. 8–12 1962 (Fig. 1 – Crude Oil variety).

[10] Smith, H. M.: Qualitative and quantitative aspects of crude oil composition. Bureau of Mines Bull. 642–1968 (pages 3–6).

[1]) Compagnie Française de Raffinage

Discussion

M. Louis: Les auteurs ont constaté dans certains pétroles du Moyen Orient, qu'ils ont étudiés, des composés non thiophéniques qui sont probablement d'origine primaire.

Je pense qu'il existe aussi des cas de sulfuration secondaire. Au sujet d'une sulfuration primaire on peut citer le bitume très sulfuré qui se trouve dans les marnes du Stampien lagunaire de la Limagne (France). Des sondages profonds (plus de 1000 mètres) l'ont rencontré sous le même état. A notre avis il s'agit d'un bitume primaire et non pas d'un produit d'altération d'une huile brute. En ce sens c'est un faux indice de pétrole, au moins dans la " Limagne de Clermont "

Un autre cas semble etre consitué par le gisement de GELA (Sicile). L'huile très sulfurée se trouve à 3000 m. et elle ne contient pas d'essence contrairement à ce que l'on pourrait penser pour une huile aussi profonde et qui est dans son réservoir depuis le Trias. Par ailleurs, à quelques dizaines de km il existe un autre gisement (RAGUSE) de pétrole moins sulfuré qui contient de l'essence bien que se trouvant à une profondeur moindre.

Au sujet de la sulfuration secondaire il existe des exemples de huiles sulfurées en contact avec des eaux peu salées. C'est le cas de LACQ (France) et de GIGNO (Italie). C'est probablement dans l'arrivée d'eau douce contenant de l'oxygéne que l'on peut rechercher la cause de la sulfuration. Les bactéries réductrices des sulfates ont sans doute été l'agent de l'apport du soufre.

Enfin on connait encore des pétroles qui contiennent du soufre à l'état libre et l'on sait combien cet élément est réactif vis à vis des hydrocarbures.

M. Bestougeff nous a parlé des fractions Hempel, mais comme il l'a indiqué le soufre est plus abondant dans les fractions lourdes. La connaissance de la chimie de ces substances serait d'une grande utilité, pour la géochimie et pour la valeur technique de ces produits.

Possibilité d'application des modèles mathématiques de formation du pétrole à la prospection dans les bassins sédimentaires

Gérard Deroo, Bernard Durand, Jean Espitalie, Régis Pelet et Bernard Tissot

Institut Français du Pétrole
Rueil-Malmaison, France

Recent work has shown the existence, for a given formation, of a depth and temperature minimum, beyond which the transformation of organic matter into petroleum becomes important. Results of observations and experiments have allowed to build a mathematical model (taking into account the geological time) to simulate the generation of petroleum. Some applications of the model are presented here.

In a sedimentary basin the search for favourable areas, concerning each formation, can be carried out from this model, provided it is calibrated by a small number of measurements on core samples. The same process allows to study the case of source-rocks of different ages, or the case of two successive phases of burial, separated by an important erosion. Examples are shown from Paris Basin and other sedimentary basins.

Finally the problem of time and velocity of petroleum generation can be met. This time is compared to the age of traps, to select the most favourable of them.

Des travaux récents ont montré que, pour une formation déterminée, il existe un seuil de profondeur et de température au-delà duquel la transformation de la matière organique en pétrole devient importante. Les résultats des observations et des expériences ont permis la réalisation d'un modèle mathématique (où intervient le temps géologique) pour simuler la formation de pétrole. Quelques applications de ce modèle sont présentées ici.

Dans un bassin sédimentaire, la recherche des zones favorables, pour chaque formation, peut être menée à partir de ce modèle, pourvu qu'il soit calé par un petit nombre de mesures effectuées sur carottes. Le même procédé permet d'étudier le cas de formations roche-mères d'âge différent, ou celui de deux phases d'enfouissement séparées par une érosion importante. Des exemples sont donnés, portant sur le Bassin de Paris et d'autres bassins sédimentaires.

On peut enfin aborder le problème de l'époque et de la vitesse de formation du pétrole, et les comparer à l'âge des pièges, pour sélectionner les plus favorables d'entre eux.

On se propose de montrer quelques applications des résultats des travaux entrepris à l'Institut Francais du Pétrole pour l'étude de la transformation de la matière organique des sédiments en pétrole. Pour la clarté de l'exposé, ces résultats vont être succinctement décrits, mais le lecteur se reportera pour tous les détails et justifications aux deux articles originaux de Louis et Tissot (1967) et Tissot (1969).

1. Rappel des résultats expérimentaux et du schéma réactionnel utilisé

1.1. Résultats expérimentaux (Louis et Tissot, 1967)

Ils ont été obtenus par l'étude de la fraction organique des argiles du Toarcien inférieur du Bassin de Paris, formation sensiblement homogène du point de vue minéralogique et pétrographique, et dont on possède des échantillons prélevés à différentes profondeurs, depuis les affleurements jusqu'à 2500 m (sondage d'Essises 1). La géologie du Bassin de Paris étant bien connue, on a pu retracer l'histoire géologique de chacun des échantillons étudiés (enfouissement des sédiments).

Dans ces conditions favorables, on a pu montrer que les facteurs déterminants de l'évolution de la matière organique étaient la pression et surtout la température; l'élévation de cette dernière favorise l'apparition des composés du pétrole aux dépens de la matière organique insoluble (kérogène) et, dans ces composés, augmente la proportion des hydrocarbures par rapport aux résines et asphaltènes. On a montré aussi que la production des composés du pétrole ne se fait pas pour l'essentiel par la dégradation directe du kérogène, mais que certains composés hétéroatomiques de masse molaire assez élevée (extrait M.A.B.) constituaient un intermédiaire obligé.

On met enfin en évidence l'effet résultant des observations précédentes: lors de l'enfouissement des sédiments (= augmentation de la température et de la pression), la vitesse de formation des composés du pétrole n'est pas constante; en particulier, cette vitesse ne devient importante qu'au-dessus d'un certain seuil de température (= au-dessous d'une certaine profondeur).

1.2. Formalisation des résultats (Tissot, 1969)

Les valeurs numériques, obtenues dans l'exemple rappelé ci-dessus, ne sont valables que pour un bassin donné et une formation donnée; en effet, la nature des fractions organique et minérale varie d'une formation à l'autre et, surtout, l'histoire géologique varie d'un bassin à l'autre; or cette dernière détermine directement, par le biais de la subsidence et du gradient géothermique, la loi de la température en fonction du temps. Pour être généralisables, nos résultats doivent être formalisés. On part du schéma réactionnel synthétique:

A ⟶ B ⟶ C
Kérogène   Composés hétéroatomiques   Composés du pétrole[1]) + lourds
                  lourds

---

[1]) (hydrocarbures + résines + asphaltènes)

où les notations simples comme $A \longrightarrow B$ recouvrent un faisceau de réactions successives

$$A \begin{array}{l} \nearrow B_1' \longrightarrow B_1'' \quad \ldots\ldots\ldots\ldots \longrightarrow B_1 \\ \dashrightarrow B_2' \longrightarrow B_2'' \quad \ldots\ldots\ldots\ldots \longrightarrow B_2 \\ \searrow B_i' \longrightarrow B_i'' \quad \ldots\ldots\ldots\ldots \longrightarrow B_i \end{array}$$

où les étapes B_i', B_i'' .... ne sont pas accessibles à l'observation. Si l'on suppose que la probabilité de la $i_{\text{ème}}$ réaction est indépendante des autres et suit une loi de Poisson (évènement rare), on montre qu'on obtient la relation

$$- \frac{d\,x_i}{dt} = K_i(T) \cdot x_i \tag{1}$$

où t   est le temps,

T   est la température,

x_i est la quantité de matière impliquée dans la $i_{\text{ème}}$ réaction,

$K_i(T)$ est une fonction de la température.

Si, de plus, on prend pour $K_i(T)$ une fonction de forme:

$$K_i(T) = A_i \, \exp\left[-\frac{E_i}{RT}\right] \tag{2}$$

qui cadre assez bien avec les indications expérimentales, on retombe sur le formalisme classique de la cinétique des réactions d'ordre un. Les x_i sont les solutions d'un système d'équations différentielles du premier ordre à coefficients variables, puisque la température dépend du temps par le biais de la subsidence.

1.3. Résolution du système différentiel

On simplifie encore le schéma réactionnel et on considère les trois réactions:

$$A \longrightarrow B \begin{array}{l} \nearrow C_1 \quad \text{composés du pétrole (hydrocarbures, résines, asphaltènes).} \\ \searrow C_2 \quad \text{composés hétéroatomiques lourds.} \end{array}$$

L'intégration du système correspondant n'est possible à l'aide de fonctions simples que si la température reste constante. On a donc été amené à simuler le système sur ordinateur pour le résoudre par intégration numérique. Le problème qui se pose immédiatement est alors celui des valeurs numériques des constantes A et E de la relation (2) et des concentrations de A, B, C_1 et C_2 à l'origine. L'ordre de grandeur de ces constantes peut être tiré, pour les A et E de nos propres expériences, pour les concentrations initiales des analyses de sédiments récents rapportées dans la littérature. Cet ordre de grandeur obtenu, on réalise l'ajustement optimum entre valeurs de C_1 calculées et effectivement mesurées (Toarcien du Bassin de Paris) par la méthode des moindres carrés.

On dispose ainsi d'un outil qui, à partir d'un schéma réactionnel très simplifié, mais directement suggéré par l'expérience, et en utilisant un formalisme raisonnable, permet de simuler avec une excellente approximation[1]) l'évolution de la matière organique du Toarcien du Bassin de Paris en composés du pétrole, compte explicitement tenu de l'histoire géologique du bassin. On donne en Figure 1 cette évolution pour le sondage d'Essises.

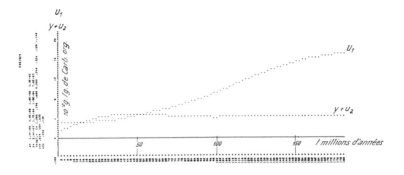

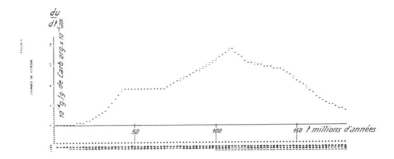

Fig. 1. Evolution de la matière organique du Toarcien du Bassin de Paris en fonction du temps pour le puits d'Essises

u_1 hydrocarbures + résines + asphaltènes

$y + u_2$ composés hétéroatomiques lourds (extractibles au mélange méthanol – acétone – benzène)

$\dfrac{du}{dt}$ vitesse de formation de u_1

t temps (en millions d'année)

---

[1]) corrélations de 0,95 entre valeurs mesurées (22 sondages) et calculées

2. Application à la recherche de zones favorables à la transformation de la matière organique

2.1. Exemple du Bassin de Paris

Ainsi qu'il a été déjà indiqué, le Toarcien est dans le Bassin de Paris une formation sensiblement homogène du point de vue minéralogique et pétrographique; de plus l'histoire géologique du bassin est simple. On peut donc penser que des facteurs, susceptibles d'influer sur la formation des composés du pétrole et qui n'auraient pas été pris en compte dans la simulation, varient peu d'un point à un autre de ce Toarcien.

La simulation sur d'autres formations du Bassin de Paris ne dispose pas des mêmes garanties. On l'a cependant tentée sur les marnes du Bajocien considérées ici comme la roche-mère du pétrole du Dogger de ce bassin.

Les courbes d'enfouissement en fonction du temps de cette formation ont été reconstituées en chaque noeud d'un maillage assez serré (Figure 2). Après simulation de la formation des composés du pétrole en chacun de ces points, il est possible de tracer des courbes "d'isotransformation" de la matière organique (en grammes par gramme de carbone organique initial) (Figure 2). Des zones plus favorables que d'autres à cette transformation peuvent être alors délimitées. La matière organique initiale ayant été répartie géographiquement de manière à peu près homogène dans tout le bassin, les secteurs où la roche-mère a été la plus productive sont ainsi mis en évidence.

On constate effectivement que tous les gisements actuellement connus dans le Dogger se trouvent à l'intérieur de la courbe d'isotransformation 0,110 et que tous les indices importants sont, à une exception près, à l'intérieur de la courbe 0,080. Les résultats ainsi obtenus tendent à prouver la valeur assez générale du schéma réactionnel utilisé et permettent d'envisager, au moins en première approximation, son utilisation pour d'autres formations et même d'autres bassins.

2.2. Exemple du bassin de Los Angeles (Californie)

On a essayé d'utiliser ici les données sur le bassin de Los Angeles tirées de l'intéressant travail de Philippi (1965). Dans cet exemple, les conditions d'application sont très différentes de celles rencontrées dans le Bassin de Paris: on y trouve en effet des séries de roches-mères d'âges variés qui ont été enfouies à des profondeurs plus grandes que pour le Toarcien pendant des temps géologiques beaucoup plus courts (de 0 à 12 millions d'années au lieu de 180).

On constate (Figure 3) que les quantités de composés du pétrole (hydrocarbures + résines + asphaltènes) calculées par simulation du schéma cinétique sont dans un

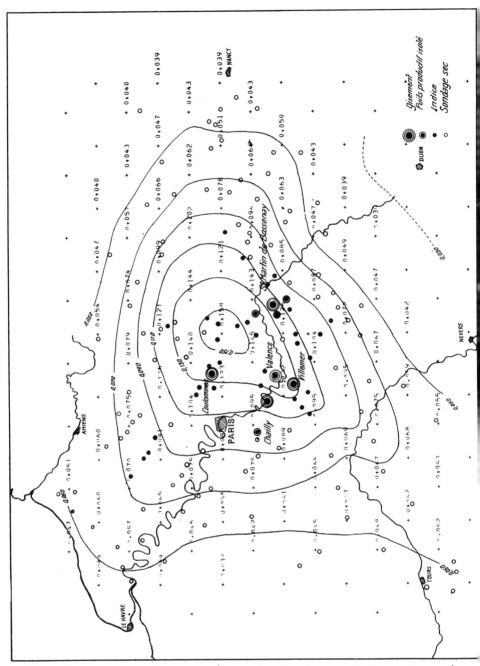

Fig. 2. Taux de transformation de la matière organique du Bajocien du Bassin de Paris, jusqu'à l'actuel (en g/g de carbone organique initial)

On a indiqué les gisements, indices et puits secs dans le Dogger (Bajocien + Bathonien)

rapport satisfaisant[1]) avec les teneurs en hydrocarbures, seules observées par Philippi (1965); les deux courbes ont en effet le même comportement en fonction de la profondeur (température) et du temps.

Bien qu'ici les constantes utilisées pour la simulation n'aient pas été ajustées au cas précis de ce bassin, les résultats ainsi obtenus semblent confirmer la possibilité de généralisation du schéma réactionnel envisagée ci-dessus (2.1.).

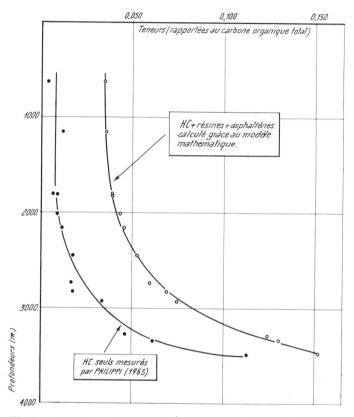

Fig. 3. Teneur en hydrocarbures + résines + asphaltènes calculée selon le schéma proposé, et teneur en hydrocarbures mesurée par Philippi (1965)

2.3. Exemple du bassin de Fort Polignac (Sahara)

Dans ce dernier cas, les roches-mères sont d'âge siluro-dévonien, les réservoirs d'âge dévonien inférieur. L'histoire géologique est plus complexe: subsidence au cours

---

[1]) Dans nos études, la teneur des extraits de roches-mères en hydrocarbures varie en effet de 20 % à 60 %, selon la profondeur d'enfouissement

du Paléozoïque, suivie à la fin de cette ère d'un plissement d'âge hercynien, et, dans certains secteurs, d'une érosion importante (Ouest du bassin); nouvelle subsidence pendant le Mésozoique.

On a considéré cette fois un point moyen pris dans chacun des principaux secteurs et pour lequel on a reconstitué une courbe d'enfouissement. Comme dans le paragraphe précédent, les constantes utilisées n'ont pas été ajustées au cas particulier. Le tableau I montre les résultats obtenus: on y a distingué les teneurs en matière organique transformée avant la phase de plissement principale, située à la fin du Paléozoique, et après celle-ci.

Tableau I.   Taux de transformation de la matière organique du silurodévonien dans diverses régions du bassin de Fort-Polignac

Région dans le bassin de Fort Polignac	Taux de transformation de la matière organique	
	A la fin du Paléozoïque	De la fin du Paléozoïque jusqu'à l'actuel
Nord-Est	0.090	0.078
Centre et Sud-Est	0.111	0.065
Nord	0.057	0.050
Nord-Ouest	0.058	0.009
Sud-Ouest	0.170	0.012

Dans l'Est du bassin, où l'enfouissement s'est poursuivi depuis le Silurien jusqu'à la fin du Crétacé, la transformation de la matière organique s'est effectuée aussi bien pendant le Paléozoïque que le Mésozoïque. C'est la zone des grands gisements. Au Nord le phénomène est analogue, mais les taux de transformation sont plus faibles. On n'y connait pas actuellement de gisement. Dans l'Ouest par contre, l'histoire géologique est différente: l'érosion qui suit la phase de plissements est importante, l'enfouissement au Mésozoïque est souvent inférieur à ce qu'il était au Paléozoïque. On constate là que la matière organique s'est transformée presque uniquement au Paléozoïque et que le rendement au cours du Mésozoïque reste négligeable. Les structures post-paléozoïques de cette région ne peuvent donc avoir piégé de pétrole que si leur position géographique leur permet d'être alimentées par une autre zone, par exemple la partie centrale du bassin.

Conclusions

A partir des observations et des expériences réalisées sur le Toarcien du Bassin de Paris, on a pu bâtir un schéma réactionnel dont la cinétique a fait l'objet d'une simulation sur ordinateur. Les valeurs obtenues, grâce à ce schéma, pour la transformation de la matière organique en pétrole montrent une très bonne corrélation avec les taux de transformation réellement observés.

Ce schéma permet d'introduire, pour la première fois, le temps de façon explicite et, par là, l'histoire géologique de chaque partie du bassin. On peut espérer ainsi généraliser ce modèle (en déterminant les constantes appropriées) à d'autres bassins sédimentaires. Les premiers essais dans ce sens sont assez encourageants.

Ce procédé permet de déterminer, dans un bassin et pour chaque formation contenant de la matière organique, les zones favorables à la genèse du pétrole, c'est-à-dire les zones où les quantités de matière organique transformées (taux de transformation X quantité de matière organique) sont importantes. Nous l'avons présenté ici brièvement pour le Dogger du Bassin de Paris et le Siluro-Dévonien du Bassin de Fort Polignac.

Mais cette utilisation ne constitue qu'une première étape. La présence de matière organique et sa transformation sont des conditions nécessaires, mais non suffisantes pour la formation de gisements de pétrole. Il faut encore que l'expulsion du pétrole hors de la roche-mère (migration primaire) ait lieu et que les pièges soient formés à temps pour le recueillir. Par exemple, un piège anticlinal doit, pour être actif, s'être formé avant que le masse du pétrole migre dans le réservoir. En d'autres termes l'âge des pièges doit être compatible avec l'époque et la vitesse de formation et d'expulsion du pétrole.

La vitesse d'*expulsion* ne nous est pas accessible à ce jour. Mais nous pouvons, en première approximation, considérer qu'un piège déjà en place, lorsque la *formation* du pétrole devient importante, pourra être efficace. Or le calcul présenté ici nous donne accès à la variation de cette quantité en fonction du temps (Figure 1). Dans le centre du Bassin de Paris et pour la formation considérée, cette époque correspond en général au Crétacé moyen; les structures présentant de l'intérêt pour le problème du Dogger devront donc être formées dès cette époque, ce qui est effectivement vérifié. Par contre, dans l'Ouest du bassin où la subsidence a été plus lente, cette époque se situe à la fin du Crétacé. C'est ainsi que l'anticlinal du Pays de Bray, bien que tardif (fin Crétacé — début Tertiaire) a pu recevoir une petite accumulation de pétrole, d'ailleurs plus lourd puisque formé à une température plus faible.

C'est seulement lorsque le schéma de transformation de la matière organique pourra être complété par un schéma d'expulsion des composés du pétrole (migration primaire) que l'on pourra valablement employer le nom de modèle mathématique de genèse du pétrole.

Bibliographie

Louis, M. et Tissot, B., 1967: Influence de la température et de la pression sur la formation
des hydrocarbures dans les argiles à kérogène. 7th World Petrol. Congress, Mexico 1967,
2, 47–60.

Philippi, G.T., 1965: On the depth, time and mechanism of petroleum generation. Geochim.
et Cosmochim. Acta, 29, 1021–1049.

Tissot, B., 1969: Premières données sur les mécanismes et la cinétique de la formation du
pétrole dans les sédiments. Simulation d'un schéma réactionnel sur ordinateur. (A paraitre,
Rev. Inst. Franc. du Pétrole, vol. XXIV).

Discussion

J. Karweil: Welche Zahlenwerte für E und A haben Sie benutzt?

B. Tissot: Pour les réactions du type B → C, une évaluation a pu être faite à partir de nos observations. Les valeurs de E se situent entre 15 et 20 kilocalories pour les hydrocarbures,
autour de 10 kilocalories pour les composés hétéro-atomiques. Les valeurs de A dépendent
de l'unité de temps; si on choisit le million d'années, elles vont selon des produits, de
10^8 à 10^2.

Pour les réactions du type A → B, les constantes sont déterminées par itération entre les résultats du calcul et les valeurs observées; on trouve une distribution des E dont la valeur moyenne
est d'environ 30 kilocalories.

M. Bajor: Zunächst werden alle Ergebnisse, mögen sie auch nachher in komplizierten Com-
putern oder mathematischen Formeln eingesetzt werden, von den Geologen oder Geochemi-
kern ausgewertet und zur Problemstellung in Beziehung gesetzt. Daher hängen ja auch die
mathematischen Endresultate von den ersten Beobachtungen ab. Um nur ein Beispiel zu
nennen: Sie interpretieren alle Ihre Analysenzahlen, Ihre Änderungen zum Beckenzentrum
hin als Folge von unterschiedlicher thermischer Reifung (Pariser Becken). Alle Änderungen
der angeführten Parameter: Extrakt/C_{org}, gesättigte/Aromaten, Extrakt I/Extrakt II, etc.
könnten aber ebensogut durch Faziesunterschiede zwischen Beckenäußere und -innere bedingt
sein. Haben wir im E des Pariser Beckens mehr kontinentales organisches Material als im Inneren, so werde folglich in den Proben vom Rand höheren Anteil an Aromaten und NSO, niedrigere Extrakt/C_{org} etc. als im Probenmaterial im Zentrum! Im Posidonienschiefer N.W.
Deutschlands konnten durch DTA Aufnahmen auch zwei Typen, wahrscheinlich faziell bedingt,
festgestellt werden (Schmitz und von Gaertner 1964). Welche Kriterien dienten zu Ihren Feststellungen, daß allein Temperatureinflüsse nicht aber auch/oder Fazies für die unterschiedlichen
Analysenwerte verantwortlich sind?

B. Tissot: Les affleurements actuels du Toarcien inférieur, situés à l'Est du bassin de Paris,
sont dûs à l'érosion principalement tertiaire. Ils ne constituent pas la bordure orientale du
bassin de déposition, qui pendant le Toarcien inférieur se situait probablement plus à l'Est:

1. L'étude sédimentologique et paléoécologique des affleurements entre Dijon et Metz a
   montré que les conditions de dépôt du Toarcien inférieur ne sont pas des conditions de
   bordure de bassin.

2. D'après les forages, la répartition des isopaques dans le bassin ne permet pas de faire, de la
   bordure orientale des affleurements actuels, la bordure du bassin au Toarcien inférieur.

3. Enfin les teneurs en matière organique du Toarcien inférieur, aussi bien que la nature des
   éléments-trace liés à celle-ci, sont tout à fait comparables dans les forages situés au centre
   géographique du bassin actuel et dans les forages et affleurements les plus orientaux.

Results of an Experimental Offshore Geochemical Prospection Study

Roland E. Gérard and Guy Feugère

Geoservices

Paris, France

The extension of Geochemical Prospection for Oil and Gas to off-shore sites is examined in a feasibility study. A previous survey where sea water was sampled and analysed for light hydrocarbon contents having been inconclusive, an area of the sea floor overlying a known productive structure was sampled. It should be pointed out that only one well was drilled in the structure.

Sediments along cores up to 4.60 metres long were analysed for light hydrocarbon (C1 to n-C4) content, petrographic and chemical characteristics, etc.. Correlations, trend analysis and a statistical sorting of the sediments show that a certain number of samples have a light hydrocarbon content which cannot be explained by normal variations around an average content (background). This background can be considered as a "geochemical noise", while the anomalous samples are related to the subsurface oil accumulation.

The conclusions of the study are:

1. Techniques similar to on-shore Geochemical Prospecting can be extended offshore.

2. At least for the area surveyed and for the purpose of prospecting, we could have limited ourselves to samples taken in the immediate vicinity of the sea floor.

Introduction

With the authorization and thanks to the facilities made available by Petrangol, a study of the light hydrocarbons contained in sea water was conducted off the coast of Angola in May, 1966. For this survey, sea water was continuously and automatically sampled. The gas extracted by mildly heating the sample under a vacuum was stored in phials pending a chromatographic analysis in a laboratory. The hydrocarbons obtained ranged from methane to propane. However, the map of strong concentrations in saturated hydrocarbons correlated more with river estuaries and their extension into the ocean than with potential oil and gas prospects.

Consequently, it was decided to run a feasibility study where the sea floor would be sampled using on-shore interpretative and analytical techniques. In March, 1968, Spafe and Orstom made a site and facilities available to us, thereby rendering this survey possible.

The site was off the coast of Gabon on the open sea, over a structure where only one (discovery) well had been drilled (Figure 1). Although the extension of on-shore interpretative techniques requires the use of an almost regular sampling grid,

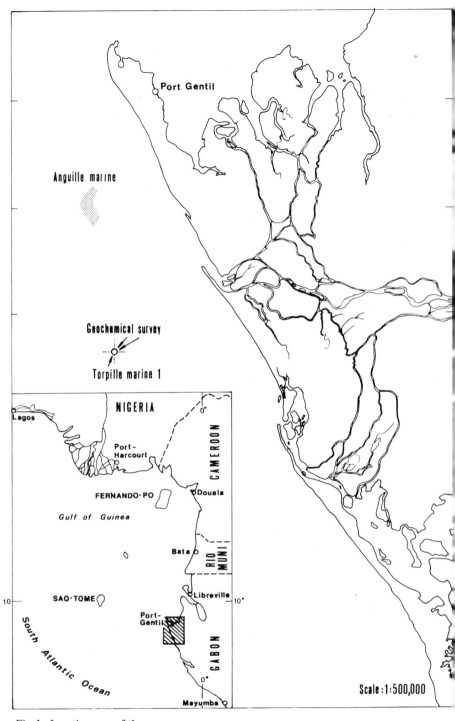

Fig. 1. Location map of the survey

only two profiles at right angles were sampled for technical and economical reasons. Since it is essential that a commercial prospection survey be reasonnably priced, special attention was paid to sampling depth, an item directly related to cost.

Experimental

Sampling

Figure 2 shows the locations where samples were attempted and recovered, as well as the sea floor depth given by echo sounder equipment. The spacing between locations is 500 meters. The sample taker was of the Kuhlenberg type, and the sea bottom cores were recovered in plastic jackets five meters long. The ship, a trawler, was localized by sextant sighting on the derrick of TRM-1. Twenty cores were recovered out of forty attempts, a 60 % recovery rate. The sampling lasted from March 12 to March 18, 1968.

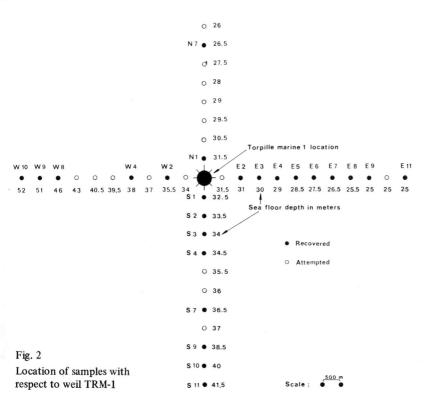

Fig. 2
Location of samples with respect to weil TRM-1

Light Hydrocarbon Extraction and Analysis

Samples from the cores were shipped to Paris in air-tight polyethylene containers. Light hydrocarbons adsorbed on the sediments were extracted in an evacuated glass system by submitting the samples to the action of hydrochloric acid and mild heat at a temperature not exceeding 80 °C for 20 minutes. The recovered gases, freed of CO_2 and acid vapors by a KOH solution, were analysed by gas chromatography using a squalane precolumn, a DC-200 (silicone oil) column and a flame ionisation detector. The carrier gas was nitrogen. The chromatographs were calibrated with a quantitative mixture of C1, C2, C3, i-C4, n-C4 and nitrogen prepared by *Air Liquide.*

Sand Content Determination

Sand content was determined by measuring the volume of sand after sedimentation in water of 50 grammes of sample treated with acid. The purpose of using such a measurement was to obtain, without much trouble, a parameter related not only to the amount of sand present in the sample, but also to its grain sorting. Also, since the sand content was used concurrently with the carbonate content to establish correlation coefficient matrices, these measurements should not be related by an equation of the type:

% sand + % clay + % carbonate = 100 %.

Moreover, selected samples were submitted to X-ray analysis in order to determine the principal mineral constituants and, therefore, to render the above sand content measurement more significant. Finally, a microscopic examination was made of the samples.

Organic Matter Determination

Vacuum dehydrated samples were extracted for 10 hours in a Soxhlet with a mixture of benzene-acetone-methanol. Total lipids content of the extract was determined by colorimetry (sulfo-phospho-vaniline method). These analyses were conducted by *Solara Industrie.*

Results

The sediments sampled are of quaternary age. They have been supposedly covered by the sea for a period of 15,000 years.

As shown by X-ray analysis, the major mineral element is quartz (about 70 %), the remainder being constituted by 5 to 8 % of clay minerals (illite, kaolinite, chlorite in decreasing quantity) and by feldspars (k-feldspars and plagiochase). The deeper the sample, the higher the clay content. The aragonite and calcite peaks on the

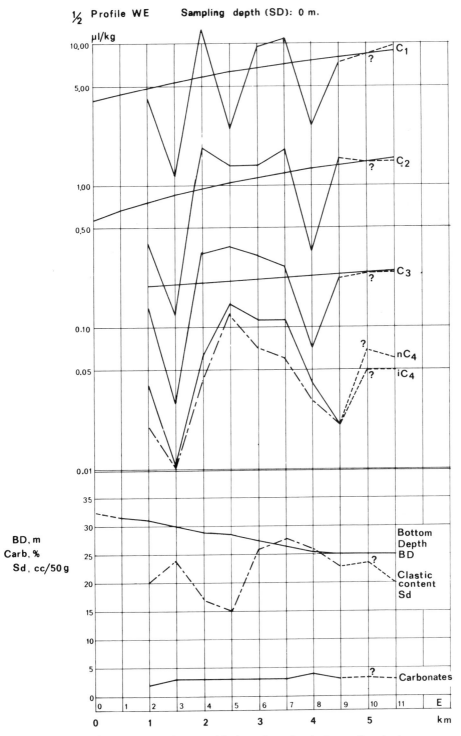

Fig. 3. Variations in the amount of saturated hydrocarbons absorbed on sediments along eastern profile

X-ray diagram most probably correspond to the fossils shown by microscopic analysis. Most of the grains of quartz are rounded and glassy. All the samples contain numerous pellets, well rounded, dull black and opaque, which have not been identified.

Light hydrocarbons from methane to n-butane were extracted from the sediments. Ethylene was sometimes present in larger quantity than methane, while the propylene content was about half the propane content. Figure 3 is an example of the results obtained on the eastern half of the WE profile. The hydrocarbon contents are expressed in microliters per kilogramme of rock.

Tables I through IV show the variations of the average methane content with sea floor depth (bottom depth), the sample depth below the sea floor (sample depth), the carbonate content and the sand content respectively. For each table, the range

Table I. Variation in the average methane contents with the depth of the sampling

C	SD		Ci			$\alpha = 0.05$	G
i			n	m	s	$t_{i, i+1}$	
1	0	0	23	10.32	6.38		
						1.5579	
2	0.5 - 0.8	0.53	20	7.49	5.39		
						0.7704	
3	1 - 1.30	1.02	23	9.12	8.01		
						0.0857	
4	1.50 - 1.80	1.53	18	8.91	7.49		$0 \leqslant , \leqslant 3.30$
						0.5862	
5	2 - 2.30	2.04	20	7.62	6.06		
						0.2918	
6	2.50 - 2.85	2.57	13	7.02	5.28		
						0.4670	
7	3 - 3.30	3.06	8	8.36	7.93		
	3.50		1	17.28			
	3.60		1	7.38			
	4		1	18.26			
	4.60		2	9.43			

C,i : numbered classes
SD : depth of the sampling, limits of the classes, average per class
n : number of samples per class
m : average per class
s : standard deviation
t : Student's ratio between two successive classes
G : limits of the groups extracted from the total number of samples

Table II. Variation in the average methane contents with the depth of the water

C	BD		Ci			α = 0.05	G
i			n	m	s	$t_{i, i+1}$	
1	25 ≤, < 28	26.5	32	4.90	4.39		25 ≤, < 31
						1.1184	
2	28 ≤, < 31	29.5	19	3.65	2.72		
						2.9538	
3	31 ≤, < 34	32.5	20	8.82	7.15		31 ≤, < 37
						0.3157	
4	34 ≤, < 37	35.5	26	9.39	5.10		
						2.7658	
5	37 ≤, < 40	38.5	9	14.00	5.33		37 ≤, < 55
						0.7106	
6	40 ≤, < 43	41.5	14	12.44	4.21		
						5.3005	
7	46 ≤, < 49	47.5	4	25.68	5.17 ˙		
						4.0938	
8	49 ≤, < 52	50.5	6	15.01	3.17		
						0.80744	
9	52 ≤, < 55	52.0	6	13.10	4.85		
						$t_{6,8}$	
						0.3425	

BD　：　bottom depth limits of the classes, average per class

Table III. Variation in the average methane contents with the carbonametry

C	Carb	C_1			α = 0.05	G
i		n	m	s	$t_{i, i+1}$	
1	0	9	12.68	4.70		0 (< 2)
					2.1585	
2	2	12	8.67	3.82		2 ≤, < 5
					0.33601	
3	3	62	9.33	6.57		
					0.8487	
4	4	28	8.03	7.07		
					0.0923	
5	5	22	8.23	8.24		
	6	1	5.65			
	10	1	10.82			
	25	1	9.06			

Carb : Carbonate content

Table IV. Variation in the average methane contents with the coarse clastic content

C i	Sd		C$_1$			$\alpha = 0.05$ $t_{i, i+1}$		G
			n	m	s			
1	$0 \leqslant, < 16$	10.80	11	11.70	6.70			
						0.2600		
2	$16 \leqslant, < 20$	17.81	16	12.36	6.35			
						1.3859		
3	$20 \leqslant, < 23$	20.40	22	9.67	5.57			$0 \leqslant, < 29$
						1.1930		
4	$23 \leqslant, < 26$	23.52	45	7.75	6.46			
						0.2953		
5	$26 \leqslant, < 29$	26.75	40	7.34	6.31			
		50	1	28.41				

Sd: clastic content, limits of the classes, average per class

of the parameter on which the methane content depends is divided into classes. The mean methane content of a class is compared with the next class mean through the use of a two-tailed t-test. This procedure yields the following results:

— the average methane content is constant with respect to variations in sampling depth and sand content.

— the average methane content does not depend on carbonate content when the latter ranges from zero to five percent, although it is possible that this is not true for a carbonate content of exactly zero.

— the average methane content depends on the sea floor depth.

As a check on this procedure, trend analysis was performed on the variations in the methane content. First, data was dichotomized into sequences of values above and below the average and/or the least square regression line; then, tests for random ordering and superimposed cyclic components were applied. The results summarised in Table V confirm the above conclusions.

The relative interdependence between methane content, bottom depth sampling depth, sample position along the WE profile, sample position along the SN profile, carbonate content and sand content was determined by analysis of the correlation coefficient matrix illustrated in Table VI. The correlations significantly different from zero are listed in Table VII. Figure 4 shows the cluster of linked variables which can be extracted from the matrix.

The matrix of partial correlation coefficients which correlate the variables two by two conditionally on some value of the remaining variables is necessary to avoid a false impression of the association between two variables (which could be marked

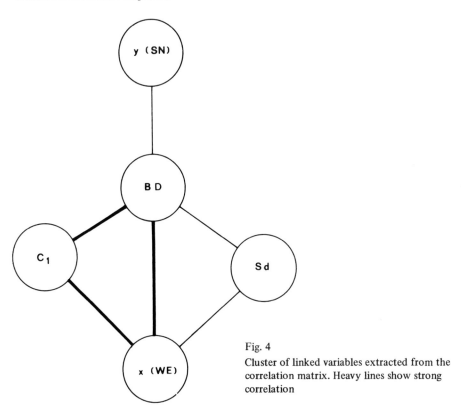

Fig. 4
Cluster of linked variables extracted from the correlation matrix. Heavy lines show strong correlation

Table V. Trend analysis of the variations in the methane contents with SD (sampling depth), BD (bottom depth), Carb (carbonate content), Sd (clastic content). Test for random order around the mean content (single value in column C_1) or the mean square regression line Starred entry in last column indicates that the sequence is "probably not random".

	C_1								n_1 +	n_2 −	u	P (u)	
SD	$C_1 = 8.54$	+	−	+	+	−	−	−	3	4	4	0.3429	
BD	$C_1 = 11.04$	−	−	−	−	+	+	+	+	+	5	4	2	0.0222	*
	$C_1 = 0.5$ BD-8.30	−	−	+	−	+	−	+	−	−	3	6	7	0.0794	
Carb	$C_1 = 9.16$	+	−	+	−	−			2	3	4	0.4000	
Sd	$C_1 = 10.04$	+	+	−	−	−			2	3	2	0.2000	

		t	E (t)	V (t)	Z				
BD	$C_1 = 0.5$ BD-8.30	4	4.66	1.27	- 0.5898				0.2777

Table VI. Matrix of the coefficients of correlation between:

Ci: methane contents
SD: sampling depths   y (SN): positions on the SN profile
BD: bottom depth   Carb: carbonate content
x (WE): positions on the WE profile Sd: clastic content

	C_1	SD	BD	x WE	y SN	Carb	Sd
C_1	1	- 0.04107	0.57248	- 0.62536	- 0.10842	- 0.07231	- 0.10701
SD		1	0.26823	0.12553	- 0.07835	0.02957	- 0.29317
BD			1	- 0.84706	- 0.42769	- 0.14373	- 0.44206
x WE				1	0.01457	0.11878	0.36153
y SN					1	0.19001	0.05319
Carb						1	0.01214
Sd							1

Table VII. Matrix of the coefficients of correlation ρ which are significantly different from zero.

	C_1 SD	BD	x WE	y SN	Carb	Sd
C_1		- 0.47; - 0.67	- 0.51; -0.71			
SD						
BD			- 0.82; - 0.87	- 0.20; - 0.54		- 0.33; - 0.57
x WE						0.21; - 0.51
y SN						
Carb						
Sd						

by the variation of a third). The linear approximation of the methane content variation is deduced from this matrix (see Table VIII) through multiple regression analysis.

Table VIII. Matrix of the coefficients of the partial correlation between:

C_1: methane contents   Carb: carbonate content
SD: sampling depth   Sd: clastic content
BD: bottom depth

	C_1	SD	BD	Carb	Sd
C_1	1	- 0.25250	0.60829	0.03828	0.15839
SD		1	- 0.09578	0.06774	- 0.15707
BD			1	- 0.28051	- 0.40676
Carb				1	- 0.04983
Sd					1

A linear approximation of the variation in the C_1 contents can be represented by the equation

$$C_1 = 0.54 \text{ BD} - 1.28 \text{ SD} - 7.66$$

or

$$C_1 = 0.19 \text{ x} - 0.11 \text{ y} - 1.28 \text{ SD} + 10.49$$

x and y being the coordinates in kilometers on the WE and SN profiles respectively.

This equation indicates that the most rapid variation of C_1 is found along an axis which forms an approximate 29° angle with the WE profile.

From this study and for the sampled area, it can be concluded that the methane content of the samples is strongly dependant on the sea floor depth: the deeper the sea bottom, the higher the methane concentration.

An analysis of the correlation between the behaviour of the saturated hydrocarbons up to n-butane and the behaviour of methane for four selected sampled depths indicates that the variations in the average hydrocarbon contents are similar to the variations in the average methane contents. The correlation coefficient used in this case is Kendall's tau, a non parametric statistic (Figure 5).

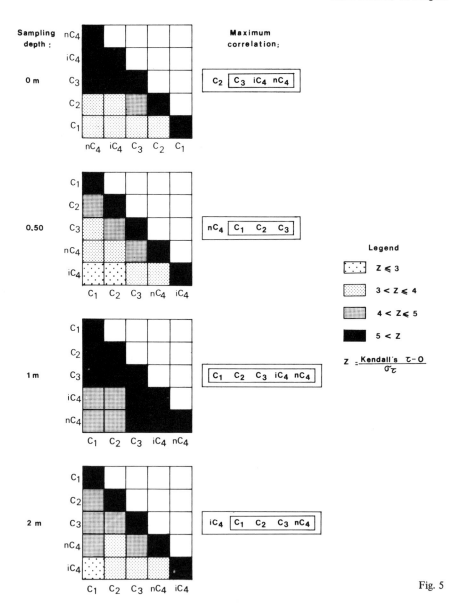

Fig. 5

It seems, therefore, that three main groups of samples may be distinguished according to the sea floor depth: one group between 25 and 31 meters deep, another between 31 and 37 and a third between 37 and 55 meters deep.

For each group and for each saturated hydrocarbons gas, the cumulative frequency distribution of the hydrocarbon contents was found to be compatible with the normal hypothesis. Figure 6 is an example of the fit of the data to the normal curve.

In each group, all the samples having a hydrocarbon content higher than the mean plus three standard deviations were considered anomalous. They are listed in Table IX together with the estimated mean (background) of the population to which they belong. The contents are standardized by the relation:

$T = (content-mean)/standard deviation.$

The purpose of this procedure is to try to circumvent the bias introduced by differences in concentration according to the type of sediment as well as the bias and the variable precision introduced by the different response of the different sediments to the desorption technique (desorption efficiency). However, it does not eliminate the sampling bias resulting from the non-recovery of certain sediments (sample taker efficiency). Figure 7 shows a geographical distribution of the anomalous samples.

The average organic matter (extractable by the benzene-acetone-methanol solvent) of the anomalous samples is 0.763 % with a range of 0.430 to 1.252. The average lipids content of this extract is 54.5 % with a range of 23.8 to 80.5. The average organic matter extracted from 3 samples having a light hydrocarbon content close to the background value is 0.717 % with a range of 0.347 to 0.802. For 7 non-anomalous samples (including the 3 above) the average organic matter content is 0.823 % with a range of 0.596 to 1.050. The average lipids content is 61.2 % with a range of 52.7 to 82.0. A comparison of these averages through the use of a two-tailed t-test (the standard deviation is estimated from the range) shows no difference between the amount of organic matter (and lipids) in anomalous samples and in non-anomalous samples.

For sample W-9, the organic matter content was measured at sample depth of 0, 1, 3 and 4 meters. The calculated correlation coefficient (between organic matter and sample depth) is not significantly different from zero ($r = 0.20947$). The same result is obtained if the 17 anomalous and non-anomalous samples are considered ($r = -0.08678$). The correlation between organic matter content and sea floor depth does not seem to be significantly different from zero ($r = 0.44669$ for the above 17 samples).

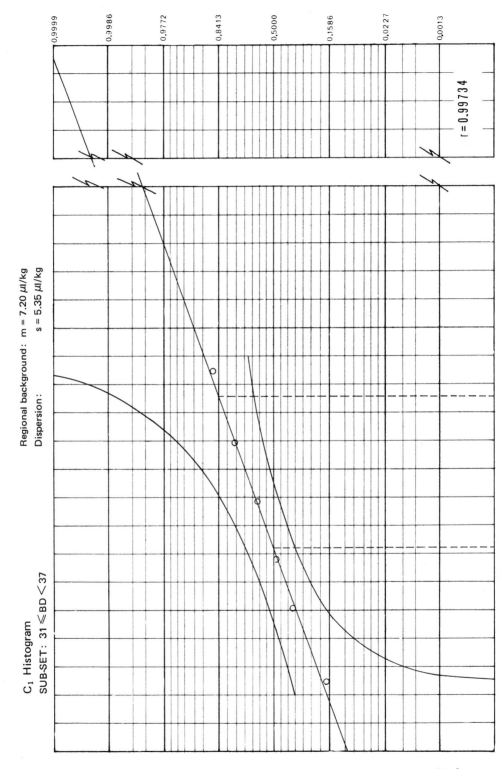

Fig. 6

Table IX. List of the anomalous samples by number (N°), sampling depth (SD), and bottom depth (BD). The contents that have been normalized in relation to the respective Regional Backgrounds are marked in columns C_1, C_2, C_3, iC_4 and nC_4 (the figures in parentheses are the raw measured contents). The values that differ by more than 2 sigmas from the Regional Background are indicated by a cross, while those that differ by more than 3 sigmas are indicated by a double cross.

N°	SD	BD	C_1		C_2		C_3		iC_4		nC_4	
E 9	2.85	25	1.87 (9.06)		2.38 (1.82)	✕	7.78 (0.82)	✕✕	7.14 (0.13)	✕✕	6.43 (0.12)	✕
N 7	0	26.5	6.15 (22.52)	✕✕	1.36 (1.28)		2.11 (0.31)	✕	2.14 (0.06)	✕	3.57 (0.08)	✕
E 6	1.5	27.5	0.57 (4.97)		4.58 (2.99)	✕✕	0.78 (0.19)		1.43 (0.05)		2.86 (0.07)	✕
E 4	0	29	3.01 (12.64)	✕✕	2.40 (1.83)	✕✕	2.22 (0.32)	✕	0.71 (0.04)		2.14 (0.06)	✕
BACKGROUND			3.16		0.56		0.12		0.03		0.03	
N 1	1.0	31.5	2.57 (20.96)	✕	8.10 (4.86)	✕✕	11.64 (1.83)	✕✕	61.90 (1.34)	✕✕	59.05 (1.28)	✕✕
N 1	1.5	31.5	4.44 (30.94)	✕✕	0.51 (0.99)		0.86 (0.32)		2.86 (0.10)	✕	4.76 (0.14)	✕✕
W 2	A	35.5	0.66 (10.71)		3.71 (2.62)	✕✕	1.14 (0.36)		2.38 (0.09)	✕	4.29 (0.13)	✕✕
W 2	B	35.5	2.39 (19.97)	✕	7.84 (4.73)	✕✕	7.36 (1.23)	✕✕	11.43 (0.28)	✕✕	16.19 (0.38)	✕✕
W 2	E	35.5	2.14 (18.64)	✕	3.00 (2.24)	✕✕	3.85 (0.70)	✕✕	5.24 (0.15)	✕✕	10.48 (0.26)	✕✕
S 7	2.5	36.5	1.03 (12.70)		3.31 (2.42)	✕✕	0.43 (0.26)		1.90 (0.08)		3.81 (0.12)	✕✕
BACKGROUND			7.20		0.73		0.20		0.04		0.04	
S 11	1	41.5	1.66 (20.80)		0.73 (2.31)		4.33 (1.36)	✕✕	3.40 (0.29)	✕✕	1.80 (0.21)	
W 8	0	46	3.18 (28.41)	✕✕	2.36 (3.66)	✕✕	1.95 (0.86)	✕	2.00 (0.22)	✕	2.40 (0.24)	✕
W 8	1.0	46	3.82 (31.62)	✕✕	2.41 (3.70)	✕✕	2.86 (1.05)	✕	3.20 (0.28)	✕✕	5.20 (0.38)	✕✕
BACKGROUND			12.50		1.70		0.45		0.12		0.12	

Conclusion

Figure 7 shows that the methane contents of the sampled sediments increase from North East to South West, a direction roughly perpendicular to the coast line and to the average current. It does not seem, therefore, that the anomalous light hydrocarbon contents are due to pollutions from the well drilled at the intersection of the two profiles. Nor does it seem that the anomalous light hydrocarbon contents correlate with some high (soluble) organic matter contents.

A tentative conclusion of this study is that geochemical prospection can be carried out offshore on sediments sampled on the sea floor. Sample depth could be confined to the 1-foot range. Interpretation techniques similar to on-shore methods can be used.

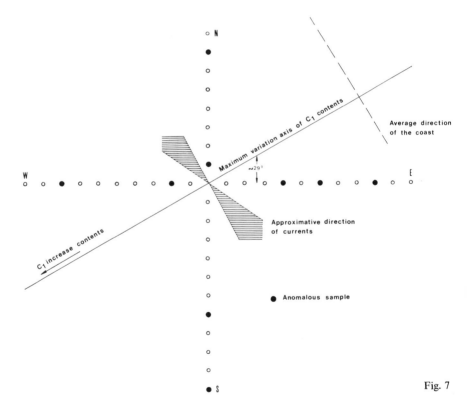

Fig. 7

References

Dunlap, H. F., Bradley, J. S., Moore, T. F.: "Marine seep detection – a new reconnaissance exploration method" Geophysics, **XXV**, No. 1, Feb. 1960, pp. 275–282.

Krumbein, W. C. and Graybill, F. A.: "An introduction to statistical models in geology", Mc Graw-Hill, 1965.

Miesch, A. T.: "Theory of error in geochemical data", Geol. Surv. Prof. Paper 574-A, 1967.

Miller, R. L. and Kahn, J. S.: "Statistical analysis in the geological sciences". John Wiley and Sons, 1965.

Swinnerton, J. W. and Linnenbom, V. J.: "Determination of the C1 to C4 hydrocarbons in sea water by gas chromatography", Journal of gas chromatography, **15,** Nov. 1968, pp. 570–573.

Thompson, R. R. and Creath, W. B.: "Low molecular weight hydrocarbons in recent and fossil shells", Geochimica et Cosmochimica Acta, **30,** 1966, pp. 1137–1152.

Welte, D. H. and Ebhart, G.: "Distribution of long chain n-paraffins and n-fatty acids in sediments from the Persian Gulf, "Geochimica et Cosmochimica Acta, Vol. **32,** 1968, pp. 465– 466.

Discussion

V. Sokolov: The direct geochemical prospecting for petroleum and gas is based on the migration of hydrocarbon gas from the petroleum and gas accumulations to the earth surface, on peculiarities of this gas composition and distribution forming as we call the "gas anomalies" over petroleum gas bearing structures.

These direct geochemical prospecting methods have the best theoretical base in comparison of any other methods. The usual geological – geophysical methods may help only to find traps, but they cannot distinguish the trap with petroleum and gas from the empty trap, which does not contain petroleum and gas.

Our experience in gas survey, taking into account geological data, shows that on average in 60 % our conclusions about the presence of petroleum or gas were quite right. But many geologists do not like the geochemical prospecting and geochemistry in general.

I think that the conditions for off-shore gas survey are much better than on land, because the rate of dissipation from the sea floor is almost the same on all area, and so we expect getting here the good, as we call contrast anomalies over petroleum and gas deposits.

I think that it is useful to arrange a special commission about geochemical prospecting and to arrange the International Meeting on Geochemical Prospecting for Petroleum and Gas in France.

M. Bajor: In den letzten Jahren wurden große Fortschritte bei der analytischen Bestimmung der Benzol und Homologe in Salzwässern erzielt (Blasejak und van der Weide 1967), die gestatten, das Wasser direkt in den Chromatographen zu spritzen und so eine sehr große Anzahl von Proben in kurzer Zeit und einfach zu untersuchen. Warum haben Sie nicht auf dieses Bestimmungsverfahren vom Benzol in den zur Sedimentoberfläche naheliegenden Wässern zurückgegriffen, anstatt auf die Analyse der C_1–C_4 Kohlenwasserstoffhomologen? Die letzten können ja leicht aus den Proben entweichen, lösen sich einigen Potenz weniger und sind daher analytisch nur schwieriger erfaßbar.

R. E. Gérard: Benzene being very soluble in water it is not thought that it would be a good geochemical indicator in sea floor sediments. On the other hand, geochemical prospecting is based on the assumption that gases migrate toward the surface rather than heavier products such as benzene. Benzene is a good indicator of oil when used in subsurface geochemical logging not in surface geochemical prospecting.

Diffusion of Paraffin, Cycloparaffin and Aromatic Hydrocarbons in Water and some Effects of Salt Concentration

Luciano Bonoli and Paul Adam Witherspoon

Istituto Ricerche "G. Donegani" Montecatini Edison S. p. A.
Novara, Italy
University of California
Berkeley, California, USA

Diffusion coefficients for five paraffin, three aromatic and three cycloparaffin hydrocarbons in pure water have been measured, starting with essentially saturated solutions, at temperatures ranging from $2°$ to $60\,°C$ and using the capillary-cell method. Measurements have also been made with benzene in pure water at different initial concentrations at temperatures ranging from $2°$ to $60\,°C$, and on four paraffin hydrocarbons in solutions with two different concentrations of NaCl (2.6 and 5.3 g $\cdot$ mole/liter at $22\,°C$) at temperatures ranging from $10°$ to $40\,°C$.

The diffusion coefficients in pure water for all hydrocarbons investigated can be correlated over the entire temperature range using the empirical Wilke-Chang equation. Because of the very low solubilities of hydrocarbons, the diffusion coefficients show little effect of initial concentration. For a forty-fold decrease in concentration, the decrease in the diffusion coefficients of benzene averages about 10 percent.

By contrast, a marked decrease in the diffusion coefficients of the paraffin hydrocarbons was found in the presence of NaCl. When the salt concentration was 2.6 g $\cdot$ mole/liter, the diffusion coefficients were about 80 percent of their value in pure water, and when the concentration was 5.3 g $\cdot$ mole/liter, the diffusion coefficients were about 65 percent of their value in pure water. This decrease can be explained as a net result of various effects of ions in water, which, in general, act as structure breakers, but also provide obstacles to movement by diffusion because of obstructions and hydrations.

Introduction

Until recently, not much data on the diffusion of hydrocarbons in water has been published. Kartsev, et al. (1959) have reported results for the diffusion of methane, ethane, propane, and normal hexane in water. Gubbins, et al. (1966) have reported data for methane, as well as the effects of electrolytes on the diffusion of methane in water. With regard to other hydrocarbons, diffusion data have been reported only by Tammann, et al. (1929) for acetylene in water, Vivian, et al. (1964) for propylene in water, Unver, et al. (1964) for ethylene, propylene and butylene in water, and Mousseau (1964) for benzene in pure water and in aqueous salt solutions at 25 °C. An extensive investigation on the solubility of hydrocarbons in water has been reported by McAuliffe (1966).

Because of this lack of data, a project has been underway for some time at the University of California at Berkeley to study the diffusion through water of the hydrocarbons found in petroleum. The first investigations were concerned with light paraffin hydrocarbons (Saraf, et al. 1963; Witherspoon and Saraf, 1965; Sahores and Witherspoon, 1966). Recently, Witherspoon, et al. (1968), and Bonoli and Witherspoon (1968) have obtained results for aromatic and cycloparaffin hydrocarbons, and in studying the diffusion of benzene, they have also investigated the effect of initial concentration on diffusion. This paper will review these results and show how they may be correlated by one empirical equation.

The next logical step is to investigate the effect of electrolytes on hydrocarbon diffusion. This paper presents new results on the diffusion of methane, ethane, propane, and n-butane in solutions of NaCl at temperatures ranging from $10°$ to $40 °C$.

Experimental Procedure

The capillary-cell method of measuring diffusion coefficients perfected by Wang (1951, 1952), Wang, et al. (1953, 1954) and Saraf, et al. (1963) has been used for this work. Various improvements in the experimental procedure have been developed, and the details have been described in several other publications (Witherspoon and Saraf, 1965; Sahores and Witherspoon, 1966; Witherspoon, et al., 1968; Bonoli and Witherspoon, 1968).

Solutions with two different concentrations of NaCl (2.6 and 5.3 g · mole/liter at $22 °C$) were prepared using standard procedures and kept in covered containers to prevent evaporation. These solutions were then saturated with the hydrocarbon[1]) under investigation using the standard bubbling techniques described by Sahores and Witherspoon (1966), and Witherspoon, et al. (1968). One of the critical problems was to maintain the same salt concentration inside the capillary cell as well as outside so that the hydrocarbons could diffuse through a homogeneous environment.

Experimental Results

Data on the diffusion coefficients of the paraffin, aromatic and cycloparaffin hydrocarbons in water, as well as results on the diffusion of benzene with different initial concentrations, have recently been reported, and are given in Tables I, II and III for the sake of completeness.

---

[1]) All hydrocarbons used were pure grade, 99 % pure or better, and were obtained from Philips Petroleum Company, Bartlesville, Oklahoma, USA.

Diffusion coefficients for methane, ethane, propane, and normal butane in solutions with NaCl concentrations of 2.6 and 5.3 g · mole/liter are given in table IV and V, respectively. In all of these tables, the data shown represent averages of a number of repetitive runs, generally 10-15. The precision shown is the standard deviation of the arithmetic mean.

Discussion of Results

A comparison of results from Table I for the diffusion coefficients of paraffin hydrocarbons in pure water with the earlier work of Sahores and Witherspoon (1966) indicates generally good agreement. The only significant differences are that the values on Table I for propane and n-pentane are about 13 % higher than those previously reported.

Table I. Experimental results for diffusion coefficients of paraffin hydrocarbons in water

| Hydrocarbon | $D \times 10^5$, cm^2/sec at temperatures of: | | | |
	4 °C	20 °C	40 °C	60 °C
Methane	0.85 ± .02	1.49 ± .04	2.38 ± .07	3.55 ± .15
Ethane	0.69 ± .01	1.20 ± .06	1.94 ± .04	2.94 ± .12
Propane	0.55 ± .03	0.97 ± .02	1.77 ± .04	2.71 ± .05
n-Butane	0.50 ± .02	0.89 ± .04	1.59 ± .04	2.51 ± .05
n-Pentane	0.46 ± .02[1])	0.84 ± .04	1.49 ± .03	2.24 ± .10

[1]) New result, not previously published

In considering the results of Tables I and II the question may arise as to the effect of the initial concentration on the diffusion process. The results of Table III indicate that there is little effect of concentration on the diffusion of benzene in water. For a thirty to forty-fold decrease in concentration, the decrease in the diffusion coefficients averages about 10 %, whereas the uncertainty in our results is about 3 %.

These results suggest that over the range of concentrations studied, the benzene molecules move through water more or less independently of each other. This is not unexpected because at its maximum solubility, one molecule of benzene is surrounded by more than 2000 molecules of water. The same conclusion can be drawn from the results of Table II. Methylcyclopentane, for example, has the lowest solubility among the aromatic and cycloparaffin hydrocarbons studied, 42.6 ppm at 25 °C (McAuliffe, 1966), yet the diffusion coefficients for these hydrocarbons are only 20 percent lower than those of benzene. These lower results for

Table II. Experimental results for diffusion coefficients of aromatic and cycloparaffin hydrocarbons in water

Hydrocarbon	$D \times 10^5$, cm^2/sec at temperatures of:				
	2 °C	10 °C	20 °C	40 °C	60°C
Benzene	0.58 ± .02	0.75 ± .02	1.02 ± .03	1.60 ± .05	2.55 ± .05
Toluene	0.45 ± .02	0.62 ± .02	0.85 ± .03	1.34 ± .05	2.15 ± .06
Ethylbenzene	0.44 ± .04	0.61 ± .05	0.81 ± .03	1.30 ± .05	1.95 ± .05
Cyclopentane	0.56 ± .02	0.64 ± .03	0.93 ± .02	1.41 ± .09	2.18 ± .07
Methylcyclo-pentane	0.48 ± .08	0.59 ± .06	0.85 ± .10	1.32 ± .12	1.92 ± .15
Cyclohexane	0.46 ± .04	0.57 ± .04	0.84 ± .05	1.31 ± .07	1.93 ± .12

Table III. Experimental results of diffusion measurements with benzene at different initial concentrations

2 °C		10 °C		20 °C	
Conc. [a]	D [b]	Conc.	D	Conc.	D
1700	0.58 ± .02	1700	0.75 ± .02	1700	1.02 ± .03
210	0.56 ± .03	60	0.68 ± .04	40	0.82 ± .04
40	0.43 ± .02				

40 °C		60 °C	
Conc.	D	Conc.	D
1700	1.60 ± .05	1700	2.55 ± .05
50	1.52 ± .05	45	2.39 ± .04

[a] Concentrations in ppm.

[b] $D \times 10^5$, cm^2/sec

methylcyclopentane may be explained by its larger molecular size and are not an effect of concentration. Haycock, et al. (1953), Watts, et al. (1955), Hildebrand and Scott (1962) have supported the concept that movement by diffusion is a "random-walk" process and later Ross and Hildebrand (1964), and Nakanishi, et al. (1965) have proposed that such a process should be controlled mainly by molecular cross-section.

Witherspoon and Saraf (1965) have found the same results in studying the diffusion of light paraffin hydrocarbons.

A considerable effort has been expended by many workers in developing methods of predicting coefficients of diffusion. Antonov (1959) has published data on the steady state diffusion of methane, ethane, propane, butane, and hexane through clays containing 25 percent water by weight. The diffusion coefficients are, of course, lower than for pure water because of the presence of clay, but these results are used by him to support the interpretation that diffusion coefficients for the paraffin gases are inversely proportional to the square root of their molecular weights.

To investigate this point, we computed the values of $D\sqrt{M}$ using the data of Table I, and have plotted these values versus carbon number as shown in Figure 1. It will be noted that at the lowest temperature studied, 4 °C, $d\sqrt{M}$ is sensibly constant. However, as temperature increases, it is evident that $d\sqrt{M}$ departs more and more from a constant value. Thus, it appears that this correlation can lead to errors whose magnitude will be very much dependent on the temperature at which diffusion takes place.

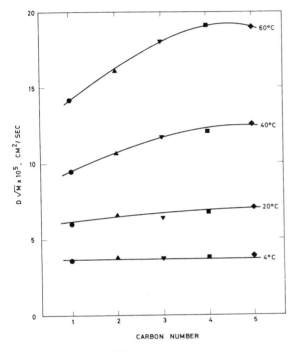

Fig. 1. Values of $D\sqrt{M}$ versus carbon number for paraffin hydrocarbons

In attempting to correlate the diffusion coefficients for paraffin hydrocarbons, Witherspoon and Saraf (1965) found that by plotting log D versus carbon number, they obtained a simple exponential relationship over a temperature range of 24.8° to 42.6 °C. Sahores and Witherspoon (1966) have also reported the same result. We have investigated this point by plotting the results of Table I as shown on Figure 2. We have arbitrarily drawn straight lines through the plotted points, but it is evident that lines with slight curvature would make a better correlation. More-over, the lines shown in Figure 2 are not parallel, and thus one cannot obtain a simple exponential relationship from these results. We therefore concluded that

the exponential relationship proposed by Witherspoon and Saraf (1965) as well as
the earlier factor $D\sqrt{M}$ = const. supported by Antonov (1959) are not entirely
satisfactory.

It is, of course, obvious that the above correlations cannot be applied to aromatic
or cycloparaffin hydrocarbons. We therefore turned our attention to other empirical correlations in an effort to learn if there might be one method that could be
applied to all the hydrocarbons of this investigation.

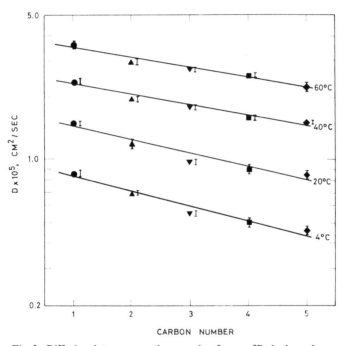

Fig. 2. Diffusion data versus carbon number for paraffin hydrocarbons

Since diffusion coefficients in liquids are increasingly important in many theoretical
and engineering calculations involving mass transfer, such as adsorption, extraction,
distillation, and chemical reactions, attempts have been made by Othmer and Thakar
(1954), Scheibel (1954), Wilke and Chang (1955) to develop empirical equations that
would enable one to predict diffusion coefficients. Wilke and Chang (1955) have proposed the following equation for diffusion in either associated or unassociated liquids:

$$D = 7.4 \times 10^{-8} \frac{(xM)^{0.5}T}{\eta\, V^{0.6}}$$

where:

x   association parameter equal to 2.6 in water and 1.0 for unassociated liquids
M   molecular weight of the solvent
T   absolute temperature, °K
η viscosity of the solvent at temperature T, cp
V   liquid molal volume of solute at normal boiling point, $cm^3/g \cdot mole$.

To examine the applicability of this equation to our results, we plotted D/T versus $\eta V^{0.6}/M^{0.5}$ for the paraffin hydrocarbons as shown on Figure 3. Although there is some scatter of points about the correlation line for associated liquids (x = 2.6), the agreement is fairly good. Figure 3 indicates that the Wilke-Chang equation will predict diffusion coefficients for the paraffin hydrocarbons from methane through pentane with a maximum error of 18 percent.

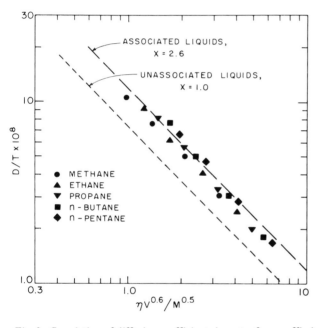

Fig. 3. Correlation of diffusion coefficients in water for paraffin hydrocarbons

Figure 4 shows the same correlation as applied to the diffusion coefficients obtained for aromatic and cycloparaffin hydrocarbons. Here, we see that our results are in good agreement with the correlation line for associated liquids. These results indicate that the Wilke-Chang equation will predict diffusion coefficients for the aromatic and cycloparaffin hydrocarbons with a maximum error of 10 percent.

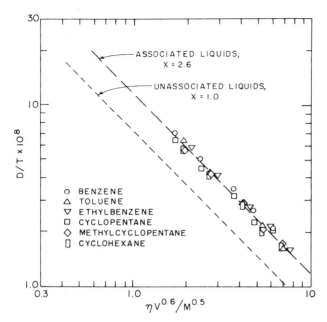

Fig. 4. Correlation of diffusion coefficients in water for aromatic and cycloparaffin hydrocarbons

Therefore, it is our conclusion that the Wilke-Chang equation provides a reliable basis for predicting the diffusion of hydrocarbons in pure water. It appears that this equation will be somewhat more reliable when applied to aromatic and cycloparaffin hydrocarbons than when applied to paraffin hydrocarbons. It must be kept in mind, however, that V does not vary as much for the aromatic and cycloparaffin hydrocarbons as it does for the paraffins of this investigation.

A comparison of the results of Table IV and V with those in Table I will reveal the marked decrease in the diffusion coefficients of paraffin hydrocarbons that is caused by the presence of NaCl. When the salt concentration is 2.6 g · mole/liter, the diffusion coefficients are about 80 percent of their value in pure water, and when the concentration is 5.3 g · mole/liter, the diffusion coefficients are only 65 percent of their value in pure water.

Gubbins, et al. (1966) have recently published data for the diffusion of methane in solutions of three different salts: KCl, $MgCl_2$, and $MgSO_4$. They also observed a decrease in the diffusion coefficients as the salinity increased which they explain as an effect of changes in the free energy of activation for diffusion. By making Arrhenius plots of the data of Table I, IV and V, we obtained activation energies of 4400, 5200 and 5500 cal/mole, respectively. In other words, we found the activation energy for diffusion to increase about 25 percent when the NaCl concentration was increased to 5.3 g · mole/liter.

Table IV. Experimental results for diffusion coefficients of paraffin hydrocarbons in salt solutions with 2.6 g·mole/ liter of NaCl

Hydrocarbon	$D \times 10^5$, cm^2/sec at temperatures of:		
	10 °C	25 °C	40 °C
Methane	0.87 ± .03	1.35 ± .06	1.97 ± .05
Ethane	0.66 ± .03	1.10 ± .04	1.61 ± .04
Propane	0.56 ± .02	0.92 ± .03	1.40 ± .05
n-Butane	0.50 ± .02	0.84 ± .04	1.22 ± .06

Table V. Experimental results for diffusion coefficients of paraffin hydrocarbons in salt solutions with 5.3 g·mole/ liter of NaCl

Hydrocarbon	$D \times 10^5$, cm^2/sec at temperatures of:		
	10 °C	25 °C	40 °C
Methane	0.68 ± .03	1.09 ± .04	1.60 ± .05
Ethane	0.47 ± .03	0.83 ± .05	1.30 ± .05
Propane	0.42 ± .02	0.74 ± .06	1.09 ± .04
n-Butane	0.41 ± .05	0.66 ± .05	1.03 ± .07

According to Wang (1954), however, the effect of an ionic solute in changing the liquid structure of water is of more importance on diffusion than changes in activation energy. Wang measured self-diffusion coefficients for water in NaCl and KI solutions using concentrations ranging from 0 to 5 g·mole/liter. He found that NaCl decreased the self-diffusion coefficients whereas KI increased them relative to values obtained with pure water.

Recently, Mousseau (1964) has measured diffusion coefficients for benzene at 25 °C in pure water as well as in KI solutions with concentrations up to a maximum of 1.8 g·mole/liter. In pure water he obtained a value of 1.10×10^{-5} cm^2/sec, which is in very good agreement with our results for benzene (see Table II). His results are also in agreement with those of Wang (1954) in that he observed a 10 percent increase in the diffusion coefficient when the maximum KI concentration was used.

Wang (1954) explains the opposite effects of NaCl and KI on diffusion from the standpoint that, in general, one should expect an ionic solute to act as a structure breaker. The immediate consequence should be an increase in diffusion coefficients for hydrocarbon in water because of the longer diffusion paths in the new structure. However, obstructions and hydrations of the salt ions can provide obstacles to movement by diffusion such that the net effect is to decrease the coefficient of diffusion.

It is apparent that the presence of salt in aqueous solutions can have a significant effect on diffusion coefficients. However, in view of the opposite effects that can occur, it is obvious that, in the absence of experimental data, care will have to be exercised in making predictions of the possible effect of any given salt on the diffusion coefficients of hydrocarbons in water.

Acknowledgement: This work was made possible through a grant from the National Science Foundation of the United States of America.

References

Antonov, P. L.; 1959: The diffusion permeability of some argillaceous rocks: Geokhim. Metody Poiskov Neft. i Gaz. Mestorozhd. AN SSSR, Tr. Soveshch, Moscow, 1958.

Arnold, D. S., Plank, C. A., Erickson, E. E. and Pike, F. P.; 1958: Solubility of benzene in water: Ind. Eng. Chem., Chem. Eng. Data Ser., 3, 253–256.

Bohon, R. L and Claussen, W. F.; 1951: The solubility of aromatic hydrocarbons in water: J. Am. Chem. Soc., 73, 1571–1578.

Bonoli, L.and Witherspoon, P. A.; 1968: Diffusion of aromatic and cycloparaffin hydrocarbons in water from 2 to 60°: J. Phys. Chem. 72, 2532–2534.

Gubbins, K.E., Bhatia, K. K. and Walker, R. D.; 1966: Diffusion of gases in electrolytic solutions: A. I. Ch. E. Journal, 12, 548–552.

Haycock, E. W., Alder, B. J. and Hildebrand, J. H.; 1953: The diffusion of iodine in carbon tetrachloride under pressure: J. Chem. Phys., 21, 1601–1604.

Hildebrand, J. H. and Scott, R. L.; 1962: Regular Solutions, Prentice-Hall, Inc., New York.

Kartsev, A. A., Tabasaranskii, Z. A., Subotta, M. I. and Morgilevskii, G. A.; 1959: Geochemical Methods of Prospecting and Exploration for Petroleum and Natural Gas, University of California Press, p. 69.

McAuliffe, C.; 1966: Solubility in water of paraffin, cycloparaffin, olefin, acetylene, cycloolefin, and aromatic hydrocarbons: J. Phys. Chem., 70, 1267–1275.

Mousseau, R. J., Jr.; 1964: Diffusion of benzene in aqueous salt solutions: M. S. Thesis, University of Pittsburgh, Pennsylavania.

Nakanishi, K., Voigt, E. M. and Hildebrand, J. H.; 1965: Quantum effect in the diffusion of gases in liquids at 25 °C: J. Chem. Phys., 42, 1860–1863.

Othmer, D. E. and Thakar, M. S.; 1953: Correlating diffusion coefficients in liquids: Ind. Eng. Chem., 45, 589–593.

Ross, M. and Hildebrand, J. H.; 1964: Diffusion of hydrogen deuterium, nitrogen, argon, methane and carbon tetrafluoride in carbon tetrachloride: J. Chem. Phys., 40, 2397–2399.

Sahores, J. J. and Witherspoon, P. A.; 1966: Diffusion of light paraffin hydrocarbons in water from 2° to 80 °C: in "Advances in Organic Geochemistry, 1966", Pergamon Press (in press).

Saraf, D. N., Witherspoon, P. A. and Cohen, L. H.; 1963: Diffusion coefficients of hydrocarbons in water: Method for measuring: Science, 142, 955–956.

Scheibel, E. G.; 1954: Liquid diffusivities: Ind. Eng. Chem., 46, 2007–2008.

Tammann, G. and Jensen, V. Z.; 1929: Über die Diffusionskoeffizienten von Gasen in Wasser und ihre Temperaturabhängigkeit: Z. Anorg. Allgem. Chem., 179, 125–144.

Unver, A. A. and Himmelblau, D. M.; 1964: Diffusion coefficients of CO_2, C_2H_4, C_3H_6 and C_4H_8 in water from 6 to 65°: J. Chem. Eng. Data, 9, 428.

Vivian, J. E. and King, C. J.; 1964: Diffusivities of slightly soluble gases in water: A. I. Ch. E. Journal, 10, 220–221.

Wang, J. H.; 1954: Effects of ions on the self-diffusion and structure of water in aqueous electrolytic solutions: J. Phys. Chem., 58, 686.

Wang, J. H.; 1952: Tracer-diffusion in liquids. I. Diffusion of tracer amount of sodium ion in aqueous potassium chloride solution: J. Am. Chem. Soc., 74, 1182–1186.

Wang, J. H.; 1951: Self-diffusion and structure of liquid water. I. Measurement of self-diffusion of liquid water with deuterium as tracer: J. Am. Chem. Soc., 73, 510–513.

Wang, J. H., Anfinsen, C. B. and Polestra, F. M.; 1954: The self-diffusion coefficients of water and ovalbumin in aqueous ovalbumin solutions at 10 °C: J. Am. Chem. Soc., 76, 4763–4765

Wang, J. H., Robinson, C. V. and Edelman, I. S.; 1953: Self-diffusion and structure of liquid water. III. Measurement of the self-diffusion of liquid water with H^2, H^3 and O^{18} as tracers: J. Am. Chem. Soc., 75, 446–470.

Watts, H., Alder, B. J. and Hildebrand, J. H.; 1955: Self-diffusion of carbon tetrachloride, isobars and isochores: J. Chem. Phys. 23, 659–661.

Wilke, C. R. and Chang, P.; 1955: Correlation of diffusion coefficients in dilute solutions: A. I. Ch. E. Journal, 1, 264–270.

Witherspoon, P. A., Bonoli, L. and Sahores, J. J.; 1968: Results on the measurement of diffusion coefficients for paraffin, aromatic and cycloparaffin hydrocarbons in water: Paper presented at All-Union Conference on Origin of Oil and Gas, Moscow, USSR, January 1968 (to be translated into Russian and published with Proceedings).

Witherspoon, P. A. and Saraf, D. N.; 1965: Diffusion of methane, ethane, propane and n-butane in water from 25 to 43°: J. Phys. Chem. 69, 3752–3755.

Evolution expérimentale d'huiles brutes et de fractions d'huiles brutes sous l'influence de la température, de la pression et de minéraux argileux

Yolande Califet[1]), Jean-Louis Oudin[1]) et Bernard Marius van der Weide[2])

[1]) Institut Français du Pétrole
Rueil-Malmaison, France
[2]) Société Nationale des Pétroles d'Aquitaine
Pau, France

Series of experiments have been performed to study the evolution of crude oils and fractions of crude oils (aliphatic hydrocarbons, aromatic hydrocarbons and resins) at 180 °C and 230 °C. Assays have been made under vacuum or in inert atmosphere, with or without pressure in presence or absence of a clay mineral (montmorillonite); in some cases water was added to the sample.

Light hydrocarbons, aliphatic hydrocarbons and asphaltic substances (resins and asphaltenes) are produced during the evolution of crude oil and aromatics. The evolution of the aliphatic hydrocarbon fractions leads to the formation of aromatics and asphaltics but this conversion takes place to a smaller extent than the conversion of the aromatic fraction. Thus the maturation of the crude oil, combining these two trends, results in an "aliphatisation".

All these results can be essentially related to a thermal cracking, since temperature increases obviously the formation of light and aliphatic hydrocarbons. The presence of heteroatomic compounds (mainly oxygenated ones) influences strongly the formation of asphaltic substances. Montmorillonite seems to catalyze these phenomena.

Des séries d'expériences ont été réalisées afin d'étudier l'évolution d'huiles et de fractions d'huiles (hydrocarbures aliphatiques, hydrocarbures aromatiques, résines) à des températures de 180 °C et 230 °C. Les essais ont été effectués sous vide ou en atmosphère inerte, avec ou sans pression, et en présence ou non d'un minéral argileux (montmorillonite) et d'eau.

On forme au cours de l'évolution de l'huile et de la fraction aromatique des hydrocarbures légers, des hydrocarbures aliphatiques et des produits lourds. L'évolution de la fraction aliphatique conduit à la formation d'hydrocarbures aromatiques et de produits lourds, mais cette transformation est moins importante que celle de la fraction aromatique. Dans l'ensemble, l'évolution de l'huile se traduit ainsi par une aliphatisation.

Les réactions de cracking thermique semblent prédominer, car la température augmente notablement la formation d'hydrocarbures aliphatiques. La présence de molécules hétéroatomiques (en particulier oxygénées) semble jouer un rôle déterminant dans la formation des produits lourds. Le phénomène est catalysé par la présence de montmorillonite.

Introduction

Les huiles de gisements profonds ont en général un caractère plus paraffinique et une densité plus faible que les huiles de gisements peu profonds (Mc Nab et al. 1952, Kartsev, 1964, Biederman, 1965). Aussi l'objectif des expériences de laboratoire décrites dans cet exposé est-il d'étudier l'évolution de la constitution chimique d'une huile ou de fractions d'huiles brutes en fonction des paramètres liés à l'enfouissement: température et pression. Simultanément l'influence d'un minéral argileux (montmorillonite) sur cette évolution a été examinée.

Partie experimentale

Les essais ont été effectués sur une huile brute de Libye, préalablement toppée à 300 °C puis désasphaltée par précipitation à l'éther de pétrole (Eb. 40–60 °C) ainsi que sur les fractions aliphatique, aromatique et hétéro-atomique (résines) isolées de cette huile par chromatographie liquide sur alumine et silicagel. Ces produits étaient chauffés pendant 72 heures à 230 °C dans des ampoules de verre sous vide d'hélium, en présence ou non d'eau salée[1]), de montmorillonite et d'eau salée[2]) enfin de montmorillonite seule. Les produits récupérés étaient séparés en leurs divers constituants : hydrocarbures aliphatiques et aromatiques, résines et asphaltènes, par chromatographie liquide.

D'autre part, des essais analogues ont été effectués à 180 °C pendant 28 jours, sous une pression liquide de 300 kg/cm^2 sur des fractions aliphatiques et aromatiques. Celles-ci étaient isolées à partir de coupes de distillation $C_{15}-C_{20}$ et $C_{20}-C_{25}$ d'une huile brute de Mirando (Eocène, Texas), essentiellement naphténique et contenant environ 9 % de produits lourds. Les échantillons étaient introduits dans de petits autoclaves (Photo 1) à la pression désirée, par l'intermédiaire d'une cellule tampon reliée à une pompe hydraulique à mercure. Ces autoclaves étaient chauffés à 180 °C dans un bain d'huile thermostatée (Photo 2). Les gaz formés étaient récupérés et analysés en CGL tandis que l'huile évoluée était séparée en ses divers constituants.

Resultats

1. Evolution d'une huile brute (tableau I)

On remarque que la teneur en hydrocarbures aliphatiques ne semble pas être affectée par le traitement. Par contre, il y a formation de produits lourds et cela

---

[1]) Solution aqueuse à 3 % de NaCl.
[2]) Pour éviter des échanges ioniques dans les expériences en présence d'eau salée, la montmorillonite est rendue sodique par traitement au NaCl.

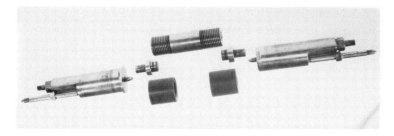

Photo 1. Autoclave pour l'évolution des huiles

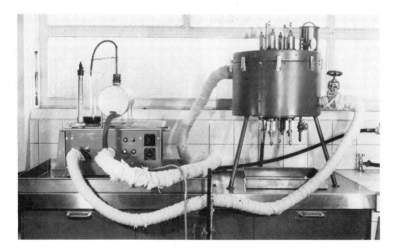

Photo 2. Appareil pour l'évolution des huiles

Tableau I.   Evolution (72 heures à 230 °C) d'une huile brute désasphaltée

	Hydrocarbures aliphatiques	Hydrocarbures aromatiques	Résines	Asphaltènes
Huile non traitée	64,2	27,3	8,5	-
Huile chauffée	65,5	22,7	6,4	5,9
Huile + montmorillonite	64,6	22,6	6,7	6,1
Huile + eau salée	66,3	18,5	6,5	8,7
Huile + montmorillonite + eau salée	64,3	16,3	6,8	12,6

aux dépens de la fraction aromatique. La présence ou l'absence de montmorillonite n'a pas d'influence ; par contre en présence d'eau on constate la formation
accrue de produits lourds, notamment d'asphaltènes.

2. Evolution de la fraction aliphatique d'une huile brute (tableau II)

On constate que la montmorillonite et l'eau ont peu d'effet sur la formation
d'hydrocarbures aromatiques et de résines, laquelle se manifeste dans tous les cas.

Tableau II.   Evolution (72 heures à 230 °C) d'une fraction aliphatique d'huile brute

	Hydrocarbures aliphatiques	Hydrocarbures aromatiques	Résines	Asphaltènes
Fraction non traitée	100,00	-	-	-
Fraction chauffée	92,9	5,2	1,9	-
Fraction + montmorillonite	89,8	7,6	2,6	-
Fraction + eau salée	89,2	7,7	3,1	-
Fraction + montmorillonite + eau salée	92,4	5,2	2,4	-

3. Evolution des fractions aliphatiques des coupes de distillation (tableaux III et IV)

Dans ces essais, la montmorillonite catalyse la formation d'hydrocarbures aromatiques et surtout de produits lourds; en particulier dans la coupe $C_{15} - C_{20}$, l'addition d'eau salée favorise d'une manière plus nette la formation de ces corps. Des
hydrocarbures gazeux sont formés en traces de C_1 à C_6, dans lesquels des n- et isoparaffines ainsi que des oléfines ont été identifiées.

Tableau III.   Evolution de la fraction aliphatique $C_{15} - C_{20}$ de Mirando (300 kg/cm^2, 180 °C, 28 jours)

	Hydrocarbures légers C_1 à C_6	Hydrocarbures aliphatiques	Hydrocarbures aromatiques	Résines	Asphaltènes
Fraction non traitée	-	100,00		-	-
Fraction chauffée	traces	99,00	0,76	0,24	-
Fraction + montmorillonite	traces	98,20	1,58	0,12	0,10
Fraction + eau salée + montmorillonite	traces	93,92	2,47	3,27	0,84

Tableau IV. Evolution de la fraction aliphatique $C_{20}-C_{25}$ de Mirando (300 kg/cm², 180 °C, 28 jours)

	Hydrocarbures légers C_1 à C_6	Hydrocarbures aliphatiques	Hydrocarbures aromatiques	Résines	Asphaltènes
Fraction non traitée	-	100,00	-	-	-
Fraction + montmorillonite	traces	96,97	1,37	1,02	-
Fraction + eau salée	traces	99,16	0,66	0,18	0,64
Fraction + montmorillonite + eau salée	traces	98,10	0,70	0,99	0,21

Les hydrocarbures aromatiques et aliphatiques récupérés des essais d'évolution ont été analysés par spectrométrie de masse (AEI type MS9). Les résultats (Figure 1) montrent que les hydrocarbures aromatiques formés à partir de la coupe $C_{20}-C_{25}$ ont une formule moyenne $C_{22}H_{33}$ (C_nH_{2n-11}). Dans les essais en présence d'eau, on

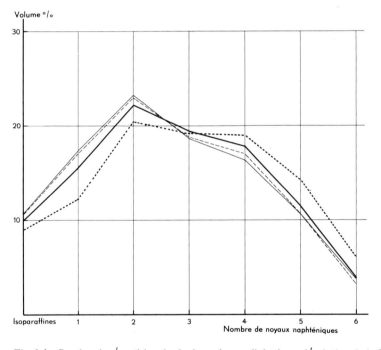

Fig. 1.1. Courbes de répartition des hydrocarbures aliphatiques (évolution de la fraction aliphatique $C_{20}-C_{25}$ de Mirando)

——————— Fraction non traitée

——————— Fraction + montmorillonite

– – – – – Fraction + eau salée

- - - - - - - - Fraction + montmorillonite + eau salée

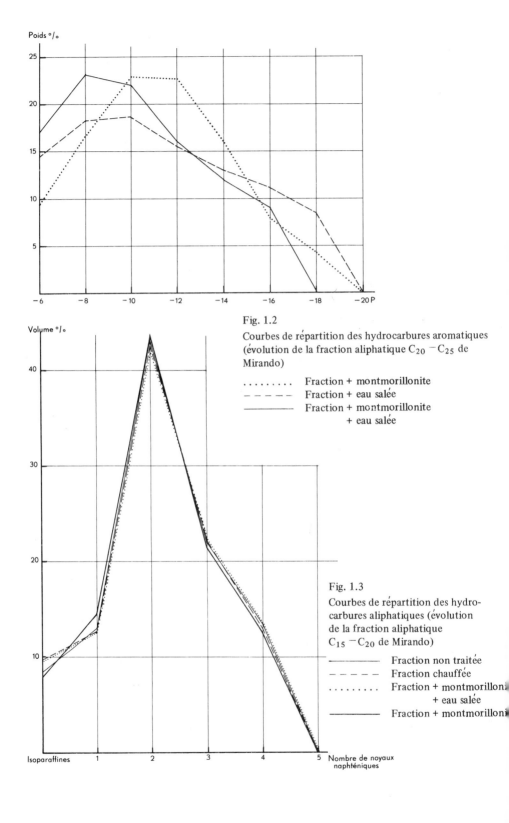

Poids °/o

Fig. 1.2

Courbes de répartition des hydrocarbures aromatiques (évolution de la fraction aliphatique $C_{20} - C_{25}$ de Mirando)

.... Fraction + montmorillonite
– – – – Fraction + eau salée
———— Fraction + montmorillonite
              + eau salée

Volume °/o

Fig. 1.3

Courbes de répartition des hydro-carbures aliphatiques (évolution de la fraction aliphatique $C_{15} - C_{20}$ de Mirando)

———— Fraction non traitée
– – – – Fraction chauffée
.... Fraction + montmorillon
              + eau salée
———— Fraction + montmorillon

Isoparaffines   1   2   3   4   5   Nombre de noyaux
                                                                     naphténiques

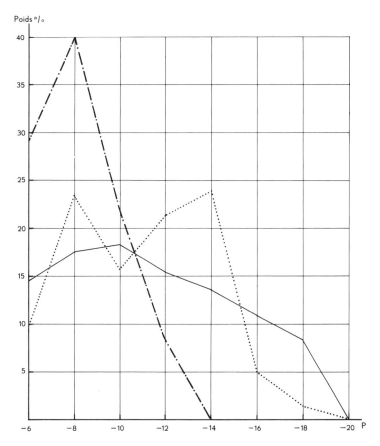

Fig. 1.4. Courbes de répartition des hydrocarbures aromatiques (évolution de la fraction aliphatique $C_{15} - C_{20}$ de Mirando)

· — · — · — · Fraction non traitée   ————— Fraction + montmorillonite
· · · · · · · · Fraction + montmorillonite   + eau salée

constate une prédominance des mono-aromatiques; en présence de montmorillonite seule on est en présence d'un mélange de mono- et di-aromatiques. A partir de la coupe $C_{15} - C_{20}$, les hydrocarbures formés sont différents d'un essai à l'autre. L'huile seule donne une prédominance de $C_n h_{2n-8}$ (famille de la tétraline); en présence de montmorillonite il y a formation d'un mélange de $C_n H_{2n-8}$ et de $C_n H_{2n-14}$ (famille du tétrahydrophénanthrène). Enfin en présence d'eau salée et de montmorillonite, la courbe est plus étalée entre les mono- et di-aromatiques.

Les hydrocarbures aliphatiques formés à partir des deux coupes $C_{15} - C_{20}$ et $C_{20} - C_{25}$ sont peu différents de ceux présents dans ces coupes avant traitement.

Toutefois le traitement de la coupe $C_{20}-C_{25}$ en présence de montmorillonite et d'eau a provoqué une légère augmentation relative des naphtènes plus lourds (3 ou 4 cycles) aux dépens des naphtènes à 1 ou 2 cycles. La chromatographie en phase gazeuse confirme également que les fractions aliphatiques récupérées des deux coupes après évolution n'ont pas subi de modifications notables par rapport aux produits de départ (Figure 2).

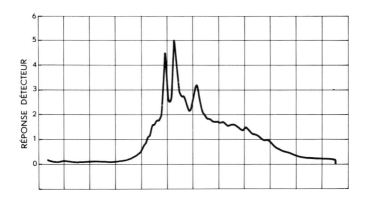

Fig. 2.1. Chromatogramme de la fraction aliphatique $C_{15}-C_{20}$ de Mirando de départ

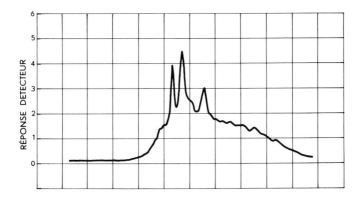

Fig. 2.2. Chromatogramme de la fraction aliphatique $C_{15}-C_{20}$ de Mirando, chauffée à 180 °C, sous 300 kg/cm² de pression pendant 30 jours

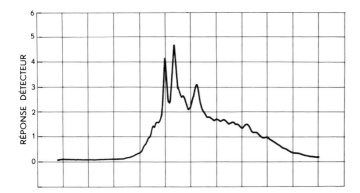

Fig. 2.3. Chromatogramme de la fraction aliphatique $C_{15} - C_{20}$ de Mirando, chauffée à 180 °C, sous 300 kg/cm² de pression pendant 30 jours avec eau salée et montmorillonite

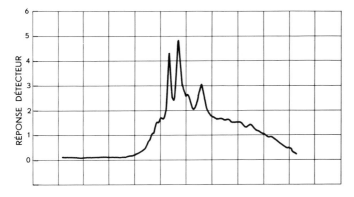

Fig. 2.4. Chromatogramme de la fraction aliphatique $C_{15} - C_{20}$ de Mirando, chauffée à 180 °C, sous 300 kg/cm² de pression pendant 30 jours avec de la montmorillonite

4. Evolution de la fraction aromatique d'une huile brute (tableau VIII)

Le traitement thermique de la fraction aromatique d'une huile brute conduit à la formation d'hydrocarbures aliphatiques, de résines et d'asphaltènes en quantités appréciables. La montmorillonite exerce un effet favorable sur la formation des hydrocarbures aliphatiques. Par contre, l'eau n'a pas d'influence notable et semble même inhiber l'action de la montmorillonite.

5. Evolution des fractions aromatiques des coupes de distillation (tableaux V et VI)

La formation d'hydrocarbures aliphatiques n'est pas influencée par la présence de montmorillonite, mais la présence d'eau salée dans la coupe $C_{20}-C_{25}$ en augmente considérablement la quantité et en modifie la nature chimique: le pourcentage de paraffines est plus faible que dans les autres essais (Figure 3). En outre, des hydrocarbures gazeux de C_1 à C_6 sont formés en traces avec une très faible proportion d'hydrocarbures isoparaffiniques.

Tableau V. Evolution de la fraction aromatique $C_{15}-C_{20}$ de Mirando (300 kg/cm², 180 °C, 28 jours)

	Hydrocarbures legers C_1 à C_6	Hydrocarbures aliphatiques	Hydrocarbures aromatiques	Résines	Asphaltènes
Fraction non traitée	-	-	100,00	-	-
Fraction chauffée	traces	0,91	95,74	3,35	-
Fraction + montmorillonite	traces	0,43	95,17	4,05	0,38
Fraction + eau salée	traces	1,47	93,57	4,96	-
Fraction + montmorillonite + eau salée	traces	0,79	92,18	6,61	0,46

Tableau VI. Evolution de la fraction aromatique $C_{20}-C_{25}$ de Mirando (300 kg/cm², 180 °C, 28 jours)

	Hydrocarbures légers C_1 à C_6	Hydrocarbures aliphatiques	Hydrocarbures aromatiques	Résines	Asphaltènes
Fraction non traitée	-	-	100,00	-	-
Fraction chauffée	traces	0,45	97,25	2,25	0,05
Fraction + montmorillonite	traces	0,33	95,38	3,69	0,60
Fraction + eau salée	traces	9,14	88,34	2,27	0,17
Fraction + montmorillonite + eau salée	traces	13,34	82,86	3,21	0,59

Les hydrocarbures aromatiques récupérés analysés en spectrométrie de masse donnent des courbes de répartition par famille et par nombre d'atomes de carbone similaires à celles de la fraction de départ (Figure 3).

Enfin les quantités de résines formées sont plus importantes en présence de montmorillonite et les asphaltènes ne se forment presque exclusivement qu'en présence de celle-ci.

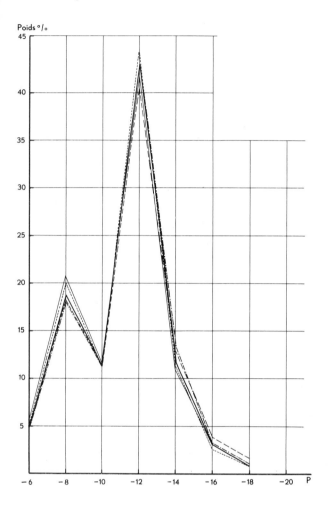

Fig. 3.1. Courbes de répartition des hydrocarbures aromatiques (évolution de la fraction aromatique $C_{15} - C_{20}$ de Mirando)

——————————— Fraction non traitée

‐ ‐ ‐ ‐ ‐ ‐ ‐ ‐ Fraction chauffée

— · — · — · Fraction + eau + montmorillonite

— — — — — Fraction + montmorillonite

——————————— Fraction + eau

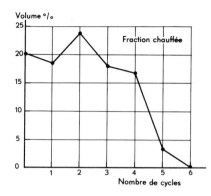

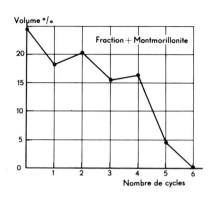

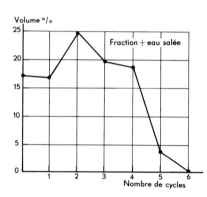

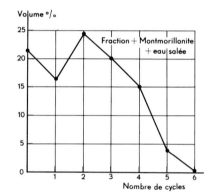

Fig. 3.2. Courbes de répartition des hydrocarbures aliphatiques (évolution de la fraction aromatique $C_{15} - C_{20}$ de Mirando)

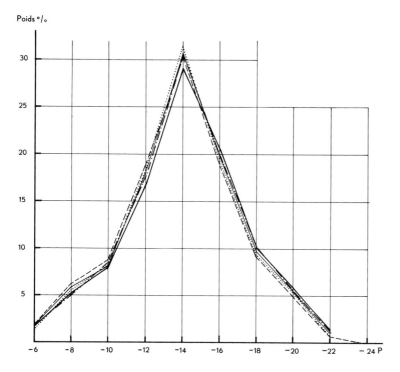

Poids °/o

Fig. 3.3. Courbes de répartition des hydrocarbures aromatiques (évolution de la fraction aromatique $C_{20} - C_{25}$ de Mirando)

—————— Fraction non traitée

. . . . Fraction chauffée

— · — · — · Fraction + eau + montmorillonite

— — — — — Fraction + montmorillonite

—————— Fraction + eau

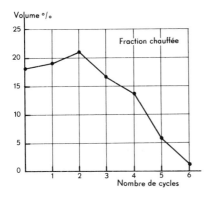

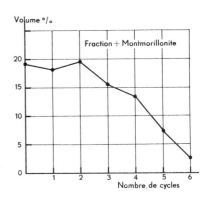

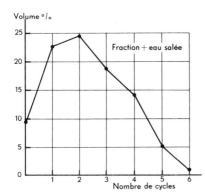

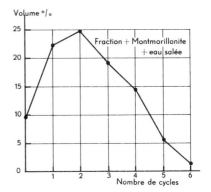

Fig. 3.4. Courbes de répartition des hydrocarbures aliphatiques (évolution de la fraction aromatique $C_{20} - C_{25}$ de Mirando)

Si l'on effectue un bilan de l'oxygène réparti entre les résines, les asphaltènes et les aromatiques pour chaque expérience, on s'aperçoit que la majeure partie des composés oxygénés présents dans la fraction aromatique de départ participe à la formation des résines et des asphaltènes (tableau VII).

Tableau VII. Bilan de l'oxygène (%) dans les différents constituants (Fraction aromatique $C_{15}-C_{20}$ de Mirando)

	Fraction non traitée	Fraction chauffée	Fraction + montmorillonite	Fraction + eau salée	Fraction + eau salée + montmorillonite
Aromatiques	0,76	0,26	0,27	0,28	0,23
Résines	-	0,33	0,31	0,48	0,51
Asphaltènes	-	-	0,03	-	0,03
Total	0,76	0,59	0,61	0,76	0,77

Tableau VIII. Evolution (72 heures à 230 °C) d'une fraction aromatique d'huile brute

	Hydrocarbures aliphatiques	Hydrocarbures aromatiques	Résines	Asphaltènes
Fraction non traitée	-	100,00	-	-
Fraction chauffée	9,7	74,00	10,6	5,7
Fraction + montmorillonite	20,6	57,8	16,5	5,1
Fraction + eau salée	8,2	73,1	12,5	6,2
Fraction + montm. + eau salée	9,9	76,9	8,7	4,5

6. Evolution de la fraction résines d'une huile brute (tableau IX)

Les essais révèlent une forte influence de la présence d'eau. On remarque aussi une proportion importante de produits lourds absorbés sur la montmorillonite et insolubles dans les solvants habituels.

Tableau IX. Evolution (72 heures à 230 °C) d'une fraction résines d'huile brute

	Hydrocarbures aliphatiques	Hydrocarbures aromatiques	Résines	Asphaltènes	Produits lourds fixés sur la montmorillonite
Fraction non chauffée	-	-	100,00	-	-
Fraction chauffée	29,1	21,5	46,4	3,0	-
Fraction + montmorillonite	9,2	24,8	48,4	1,5	16,1
Fraction + eau salée	13,5	11,9	34,1	40,5	-
Fraction + montm. + eau salée	16,0	20,6	34,2	15,4	13,8

Conclusions

Les résultats des expériences décrites permettent de dégager un certain nombre d'observations.

Des hydrocarbures légers jusqu'en C_6 sont formés: paraffines, isoparaffines et oléfines.

Dans toutes les expériences d'évolution d'huile brute, de fractions aromatiques et de résines, des hydrocarbures aliphatiques (paraffiniques, isoparaffiniques et naphténiques) et des produits lourds sont formés en quantités appréciables. Le taux de transformation global de ces fractions est supérieur à celui qui est observé sur les fractions aliphatiques. On peut supposer que les fractions aromatiques et naphténoaromatiques jouent un rôle essentiel dans l'évolution thermique des huiles brutes: sous l'action du cracking thermique, les hydrocarbures aliphatiques seraient formés après rupture des chaînes alkyles fixées sur les cycles aromatiques ou naphténoaromatiques. Les fragments résiduels se condenseraient alors en produits lourds à structure graphitique, type résines, asphaltènes et produits insolubles.

On peut imaginer la formation des naphtènes par cyclisation des chaînes paraffiniques ou par saturation des noyaux aromatiques ou naphténo-aromatiques par les atomes d'hydrogène libérés au cours de la condensation des cycles aromatiques.

Les composés oxygénés des fractions aromatiques participent dans la majeure partie à la formation des résines et asphaltènes. L'action catalytique de la montmorillonite se fait généralement sentir au niveau de ces produits, tandis que l'eau salée paraît également exercer une influence importante, seule ou mélangée à la montmorillonite On relève toutefois plusieurs cas de contradiction entre les résultats des deux séries d'expériences et qui résultent certainement des conditions expérimentales différentes. En effet, toutes les expériences concernant l'huile de Libye ont été effectuées dans des ampoules évacuées si bien que les réactions d'évolution ont dû se dérouler en grande partie en phase gazeuse. Par contre les essais d'évolution sur les différentes fractions des coupes de distillation (huile de Mirando) ont été faits en milieu essentiellement liquide.

Les premiers résultats apportent une série d'éléments de base qui permettent de prévoir les expériences à venir, telles que l'évolution de produits purs aromatiques ou naphténo-aromatiques avec chaînes alkyles, de produits purs oxygénés et de paraffines.

Bibliographie

Mac Nab, J.G., Smith, P.V. et Betts, R.L. 1952: Evolution of petroleum: Ind. Eng. Chem., 44, 2256.

Kartsev, A.A. 1964: Geochemical tranformation of petroleum: Advances in Organic Geochemistry, edited by U. Colombo and G.D. Hobson, Pergamon Press, Oxford, 1964, p. 11–14.

Biederman, E.W. 1965: Crude oil composition, a clue to migration: World Oil, dec. 1965, p. 78–82.

The Distribution of Hydrocarbons in the Gasoline Fraction obtained upon Thermocatalysis of Fatty Acids

Alexandr A. Petrov, Tatjana V. Tichomolova, Serafima D. Pustilnikova

The Institute of Geology and Exploitation of Combustible Fuels
Moscow, U.S.S.R.

One aspect of the problem of the origin of oil that is very important but has been insufficiently investigated is the way in which light hydrocarbons are formed. As the content of light hydrocarbons in living organisms is insignificant one can suggest that they are mainly formed in the processes of more or less drastic changes in the hydrocarbon molecules of the initial organic matter.

The study of the formation of oil gasoline fractions must be undertaken in two directions. On the one hand it is necessary to study in detail the component composition of oil gasolines, as only the knowledge of composition and distribution of hydrocarbons permits us to draw conclusions about the chemical reactions taking part in the formation of light fractions. On the other hand it is necessary to study the composition of the gasoline fraction formed during the model experiments of the processes of oil formation.

The component composition and distribution of hydrocarbons of petroleums is described in a series of recently published articles [3, 4, 5]. From the distribution of hydrocarbon isomers one can see that in the formation of gasoline fractions of oil the main reactions are thermal and catalytic cracking and isomerisation [3, 4, 6]. During the experiments on the thermocatalysis of organic acids the gasoline fractions were usually not determined or only their group analysis [1, 2] was made.

The task of the investigations described in this article was the isolation of gasoline fractions from the products of the thermocatalysis of fatty acids and the determination of individual hydrocarbons in their composition.

For the experimental verification of the influence of the initial substance structure on the composition of the gasoline fraction formed during these experiments, oleic acid (experiment N 1), stearic acid (experiment N 2) and a mixture of these two acids in the ratio 1 : 1 (experiment N 3) were taken. As is known, the highest saturated and unsaturated acids are the main components of the lipid fraction of organic matter of sedimentary rocks.

The Conditions of the Experiments

The experiments were carried out in an atmosphere of nitrogen in an autoclave with a capacity of 1 litre. Industrial aluminium silicate was used as the catalyst, the acid catalyst ratio was 1 : 3.

The duration of each experiment was 100 hours, at the temperature of 250 °C.
For the extraction of the gasoline fraction acetone was used. After the extraction
acetone was washed off by water and the gasoline fraction was distilled from the
catalyst.

The gasoline fraction under analysis (boiling point 70–130°) was isolated by preparative gas chromatography. The analysis of this fraction was carried out by capillary
gas chromatography. The copper column was 50 m long and had an effectiveness of
about 50 thousand theoretical plates. The stationary phase was squalane, and a
flame-ionisation detector was used. Qualitative identification of peaks was carried
out by the addition of individual hydrocarbons.

The Discussion of the Results

The composition and distribution of the most important hydrocarbons are given in
the Tables 1–4. Analogous data about the distribution of hydrocarbons in the gasoline fraction of some typical oils are given. For comparison the oil compositions are
presented in such a way that the concentration of normal alkanes (per sum of isomers) should correspond to the concentration of normal alkanes in the products of
thermocatalysis.

The total data of the gasoline composition after thermocatalysis are the following:
alkanes 60–70 %, cyclanes (30–40%). Aromatic hydrocarbons have not been
determined.

By analysing the data of the Tables 1–4 it is easy to notice the similarity between
gasolines obtained by thermocatalysis and gasoline of oils. In both cases the products are represented by a number of hydrocarbons. In their quantitative distribution one can see many common phenomena. The data about concentration of normal alkanes are of special interest, as from our point of view these data may be of
great importance for the problems of the origin of oil and for the problems of
their classification as well.

Table 1. The Distribution of Heptane Isomers (in %)

| Hydrocarbons | Gasolines of thermocatalysis | | Gasolines of oil fields | |
	Experiment N 1	Experiment N 2	Neftyanie kamni	East Echabi
Normal heptane	3	20	5	19
2–methylhexane	42	31	28	24
3–methylhexane	39	28	45	37
3–Ethylpentane	traces	3	6	1
2,4–Dimethylpentane	4	10	2	1
2,3–Dimethylpentane	12	8	11	12
2,2–Dimethylpentane	traces	traces	1,5	2
3,3–Dimethylpentane	traces	traces	1	3
2,2,3–Trimethylbutane	traces	traces	0,5	1

Table 2. The Distribution of Octane Isomers (in %)

Hydrocarbons	Gasoline fraction obtained upon thermocatalysis		Gasoline fractions of oils			
	Experiment N 1	Experiment N 2	Experiment N 3	Neftyanie kamni	Markovo	East Echabi
Normal octane	3	32	16	2	38	11
2–Methylheptane	34	21	29	10	28	31
3–Methylheptane	31	16	22	45	15	22
4–Methylheptane	9	7	8	18	8	12
3–Ethylhexane	1	1	2	1	3	3
2,5–Dimethylhexane	6	4	9	5	2	6
2,4–Dimethylhexane	9	3	6	6	3	7
2,3–Dimethylhexane	4	4	4	7	1	3
3,4–Dimethylhexane	2	2	1	3	1	2
3,3–Dimethylhexane	1	2	1	2	1	1
2,2–Dimethylhexane	traces	traces	2	0,5	0,5	2

Table 3. The Distribution of Naphthenes C_7 (in %)

Hydrocarbon	Experiment N 1	Experiment N 3	Gasoline fractions from Markovo oil
Methylcyclohexane	59	55	66
The sum of cyclopentanes C_7	41	45	34
Ethylcyclopentane	18	18	15
1,3–Dimethylcyclopentane cis	29	28	22
1,3–Dimethylcyclopentane trans	22	26	16
1,2–Dimethylcyclopentane cis	13	10	4
1,2–Dimethylcyclopentane trans	18	14	29
1,1–Dimethylcyclopentane	traces	4	14

When using stearic acid as initial material, a gasoline fraction containing 32 % of normal octane was formed, which greatly exceeds equilibrium value for the temperature intervals 100–300 °C. The majority of investigated oils [3–5] belong to this very type.

In the case when oleic acid is the initial product, the content of normal alkanes in the gasoline fraction was unimportant. In the experiment with the mixture of acids the normal-alkane content as it was expected had an intermediate value.

Among branched alkanes in the products of thermocatalysis as well as in gasoline fractions of the oil monomethyl-substituted isomers prevailed.

Table 4. The Distribution of Naphthenes C_8 (in %)

Hydrocarbon	Experiment N 1	Experiment N 3	Gasoline fractions from Markovo oil
The sum of cyclohexanes C_8	50	62	45
1,3 + 1,4–Dimethylcyclohexanes*)	91	88	84
1,2–Dimethylcyclohexanes*)	9	12	16
The sum of cyclopentanes C_8	50	38	55
1, 1,3–Trimethylcyclpentane	28	3	16
1, 1,2–Trimethylcyclopentane	traces	traces	4
1, 2,4–Trimethylcyclopentane*)	24	20	18
1, 2, 3–Trimethylcyclopentane*)	15	24	25
1,1–Methyl, ethylcyclopentane	traces	traces	3
1–Methyl, 3–ethylcyclopentanes*)	24	39	25
1–Methyl, 2–ethylcyclopentanes*)	9	14	9

*) The sum of stereoisomers

One can see the equal character of hydrocarbon distribution in oil gasolines and in thermocatalysis gasolines from the data on cyclic hydrocarbons. For example, in natural gasolines polymethyl-substituted cyclanes usually prevail; the same phenomenon has been noticed in gasolines formed by thermocatalysis. The ratio between cyclohexane hydrocarbons and cyclopentane hydrocarbons is of the same character too.

The structure of the initial acid mostly affects the composition of the alkane part of thermocatalysis gasolines.

Isomerisation processes and redistribution of hydrogen, which are characteristic of unsaturated hydrocarbons under these conditions, lead to the small concentration of normal alkanes formed from oleic acid. Heptene–1 is treated in this way; during the thermocatalysis a mixture of 2 and 3–methylhexane containing only traces of normal heptane was formed. Saturated hydrocarbons under the same conditions are more stable [7]

Ultimately, the final composition of light oil fractions depends on two processes: the primary genesis and further metamorphism of high hydrocarbons [5, 8].

The influence of metamorphism is especially noticeable on the gasoline composition of paraffinic oils having very high concentrations of normal alkanes (50–60 % per sum of isomers).

It is interesting to notice that gasoline containing normal heptane of 80 % per sum of isomers was formed during the [5] thermal decomposition of high-boiling oil hydrocarbons.

The above results were obtained when studying the decomposition of heavy hydrocarbons formed by the thermocatalysis of fatty acids.

References

[1] Bedov, Yu.A., Pustilnikova, S.D., Ratnikova, L.V., Petrov, Al.A.: 1962. Nephtekhimiya, 2, N 3.

[2] Bogomolov, A.I., Khotintseva, L.I., Panina, K.I.: 1960, VNIGRI Geochimicheskii sbornik N 6.

[3] Bryanskaya, E.K., Zakharenko, V.A., Petrov, Al.A.: 1966. Nephtekhimiya 6, N 6, 904.

[4] Martin, R.L., Winters, J.C., William, J.A.: VI. World Petroleum Congress, Frankfurt, Sec V., (1963).

[5] Olenina, Z.K., Petrov, Al.A.: 1967, Nephtekhimiya 7, N 3, 323.

[6] Petrov, Al.A., Zakharenko, V.A., Bryanskaya, E.K.: 1967, The Oil and Gas Genesis, M.

[7] Petrov, Al.A.: The Ac. of Sci of the USSR, 1960. Catalytical isomerization of hydrocarbons.

[8] Bogomolov, A.I., Shimanskii, V.K.: Geochimiya, N 1, 1966.

Coal-Rank and Burial-Metamorphic Mineral Facies

Hanan J. Kisch

Department of Petrology, Mineralogy and Crystallography,
Geologisch en Mineralogisch Instituut der Rijksuniversiteit
Leiden, The Netherlands

Progressive geochemical coalification is essentially an effect of burial metamorphism (or late diagenesis, or epigenesis) during deep burial. Though to a large extent controlled by a similar range of physical conditions during deep burial, coal rank and progressive burial-metamorphic modification of the mineralogy of associated sedimentary rocks have generally been studied separately: scant attention has hitherto been paid to their mutual relations.

This paper considers the relation of two types of burial-metamorphic mineral modification with the rank of associated coals. Relevant mineral data have been plotted on a coal-rank scale.

1. *Replacement of kaolinite by illite, chlorite, and pyrophyllite.* In the southern Bowen Basin, Queensland, the replacement of kaolinite in Permian rocks rich in igneous detritus is noticeable in association with ess coals (approx. 89 % C, 16–17 % V.M.), and virtually completed in association with lean coals (approx. 90–91 % C, 14–15 % V.M.). In the Münsterland 1 bore, Westphalia, kaolinite disappears in association with low-rank anthracites (approx. 91–92 % C, 6–7 % V.M.). In the kaolinite-coal tonsteins of Western Germany kaolinite persists at least into high-rank anthracites. On other areas pyrophyllite (formed from kaolinite), and some other mineral assemblages of the greenschist facies of regional metamorphism are associated with meta-anthracites.

2. *Appearance of the diagnostic mineral assemblage laumontite + quartz of the zeolite facies of burial metamorphism, and the replacement of analcime + quartz by albite* in tuffs and feldspathic-lithic rocks. Analcime + quartz is associated with lower rank coals than laumontite + quartz (and albite) in any one area. However, in the various regions considered, this change is associated with coal ranks ranging from flame coal (approx. 39 % V.M.) in the Lena Coal Basin, northern Yakutia, through gas-flame coal (approx. 36–37 % V.M.) in the Sydney Basin, New South Wales, to gas coal (approx. 31 % V.M.) in the Tamworth Trough, New South Wales.

The range of occurrence of kaolinite, and the laumonite + quartz zone thus overlap in association with coals of at least the gas-fat-ess coal ranks.

Differences in coal rank associated with particular burial-metamorphic reconstitution reactions are ascribed to chemical factors under the relatively low P–T conditions of burial metamorphism, such as the role of availability of cations (i.e., the primary mineralogical nature of the sediment), and the influence of the partial pressures of water and CO_2 on zeolitic reactions; and to dissimilar effects of pressure and time on coalification and mineral reactions (e.g., late coalification).

Co-ordinated studies of coal rank and burial-metamorphic mineral facies may help to clarify the conditions of their formative processes during deep burial.

Introduction

The increased interest in coal rank during recent years has led to major advances in the knowledge of parameters of coal rank, and of the regional variation and physical controls of geochemical coalification.

Essentially, progressive geochemical coalification is a burial-metamorphic (or late-diagenetic[1]) process: the effect of deep burial and incipient metamorphism on one type of sediment — a very sensitive one. Concurrently, the mineral composition of several other sedimentary rock types is progressively modified.

However, coalification has mainly been studied on its own merits, and the correlation of coal rank with modification stages of the mineralogy of other sedimentary rocks is still in the beginning stage. This paper reports on the relation of some diagnostic burial-metamorphic mineral assemblages to the rank of associated coals. Two types of burial-metamorphic silicate-mineral processes are considered:

1. *Modification of clay mineralogy,* particularly the replacement of kaolinite by illite, chlorite, and pyrophyllite.
2. *Appearance of zeolite-facies mineral assemblages,* particularly the diagnostic assemblages:
   - analcime + quartz
   - heulandite (-clinoptilolite) + quartz } upper zone of the zeolite facies
   - laumontite + quartz (and albite) —   lower zone of the zeolite facies

Coal Rank as a Standard for Burial Metamorphism

As in regional-metamorphic facies, burial-metamorphic mineral assemblages are controlled by pressure, temperature, and chemical composition.

However, the relatively low P-T conditions of burial metamorphism, and the resulting low mineral-reaction rates and importance of reaction kinetics confer some distinctive features on burial-metamorphic mineral facies. Mineral relics and metastable new-formed minerals are common: approach to thermodynamic equilibrium is often incomplete (cf. Coombs *et al.,* 1959; Kossovskaya and Shutov, 1963; Turner, 1968). Reaction conditions will greatly depend on the primary *mineralogical* nature of the sediment (as distinguished from chemical composition), availability of cations required for the alteration processes, and related factors.

---

[1]) Burial metamorphism is here used after Coombs (1961) for all mineral processes of regional extent, taking place at temperatures appreciably different from deposition conditions, up to the onset of regional metamorphism. In this sense it is used as a synonym of late diagenesis, also covering epigenesis (Strachov; Ruchin; Kossovskaya and Shutov), epigenetic diagenesis (Packham and Crook), katagenesis (Strachov), anadiagenesis (Fairbridge), eometamorphism (Landes), late-burial or pre-metamorphic stage (Dapples), and deep-burial stage (Müller) of other authors.

Other complications are connected with the partial pressures (or chemical activities) of water and CO_2. Low P_{H_2O}/P_{load} ratios — which could prevail in burial meta-morphism — and high salinity of pore solutions reduce the chemical activity of water, and would lower the equilibrium temperature of dehydration reactions (Coombs et al., 1959; Hay, 1966). Variation in the P_{CO_2}/P_{H_2O} ratio influences the relative extents of some critical Ca-zeolite composition fields (Zen, 1961; MacNamara, 1965).

Such factors may exert considerable effect on the nature of mineral assemblages formed in sedimentary rocks at given conditions of temperature and pressure (i.e. depth of burial and geothermal gradient).

This is where reference to rank of the associated coals has a useful application. The main control of progressive geochemical coalification is the increase in temperature towards depth — the geothermal gradient (Huck and Karweil, 1955, 1962; Karweil, 1956, Teichmüller and Teichmüller, 1966a). Coalification is unaffected — as far as known — by factors such as composition and salinity of pore solutions, and the composition of the volatile phases, possibly excluding extremely high P_{CO_2}/P_{H_2O} ratios. The effect of country-rock lithology is relatively minor (Damberger, 1965; Timofeev and Bogolyubova, 1966). Moreover, coal rank as determined on the maceral vitrinite is independent of the petrographic composition of the coal.

Admittedly, progressive coalification and burial-metamorphic mineral reactions are not affected in identical ways by temperature and pressure. For instance, static pressure has only a minor, or even a retarding effect on coalification reactions (Huck and Patteisky, 1954), whereas it promotes mineral-reconstitution processes, such as dehydration reactions (cf. Coombs et al., 1959).

Coalification is also more continuous in time than are mineral reactions: coal rank is further increased — though very slowly — by late coalification (Nachinkohlung) subsequent to uplift from maximum burial depth (cf. Karweil, 1956). The condi-tions under which continued late coalification takes place probably modify the burial-metamorphic mineral assemblages to a much lesser extent.

Coalification is also irreversible: there is no retrogressive coalification to compare with retrogressive mineral reactions.

However, as a first step one must attempt to establish the associations between diagnostic burial-metamorphic minerals and mineral assemblages, and the rank of associated coals, without taking such genetic considerations into account.

Coal Rank Scale

Maximum depth of burial of sedimentary sequences is notoriously hard to esta-blish. The geological extrapolations involve assumptions about the once superim-posed and subsequently removed overburden, and about the tectonic development of the area. In the present paper, therefore, the burial-metamorphic mineralogy is not interpreted in terms of maximum depths of burial, but is plotted directly against the rank of the associated coals.

The vertical coal-rank scale used is derived from Karweil's (1956) calculated volatile-matter vs. relative-depth curve[1]) as indicated in Fig. 1: the relevant rank parameter (volatile matter) is plotted along the linear relative-depth scale. The resulting

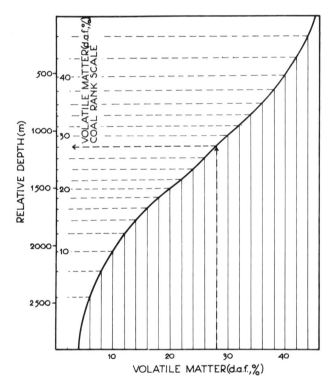

Fig. 1. Derivation of the vertical coal-rank scale from Karweil's (1956, Fig. 1; after Huck and Karweil, 1955) calculated volatile matter versus relative depth curve

---

[1]) This curve, after Huck and Karweil (1955), has been calculated assuming a decrease of 2,2 % volatile matter per 100 m increase in depth in the fat coal range, and an average geothermal gradient of 40 °C/km from the Upper Carboniferous to the present. The curve agrees with observed coalification gradients in Carboniferous coal measures of Western Europe.

vertical coal-rank scale is in principle linear with depth for the coalification gradients in the Carboniferous coal measures in Western Europe, but the intervals of relative depth will diverge for areas with different coalification gradients.

Range of Coal Rank in Burial Metamorphism

Coals of meta-anthracite rank are associated with mineral assemblages of the greenschist facies of regional metamorphism in Rhode Island (Quinn and Glass, 1958). Pyrophyllite – characteristic for the greenschist facies (Winkler, 1967) – is associated with high-rank anthracites and meta-anthracites in Pennsylvania (Spackman and Moses, 1961) and Western Germany (Stadler, Teichmüller and Teichmüller, unpublished, quoted in Teichmüller and Teichmüller, 1966a, 1966b). Carbonaceous matter in greenschist facies pelites from South and Western Australia is generally well-ordered graphite (Kisch and Taylor, un publ. ms; see also Schüller, 1961; Szádeczky-Kardoss, 1952).

Logvinenko (1956) found that the highest of three stages of late-diagenetic ("epigenetic") mineral alteration in the Donbas is associated with lean and anthracite coals.

The range of burial metamorphism or late diagenesis up to the greenschist facies thus seems to be associated with coalification up to approximately meta-anthracite rank.

Coal Rank and Burial-Metamorphic (Late-Diagenetic) Clay Mineralogy

The disappearance of kaolinite and montmorillonite during late diagenesis is well documented: with increasing pressure and temperature, these clay minerals give way to illite-muscovite and chlorite. Some examples from deep drillings are compiled in Fig. 2.

The disappearance of kaolinite during late diagenesis is especially suitable for correlation with coal rank, as kaolinite is the predominant primary clay mineral in floor rocks and shale partings of coal seams (e.g. Kossovskaya, Shutov and Alexandrova, 1964) – an extreme case being the kaolinite-coal tonsteins, with their characteristic kaolinite crystals and pellets.

Clay mineralogy has been studied and correlated with coal rank in the gas-flame coal to anthracite range in the Münsterland 1 bore in Westphalia (Scherp, 1963; Stadler, 1963; Esch, 1966), in the southern Bowen Basin of Queensland (Kisch, 1966a, 1968), and in various kaolinite-coal tonsteins from Western Europe (Eckhardt, 1963; Bouroz, 1962). Relevant mineral data from these studies are plotted on the coal-rank scale in Fig. 3.

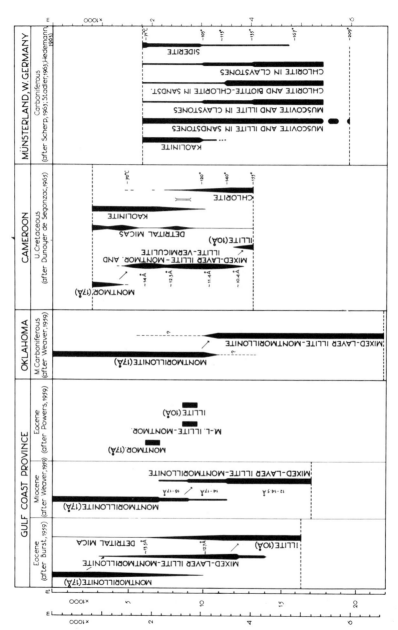

Fig. 2. Effect of late diagensis on the distribution of clay minerals with depth in some deep drillings.

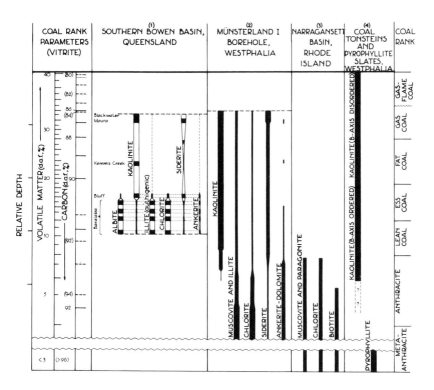

Fig. 3. Schematic distribution of clay and carbonate minerals with respect to rank of associated coal (vitrite) in four late-Paleozoic areas. Coalification gradient is based on Karweil's (1956) curve (Fig. 1). Carbon contents for vitrites of stated volatile-matter yield after Teichmüller (1963, Fig. 1–2), and (in brackets) after Kötter (1960). Data schematized after [1] Kisch, 1968; [2] Scherp, 1963; Stadler, 1963; Esch, 1966; [3] Quinn and Glass, 1958; [4] Eckhardt, 1964; Teichmüller and Teichmüller, 1966a, 1966b.

Kaolinite gives way to illite (muscovite), chlorite and/or pyrophyllite with increasing rank of the associated coals, as expected. However, in the various areas, the change in clay mineralogy correlates with rather different ranks of coal, varying from lean coal to meta-anthracite.

These discrepancies could be ascribed for a large part to the primary mineralogical nature of the sediments, and the differences in availability in cations from detrital components. The alteration of kaolinite to illite-muscovite and chlorite requires cations such as K and (Mg, Fe), respectively. These cations must be supplied by unstable detrital fragments, or by circulating pore solutions.

If no cations are available for the alteration reactions, kaolinite will persist to the temperatures of deeper burial levels (Fig. 4, after Hemley and Jones, 1964). Ultimately, at the onset of greenschist facies conditions, the remaining kaolinite will be replaced by pyrophyllite (Reed and Hemley, 1966; Kossovskaya and Shutov, 1963; Winkler, 1967).

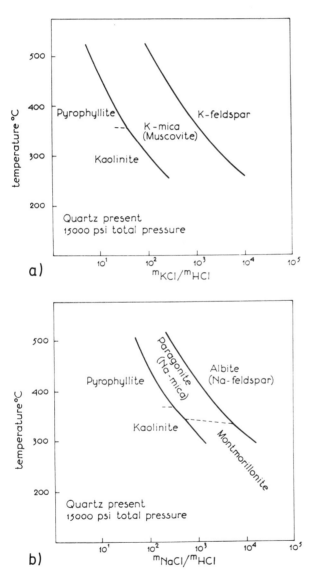

Fig. 4. Reaction curves for the systems K_2O-Al_2O_3-SiO_2-H_2O (A) and Na_2O-Al_2O_3-SiO_2-H_2O (B). Dashed line indicates experimental decomposition temperature of kaolinite in 0.5 m KCl and NaCl solutions. After Hemley and Jones (1964).

Kossovskaya and Shutov (1963) take the nature of the detrital constituents into account in their system of late diagenesis: in the "rock families" rich in feldspathic detritus, kaolinite and montmorillonite disappear at an earlier stage than in the kaolinite-quartz rocks (Fig. 5). However, in the areas considered in this paper, the burial-metamorphic disappearance of kaolinite in *both* these "rock families" is associated with somewhat higher coal ranks (lean coal to meta-anthracite) than the coking coal to anthracite indicated by the correlation of mineral zones and coal type after Kossovskaya, Logvinenko and Shutov (1957) (Fig. 5).

In the Upper Permian sedimentary rocks of the southern Bowen Basin — rich in unstable detritus of igneous origin, which supplied alkalis and magnesium-iron — kaolinite disappears already in association with lean coal rank (Kisch, 1966a, 1968).

Absence of kaolinite, and predominance of sericite-chlorite cements in sandstones and argillites associated with lean coals and anthracites has also been described from the Donbas (Logvinenko, 1956; Doluda, 1963) (cf. Fig. 5), and the Petchora Basin (Kossovskaya, Shutov and Alexandrova, 1964).

The case of little or no availability of cations is represented by the kaolinite-coal tonsteins of the Western European coal measures. Here no noticeable replacement of kaolinite by illite and chlorite takes place as coal rank increases: the kaolinite persists up to anthracite rank, while its b-axis disorder progressively decreases up to fat coal rank (Eckhardt, 1963). At meta-anthracite rank, replacement by pyrophyllite may take place (e.g., Spackman and Moses, 1961).

Some regional variation of burial-metamorphic clay-mineral zonation with respect to coal rank may also be due to the different response of coal and mineral reconstitution to pressure and late coalification, as mentioned above.

Coal Rank and Zeolite Mineral Facies

Another group of burial-metamorphic mineral modifications may take place in feldspathic-lithic arenites and siltstones, and in tuffaceous rocks, with the appearance of a succesion of diagnostic zeolites and other Ca-aluminosilicates, particularly analcime (approx. Na $[AlSi_2O_6] \cdot H_2O$), heulandite $(Ca_{,Na_2})$ $[Al_2Si_7O_{18}] \cdot 6H_2O$ and its alkali- and Si-richer variety clinoptilolite, laumontite Ca $[Al_2Si_4O_{12}] \cdot 4-3\frac{1}{2}H_2O$, prehnite $Ca_2(Al, Fe^{3+})$ $[AlSi_3O_{10}/(OH)_2]$, and pumpellyite $Ca_2(Al, Mg, Fe^{2+})_3$ $[SiO_4/Si_2O_7/(OH)_2/(H_2O, OH)]$.

The aluminosicate minerals appearing with increasing depth of burial tend to be progressively less hydrous and more dense (cf. Coombs *et al.*, 1959, Fig. 3; Kossovskaya and Shutov, 1963, Fig. 2).

On the basis of Coombs' work, Turner (in Fyfe *et al.*, 1958) and Coombs *et al.* (1959) established a zeolite facies of burial metamorphism, later slightly modified by Winkler (1967, p. 153 ff.).

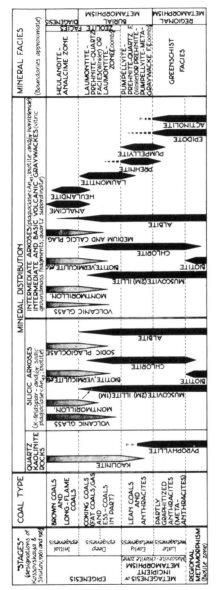

Fig. 5. Correlation of the distribution of some primary (in grey) and new-formed (in black) silicate minerals in various terrigenic and volcanic sedimentary rock types in late diagenesis, compiled and schematized after Kossovskaya and Shutov (1961, 1963). Broken bars indicate extension of some mineral zones after Coombs (1961). Correlation of mineral zones in terrigenic rocks with coal type after Kossovskaya, Logvinenko and Shutov (1957). Not drawn to scale.

The upper zones of the zeolite facies are characterized by the mineral assemblages
— analcime + quartz; heulandite (-clinoptilolite) + quartz;
the lower zone (laumontite-prehnite-quartz facies of Winkler) by
—laumonite + quartz ± prehnite (and albite).

Montmorillonite and kaolinite are still present in rocks with different composition.
Some zeolite-facies mineral assemblages are shown in the ACF diagrams Fig. 6
(after Coombs, 1961).

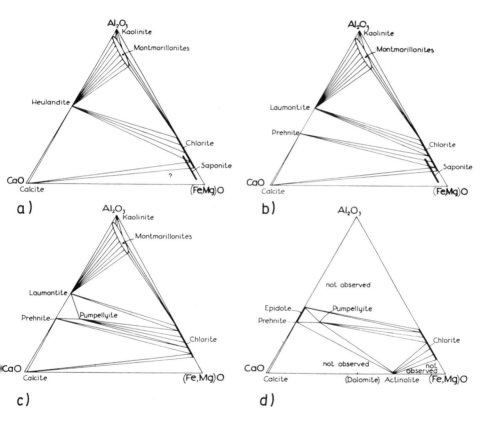

Fig. 6. Schematic Al_2O_3-CaO-(Fe, Mg)O diagrams showing mineral assemblages in low-grade
rocks with excess quartz, sodic and potassic phases. a) Heulandite zone. b) and c) Laumontit
zone (laumontite-prehnite-quartz facies). d) Higher grade part of prehnite-pumpellyite-meta-
graywacke facies (pumpellyite-prehnite-quartz facies). After Coombs (1961), Fig. 4. Facies
designations after Winkler (1967), in brackets.

Table I. Rank of Coals associated with some Analcime, Heulandite-Clinoptilolite and Laumontite Occurrences.

District / Geologic Formation and age	Zeolite mineral [numbered references]	Coal-rank parameters (dry, ash-free) Volatile matter, %	Carbon %	Calorific value, kcal/kg	Nature of coal-rank data [numbered references]
Lena Coal Basin, Northern Yakutia					
1. Cretaceous – "Zone of long-flame coals" [1]	stilbite, heulandite, very little laumontite [1]	> 39	< 80	< 8000	vitrite comp. in rank stage 1 [2]
2. Cretaceous – "Zone of gas and steam-fat coals" [1]	abundant laumontite [1]	40–29	80–87	7900–8700	vitrite comp. in rank stages II and III [2]
Sydney Basin, New South Wales (Illawarra area)					
a. Illawarra Coal Measures (Upper Permian), lower part	laumontite [3]	32.6–29.4	87.4–89.1	8620–8800	6 vitrite concentrates from 2 coal seams [3] extrapolated 600 m downwards from a).
b. Gerringong Volcanics (Upper Permian), base	laumontite [3]	≈ 17			7 vitrite concentrates from 3 coal seams in upper part of Newcastle C.M. [3]
Sydney Basin, New South Wales (Lake Macquarie) Newcastle Coal Measures (Upper Permian), middle part	analcime [4][3]	40.2–38.7 / 39.9–37.7	82.7–83.7 / 84.2–84.4	8100–8200 / 8399–8410	2 vitrite concentrates from 3 coal seams in lower part of Newcastle C.M. [3]
Lower Hunter Valley, New South Wales (Seaham) Glacial Stage Beds (Upper Carboniferous)	laumontite and ? clinoptilolite [5][3]	≈ 35	≈ 84		vitrite calculated from reflectance and whole-coal composition [3]
Werrie Basin, Tamworth Trough, New South Wales					
a. Lower Permian, ≈ 1670 m above base of Currabubula Formation (Upper Carboniferous)	analcime, heulandite [6][3]	≈ 36½	≈ 82½		vitrite calculated from reflectance and whole-coal composition [3]
b. Currabubula Fm (Upper Carboniferous) ≈ 1430 m above base of Fm	base of analcime zone [6]	≈ 31			extrapolated 240 m downwards from a).
c. Currabubula Fm (Upper Carboniferous) ≈ 900 m above base of Fm	top of laumontite zone [6][3]	≈ 20			extrapolated 770 m downwards from a).
Kushiro Coal Basin, Hokkaido Harutori coal-bearing Formation (Eocene)	clinoptilolite [7]	54.2–55.2		7840–7710	2 vitrite-rich whole-coal samples [8]
Cave Hills, Harding County, South Dakota Tongue River Formation (Paleocene)	analcime [9]				"lignite" [9]
Colville River area, Northern Alaska Colville Group (Upper Cretaceous)	analcime [10]	37–43			range for sub-bituminous coals from Colville River area ([11], Table 6)
Duingen, Lower Saxony, Western Germany Wealden (Lower Cretaceous)	analcime	42–46	79		vitrite concentrate [12]
Pursglove, Monongahela County, West Virginia Pittsburgh Seam (Upper Carboniferous)	analcime [13]	39.7–39.2		8410–8500	size fractions of whole-coal sample ([14], Table 3)
Colston Bassett, S.E. Nottinghamshire, England Lower Coal Measures (Upper Carboniferous)	analcime [15]	39–40	83		whole coal, extrapolated from data in [16] (Tables VI and App. IV) and from

References to Table I

[1]   Zaporozhtseva et al., 1963, Litolog. i. Polezn. Iskop, **1963** (2), 161–177.
[2]   Ammosov et al., 1964, ("Industrial-genetic classification of Soviet coals"); Moscow, Nauka.
[3]   Kisch, 1966, Geol. Mag.,**103** (5), 414–422.
[4]   Loughnan, 1966, Amer. Mineral.,**51** (3–4), 486–494.
[5]   Coombs, 1958, Austr. Jour. Science, **21**, 18–19.
[6]   Wilkinson and Whetten, 1964, Jour. Sedim. Petrol.,**34** (3), 543–553.
      Whetten, 1965, Geol. Soc. Amer. Bull.,**76**, 43–56.
[7]   Iijima, 1961, Japan. Jour. Geol. and Geogr., **32** (3–4), 507–522.
[8]   Dr. A. Iijima (Geological Institute, University of Tokyo), written communication, April 1968.
[9]   Rozendal, 1956, Proc. South Dakota Acad. Science,**35** (2), 39–41.
[10]   Reynolds and Anderson, 1967, Jour. Sedim. Petrol., 37 (3), 966–969.
[11]   Barnes, 1967, "Coal resources of Alaska", U.S. Geol. Survey Bull. **1245–B**.
[12]   Teichmüller and Teichmüller, 1950, Zeit. deut. geol. Ges., **100**, 498–517.
[13]   Foster and Feicht, 1946, Amer. Mineral.,**31**, 357–364.
[14]   Aresco et al., 1955, U.S. Bureau of Mines Report of Investigations **5085**.
[15]   Sabine, 1963, Geol. Mag.,**100** (6), 551–555.
[16]   Dawe and Coles, 1948, Jour. Inst. Fuel,**22** (122), 12–23.
[17]   A. Milner (Area Chief Scientist, National Coal Board, South Nottinghamshire Area)
      and E. Skipsey (Coal Scientist, National Coal Board, East Midlands Geological
      Outstation), written communication, June 1968.

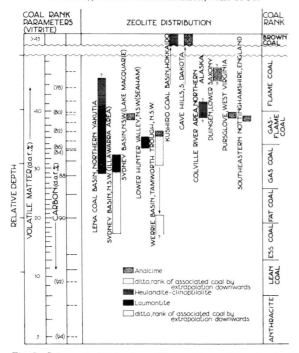

Fig. 7. Schematic distribution of the zeolites analcime, heulandite-clinoptilolite, and laumontite with respect to rank of associated coal (vitrite). Data are listed in Table I. Coalification gradient as in Fig. 3.

Occurrence of the critical zeolitic mineral assemblages, and the rank of the associated coals have been compiled in Table I, and plotted along the coal-rank scale in Fig. 7 for coal-measure areas in northern Yakutia (Zaporozhtseva *et al.,* 1963) and eastern New South Wales (Kisch, 1966 b), and for additional isolated analcime and heulandite-clinoptilolite occurrences in coal measures. For a few New South Wales zeolite-bearing localities which underlie coal seams by a few hundred meters, the coal ranks have been extrapolated downwards using Karweil's (1956) curve (Kisch, 1966 b).

The general distribution shows that *analcime is associated with lower rank coals than laumontite + quartz.* Analcime is associated with ranks up to gas coal (down to 30 % V.M. in vitrite), and laumontite with flame coal to at least ess coal rank (less than 40 % V.M. in vitrite). If however data from various areas are compared, it is clear that the boundary between the coal ranks associated with analcime + quartz and with laumontite + quartz assemblages is not very sharp: all the occurrence considered show an overlap in the 40–30 % V.M. in vitrite range, i.e. the flame to gas coal range.

In Northern Yakutia the boundary between rocks with heulandite and stilbite, and rocks with abundant laumontite corresponds with coal of approx. 39–40 % V.M., i.e. flame coal to gas-flame coal rank.

In the Sydney Basin and the Lower Hunter Valley, NSW, the one known occurrence of the analcime + quartz assemblage is associated with 38–40 % V.M. in vitrite; the laumontite + quartz sequences with less than about 36 % V.M. The transition thus seems to correspond here with about 36–37 % V.M. in vitrite, i.e. gas-flame coal rank.

In the Currabubula area, Tamworth Trough, the base of the analcime zone corresponds with a higher coal rank, about 31 % V.M. in vitrite – extrapolated downwards –, i.e. gas coal rank.

The isolated analcime and clinoptilolite occurrences compiled from various areas are associated with low-rank coals: flame coals and brown coals with over 39 % V.M. (d.a.f.).

The rank of coals associated with the *lower* limit of the laumontite + quartz assemblage remains to be established; downward extrapolations of coal rank in Illawarra area, Sydney Basin (Kisch, 1966 b; cf. Fig. 7) suggest that it extends to at least ess coal rank.

Discrepancies between the coal ranks associated with which the critical laumontite + quartz assemblage appears in various areas are tentatively ascribed to two chief factors:

1. *The effect of different P_{CO_2}/P_{H_2O} ratios during burial metamorphism.* High P_{CO_2}/P_{H_2O} ratios would favour binding of calcium as Ca-carbonate instead of Ca-zeolite:

2 Ca$[Al_2 Si_7 O_{18}]$. 6H_2O + 2CO_2 ⇌ $Al_4[Si_4 O_{10}/(OH)_8]$ + 2 $CaCO_3$ + 10 SiO_2 + 8H_2O
    heulandite   kaolinite   calcite   quartz

2 Ca$[Al_2 Si_4 O_{12}]$. 4–3$\frac{1}{2}$ H_2O + 2CO_2 ⇌ $Al_4[Si_4 O_{10}/(OH)_8]$ + 2$CaCO_3$ + 4SiO_2 + 3–4H_2O
    laumontite   kaolinite   calcite   quartz

Thus the appearance of the laumontite + quartz mineral assemblage would be delayed. Under regionally high P_{CO_2}/P_{H_2O} ratios the diagnostic Ca-zeolite assemblages may even not appear at all under zeolite-facies P-T conditions in sedimentary rocks of otherwise suitable mineral composition (Coombs, 1961; Zen, 1961; MacNamara, 1965). This seems to be the case in the higher grade — lean-coal bearing — southern Bowen Basin sequence at Baralaba: the mineral composition of many of these rocks seems otherwise favourable for the formation of zeolitic assemblages (Kisch, 1968).

Reduced chemical activity of water — through low P_{H_2O}/P_{total} ratios or highly saline solutions — would lower temperatures of critical zeolite equilibria; it would e.g. restrict the stability of the analcime + quartz and the heulandite (-clinoptilolite) + quartz mineral assemblages (Coombs *et al.*, 1959; Campbell and Fyfe, 1965; Hay, 1966).

2. *Different rates of rank increase and mineral reactions during burial metamorphism,* particularly the continued — though very slow — coal-rank increase during "late coalification". If no appreciable parallel progressive modification of the associated burial-metamorphic mineral assemblages took place, the coal rank associated with a given mineral-facies boundary could be expected to be higher in older than in younger strata.

The zeolite mineral-assemblage boundary seems in fact associated with progressively higher rank coals going down the stratigraphic time scale from the Cretaceous of Northern Yakutia, through the Upper Permian of the Sydney Basin, to the Lower Permian and Upper Carboniferous of the Tamworth Trough (Fig. 7). However, present scanty data are hardly sufficient to substantiate such a suggestion.

Correlation of Burial-Metamorphic Mineral Assemblages and Coal Rank

The mineral assemblage analcime + quartz appears to be associated with lower ranks of coal than laumontite + quartz in any one area. When all occurrences from various regions are considered, the coal ranks associated with these mineral assemblages show a range of overlap. However, disregarding the Lower Permian-Carboniferous Tamworth Trough occurrences, the present evidence indicates *disappearance of the analcime + quartz assemblage at gas-flame coal rank* (about 36–40 % V.M. in vitrite) in the post-Carboniferous sequences.

This rank range has an additional interest in being also the upper rank limiting the occurrence of large oil fields — "dead line" or "oil phase-out zone" — in the carbon ratio theory; in association with higher rank coals only small oil fields (up to about 30 % V.M.) and gas fields are found (cf. White, 1935; Teichmüller and Teichmüller, 1966 b; Landes, 1967). The nature of the zeolite mineral assemblages therefore is a potential indicator as to degree of oil alteration.

Replacement of kaolinite by chlorite and illite takes place at much higher coal ranks: lean coal (Baralaba) to meta-anthracite (kaolinite-coal tonsteins), depending — among other factors — on the supply of cations, i.e. on the primary mineralogical nature of the sediments. In terms of coal rank the ranges of occurrence of kaolinite and of the diagnostic laumontite + quartz mineral assemblage overlap in at least the gas-fat-ess coal ranks — and possibly more if the lower limit of the laumontite + quartz assemblage will prove to be associated with higher than ess coal rank.

Many factors involved in correlation of burial-metamorphic mineral assemblages and coal rank sill await elucidation, particularly the complications due to the different rates of the processes. Nevertheless, it seems clear that use of coal rank — essentially dependent on temperatures and time — as a measuring scale may help in clarification of burial-metamorphic mineral facies, and of the factors influencing burial-metamorphic mineral reactions *apart* from pressure and temperature. It may be a valuable tool in the correlation of stages of burial metamorphism in different types of sedimentary rocks.

References[1])

Ammosov, I.I., Babashkin, B.G., Grechishnikov, N.P. et al. (1964): Promyshlenno-geneticheskaya klassifikatsiya uglei SSSR — Osnovy klassifikatsii (industrial-genetic classification of Soviet coals — Principles of classification): Moscow, Nauka.

Bouroz, Alexis (1962): Sur la pluralité d'origine des tonstein (A propos d'une cinérite oligocène du Japon): Soc. géol. Nord Annales, **82**, pp. 77–94.

Burst, J.F. (1959): Postdiagenetic clay mineral environmental relationships in the Gulf Coast Eocene: Clays and Clay Min., Proc. 6th Nat. Conf., London, Pergamon Press, pp. 327–341.

Campbell, A.S. and Fyfe, W.S. (1965): Analcime-albite equilibria: Am. Jour. Sci., **263** (9), pp. 807–16.

Coombs, D.S. (1961): Some recent work on the lower grades of metamorphism: Aust. Jour. Sci., **24**, pp. 203–215.

---

[1]) References belonging to Table I are not again included.

Coombs, D.S., Ellis, A.J., Fyfe, W.S., Taylor, A.M. (1959): The zeolite facies, with comments on the interpretation of hydrothermal syntheses: Geochim. Cosmochim. Acta, 17, pp. 53–107.

Damberger, Heinz (1965): Die Abhängigkeit des Inkohlungsgradienten vom Gesteinsaufbau: Vortrag Frühjahrstagung der Deutschen geol. Gesell. in Saarbrücken, 27–29.5.1965.

Doluda, M.Ye. (1963): Izmeneye porod vize yugo-zapadnoy okrainy Donbassa v stadiyu epigeneza (Epigenetic alteration of Upper Visean rocks of the southwest margin of the Donbas): Akad. Nauk SSSR Doklady, 150 (6), pp. 1349–1351.

Dunoyer de Segonzac, G. (1964): Les argiles du Crétacé supérieur dans le bassin de Douala (Cameroun): Problèmes de diagenèse: Serv. Carte géol. Alsace Lorraine Bull., 17 (4), pp. 287–310.

Eckhardt, F.-J. (1964): Über den Einfluß der Temperatur auf den kristallographischen Ordnungsgrad von Kaolinit: Internat. Clay Conf. 1963, Oxford, Pergamon Press, 2, pp. 137–145.

Esch, H. (1966): Vergleichende Diagenese-Studien an Sandsteinen und Schiefertonen des Oberkarbon in Nordwestdeutschland und den East Midlands in England: Fortschr. Geologie Rheinland und Westfalen, 13 (2), pp. 1013–1084.

Fyfe, W.S., Turner, F.J. and Verhoogen, J. (1958): Metamorphic reactions and metamorphic facies: Geol. Soc. America Mem. 73, 259 pp.

Hay, R.L. (1966): Zeolites and zeolitic reactions in sedimentary rocks: Geol. Soc. America, Spec. Paper, no. 85, 130 pp.

Hedemann, H.-A. (1963): Die Gebirgstemperaturen in der Bohrung Münsterland und die geothermische Tiefenstufe: Fortschr. Geologie Rheinland und Westfalen, 11, pp. 403–418.

Hemley, J.J. and Jones, W.R. (1964): Chemical aspects of hydrothermal alteration with emphasis on hydrogen metasomatism: Econ. Geology, 59 (4), pp. 538–569.

Huck, G. and Karweil, J. (1955): Physikalisch-chemische Probleme der Inkohlung: Brennstoff-Chemie, 36 (1–2), pp. 1–11.

Huck, G. and Karweil, J. (1962): Probleme und Ereignisse der künstlichen Inkohlung im Bereich der Steinkohlen: Fortschr. Geologie Rheinland und Westfalen, 3 (2), pp. 717–724.

Huck, G. and Patteisky, K. (1964): Inkohlungsreaktionen unter Druck: Fortschr. Geologie Rheinland und Westfalen, 12, pp. 551–558.

Karweil, J. (1956): Die Metamorphose der Kohlen vom Standpunkt der physikalischen Chemie: Deutsche Geol. Gesell. Zeitschr., 107 (1955), pp. 132–139.

Kisch, H.J. (1966a): Chlorite-illite tonstein in high-rank coals from Queensland, Australia: notes on regional epigenetic grade and coal rank: Amer. Jour. Sci., 264 (5), pp. 386–397.

Kisch, H.J. (1966b): Zeolite facies and regional rank of bituminous coals: Geol. Mag. 103 (5), pp. 414–422.

Kisch, H.J. (1968): Coal rank and lowest-grade regional metamorphism in the southern Bowen Basin, Queensland, Australia: Geologie en Mijnbouw, 47 (1), pp. 28–36.

Kossovskaya, A.G., Logvinenko, N.V. and Shutov, V.D. (1957): O stadyakh formirovaniya i izmeneniya terrigennykh porod (Stages of formation and alteration in terrigenous rocks): Akd. Nauk SSSR Doklady, 116 (2), pp. 293–296.

Kossovskaya, A.G. and Shutov, V.D. (1961): O korrelyatsii zon regionalnogo epigeneza i metageneza v terrigennykh i vulkanogennykh porodakh (The correlation of zones of regional epigenesis and metagenesis in terrigenous and volcanic rocks): Akad. Nauk. SSSR Doklady, 139 (3), pp. 677–680.

Kossovskaya, A.G. and Shutov, V.D. (1963): Fatsii regional'nogo epigeneza i metageneza (Facies of regional epigenesis and metagenesis): Akad. Nauk SSSR Izv., Ser. geol., **28** (7), pp. 3–18.

Kossovskaya, A.G., Shutov, V.D. and Alexandrova, V.A. (1964): Dependence of the mineral composition of the clays in the coal-bearing formations on the sedimentation conditions: 5me Congr. Internat. Strat. et Géol. Carbonif., Paris 1963, Comptes rendus, **2**, pp. 519–529.

Kötter, K. (1960): Die mikroskopische Reflexionsmessung mit dem Photomultiplier und ihre Anwendung auf die Kohlenuntersuchung: Brennstoff-Chemie, **41**, pp. 263–272.

Landes, K.K. (1967): Eometamorphism, and oil and gas in time and space: Am. Assoc. Petroleum Geologists Bull., **51** (6), 828–841.

Logvinenko, N.V. (1956): O pozdnem diageneze (epigeneze) donetskikh karbonovykh porod (On the late diagenesis (epigenesis) of Carboniferous rocks of the Donbas): Akad. Nauk SSSR Doklady, **139** (3), pp. 677–680.

MacNamara, M. (1965): The lower greenschist facies in the Scottish Highlands: Geol. Fören. i Stockholm. Förh., **87** (3), pp. 347–389.

Powers, M.C. (1959): Adjustment of clays to chemical change and the concept of the equivalence level: Clays and Clay Min., Proc. 6th nat. Conf., London, Pergamon Press, pp. 309–326.

Quinn, A.W. and Glass, H.W. (1958): Rank of coal and metamorphic grade of rocks of the Narragansett basin of Rhode Island: Econ. Geology, **53**, pp. 563–576.

Reed, B.L. and Hemley, J.J. (1966): Occurrence of pyrophyllite in the Kekiktuk Conglomerate, Brocks Range, northeastern Alaska: U.S. Geol. Survey Prof. Paper **550**–C, pp. C 162–C 165.

Scherp, Adalbert (1963): Die Petrographie der paläozoischen Sandsteine in der Bohrung Münsterland 1 und ihre Diagenese in Abhängigkeit von der Teufe: Fortschr. Geologie Rheinland und Westfalen, **11**, pp. 251–282.

Schüller, A. (1961): Die Druck-Temperatur- und Energiefelder der Metamorphose: Neues Jahrb. Mineralogie Abh., **96**, pp. 250–290.

Spackman, W. and Moses, R.G. (1961): The nature and occurrence of ash-forming minerals in anthracite: Mineral Indus. Expt Sta., Penn. State Univ., Bull. **75** (Proceedings of the Anthracite Conference), pp. 1–15.

Stadler, G. (1963): Die Petrographie der oberkarbonischen Tonsteine in der Bohrung Münsterland 1: Fortschr. Geologie Rheinland und Westfalen, **11**, pp. 283–292.

Szádeczky-Kardoss, E. (1952): Gesteinsumwandlung und Kohlengesteine; Acad. Sci. Hungaricae Acta Geol., **1**, pp. 205–225.

Teichmüller, M. (1963): Die Kohlenflöze der Bohrung Münsterland 1: Fortschr. Geologie Rheinland und Westfalen, **11**, pp. 129–178.

Teichmüller, Marlies and Teichmüller, Rolf (1966a): Geological causes of coalification: Adv. Chem. Ser., **55** (Coal Science), pp. 133–155.

Teichmüller, Marlies and Teichmüller, Rolf (1966b): Inkohlungsuntersuchungen im Dienst der angewandten Geologie: Freiberger Forschungsh., no. C210, pp. 155–195.

Timofeev, P.P. and Bogolyubova, L.I. (1966): Secondary transformations of organic matter under different facies conditions: Lithol. and Mineral Resourc., (transl. from Litologiya i Poleznye Iskopaemye), **1966** (5), pp. 577–584.

Turner, F.J. (1968): Metamorphic petrology: mineralogical and field aspects: New York, MacGraw-Hill Book Comp., 403 pp.

Weaver, C.E. (1959): The clay petrology of sediments: Clays and Clay Min., Proc. 6th nat. Conf., London, Pergamon Press, pp. 154–187.

White, David (1935): Metamorphism of organic sediments and derived oils: Am. Assoc. Petroleum Geologists Bull., 19, pp. 589–617.

Winkler, H.G.F. (1967): Die Genese der metamorphen Gesteine, 2. Auflage: Berlin, Springer-Verlag, 237 pp.

Zaporozhtseva, A.S., Vishnevskaya, T.N. and Glushinskii, P.I. (1963): Tseolity melovykh otlozhenii severa Yakutii (Zeolites from Cretaceous formations in Norhtern Yakutia): Litologiya i Poleznye Iskopaemye, 1963 (2), pp. 161–177.

Zen, E-an, (1961): The zeolite facies – an interpretation: Am. Jour. Sci., 259, pp. 401–409.

Discussion

H.R. von Gaertner: Die vorgetragenen Parallelen zwischen Inkohlung und Mineralfazies führen im Augenblick noch zu kaum tragbaren Konsequenzen. Für Laumontit und Pumpellyit liegen aus Gleichgewichtsreaktionen die Bildungstemperaturen fest. Man kommt dann zu Temperaturen von 250–350 °C für Inkohlung mit 30–40 % flüchtige Bestandteile, was höchst unwahrscheinlich scheint. Die Parallelisierungen müssen wohl noch überprüft werden.

H.J. Kisch: The mineral-reaction equilibria that appear to be associated with coal ranks of 30–40 % volatile matter are:

analcime + quartz $\longleftrightarrow$ albite + water (1)
heulandite $\longleftrightarrow$ laumontite + quartz + water (2).

Earlier authors have given excessively high equilibrium temperatures for these reactions, e.g. 280–295 °C at 1000–4000 bars P_{H_2O} in Winkler (1964, *Beitr. Mineralog. u. Petrol.,* 10, pp. 76–77).

However, subsequent studies by Campbell and Fyfe (1965, *op. cit.*) indicate that reaction (1) is in equilibrium near 190 °C at up to 1000 bars P_{H_2O}, and at lower temperatures with increasing pressure (e.g. 150 °C at about 2900 bars P_{H_2O}). According to recent work by Nitsch – in Winkler (1968, *Geol. Rundschau,* 57, pp. 1002–1019) – the upper temperature limit of heulandite, and the lower temperature limit of laumontite with quartz and water, lies at about 200 °C, and is little affected by pressure.

These new mineral-equilibrium data greatly reduce the alleged discrepancy between coalification temperatures, and equilibrium temperatures for the associated zeolitic mineral reactions.

The Chemical Aspects of Coal Metamorphism (A prepared contribution)

Mass spectral evidence on chemical fossils in coals

Peter H. Given

Pennsylvania State University
Pennsylvania, USA

At the London meeting two years ago, I described a laser mass spectrometer system for the structural study of heterogeneous solids, developed by F. J. Vastola, R. R. Dutcher and myself. The sample is mounted within the ionization chamber of a time-of-flight mass spectrometer, and a small area is irradiated with a pulse of energy from a laser projected through the objective of a microscope. A low ionization potential is used, to minimize fragmentation of the primary products of pyrolysis and simplify interpretation. The technique has been applied to the study of coals, and some results of geochemical significance have recently appeared.

All coals studied gave large peaks at M/e = 50 and 74, and a smaller one at 26; these are attributed to acetylene, di- and triacetylene. The ratio of intensities, 50/74, varies little with coal rank, indicating a common origin for the substances responsible, C_4H_2 and C_6H_2. This origin is believed to be the fragmentation of benzene rings in mono- and poly-cyclic aromatic structures. This has been confirmed by Dr. J. Romováček (while on leave from the University of Chemical Technology, Prague), who exchanged some of the hydrogen in a coal for deuterium using Yavorsky's reagent, $BF_3 \cdot D_3PO_4$, which acts preferentially on hydrogen attached to aromatic nuclei. Appreciable shifts of intensity from 50 and 74 to 51/52 and 75/76 were observed.

In addition to peaks at 78, 92, 106, etc. and 128, 142, etc. (homologous series of methyl-benzenes and naphthalenes) there are groups of peaks at M/e values of 93-94, 107-110 and 121-124, which must be due to mono- and dihydroxy benzenes, without and with methyl substituents. The dihydroxy peaks, 110 and 124, are the most prominent in these regions of the spectra of the lowest rank coals, and decrease in intensity relative to the monohydroxy and hydrocarbon peaks at higher rank. Chemical evidence has shown previously that 50-80 % of the oxygen in bituminous vitrinites occurs as phenolic hydroxyl. But the mass spectral data reported here constitute the first evidence of the occurrence of more than one OH group in one benzene ring. Of course the basic monomer units of the lignin polymer have di- or trihydroxy-phenylpropane skeletons, so perhaps we have detected a veritable chemical fossil of the original plant structure (the methoxyl groups detected chemically in lignites and sub-bituminous coals, and confirmed by the peak at 31 in the mass spectra, are no doubt also chemical fossils of lignin structure). We are encouraged to think that the chemical structures of coals may bear a more interpretable relation to the biochemical precursors than we had once dared to believe.

Relation between Distribution of Heavy n-Paraffins and Coalification in Carboniferous Coals from the Saar District, Germany

Detlev Leythaeuser [1]) and Dietrich H. Welte [2])

Institut für Geologie der Universität Würzburg
Würzburg, Germany

55 samples of sub-bituminous to medium volatile bituminous coals from the Upper Carboniferous of the Saar district have been investigated for their heavy n-paraffin content with ether (soxhlet), column chromatography on Al_2O_3 and SiO_2, separation with molecular sieves or urea adduction and gas liquid chromatography. Many of the results thus obtained show distinct relations to coalification, e.g. the maximum extraction yields in coal with 30 % volatile matter (d.a.f.), the continuous decrease of the saturated hydrocarbon fraction from column chromatography and the increase of the corresponding aromatic hydrocarbons with increasing coalification. The results of the gas-chromatographic analysis of the heavy n-paraffins reveal strong correlation to rank of coal:

1. n-Paraffins from sub-bituminous Stefanian coals tend to have broad distribution curves, mostly without a sharp maximum. Distribution curves from the coals of the Westfalian D continuing to those of Westfalian C become steeper. At the same time they increasingly tend to show a distinct maximum.

2. As coalification progresses up to a rank of 30 % volatile matter (d. a. f.), there is some evidence for a decrease of the high molecular n-paraffins relative to their lower homologues. With further coalification an opposite trend can be oberserved.

3. The preference of the odd numbered n-paraffins strongly corresponds with rank of coal. The CPI-values in the range from C_{23} to C_{29} systematically decrease during coalification from 1.59 to 1.00.

A. Introduction

Heavy n-paraffins (straight chain saturated hydrocarbons of the formula C_nH_{2n+2} with 15 to 30 carbon numbers per molecule) are common and well known constituents of crude oils and nearly all sedimentary rocks. They are used especially for the characterisation of possible source beds (e.g. Bray/Evans 1961, Hunt 1961, Martin/Winters/Williams 1964, Welte 1964, 1967). According to Welte (1967) the amount of n-paraffins, the shape of their distribution curves, and the preference of odd numbered n-paraffins (CPI = carbon preference index) are valuable maturity indicators. But there is no sufficient information on which geological conditions these properties depend.

---

[1]) Present address: Atlantic Richfield Company, P. O. Box 2819, Dallas, Texas 75221, USA

[2]) Present address: Chevron Oil Field Research Co. P. O. Box 446, La Habra, California 90631, USA

Coals are well suited materials for the investigation of the geochemistry of heavy
n-paraffins and for defining more clearly the influence of the main geological factors, like source material and depth of burial upon the geochemistry of n-paraffins.
The nature of the source material which is derived mainly from autochthonous
plant debris, can be determined by means of coal microscopy. Furthermore its
chemical and structural transformation process during diagenesis can be traced by
chemical and physical indicators as used for coal rank determinations. When this
work was started there was very little known about the n-paraffin content and
distribution in coals and it was just recently when Brooks and Smith (1967) published one of the first papers about this subject matter. The information that was
available till then was only in respect to the overall chemical composition (Steinbrecher / Behling 1958, Boyer et al. 1961, Halleux/de Greef 1963, Kröger 1963,
Ouchi/Imuta 1963, Bertling 1964, Pauly 1968).

From a geological point of view, coal samples taken from the seams of one individual coal bearing sedimentary basin seem to be most promising for that purpose.
The Upper Carboniferous of the Saar district seems well suited, because of the
monotonous continental facies of its sediments, without any marine influences.

B. Samples

The bulk of the coal samples investigated were taken from cores of deep bore holes
of the Saarbergwerke AG, Saarbrücken. The Upper Carboniferous of the Saar
district (Westfalian C, D and Stefanian A, B, C) consists of about 4500 m of clastic
sedimentary rocks, mostly carbonaceous shales and also siltstones, sandstones and
conglomerates interlayered with many coal seams. This sequence has been deposited in a limnic to fluviatile environment in a continental basin (Kneuper 1964).
The rank of the 51 coal samples investigated ranges from 5.6 to 0.7 % moisture
content. Coalification has mainly taken place before folding of these sediments
(Damberger/Kneuper/Teichmüller, M. u. R. 1964, Teichmüller, M. u. R. 1966,
Damberger 1967). In addition, four high rank coals (27.5 – 18.0 % volatile matter
content d. a. f.) of the Carboniferous of the "Ruhr"-area were chosen.

C. Analytical Procedure

The analytical methods used are those frequently applied in petroleum geochemistry. For details see the literature quoted (e. g. Smith 1954, Evans/Kenny/Mein-
schein/Bray 1957, Ferguson 1962, Van der Wiel 1965). The steps of the analytical
process are: Solvent extraction of the fine ground sample with diethyl ether (soxhlet, 8 hr), column chromatographic separation on Al_2O_3 and SiO_2 into three
fractions (saturated hydrocarbons, aromatic hydrocarbons, asphaltic compounds),
separation of n-paraffins by molecular sieves or urea adduction and finally gas
liquid chromatographic analysis of heavy n-paraffins. The results of this analysis

were plotted as distribution curves, from which the CPI values (preference index of odd numbered n-paraffins n-C_{23} to n-C_{29}) were calculated according to Bray/ Evans (1961) and Kvenvolden (1966).

As the basis for the correlation of the geochemical results the mean value of moisture content (%) calculated after Damberger (1964, 1967) was chosen as rank parameter. He plotted the moisture contents of a great number of Saar coals against their carbon contents, calorific values and maximum internal moisture contents (water retaining capacities). Using these diagrams, all the coalification parameters of the samples investigated here, were transformed into a calculated mean moisture content. According to statistical investigations by Damberger (1967) this value is most suitable for characterising the rank of the Carboniferous coals of the Saar region.

D. Discussion of Results

1. Yield and composition of extracts

The *yields* of the ether *extraction* of the coals from the Saar district range from 0.2 to 1.0 % a. f., depending upon the rank of the coals analysed. Figure 1 shows the relation between the extraction yields and the content of volatile matter of coal. At a point of 30 % volatile matter the extraction yield reaches a maximum. With further coalification there is a continuous decrease of extraction yields. After Van Krevelen (1965) some solvents have an optimum extracting effect at a specific degree of coalification. The extracts obtained by poor solvents such as ether, are considered to have formed from resins and waxes of the coal (Van Krevelen 1961). Furthermore from Figure 1 the results of the column chromatographic separation can be seen.

The *composition* of the *extracts* is also related to rank of coal: The content of saturated hydrocarbons (25–3 % of extract) decreases and the content of aromatic hydrocarbons (26–50 % of extract) increases with coalification progress, while the asphaltic compounds (25 - 60 % of extract) vary considerably without a consistent trend. The aliphatic hydrocarbons of coal tars after Bertling (1964) are derived from waxes of plant origin in the coal, whereas the aromatic compounds come from resin components. The same derivation is assumed also for the extracts yielded under analytical conditions applied here. From Figure 2 the general decrease of the saturated hydrocarbons from 25 % to 3 % of extract can be seen with increasing rank of the coal from 3.6 % to 0.8 % moisture content respectively. Some samples show strikingly high saturated hydrocarbon contents. These coals reveal special properties of their parent material by microscopic examination: No. 46,57 and 100 have high contents of spore and exine materials and No. 57 has additional resin enclosures. The vitrinitic groundmass of these coals shows little

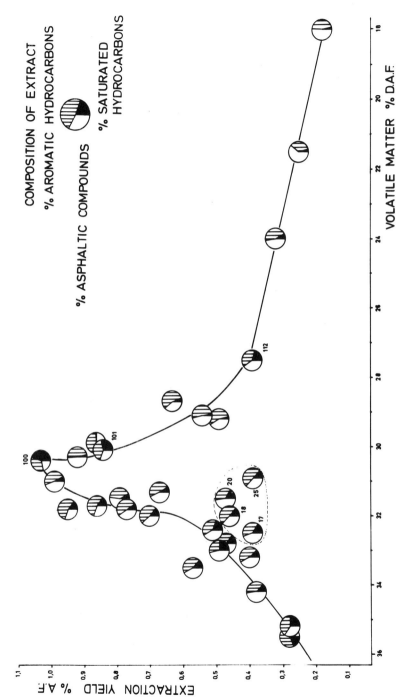

Fig. 1. Coals from the Upper Carboniferous of the Saar district. Extraction yields (% a. f.) and composition of extracts (obtained by column chromatographic separation) in relation to the volatile matter content of coals. Samples with less than 28 % volatile matter content are taken from the Upper Carboniferous of the Ruhr district. Samples deviating from the general trend are emphasized by their numbers.

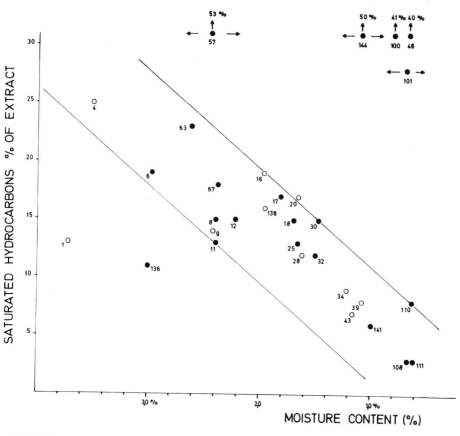

Fig. 2. Coals from the Upper Carboniferous of the Saar district. Saturated hydrocarbon content (% of extract) in relation to rank of coal (% moisture content). Among the samples deviating from the general trend, N. B.: No. 46 = cannel coal, No. 144 = spore rich bituminous coal impregnated on fissures with crude oil. For some of these samples only the approximate position in the rank scale could be given because of a lack of exact rank data.

fluorescence, which is possibly caused by an impregnation with bituminous substances. No. 144 is a bituminous coal rich in spores. The fissures of the coal were impregnated with crude oil.

The mean values of the heavy *n-paraffin recoveries* from coals (a. f.) of different stratigraphic units of the Upper Carboniferous are: Westfalian C = 150 ppm, Westfalian D = 250 ppm, and Stefanian = 110 ppm.

The heavy n-paraffins are generally considered to come mainly from the exinites of the original coal (Boyer et al. 1961, Ouchi/Imuta 1963).

2. Distribution of heavy n-paraffins in relation to rank of coal

Some examples of heavy n-paraffin distribution curves are given in Figure 3 und 4. Those of the coals of the Stefanian (Figure 3) show a relatively broad distribution curve mostly without any distinct maximum and always with a clear predominance of odd numbered n-paraffins $n-C_{19}$ to $n-C_{29}$. It is evident, that CPI values decrease with increasing rank of coal. All distribution curves have strikingly high C_{17} peaks. This is probably due to a contribution from pristane which was very abundant in some samples. Therefore high C_{17} peaks in the figures are drawn in dashed lines, because of a possible contribution from pristane.

The n-paraffin distribution curves from coals of Westfalian D occupy an intermediate position with respect to their shape and CPI values between the foregoing coals and the coals of Westfalian C (Figure 4). These coal samples reveal much sharper distribution curves with less preference of odd numbered n-paraffins. CPI

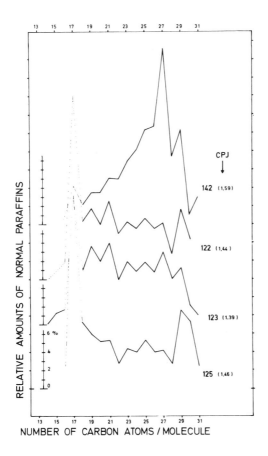

Fig. 3

Normal paraffin distribution curves of Carboniferous coal samples taken from the *Stefanian* of the Saar district. Succesion from No. 142 to No. 125 corresponds to increasing coalification.

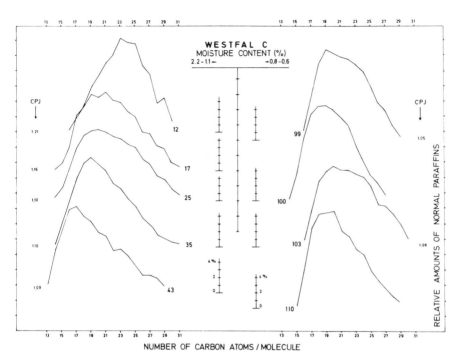

Fig. 4. Normal paraffin distribution curves of Carboniferous coal samples taken from the *Westfalian C.* of the Saar district. Left — high volatile bituminous coals, right — medium volatile bituminous coals.

values again decrease with coalification progress. The maxima within the distribution curves are shifted with increasing coalification to lower homologues up to a rank of about 1.1 % moisture content. At the same time distribution curves get steeper (Figure 4, left side). With further coalification progress the maxima shift again to higher homologues (more than n-C_{18}, Figure 4 right side).

Summarizing this comparative view of some typical examples of distribution curves of heavy n-paraffins, it is evident, that the position of the maximum of the curves as well as the CPI index of the odd numbered homologues n-C_{23} to n-C_{29} reveal definite relations to the degree of coalification of the sample investigated. Figure 5 demonstrates, that the position of the maximum of the n-paraffin distribution curve is shifted continuously with increasing rank from n-C_{23} at a rank of 3.6 % moisture content to n-C_{17} at 1.2 % moisture content. The broad range of variation of these maxima may be caused by two factors: Analytical errors and variation of the petrographic composition of the coal seams. Samples No. 134—141 deviating

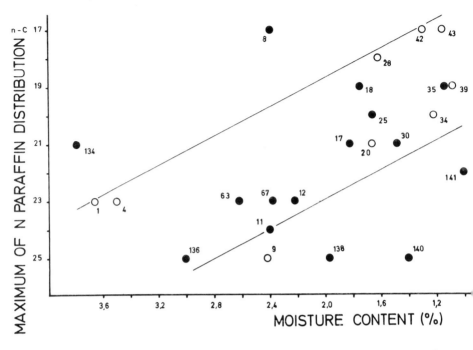

Fig. 5. The position of the maximum within the n-paraffin distribution curves of Carboniferous coals from the Saar district in relation to rank of coal (% moisture content)

from the general trend are out a borehole with a tectonically very disturbed sequence. Tectonical stress may have influenced the coal structure in such a way, that the resulting increased porosity favoured migration of short chain n-paraffins. – Figure 5 does not show the retrogressive tendency of maximum displacement in the range of medium volatile bituminous coals, i.e. the subsequent increase of the mean molecular chain length of the n-paraffin fraction. This development may only be mentioned here, because coals of this rank are scarcely available in the Saar Carboniferous. On the other hand the few high rank coal samples of the Ruhr district, investigated for comparison, are not supporting this trend sufficiently.

Coals from different stratigraphic units of the Carboniferous of the Saar district have different ranges of CPI values (Figure 6): Highest values from 1.44 to 1.59 have been obtained from samples of the Stefanian B, those of Stefanian A have values from 1.39 to 1.46, while those of Westfalian D show indices from 1.22 to 1.34 and the lowest ones are revealed by the samples of Westfalian C coal seams with 1.02 to 1.25. This decrease of CPI values from Stefanian B to Westfalian C,

i. e. from stratigraphically younger to older seams, corresponds generally to increasing coalification. Figure 7 demonstrates clearly a close relation between CPI values and rank of coal: It diminishes continously from 1.59 at a rank of 5.6 % moisture content and approaches 1.0 at a rank of 1.0 % moisture content.

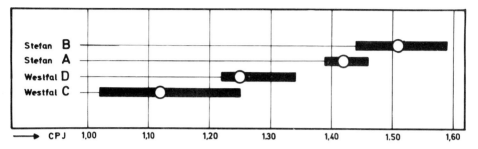

Fig. 6. Ratios of odd-to even-carbon-numbered paraffins (CPI) n-C_{23} to n-C_{29} in coals from the different stratigraphic units of the Upper Carboniferous of the Saar district. Range of variation and mean values are plotted.

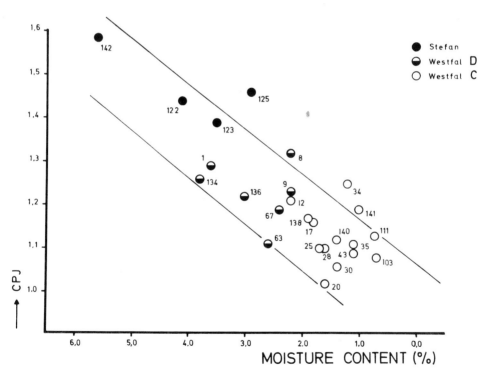

Fig. 7. Ratios of odd- to even-carbon-numbered paraffins (CPI) n-C_{23} to n-C_{29} in Carboniferous coals of the Saar district in relation to rank of coal.

A closer examination of this graph also reveals source bound influences. When comparing the CPI values of only small sections of the rank scale (for example those between 4.0 and 3.0 % moisture content), it is obvious that coals from Stefanian generally yield higher CPI values than those of the Westfalian D. The latter ones in turn provide higher values than the Westfalian C coals (e.g. No. 122, 123, 125 compared with No. 1, 134, 136 and No. 8, 9, 67, 63 compared with No. 12, 138, 17, 25). These differences may be caused by changes in the source material due to environmental alterations during the Upper Carboniferous. The amount of higher organised plants in the peat forming plant communities, increased during Saar Carboniferous with the beginning of Westfalian D and especially during Stefanian time (Patteisky 1953). These plants, especially the Cordaites, were able to form resinic tissues. This change of the composition of the peat forming plant communities may be the result of an increasingly dryer climate towards the end of Upper Carboniferous.

E. Summary

Most of the organic-geochemical properties of the coals from the Upper Carboniferous of the Saar district show distinct relations to rank of coal. With coalification progress extraction yields increase up to a maximum at a rank of 30 % volatile matter. From that point on with further coalification a continuous decrease of extraction yield can be observed. The composition of extracts varies regularly with the increase of coalification: There is a decrease of the saturated hydrocarbons and an increase of the aromatic hydrocarbons. The most important result of this investigation of coal samples may be the evidence of more defined relations between distribution of heavy n-paraffins and rank of coal:

1. The shape of the n-paraffin distribution curves obtained from the coals of the Stefanian is mostly broad without any distinct maximum. Curves get steeper from coals of Westfalian D increasingly to those of Westfalian C. At the same time a tendency to reveal a clear maximum within the distribution curve is evident.

2. With increasing coalification there is a trend of decrease of heavier n-paraffin homologues up to the transition of high volatile to medium volatile bituminous coals. This is indicated by a displacement of the maximum of the distribution curve in the direction to lower homologues. With further coalification a retrogressive trend may be observed.

3. The preference of odd numbered homologues $n-C_{23}$ to $n-C_{29}$ (CPI) decreases continuously with increasing rank.

Acknowledgement: This paper is a part of the doctorate thesis of the first listed author. It was undertaken in connection with a cooperative research program together with the Saarbergwerke AG, Saarbrücken. "On the origin and occurrence of coalification gas in the Carboniferous of the Saar district." For financial support we wish to thank the Saarbergwerke AG, Saarbrücken. Dr. G. Kneuper, Saarbrücken, generously furnished the coal samples and pertinent geological informations. Most of the rank determinations were kindly made by Dr. M. Teichmüller and the microscopic examinations were done by Dr. M. Wolf, Krefeld. To all of them we want to express our thanks for their interest and assistance concerning the work.

References

Bertling, H.: Über die Konstitution von Schnellschwelteeren. Dissertation Technische Hochschule Aachen (1964).

Boyer, A. F., Ferrand, R., Ladam, A., Payen, P.: Quelques indices sur la structure des carbons d'après l'analyse de leurs produits de dégradation. Chimie et Industrie **86**, 5. pp. 523-530, (1961).

Bray, E. E., Evans, E. D.: Distribution of heavy n-paraffins as a clue to recognition of source beds. Geochim. et Cosmochim. Acta **22**, 1, pp. 2-15 (1961).

Brooks, J. D., Smith, J. W.: The diagenesis of plant lipids during the formation of coal, petroleum and natural gas. I, Changes in the n-paraffin hydrocarbons. Geochim. et Cosmochim. Acta 31, 12, pp. 2389–2397 (1967).

Damberger, H., Kneuper, G., Teichmüller, M. und R.: Das Inkohlungsbild des Saarkarbons. Glückauf Jg. 100, pp. 209-217 (1964).

Damberger, H.: Inkohlungsmerkmale, ihre statistische Bewertung und ihre Anwendbarkeit bei der tektonischen Analyse im saarländischen Steinkohlengebirge. Ausarbeitung Nr. 7 zum Gasforschungsprogramm, Saarbrücken 1967, unpublished.

Evans, E. D., Kenny, G. S., Meinschein, W. G., Bray, E. E.: Distribution of n-paraffins and separation of saturated hydrocarbons from recent marin sediments. Anal. Chem. **29**, 12, pp. 1858–1861 (1957).

Ferguson, W. S.: Analytical problems in determining hydrocarbons in sediments. Bull. Amer. Assoc. Petr. Geol. **46**, 9, pp. 1613–1620 (1962).

Halleux, A., de Greef, H.: Über die Extraktion eines Vitrinits und die chemische Analyse der Fraktionen. Fuel **42**, 3, pp. 185–202 (1963).

Hunt, J. M.: Distribution of hydrocarbons in sedimentary rocks. Geochim. et Cosmochim. Acta **22**, pp. 37–39 (1961).

Kneuper, G.: Grundzüge der Sedimentation und Tektonik im Oberkarbon des Saarbrücker Hauptsattels. Oberrhein. geol. Abh. **13**, pp. 1–49 (1964).

Van Krevelen, D. W.: Coal. Elsevier Publishing Company New York 1961.

Van Krevelen, D. W.: Chemical structure and properties of coal XXVIII—Coal constitution and solvent extraction.

Kröger, C.: Eigenschaften von Hochvakuumteeren, Extrakten und Restkohlen sowie von Chlorierungs- und Sulfonierungsprodukten der Steinkohlen. Forschungsberichte des Landes Nordrhein-Westfalen Nr. 1142, Westdeutscher Verlag Köln 1963.

Kvenvolden, K. A.: Molecular distribution of normal fatty acids and paraffins in some Lower Cretaceous sediments. Nature **209**, pp. 573–577 (1966).

Leythaeuser, D.: Die Verteilung höherer n-Paraffine und anderer schwerflüchtiger Kohlenwasserstoffe in Kohlen und Gesteinen des saarländischen Karbons und Devons in Abhängigkeit von den geologischen Verhältnissen. Dissertation Universität Würzburg (1968).

Martin, R. L., Winters, J. C., Williams, J. A.: Composition of crude oils by gas chromatography: Geological significance of hydrocarbon distribution. Proc. 6th Wld. Petroleum Congr., Sect. V, Pap. 13, (1964).

Ouchi, K., Imuta, K.: The analysis of benzene extracts of Yubari coal II Analysis by gas chromatography. Fuel 42, 6, pp. 445–456 (1963).

Patteisky, K.: Die Veränderungen der Steinkohlen beim Ablauf der Inkohlung. Brennstoff-Chemie 34, pp. 75–82 und 102–108 (1953).

Pauly, W.: Gaschromatographische und massenspektroskopische Untersuchung von Kohleextrakten. Dissertation Universität Köln 1968.

Smith, P. V. jr.: Studies on the origin of petroleum: Occurrence of hydrocarbons in recent sediments. Bull. Amer. Assoc. Petr. Geol. 38, 3. pp. 377–404 (1954).

Steinbrecher, H., Behling, R. D.: Das Ölbitumen einer Fett- und Gasflammkohle. Brennstoff-Chemie 39, 9–10, pp. 146–148 (1958).

Teichmüller, M. und R.: Die Inkohlung im saar-lothringischen Karbon, verglichen mit der im Ruhrkarbon. Zschr. Dtsch. Geol. Ges. 117, pp. 243–279 (1966).

Welte, D. H.: Nichtflüchtige Kohlenwasserstoffe in Kernproben des Devons und Karbons der Bohrung Münsterland I. Fortschr. Geol. Rheinl. u. Westf. 12, pp. 559–568 (1964).

Welte, D. H.: Zur Entwicklungsgeschichte von Erdölen auf Grund geochemisch-geologischer Untersuchungen. Erdöl und Kohle, Erdgas, Petrochemie Jahrgang 20, pp. 65–77 (1967).

Van der Wiel, A.: Molekularsiebe und Gas-Flüssigkeits-Chromatographie als Hilfsmittel zur Bestimmung der Konstitution von Paraffinen. Erdöl und Kohle, Erdgas, Petrochemie 8, pp. 632–637 (1965).

Discussion

M. Teichmüller: Die Untersuchungen des Autors sind sehr wichtig, da sie die enge Beziehungen zwischen der Metamorphose der Kohle und der Erdölsubstanzen zeigen. Viele Vorträge dieser Tagung haben gezeigt, daß die Bildung, Diagenese und Metamorphose des Erdöls durch die Versenkungstiefe und zwar in erster Linie durch die Erdtemperatur bestimmt wird, und daß daneben die Zeit als Metamorphose-Faktor eine Rolle spielt. Diese Ergebnisse sind direkt vergleichbar mit den Ergebnissen die man seit vielen Jahren durch Untersuchungen der Kohle gewonnen hat.

Der Autor hat sich für seine vergleichenden Untersuchungen ganz besonders günstige Kohlenproben ausgesucht: Nach den chemischen und mikroskopischen Untersuchungen sind die Saar Kohlen – verglichen z.b. mit den Ruhrkohlen – sozusagen anormal, insofern als sie z.b. ein relativ geringes Reflexionsvermögen des Vitrinits haben, besonders viel Flüchtige Bestandteile ergeben, und sich durch hohe Blähgrade bei der Verkohlung auszeichnen, wenn man gleiche Inkohlungsgrade zu Grunde legt. Auch findet man an der Saar auffallend viel höhere Kohlenwasserstoffe im Grubengas. Ja, man hat sogar Erdöl-Spuren auf Kluften in den Flözen gefunden. Alles spricht dafür, daß die Saarkohlen besonders reichlich bituminöse („erdölige") Substanz enthalten, die übrigens nicht nur in den liptinitischen Mazeralen enthalten ist, sondern hier zu einem großen Teil wohl auch im Vitrinit (daher das relativ schwache Reflektionsvermögen, bzw. hoher Gehalt an Flüchtigen Bestandteile hoher Blähgrad usw.). Dementsprechend hat Kröger in Saar-Vitriten seine „Harz-Wachs-Komponente" in relativ großen Mengen gefunden. Die Frage ist: woher kommen die „öligen" Stoffe: Sind sie autochthon in der Kohle, oder sind sie aus den Nebengesteinen eingewandert?

D. Leythaeuser: Auf Grund meiner geochemischen Untersuchungsergebnisse kann ich diese Frage nicht direkt beantworten. Ich glaube, jedoch, daß diese „öligen" Stoffe als flüssige Reaktionsprodukte chemischer Inkohlungsprozesse anzusehen sind, d.h. sie sind in der Kohle selbst entstanden. Unter normalen Verhältnissen ist es aber diesen höhermolekularen Kohlenwasserstoffen nicht möglich, ihren Ursprungsort auf dem Wege einer Migration zu verlassen. Der im Vergleich zu den Erdölmuttergesteinen wesentlich geringere mittlere Porendurchmesser sowie die höhere Adsorptionskapazität der Kohle vereiteln dies weitgehend.

Nur unter besonderen Bedingungen, z.B. bei tektonisch stark beanspruchten Flözkohlen dürfte eine Migration flüssiger Inkohlungsprodukte aus der Kohle in das benachbarte Nebengestein möglich sein. Die tektonische Überprägung beeinflußt die Kohlestruktur bis in den submikroskopischen Bereich, wie Jüntgen/Karweil (1963) [1] festgestellt haben.

H. Jüntgen: Sie haben bei Kohlen aus gestörter Lagerung abweichende Ergebnisse beobachtet. Nun weiß man aus anderen Messungen, daß gestörte Kohlen ein abweichendes, d.h. größeres Porensystem aufweisen. Führen Sie Ihre Unterschiede auf abweichende geochemische Reaktionen infolge des geänderten Porensystems oder auf eine unterschiedliche Extraktionsausbeute an den verschiedenen Stoffen zurück?

---

[1] Jüntgen, H., Karweil, J.: Porenverteilung und innere Oberfläche der Kohlen der Bohrung Münsterland 1. Fortschr. Geol. Rheinl. Westf., **11** (1963).

D. Leythaeuser: Die Wirkung dieser beiden Einflußgrößen kann ich auf Grund der Auswertung meiner Daten nicht abgrenzen. Dazu reichen einmal die zur Verfügung stehenden Daten nicht aus, zum anderen wären zusätzliche Spezialuntersuchungen nötig.

Ein durch tektonische Beanspruchung vergrößerstes Porensystem der Kohlen dürfte u. U. auch höheren Paraffinen eine Migration aus der Kohlensubstanz ermöglichen. So ließen sich die beobachteten Abweichungen dieser Kohlen im Hinblick auf die relative Verteilung der n-Paraffinhomologen erklären.

Darüberhinaus hat sicherlich auch das vergrößerte Porensystem dieser Kohle den Lösungsmittel-Angriff erleichtert und einer Abtransport der Extraktionsprodukte begünstigt.

Untersuchungen zum Gasabspaltevermögen des organischen Materials in Gesteinen und Kohlen des saarländischen Karbons und Devons

Hermann Wehner[1]) und Dietrich H. Welte[2])

Institut für Geologie der Universität Würzburg
Würzburg, Germany

The aim of this work was to determine amount and kind of gases which are released during artificial coalification from the organic material of paleozoic rock samples from the Saar-Region (Germany).

Method: After heating the powdered samples up to 300 °C in a carbon dioxide- or nitrogen-athmosphere, the volume of the evolved gas was measured and its composition determined by use of GLC.

Results:

1. The yield of the gas, relative to the total organic content, depends on the degree of coalification of the organic material. Samples taken from locations close to bituminous coals with a medium or high amount of volatile matter produce large quantities

   of gas $\left(\text{about } 200 \; \dfrac{\text{ml gas/kg rock sample}}{\% \text{ organ. C of the rock}} \right)$

2. The composition of the organic material (determined by ether-extraction and following chromatography on aluminum oxide and silica gel) influences quantity and quality of the gas. The greater the part of saturated hydrocarbons, the greater is the obtained gas volume and its content of higher alkanes (butanes).

3. The composition of the gas depends on the degree of coalification of the organic material. With increasing rank of coal there is a decrease of the higher homologues of methane.

4. Quantity and quality of the gas depend on the source material and on the physical and chemical conditions existing during sedimentation and diagenesis of the sediments. Devonian limestones yielded much more gas, relative to the total organic content, and gas richer in hydrocarbons in the range $C_2 - C_4$, than overlying clastic Carboniferous samples.

5. In addition to the rock samples also coals have been subjected to artificial coalification. Considering these data and the known coal/rock distribution ratio in the Saar-Region, one can assume that 40 % to 80 % of the total mine gas (dependent on the content of coal seams of a certain section) evolved from the organic material of the sediments during the course of coalification.

Ziel der Untersuchungen war, festzustellen, wieviel und welche Gase bei einer künstlichen Inkohlung aus dem organischen Material der Nebengesteine des Saarkarbons abgegeben werden.

---

[1]) Neue Anschrift: Niedersächsisches Landesamt für Bodenforschung, 3-Hannover-Buchholz
[2]) Neue Anschrift: Chevron Oil Field Research Company, La Habra, California

Methode: Nach Aufheizung der feingemahlenen Proben im Autoklaven unter Kohlendioxid oder Stickstoff auf Temperaturen bis 300 °C wurde das sich entwickelnde Gas volumetrisch gemessen und gaschromatographisch analysiert.

Ergebnisse:

1. Die Gasmengen pro Kohlenstoffeinheit sind abhängig vom Inkohlungsgrad der organischen Substanz. Proben aus der Nachbarschaft von Gaskohlen liefern das meiste Gas

$$\left(ca. \ 200 \ \frac{ml \ Gas/kg \ Gestein}{\% \ organ. \ C \ d. \ Gesteins} \right)$$

2. Der Gehalt des organischen Materials an gesättigten Kohlenwasserstoffen (durch Extraktion bestimmt) ist von Einfluß auf Gasmenge und -zusammensetzung. Je höher der Anteil der gesättigten Kohlenwasserstoffe liegt, desto größer ist die Gasmenge und ihr Gehalt an höheren Paraffinen (Butane).

3. Die Gaszusammensetzung hängt vom Inkohlungsgrad des organischen Materials ab. Mit zunehmender Inkohlung verringert sich der Anteil der höheren Homologe des Methans.

4. Art und Menge der Gase hängen vom Ausgangsmaterial und von den physikalischen und chemischen Bedingungen ab, die während der Sedimentation und im Verlauf der Diagenese der Sedimente herrschten. Devonische Kalksteine liefern, in Bezug auf den gesamten organischen Inhalt mehr Gas als die überlagernden plastischen Karbon-Gesteine. Außerdem sind darin die Kohlenwasserstoffe der Reihe $C_2 - C_4$ stärker vertreten.

5. Nach Vergleichsuntersuchungen an Kohlen und unter Berücksichtigung der bekannten Kohle-Nebengesteins-Verteilung des Saarkarbons können, je nach Flözreichtum eines Profils, 40 % bis 80 % des durch die Inkohlung entstandenen Gases aus dem Nebengestein stammen.

Einleitung

Für den Steinkohlenbergbau ist die Kenntnis der beim Abbau zu erwartenden Grubengasmengen äußerst wichtig. Daher wurde schon häufiger versucht, aus der Änderung der Elementarzusammensetzung der Kohlen bei fortschreitender Inkohlung Art und Menge der dabei freiwerdenden Gase zu berechnen (Patteisky) (1951), Uspenskij (1954), Jüntgen & Karweil (1966), Kröger & Hortig (1966)). Außer der Kohle ist jedoch auch das in den Begleitgesteinen verteilte organische Material der Inkohlung unterworfen und daher als Gaslieferant anzusehen (Patteisky, 1951).

Darüber genauere Auskunft zu erhalten, war u. a. ein Anliegen des Gasforschungsprogrammes der Saarbergwerke, das sich die Aufgabe stellte, die Herkunft und das Auftreten von Grubengas im saarländischen Steinkohlengebirge zu klären. Die zur Verfügung stehenden Bohrkerne stammten daher aus Über- und Untertagebohrungen, die im Saarkarbon und -devon abgeteuft wurden.

Durch eine Temperaturbehandlung sollte die in den Gesteinen eingebettete organische Substanz künstlich inkohlt und das dabei auftretende Gas volumetrisch gemessen und analysiert werden. Es sollten also die Verhältnisse nachgeahmt werden, die bei einer erneuten Tieferversenkung der Karbonsedimente auftreten würden, bzw. die Veränderungen rekonstruiert werden, die sich durch die bisherige Versenkung ergaben.

Dazu wurden die Proben, zumeist Sandsteine und Schiefertone, feingemahlen und in einer CO_2-Athmosphäre in einem Autoklaven erhitzt. Mit CO_2-Spülgas wurde das entstandene Gasgemisch über eine Waschanlage mit Kalilauge in eine Bürette gedrückt. Das bei dem Versuch entstandene Kohlendioxid konnte also nicht gemessen werden, da es zusammen mit dem Spülgas in der Kalilauge absorbiert wurde. Im Folgenden ist unter „Gasmenge" also immer das CO_2-freie Gas gemeint. Es wurde gaschromatographisch analysiert, wobei Molekularsiebe 5 A, Silikagel und Tetraisobutylen auf Chromosorb als Säulenfüllungen dienten.

Ergebnisse

Die abspaltbare Gasmenge von Proben gleicher Inkohlungstufe wird hauptsächlich durch ihren Gehalt an organischer Substanz bestimmt. Die kohlenstofärmste, klastische Probe (0,12 % organ. C) lieferte 20 ml Gas pro kg Gestein, die kohlenstoffreichste, ein kohliger Schieferton mit 24,64 % organ. C entwickelte 702 ml/kg Gas. Bei mittleren Gehalten der Schiefertone von ca. 3 % organ. C bildeten sich ca. 200 ml/kg. Die in der Regel kohlenstofärmeren Sandsteine (ca. 1 % organ. C) liefern 100 ml/kg Gestein. Die kohlenstoffarmen devonischen Karbonate (ca. 0,24 % organ. C) entbinden im Mittel 40 ml/kg (Bild 1).

Die Gasmenge wird weiterhin durch den Gehalt der Proben an gesättigten Kohlenwasserstoffen bestimmt, der zwischen 7 ppm und 460 ppm liegt (Leythaeuser, 1968). Diesen Werten sind Gasmengen von 14 ml/kg, bzw. 702 ml/kg Gestein zugeordnet (Bild 2).

Der Inkohlungsgrad der organischen Substanz beeinflußt ebenfalls die abspaltbare Gasmenge (Bild 3). Proben, deren Inkohlungsgrad (aus Mangel an geeigneten Daten wurde der Inkohlungsgrad benachbarter Flöze mit Vorbehalten zum Vergleich herangezogen) zwischen 37 und 35 % Flüchtigen Bestandteilen liegt, liefern eine Gasmenge von ca. 90 ml/organ. $C \left(\dfrac{\text{ml Gas/kg Gestein}}{\text{\% organ. C d. Gesteins}} \right)$. Bei etwa 32 % Flücht. Best. wird ein Maximum von ca. 200 ml/organ. C durchschritten, dann sinkt die Gasmenge bei Proben mit 31 bis 29 % Flücht. Best. wieder auf 100 ml/organ. C ab. Bei ca. 23 % Flücht. Best. (Ruhrkarbon-Proben) wird ein Wert von etwa 70 ml/organ. C erreicht. In der Bohrung Saar 1 treten die höchsten Inkohlungstadien, einschließlich des Metaanthrazitstadiums, auf. Hier sinken die Gasausbeuten der klastischen Proben bis auf 15 ml/organ. C (Bild 4).

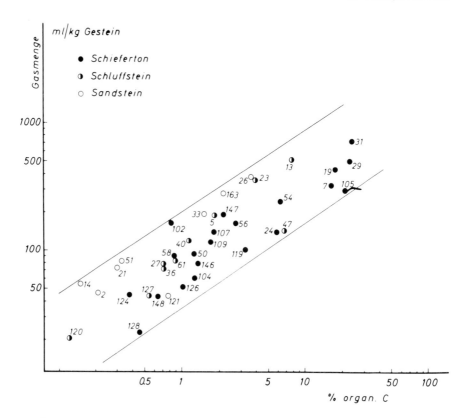

Bild 1. Abhängigkeit der Gasmenge vom organischen Kohlenstoffgehalt eines Gesteins

Die devonische Karbonatfolge der Bohrung Saar 1 lieferte auf Grund der geringen
Kohlenstoffgehalte (~ 0,24 %) auch nur geringe Gasmengen (~ 40 ml/kg Gestein).
Auf die Kohlenstoffeinheit bezogen ist dies jedoch mehr (± > 100 ml/organ. C),
als die unmittelbar darüberliegenden klastischen Serien des Oberkarbons (± < 100 ml/
organ. C) abgeben.

Unter den Kohlen brachte eine Kännelkohle mit 7270 ml/kg die größte, eine Gaskohle aus der Grube Camphausen mit 2155 ml/kg die geringste Gasausbeute.

Die *Zusammensetzung* der brennbaren Gase umfaßt gesättigte und ungesättigte,
Normal- und Iso-Kettenkohlenwasserstoffe mit maximal 6 C-Atomen. Der Anteil
der einzelnen Komponenten am Gasgemisch hängt vom Inkohlungsgrad des organischen Materials ab. Der Methananteil z. B. steigt von etwa 30 % auf 96 % (bezogen auf die Gesamtmenge der Paraffine) mit zunehmender Inkohlung, bei einer
Differenz im Inkohlungsgrad von ca. 30 % Flücht. Best. (nach begleitenden Flözen)

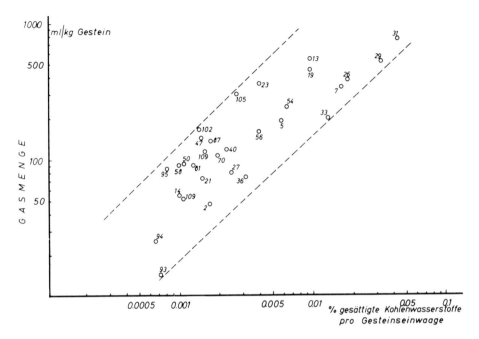

Bild 2. Gasmenge in Abhängigkeit vom Gehalt eines Gesteins an gesättigten Kohlenwasserstoffen

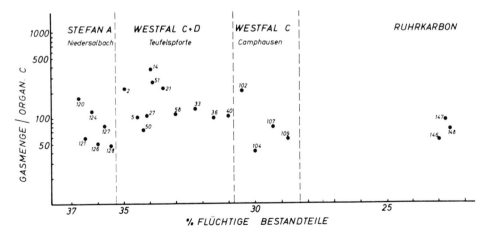

Bild 3. Gasmengen pro Kohlenstoffeinheit aus Nebengesteinen (% C > 2 %) des Saarkarbons

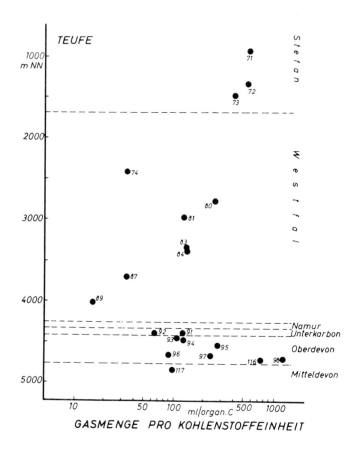

Bild 4. Gasmenge in ml/Org. C in Beziehung zur Teufe und Stratigraphie

(Bild 5). Entsprechend wird der Anteil der höheren Paraffine am Gasgemisch geringer. Der Gehalt der Butane nimmt z.B. von ca. 25 % im Gasflammkohlenstadium auf 1 % oder geringer im Metaanthrazitstadium ab. In den Gasen aus den Devonkalken steigt er jedoch wieder bis auf 7 %, während der Methangehalt auf 70 bis 80 % zurückgeht (Bild 6).

Die Menge an höheren Homologen des Methans zeigt eine Beziehung zu der ätherlöslichen organischen Substanz dergestalt, daß, bei vergleichbarem Inkohlungsgrad, mit deren Zunahme auch der Gehalt an höheren gasförmigen Paraffinen ansteigt (Bild 7).

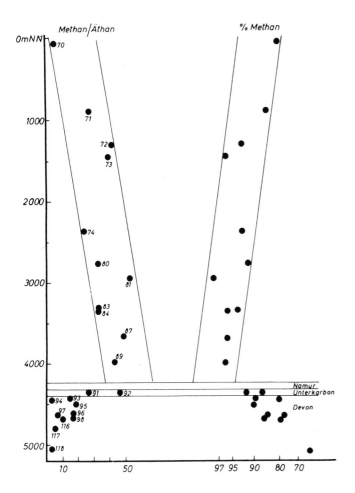

Bild 5. Beziehung zwischen Inkohlung, Lithologie und Gaszusammensetzung

Dieser Zusammenhang ergab sich bei der Untersuchung einiger Kohlen, die durch ihren hohen Anteil an gesättigten Kohlenwasserstoffen im Extrakt (bis 50 %) auffielen (Leythaeuser, 1968). Die Butangehalte dieser Proben schwanken zwischen 9 % und 12 %, während bei den Kohlen, die den Durchschnitt repräsentieren (5–15 % gesättigte Kohlenwasserstoffe), die Butane einen Anteil von nur 5–6 % am brennbaren Gas haben.

29 Geochemistry 68

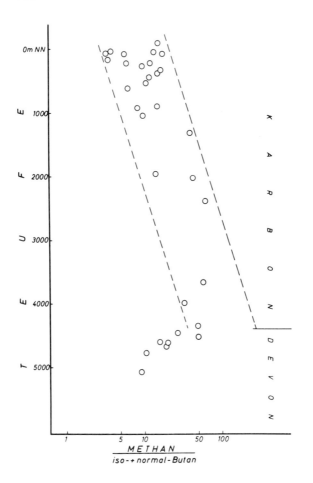

Bild 6
Das Verhältnis Methan/
i – + n-Butan in Bezie-
hung zur Teufe

Diskussion und Deutung

a) Einfluß des Inkohlungsgrades auf Gasmenge und -zusammensetzung

Die chemische Inkohlung, am Karweilschen Kohlenmodell dargestellt, besteht darin, daß sich bei gleichbleibender Größe des aromatischen Kernsystems die Zahl der Methylengruppen verringert. Gleichzeitig ändert sich durch die zunehmend dichtere Packung der Aromatkomplexe der strukturelle Aufbau der Kohle (Huck & Karweil, 1953). Diese Veränderungen im chemischen und physikalischen Zustand des organischen Materials sind von Einfluß auf Menge und Art der abspaltbaren flüchtigen Kohlenwasserstoffe.

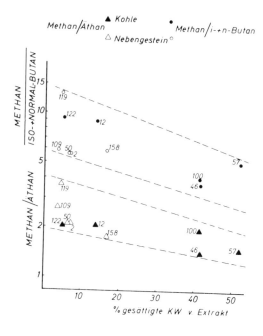

Bild 7

Beziehung zwischen Bitumenge-
halt und Gaszusammensetzung

Es ist aus der Bergbau-Praxis bekannt, daß die stärkste Methanausgasung in Gas-
und Fettkohlenflözen zu verzeichnen ist (Patteisky, 1955). Auch bei einer künstlichen Entgasung erhielt Girling (1963) die größten Gasausbeuten von Kohlen mittleren Inkohlungsgrades.

Dieser Trend zeigt sich ebenfalls, wenn auch weniger deutlich, beim Gasbildungsver-
mögen der organischen Substanz der Nebengesteine (Bild 3). In Bild 3 wurden nur
Gesteine mit weniger als 2 % organ. C aufgenommen, um damit eine bessere Ver-
gleichsbasis für die Proben zu haben.

Auf der Abszisse wurde der Inkohlungsgrad benachbarter Kohlen aufgetragen, d.h.
es wurde vorausgesetzt, daß der organische Inhalt der Gesteine durch die erhöhten
Temperaturen im Schichtverband ähnlich beeinflußt wird wie die Kohlen.

Eine mögliche Deutung des Ausgasungsmaximums gibt bereits Bode (1939). Danach würden die Protobitumina im Verlauf der Inkohlung erst im Bereich der Gaskohle tiefgreifende Veränderungen erleiden. Dies könnte die beobachteten Erschei-
nungen erklären.

Bild 4 zeigt die Abnahme der Gasmenge pro Kohlenstoffeinheit von Oberkarbon-
proben mit zunehmender Teufe. Inkohlungsmäßig wird hier bei den Kohlen der
Bereich von ca. 88 % bis 96 % Kohlenstoff überstrichen.

Daß die Gasmengen mit zunehmender Teufe geringer werden, erklärt sich aus dem abnehmenden H/C-Verhältnis der organischen Substanz mit steigender Inkohlung. Das heißt also, daß aus fortschreitendem Mangel an verfügbarem Wasserstoff die Abspaltung der wasserstoffreichen Gase abnimmt. Damit wird verständlich, daß der Inkohlungsgrad des organischen Materials nicht nur einen Einfluß auf die Menge, sondern auch auf die Art des bei den Inkohlungsversuchen gebildeten Gases haben muß.

Eine Verarmung der Restgase (im Porenraum der Gesteine und Kohlen gespeichertes Gas) an höheren gasförmigen Paraffinen konnte Gedenk (1963) an Gasanalysen von Proben der Bohrung Münsterland 1 zeigen. Als Inkohlungsmaßstab verwendete er die zunehmende Teufe. Ein ähnliches Ergebnis zeigt Bild 6 für die Abnahme des Butan-Gehaltes in den Gasen der künstlichen Inkohlung bis hinab zur Devongrenze. Für Proben aus einer Tiefbohrung ist in Bild 5 eine Zunahme des Methangehaltes bis zum Unterkarbon dargestellt.

b) Einfluß der Lithologie auf Gasmenge und -zusammensetzung

In den Bildern 5 und 6 kommt neben dem Inkohlungszustand gleichzeitig der Einfluß der Lithologie zum Ausdruck. Die devonischen Kalksteine liefern, bezogen auf die Kohlenstoffeinheit, deutlich mehr Gas als die überlagernden oberkarbonischen Schiefertone und Sandsteine. Dieses Gas ist außerdem stärker mit höheren Homologen des Methans angereichert.

Es ist bekannt (Gehman, 1962, Rodionova & Chetverikova, 1962), daß Kalksteine nur etwa 1/4 der Menge an organischem Material enthalten im Vergleich zu Schiefertonen. Der Anteil der Kohlenwasserstoffe an dieser organischen Substanz liegt jedoch bei Kalksteinen bedeutend höher. Gehman macht für diese Verteilung das Adsorptionsvermögen der Tonminerale verantwortlich, die Komponenten mit polaren Gruppen verstärkt zurückhalten.

Weiterhin kann im vorliegenden Fall das marine Milieu der Devonkalke dem limnisch-terrestrischen Verhältnissen des Westfals gegenüber gestellt werden. Der organische Inhalt mariner Sedimente ist auf Grund des planktonischen Ausgangsmaterials wasserstoffreicher als der der Sedimente, die eine starke Zufuhr organischen Materials vom Lande erfahren. Makroskopisch macht sich dieser Unterschied im Vorhandensein von kohligen Partikeln im Oberkarbon und deren völligem Fehlen im Devon bemerkbar.

Zusammenfassend läßt sich sagen, daß die verschiedenen durch die Lithologie, bzw. das syn- und postsedimentäre Milieu bewirkten physikalisch-chemischen Bedingungen den Abbau des organischen Materials beeinflussen. Der Typ des organischen Restmaterials spiegelt die lithologische Fazies des ursprünglichen Sediments und die nachfolgende Diagenese bzw. Metamorphose wider (Rodionova & Chetverikova, 1962).

c) Einfluß des Ausgangsmaterials

Das Ausgangsmaterial für die autochthone organische Substanz der Kohlen und Gesteine ist von unterschiedlicher chemischer Natur. Ganz grob kann man die daraus bei der Inkohlung entstehenden Stoffe einem kohligen Typ und einem bituminösen Typ von organischem Material zuordnen. Dabei bildet sich der kohlige Typ vorwiegend aus Lignin und Zellulose und besteht daher hauptsächlich aus kondensierten aromatischen Ringen, die durch Äther- und Alkoxy-Brücken verbunden sind. Der bituminöse Typ dagegen, aus Fetten, Wachsen, Harzen und Eiweißen hervorgegangen, ist durch eine offenere Kettenstruktur gekennzeichnet (Forsman, 1963) und wasserstoffreicher als der kohlige Typ. Diese beiden Arten der organischen Substanz liegen in Kohlen und Gesteinen in welchselnden Mengenverhältnissen vor.

In Bild 1 ist die Abhängigkeit der Gasmenge (ml/kg Gestein) vom organischen Inhalt eines Gesteins aufgetragen. Nach dem bisher gesagten ist ein guter Zusammenhang nur dann zu erwarten, wenn einmal alle Proben gleich hoch inkohlt sind und zum anderen die organische Substanz sich genetisch vom gleichen Ausgangsmaterial herleitet. Beide Bedingungen wurden vom Probenmaterial nicht erfüllt. Die untersuchten Gesteine stammen aus verschiedenen Tiefbohrungen, wobei der Inkohlungsgrad benachbarter Kohlen zwischen 37 % und 29 % Flücht. Best. schwankt. Damit ist zu erwarten, daß der organische Inhalt der Gesteine ebenfalls einen unterschiedlichen Inkohlungszustand aufweist, da das organische Material in Sedimenten, ähnlich wie die Kohle, mit größerer Versenkungsteufe eine Inkohlungszunahme erfährt (Welte, 1967).

Der Kohlenstoffgehalt der Proben schwankt zwischen 0.1 % und 25 %, d.h. im ersten Fall liegt das organische Material in feiner Verteilung vor, im zweiten Fall durchsetzt es das Gestein in Form von Kohleflözchen. Daraus resultieren Unterschiede im Chemismus und damit im Gasabspaltevermögen der organischen Substanz.

Dieser Trend läßt sich aus Bild 1 ablesen. Der aufgezeigte Zusammenhang zwischen organischem Kohlenstoffgehalt und Gasmenge/kg Gestein ist nicht linear, sondern eine logarithmische Funktion. Sehr kohlenstoffreiche Proben (% organ. C > 2), im Extremfalle Kohlen, liefern weniger Gas pro Kohlenstoffeinheit als Gesteine mit % organ. C < 2. Diese Grenze von 2 % ist nur als grobe Richtzahl gedacht.

d) Beziehungen zwischen schwer- und leichtflüchtigen Kohlenwasserstoffen

Den Zusammenhang zwischen dem Gehalt der Proben an gesättigten Kohlenwasserstoffen, die durch Ätherextraktion gewonnen wurden (Leythaeuser, 1968) und den Gasmengen (ml/kg) der untersuchten Gesteine zeigt Bild 2. Im Gegensatz zu der in Bild 1 dargestellten Beziehung ergibt sich hier eine lineare Abhängigkeit, obwohl

Proben eingetragen sind, deren Inkohlungszustand vermutlich in größeren Grenzen schwankt als der der Gesteine in Bild 1. Begleitende Kohlen befinden sich im Gasflammkohlen- bis Metaanthrazitstadium.

Dies legt die Vermutung nahe, daß die leichtflüchtigen Paraffine mindestens z.T. aus dem löslichen Anteil der organischen Substanz stammen. Daneben werden aber auch, wie Abelson (1962/63) und Welte (1965) zeigten, durch eine Erhitzung des unlöslichen organischen Materials der Sedimente (Kerogen) schwerflüchtige und leichtflüchtige Paraffine neu gebildet. Zusammenfassend läßt sich sagen, daß eine mehr aliphatische Struktur des organischen Materials die erhöhte Produktion sowohl von leicht- und schwerflüchtigen Kohlenwasserstoffen begünstigt.

Das dafür besonders in Frage kommende Ausgangsmaterial nennt Kröger (1964) den „Wachs-Harz-Komplex", der in seinem Chemismus ungefähr den Exiniten entspricht.

In diesem Zusammenhang ist interessant, daß nach Pickhardt (1967) die figurierte organische Substanz der Nebengesteine stets ein höheres Exinit/Vitrinit-Verhältnis aufweist als benachbarte Kohlen. Die Mazeralzusammensetzung des organischen Materials der Nebengesteine begünstigt also, im Vergleich zur Kohle, die vermehrte Gaslieferung.

Neben der Gasmenge zeigt auch die Gaszusammensetzung eine Beziehung zu dem ätherlöslichen Anteil des organischen Materials, speziell zu den gesättigten Kohlenwasserstoffen. In Bild 7 sind die Quotienten Methan/Σ Butane und Methan/Äthan aufgetragen.

In Zusammenhang mit Bild 2, die die Beziehung zwischen Gasmenge und extrahierbaren gesättigten Kohlenwasserstoffen zeigt, läßt sich der Schluß ziehen, daß vor allem die höheren gasförmigen Paraffine, zusammen mit den schwerflüchtigen gesättigten Kohlenwasserstoffen aus dem bituminösen Anteil der organischen Substanz stammen. Methan und Äthan dagegen können auch als Seitengruppen von hochkondensierten Aromatkomplexen abgespalten werden. Denn sonst dürfte nur die Gasmenge, nicht aber die Gaszusammensetzung eine Beziehung zu den gesättigten, schwerflüchtigen Kohlenwasserstoffen zeigen.

Abschätzung der Gasmenge aus Kohle und Nebengestein

Wenn im Folgenden versucht werden soll, mit den Versuchsergebnissen eine Gasmengenberechnung durchzuführen, so können die angegebenen Zahlen nur einen groben Anhaltspunkt über die aus der Kohle und dem organischen Material der Gesteine entstandenen Gasmengen geben.

Wie das Auftreten von ungesättigten Kohlenwasserstoffen beweist, können die durchgeführten Inkohlungsversuche nicht für sich in Anspruch nehmen, die natürliche Inkohlung perfekt nachzuvollziehen. Unbekannte Einflüsse von seiten des Probenmaterials und experimentell bedingte Unterschiede zur natürlichen Inkohlung erschweren die Deutung der Ergebnisse.

Wie Bild 1 zeigt, hängt die beim Inkohlungsversuch gebildete Gasmenge vom organischen Inhalt der Proben ab. Es mußten also Mittelwerte für die grob- und feinklastischen Gesteine gebildet werden, die auf Grund der relativ wenigen Unterlagen einen Unsicherheitsfaktor darstellen. Ebenso bleibt der Kohlendioxid-Anteil unberücksichtigt. Er liegt jedoch auch in natürlichen Grubengasen im allgemeinen unter 10 Vol. %.

Die Kohle- und Nebengesteinsproben wurden alle den gleichen Bedingungen unterworfen, so daß eine Gegenüberstellung der Gasmengen, die aus der Kohle, bzw. aus dem organischen Material des Nebengesteins bei einem Inkohlungsschritt abgegeben werden, erlaubt ist.

In die Berechnung gehen folgende Werte ein:

Tabelle I

	organ. C (%)		Gasmenge (ml/kg)	
	Sandstein	Schieferton	Sandstein	Schieferton
Stefan	0.5	1.0	75	90
Westfal D	0.5	3.0	75	200
Westfal C	1.7	5.0	200	300

Wichte des Sandsteins (lufttrocken): 2.63 g/cm^3 Patteisky (1951)
Wichte des Schiefertons (lufttrocken): 2.71 g/cm^3 Patteisky (1951)
Wichte der Kohle (20 % Asche) 1.60 g/cm^3 v. Krevelen (1961)
Gasmenge aus der Kohle (Mittelwert)   4966 ml/kg

Eine Gesteinssäule mit 1 m^2 Querschnitt, 100 m Höhe und der in Bild 8 angegebenen lithologischen Zusammensetzung wird damit unter den beschriebenen Versuchsbedingungen folgende Gasmengen (Nm^3 Gas) liefern:

Tabelle II

	Kohle	Sandstein	Schieferton	Gasmenge aus Nebengestein	Gesamtgasmenge	Anteil d. Nebengesteins
Stefan	6.0	3.1	19.5	22.6	28.6	79 %
Westfal D	63.6	4.3	35.0	39.3	102.9	38 %
Westfal C	73.1	9.7	51.2	60.9	134.0	45 %

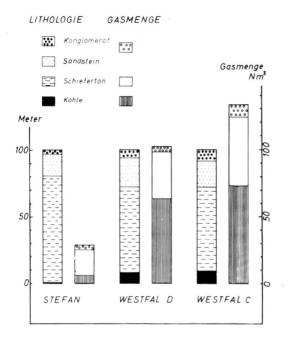

Bild 8
Gasmengen aus Kohle und
Nebengestein des Saar-
karbons

Der Inkohlungsfortschritt, den das organische Material bei der Bombenbehandlung erfährt, ist nicht bekannt. Er wurde daher mit Hilfe der gemessenen Gasausbeute abgeschätzt. Nach Patijn (1964) geben 0.03 km^3 einer Gasflamm- oder Gaskohle beim Verlust von 1 % Flücht Best. bei fortschreitender Inkohlung 156 x 10^6 Nm^3 Gas ab. Mit der in Tabelle I angegebenen Gasausbeute der Kohle würden 0.03 km^3 dieser Kohle 238 x 10^6 Nm^3 Gas liefern, was einem Verlust von 1.5 % Flücht. Best. entspräche.

Damit wurde gezeigt, daß, je nach Flözreichtum eines Profils, ein wechselnder aber stets beträchtlicher Teil des Grubengases vom organischen Material des Nebenge-steins abgegeben wird.

Anmerkung: Diese Arbeit wurde durch die Saarbergwerke AG ermöglicht und gefördert. Dafür sei Herrn Priv. Doz. Dr. G. Kneuper herzlich gedankt.

Literatur

Abelson, P.H. und Hoering, T.C.: Hydrocarbons from kerogen. Ann. Rept. Carnegie Inst. Washington Yearbook 62, 229, (1962/63).

Bode, H.: Inkohlungsvorgang und Entstehung von Grubengas. Glückauf, 75, 401–409, (1939).

Forsman, J.P.: Geochemistry of kerogen. Organic Geochemistry (ed. by Breger), Pergamon Press (1963).

Gedenk, R.: Die Zusammensetzung des Restgases in Kohlen und Nebengestein der Bohrung Münsterland 1. Fortschr. Geol. Rheinl. Westf., 11, 205–238, (1963).

Gehman, H.H. jr.: Organic matter in limestones. Geochim. et Cosmochim. Acta, 26, 889–903, (1962).

Girling, G.W.: Entwicklung flüchtiger Kohlenwasserstoffe beim Erhitzen von Kohle. J. appl. Chem., 13/2., 77–91, (1963).

Huck, G. und Karweil, J.: Versuch einer Modellvorstellung vom Feinbau der Kohle. Brennstoff-Chemie, 34, (1953).

Hunt, J.M.: Distribution of hydrocarbons ind sedimentary rocks. Geochim. et Cosmochim. Acta, 22, 37–49, (1961).

Jüntgen, H. und Karweil, J.: Gasbildung und Gasspeicherung in Steinkohlenflözen. I und II. I. Erdöl und Kohle, 19/4, 251–258, (1966). II. Erdöl und Kohle, 19/5, 339–344, (1966).

Kröger, C: Zur Struktur und Konstitution der Steinkohlen. Erdöl und Kohle, 17/10, 802–811, (1964).

Kröger, C. und Hortig, H.P.: Zur Berechnung der Inkohlungsgasmengen. Brennstoff-Chemie, 47/7, 193–195, (1966).

Patijn, R.H.: Die Entstehung von Erdgas infolge der Nachinkohlung im Nordosten der Niederlande. Erdöl und Kohle, 17/1, 2–9, (1964).

Patteisky, K.: Die Art des Vorhandenseins des Grubengases im Gebirge und seines Austretens. Bergbau-Archiv, 12/2, (1951).

Patteisky, K.: Veränderungen des Inkohlungsgrades der Ruhrkohlen mit dem stratigraphischen Alter, der Teufe sowie der tektonischen Lage. Z. dtsch. geol. Ges., 107, 120–131, (1955).

Pickhardt, W.: Unveröffentl. Untersuchungsbericht, Essen (1967).

Rodionova, K.F. und Chetverikova, O.P.: On the composition of residual organic matter in the paleozoic rocks of the Middle Wolga Region. Geochemistry, 10, 1024–1029, (1962).

Uspenskij, V.A.: Erfahrungen bei der Aufstellung einer Stoffbilanz der Vorgänge, die bei der Metamorphose der Kohlenflöze erfolgen. Izvestija Akademii nauk SSSR, Serija geologiĉeskaja Nr. 6, 94–101, (1954).

Welte, D.H.: Kohlenwasserstoffgenese in Sedimentgesteinen: Untersuchungen über den thermischen Abbau von Kerogen unter besonderer Berücksichtigung der n-Paraffinbildung. Geol. Rdsch., 55/1, 131–144, (1965).

Welte, D.H.: Inkohlungsuntersuchungen am feinverteilten organischen Material in Gesteinsproben aus dem Saargebiet. Ausarb. Nr. 26 Gasforschungsprogr., Saarbrücken (1967).

Zur Übertragbarkeit von Laboratoriums-Untersuchungen auf geochemische Prozesse der Gasbildung aus Steinkohle und über den Einfluß von Sauerstoff auf die Gasbildung

Peter Hanbaba [1]) und Harald Jüntgen

Mitteilung aus der Bergbau-Forschung GmbH, Forschungsinstitut des Steinkohlenbergbauvereins Essen-Kray, Germany

The chemical reactions of the gas release from hard coal under geological conditions *(coalification)* on the one hand and in the laboratory *(pyrolysis)* on the other hand are differentiated by the time of reaction and the range of temperature. With a continuing rise of temperature the time and temperature are related through a new parameter, the rate of heating. In the range of heating rates between $5 \cdot 10^{-3}$ °C/min and 10^5 °C/min the measurement of the release of Ethane shows that the range of temperature of the reaction shifts towards lower temperatures with a falling heating rate in accordance with our theory. By extrapolating values for the rate of heating of sinking earth clods (10^{-11} °C/min) we can obtain temperatures for the release of gases between 100 and 200 degrees Centigrade. Taking into consideration the different gas releasing reactions, we arrived at a theory in which the release of gas during the coalification can be traced back to the gas release of gas during the pyrolysis. In this way the results obtained in the laboratory can be applied to geochemical processes.

The measurement of gas formation in the presence of oxygen is carried out in a differential reactor through which air flows. In comparison with experiments carried out in the absence of oxygen we observed a decrease in the volume of the hydrocarbons released. This effect increases as the grain size of the coal pyrolysed decreases. From this we concluded that oxygen does not react with the gaseous products, but penetrates into the interior of the grain and reacts there with the coal. Furthermore the release of unsaturated hydrocarbons is shifted into a lower temperature range by the oxydative reaction. We have discussed these observations in view of the occurence of unsaturated hydrocarbons in weathered lignite and bitumious coal seams under the condition of spontaneous ignition.

Die chemischen Reaktionen der Gasbildung aus Steinkohlen unter geologischen Bedingungen *(Inkohlung)* einerseits und im Laboratorium *(Pyrolyse)* andererseits unterscheiden sich durch ihren Zeitbedarf und den Temperaturbereich. Bei kontinuierlicher Temperatursteigerung sind Zeit und Temperatur durch eine neue Einflußgröße, die „Aufheizgeschwindigkeit", verknüpft. Die Messung der Abspaltung von Äthan bei Aufheizgeschwindigkeiten zwischen minimal $5 \cdot 10^{-3}$ grd/min und maximal 10^5 grd/min zeigt, daß sich der Temperaturbereich dieser Reaktion mit fallender Aufheizgeschwindigkeit im Einklang mit der Theorie zu niedrigeren Temperaturen verschiebt. Bei Extrapolation auf die Aufheizgeschwindigkeiten ab-

---

[1]) Neue Anschrift: Brown Boverie & Cie, Mannheim

sinkender Erdschollen (10^{-11} grd/min) erhält man Temperaturen für die Gasbildung zwischen 100 und 200 °C. Die Berücksichtigung der verschiedenen Abspaltreaktionen führt zu einer Theorie, nach der die Gasbildung während der Inkohlung auf die Gasbildung bei der Pyrolyse zurückgeführt werden kann. Damit lassen sich im Laboratorium erhaltene Meßergebnisse grundsätzlich auf geochemische Vorgänge anwenden.

Die im einzelnen beschriebene Messung der Gasentbindung in Anwesenheit von Sauerstoff wird in einem durchströmten Differentialreaktor ausgeführt. Man beobachtet gegenüber der Pyrolyse unter Luftabschluß eine Verminderung des Volumens der abgespaltenen Kohlenwasserstoffe. Dieser Effekt nimmt mit fallender Korngröße der eingesetzten Steinkohle zu. Daraus wird geschlossen, daß der Sauerstoff nicht mit den gasförmigen Reaktionsprodukten reagiert, sondern einen im Korninnern stattfindenden oxydativen Abbau der Steinkohle bewirkt. Außerdem verschiebt die oxydative Beeinflussung die Abspaltung von ungesättigten Kohlenwasserstoffen in einem tieferen Temperaturbereich. Diese Beobachtung wird im Hinblick auf das Auftreten von ungesättigten Kohlenwasserstoffen in verwitterten Braunkohlenflözen und in Steinkohlenflözen bei beginnender Selbstentzündung diskutiert.

1. Einführung

Die Zusammensetzung der während der geochemischen Phase der Steinkohlengenese entstandenen Flözgase entspricht ziemlich genau der Analyse von Gasen, die bei einer thermischen Behandlung von Steinkohle, der sog. Pyrolyse, entstehen, wenn man sich auf die niedrigen aliphatischen Kohlenwasserstoffe beschränkt. Diese Ähnlichkeit in der Zusammensetzung der Gase wirft die Frage auf, ob ein Zusammenhang zwischen Pyrolyse und Inkohlung besteht und ob es grundsätzlich möglich ist, durch gezielte Arbeiten im Laboratorium die Vorgänge aufzuklären, die für die Inkohlung maßgeblich sind. Im folgenden soll zunächst die aufgeworfene Frage beantwortet und anschließend der spezielle Einfluß des Sauerstoffs auf die Gasbildung aus Steinkohle behandelt werden.

2. Versuchsführung der Experimente

Zur Lösung der gestellten Aufgabe betrachten wir nicht nur die summarischen Befunde der Gesamtanalyse der Gase, sondern versuchen, aus reaktionskinetischen Befunden Aufschlüsse über den Zusammenhang von Pyrolyse und Inkohlung zu gewinnen. Unter chemischer Kinetik versteht man bekanntlich den zeitlichen Ablauf von chemischen Reaktionen in Abhängigkeit von verschiedenen Einflußgrößen, z.B. der Temperatur, dem Druck und der Konzentration der Reaktionspartner. Um Experimente zur Kinetik ausführen zu können, müssen ganz definierte Versuchsbedingungen gewählt werden. Diese stellen sich in der von uns verwendeten Apparatur ein, die in Bild 1 dargestellt ist. Die Kohleprobe befindet sich in einem Glasrohr, als Festbett angeordnet, und wird durch das Trägergas Helium durchströmt, dessen

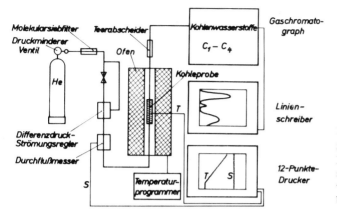

Bild 1

Schema der Apparatur zur
Messung der Entbindungsge-
schwindigkeit von Kohlen-
wasserstoffen aus Steinkohle
bei linearer Aufheizung

Geschwindigkeit gemessen wird. Während des Versuches wird die Kohleprobe nach
einem fest eingestellten und reproduzierbaren Temperatur-Zeit-Programm erhitzt.
Wir wählen für die Versuche, die von Zimmertemperatur bis zu einer Endtempera-
tur von etwa 800 °C ablaufen, verschiedene konstante Aufheizgeschwindigkeiten
zwischen 10^{-3} und 1 grd/min. Während dieser Erhitzung entstehen Gase aus der
Kohle, die mit Hilfe des Trägergases schnell herausgespült und einer Analysenanord-
nung zugeführt werden. Da wir uns auf die Messung der Kohlenwasserstoffe beschränken, benutzen wir dazu einen Gaschromatographen, mit dem sich Kohlenwasserstoffe mit 1 bis 4 Kohlenstoffatomen mit höchster Empfindlichkeit (0,1 ppm)
nachweisen lassen. Aus der Strömungsgeschwindigkeit des Trägergases sowie dem
gefundenen Anteil der Kohlenwasserstoffe kann man für jedes einzelne Gas die Ent-
bindungsgeschwindigkeit in cm^3 Gas/g Kohle und min in Abhängigkeit von Zeit
oder Temperatur berechnen. Auf Grund der zeitlinearen Temperatursteigerung
läßt sich daraus ferner eine auf die Temperatureinheit bezogene Gasbildungsge-
schwindigkeit in cm^3 Gas/g Kohle und °C bestimmen.

3. Meßergebnisse zum Entgasungsverlauf als Funktion der Temperatur

3.1. Gesamtzusammensetzung der Gase

Für vier untersuchte Steinkohlen mit unterschiedlichem Inkohlungsgrad sind die
bei einer Aufheizung mit einer Aufheizgeschwindigkeit von $2,5 \cdot 10^{-3}$ grd/min erhaltenen Gasmengen in cm^3/g Kohle in der Tabelle in Bild 2 zusammengefaßt. Man
sieht, daß, wie bei den Inkohlungsgasen, Methan in außerordentlich großem Über-
schuß vorhanden ist. Absolut- und Relativmenge der höheren Kohlenwasserstoffe
nehmen mit steigendem Inkohlungsgrad besonders im Bereich der Anthrazite stark
ab. Im Gegensatz zu den Inkohlungsgasen treten auch nennenswerte Mengen von
ungesättigten Kohlenwasserstoffen auf.

GAS	FÜRST LEOPOLD 39,5 % FL.BEST.	GUSTAV 29 % FL.BEST.	DICKEBANK 19 % FL.BEST.	HEINRICH 10 % FL.BEST.
CH_4	59,4	66,6	61,5	41,0
C_2H_4	1,39	1,29	1,05	0,27
C_2H_6	5,27	5,32	3,33	0,75
C_3H_6	1,41	1,16	0,61	0,11
C_3H_8	1,47	1,32	0,60	0,070
$n-C_4H_{10}$	0,48	0,36	0,12	0,010
$i-C_4H_{10}$	0,07	0,077	0,05	0,006
$i-C_4H_8$	0,57	0,44	0,17	0,020
$trans-2-C_4H_8$	0,16	0,13	0,077	0,016
$cis-2-C_4H_8$	0,11	0,081	0,046	0,009

Bild 2
Die aus Steinkohlen bei einer Aufheizgeschwindigkeit von $2,5 \cdot 10^{-3}$ grd/min im Temperaturbereich zwischen 20 und 800 °C gebildeten Gasvolumina pro Gramm Kohle (Ncm^3/g)

3.2. Aussagen der kinetischen Messungen über die Entbindung der Gase aus der Steinkohle

Die Gasentbindung läßt sich im allgemeinen als eine chemische Reaktion 1. Ordnung, bezogen auf die in der Kohle vorhandenen reaktionsfähigen Gruppen, darstellen, die zur Abspaltung des betrachteten Gases Anlaß geben. Als irreversible Reaktion ist sie in erster Näherung vom Partialdruck in der Gasphase unabhängig. Für die Entgasungsgeschwindigkeit pro Temperatureinheit läßt sich folgende Gleichung

$$\frac{dV}{dT} = \frac{k}{m} (V - V_0) \qquad (1)$$

ableiten.

V   abgespaltene Gasmenge [cm^3/g Kohle]
T   absolute Temperatur [°K]
k   Reaktionsgeschwindigkeitskonstante [1/min]
m   Aufheizgeschwindigkeit [°C/min]
V_0 Gesamtmenge des abgespaltenen Gases [cm^3/g Kohle]

Die für die Reaktionsgeschwindigkeit maßgebliche Konstante K hängt nach dem Arrhenius-Gesetz von der Temperatur ab:

$$k = k_0 \, e^{-\frac{E}{RT}} \qquad (2)$$

Darin bedeutet

E   Aktivierungsenergie
k_0 Frequenzfaktor

Die gefundenen Meßkurven sind am Beispiel der Entbindung von Äthylen und Äthan im Bild 3 dargestellt. Für Äthan (ausgezeichnete Kurve) erhält man zwei Temperaturbereiche, in denen eine Gasentbindung stattfindet, für Äthylen nur einen. Die gemessenen Entgasungskurven lassen sich, wie früher gezeigt worden ist, durch Gleichungen (1) und (2) mathematisch beschreiben [1]. Aus der Temperaturlage T_M des Maximums der Reaktionsgeschwindigkeit und der Form der gemessenen Kurve erhält man Werte für die Aktivierungsenergie und den Frequenzfaktor der abgelaufenen Reaktion [2]. Auf Grund der Größe der gefundenen Werte kann man darüber entscheiden, welcher physikalisch-chemische Mechanismus den beiden verschiedenen Entgasungsprozessen zugrunde liegt.

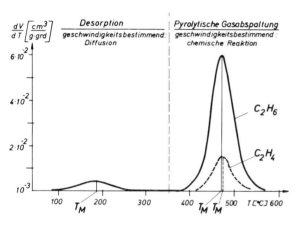

Bild 3
Entbindung von Äthan und Äthylen beim Aufheizen der Fettkohle Dickebank

Im einzelnen ergibt sich, daß der bei tieferen Temperaturen beobachtete kleinere Peak auf eine Desorption von Gas zurückzuführen ist, das sich in der geothermischen Phase der Inkohlung gebildet hat und das bei Gewinnung der Kohle adsorptiv in ihrem Hohlraumsystem gespeichert war [3]. Für die Geschwindigkeit der Entbindung dieses Gases ist die Diffusion der Gase in den Engstellen des Hohlraumsystems geschwindigkeitsbestimmend. Die hier gemessenen Gase lassen also unmittelbar Rückschlüsse auf die bei der Inkohlung entstehenden Produkte zu. Allerdings läßt sich über deren Menge aus diesen Messungen nichts aussagen, da sie nicht von der ursprünglich gebildeten, sondern nur von der durch Adsorption gespeicherten abhängt. Interessant ist, daß im Normalfall nur gesättigte, keine ungesättigten Kohlenwasserstoffe adsorptiv gespeichert sind. Sie sind also bei der Inkohlung nicht entstanden oder haben sich in den langen Zeiträumen zu gesättigten Kohlenwasserstoffen umgesetzt.

Der Peak im höheren Temperaturbereich ist einer chemischen Reaktion zuzuordnen, durch die das Gas unmittelbar unter Veränderung der Kohlestruktur entsteht. In diesem Prozeß bilden sich, wie man sieht, auch ungesättigte Gase. Bei der verwendeten Aufheizgeschwindigkeit liegt das Maximum der Entgasungsgeschwindigkeit etwa 250 °C oberhalb des Desorptionsbereiches.

4. Übertragung der gemessenen Pyrolysereaktionen auf die Reaktionen der geothermischen Steinkohlengenese

Zur Beantwortung der Frage, ob wir für die Gasbildung während der geothermischen Steinkohlenentstehung dieselben Reaktionen zugrunde legen können, die sich bei der pyrolytischen Gasbildung aus Steinkohle abspielen, muß zunächst der Temperaturbereich beider Vorgänge diskutiert werden. Bekanntlich spielt sich die geochemische Phase der Steinkohlengenese in Teufen zwischen 1000 und 4000 m und damit bei Temperaturen zwischen 60 und 200 °C ab. Eben war aber gezeigt worden, daß man für die Pyrolysereaktionen experimentell im Laboratorium einen Temperaturbereich zwischen 400 und 600 °C findet. Messungen und theoretische Betrachtungen haben jedoch ergeben, daß der Temperaturbereich der Gasabspaltungsreaktionen sehr stark von der Aufheizgeschwindigkeit der Steinkohle abhängt. Bild 4 zeigt die gewonnenen Ergebnisse im einzelnen [4]. Aufgetragen ist hier die Temperatur T_M in °C der maximalen Entgasungsgeschwindigkeit von Äthan aus einer Fettkohle gegen die Aufheizgeschwindigkeit, die im logarithmischen Maßstab dargestellt ist. Eingezeichnet sind Meßpunkte, die bei Aufheizgeschwindigkeiten zwischen 10^{-3} und 10^{+5} grd/min gewonnen worden sind. Sie liegen sehr gut auf der theoretisch berechneten Kurve, so daß die Berechtigung besteht, diese bis zu den Aufheizgeschwindigkeiten während der Inkohlung, die in Größenordnungen

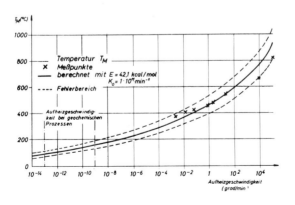

Bild 4
Temperatur T_M der maximalen Entgasungsgeschwindigkeit von Äthan aus einer Fettkohle als Funktion der Aufhiezgeschwindigkeit. Vergleich von gemessenen und theoretisch berechneten Werten. Extrapolation auf die bei geochemischen Vorgängen herrschenden Aufheizgeschwindigkeiten

von 10^{-11} grd/min liegen, zu extrapolieren. Es läßt sich nun überraschenderweise feststellen, daß bei dieser Aufheizgeschwindigkeit die im Laboratorium während der Pyrolyse vor sich gehenden Reaktionen genau in dem Temperaturbereich ablaufen, der während der Steinkohlengenese geherrscht hat.

Auf Grund dieses Ergebnisses sind quantitative Rechnungen ausgeführt worden, um aus den gemessenen Pyrolysereaktionen den zeitlichen Verlauf der geochemischen Gasbildung abzuleiten [5, 6]. Ohne auf Einzelheiten einzugehen, sei nur soviel erwähnt, daß man durch ein Zusammenspiel verschiedener Gasabspaltungsreaktionen mit unterschiedlicher Aktivierungsenergie und damit auch mit unterschiedlicher Temperaturlage des Maximums der Reaktionsgeschwindigkeit, die schon früher von Huck und Karweil [7, 8] auf anderem Wege gedeutete Veränderung der Flüchtigen Bestandteile in Abhängigkeit von der Teufe für die spezielle Situation des Ruhrgebiets befriedigend genau wiedergeben kann. Bild 5 zeigt das Ergebnis solcher Rechnungen. Man sieht, daß die mittlere ausgezogene Kurve, bei der wir verschiedene Reaktionen berücksichtigt haben, deren Aktivierungsenergie zwischen 50 und 65 kcal/mol schwankt, die gefundenen Flüchtigen Bestandteile als Funktion der Teufe genau so gut wiedergibt wie die von den genannten Autoren nach ihrer Theorie berechnete.

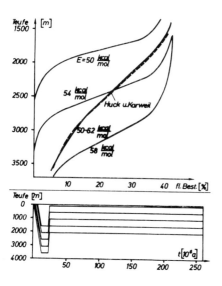

Bild 5. Berechnung des Fortschritts der geochemischen Phase der Inkohlung in Abhängigkeit von der Teufe unter den Versenkungsverhältnissen des Ruhrgebietes. Vergleich von theoretisch berechneten Kurven nach der hier mitgeteilten Theorie mit den von Huck und Karweil nach ihrer Theorie erhaltenen

5. Einfluß von anwesendem Sauerstoff auf die Zusammensetzung der Inkohlungsgase

Die eben nachgewiesene grundsätzliche Übertragbarkeit von laboratoriumsmäßigen Untersuchungen zur Steinkohlenpyrolyse auf Reaktionen unter geologischen Bedingungen haben uns ermutigt, auch spezielle Probleme, z.B. die Wirkung von Sauerstoff auf die Gasentbindung, zu untersuchen. Dazu wurden die Versuche in der beschriebenen Apparatur unter Verwendung von Luft als Spülgas mit verschiedenen Korngrößen der einzelnen Kohlen durchgeführt. Bilder 6, 7 und 8 zeigen den Unterschied zwischen den mit Helium und den mit Sauerstoff als Trägergas erhaltenen Entgasungskurven verschiedener Kohlenwasserstoffe in Abhängigkeit von der Korngröße der verwendeten Kohle. Aus Bild 6 geht hervor, daß bei Gegenwart von Sauerstoff die Methanbildung bereits früher einsetzt und bei tieferen Temperaturen ihren Abschluß erreicht. Außerdem ist das Gesamtvolumen des gebildeten Methans vermindert. Es fällt sehr stark mit abnehmender Korngröße der verwendeten Kohle ab.

Durch die Gegenwart von Sauerstoff wird allerdings nur der Peak, der der Pyrolyse zuzuordnen ist, beeinflußt, nicht dagegen der Desorptions-Peak. Die angegebenen Zahlen zeigen das Verhältnis zwischen dem in Gegenwart von Sauerstoff gefundenen und dem bei Abwesenheit von Sauerstoff gebildeten Gas an.

Bild 7 stellt ähnliche Befunde für die Äthan-Bildung dar. Die hier deutlich unterschiedlichen Desorptionskurven sind nicht auf den Einfluß des Sauerstoffs, sondern auf die unterschiedliche Korngröße der Kohle zurückzuführen. Der Desorptions-Peak ist nämlich zu umso höheren Temperaturen verschoben, je größer die Korngröße der untersuchten Steinkohle ist.

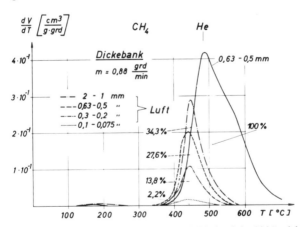

Bild 6. Methanbindung aus Flözkohle Dickebank in Abhängigkeit von der Temperatur bei Anwesenheit (gestrichelte Kurve) und Abwesenheit (durchgezogene Kurve) von Sauerstoff. Die Zahlen geben den in % ausgedrückten Anteil der Methanentbindung bezogen auf die Abwesenheit von Sauerstoff an.

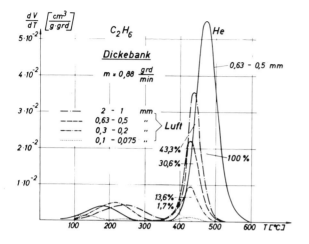

Bild 7
Äthanbindung aus Flözkohle Dickebank in Abhängigkeit von der Temperatur bei Anwesenheit (gestrichelte Kurve) und Abwesenheit (durchgezogene Kurve) von Sauerstoff. Die Zahlen geben den in % ausgedrückten Anteil der Äthanentbindung bezogen auf Abwesenheit von Sauerstoff an

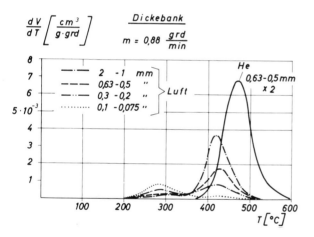

Bild 8
Äthylenentbindung aus Flözkohle Dickebank in Abhängigkeit von der Temperatur bei Anwesenheit (gestrichelte Kurve) und Abwesenheit (durchgezogene Kurve) von Sauerstoff

Besonders interessant erscheint der Einfluß des Sauerstoffs auf die Abspaltung von Äthylen. Wie im Bild 8 näher erläutert, wird auch in diesem Fall mit abfallender Korngröße zunehmend das pyrolytisch gebildete Äthylen verringert, zusätzlich tritt aber bei Temperaturen zwischen 200 und 350 °C eine neue Entgasungsreaktion auf. Die in diesem Temperaturbereich abgespaltene Gasmenge nimmt mit abnehmender Korngröße der Steinkohle deutlich zu. Bild 9 zeigt, daß dieser neuartige Mechanismus der Äthylen-Bildung bei allen untersuchten Steinkohlen erfolgt und sich besonders deutlich bei der Gasflammkohle Fürst Leopold abspielt.

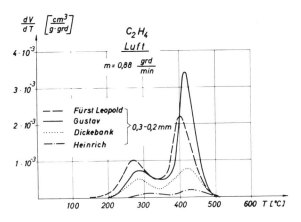

Bild 9. Äthylenentbindung aus vier Flözkohlen unterschiedlichen Inkohlungsgrades (Körnung 0,2 – 0,3 mm) in Abhängigkeit von der Temperatur

6. Diskussion der gewonnenen Ergebnisse zur Rolle des Sauerstoffs

Die Verminderung des abgespaltenen Volumens von Kohlenwasserstoffen in Gegenwart von Sauerstoff kommt sicher dadurch zustande, daß der Sauerstoff innerhalb des Korns mit der Kohlesubstanz unter oxidativem Abbau derjenigen reaktionsfähigen Gruppen reagiert, die bei der Pyrolyse zur Abspaltung von Kohlenwasserstoffen führen. Entsprechend muß sich der Anteil von CO_2 und CO im Gas erhöhen, der jedoch hier nicht gemessen worden ist. Daß sich die Abbaureaktionen zum großen Teil im Korninnern abspielen, geht aus der beobachteten Korngrößenabhängigkeit des Prozesses hervor: So bildet sich z.b. aus kleinen Körnern von 0,09 mm Durchmesser in Gegenwart von Luft nur noch 2,2 % des Methanvolumens, das bei Abwesenheit von Luft erhalten wird. Bei größeren Partikeln mit 1,5 mm Durchmesser findet man bei Einwirkung von Luft immerhin noch 34 % der bei Pyrolyse unter Helium-Atmosphäre gebildeten Methanmenge wieder. Dieses Ergebnis stimmt mit der bei anderen Oxidationsversuchen gemachten Erfahrung überein, daß Sauerstoff nur sehr langsam in die Kohlesubstanz eindringen kann [9, 10, 11]. Entsprechend wird man unter geologischen Bedingungen eine Beeinflussung der Zusammensetzung der Flözgase durch Sauerstoff nur in unmittelbarer Nähe der Erdoberfläche oder von Zonen tektonischer Beanspruchung finden.

Geologisch besonders interessant erscheint die Beobachtung, daß sich die Bildung ungesättigter Kohlenwasserstoffe bei Gegenwart von Sauerstoff zu niedrigeren Temperaturen hin verschiebt. Man kann annehmen, daß in diesem Temperaturbereich ein gewiß geringerer Teil der Kohlesubstanz partiell zu ungesättigten Verbindungen oxidiert wird. Diese sind auch spurenweise bereits in Verwitterungszonen von Braunkohlenflözen [12] gefunden worden und treten in Steinkohlenflözen auf, wenn Selbstentzündlichkeitsbrände vorliegen [13, 14]. Vielleicht ließe sich das Auftreten oder das Fehlen von ungesättigten Kohlenwasserstoffen auch als Kriterium dafür verwenden, ob in der Kohle befindlicher Stickstoff primär aus der Kohlesubstanz oder sekundär durch Sauerstoffeinwirkung entstanden ist. Eine Schwierigkeit des Nachweises der ungesättigten Kohlenwasserstoffe besteht allerdings in ihrer außerordentlich niedrigen Konzentration unterhalb eines ppm, die sich durch Anwendung hochempfindlicher Gaschromatographen meistern läßt.

Literatur

[1] Jüntgen, H.: Reaktionskinetische Überlegungen zur Deutung von Pyrolyse-Reaktionen. Erdöl und Kohle 17 (1964), 180/86.

[2] Van Heek, K. H., Jüntgen, H. und Peters, W.: Kinetik nicht-isotherm ablaufender Reaktionen am Beispiel thermischer Zersetzungsreaktionen. Ber. Bunsenges. f. phys. Chemie 71 (1967), 113/21.

[3] Hanbaba, P., Jüntgen, H. und Peters, W.: Nichtisotherme instationäre Messung der aktivierten Diffusion von Gasen in Festkörpern am Beispiel der Steinkohle. Ber. Bunsenges. f. phys. Chemie 72 (1968), 554/62.

[4] Jüntgen, H. und van Heek, K. H.: Gas Release from Coal as a Function of the Rate of Heating Fuel (London) XLVII (1968), 103/17.

[5] Hanbaba, P.: Reaktionskinetische Untersuchungen zur Kohlenwasserstoffentbindung aus Steinkohlen bei niedrigen Aufheizgeschwindigkeiten. Dissertation, Aachen 1967.

[6] Hanbaba, P. und Jüntgen, H.: Physikalische und chemische Vorgänge bei der Gasentbindung aus Steinkohle. Erdöl und Kohle 22 (1969) im Druck.

[7] Huck, G. und Karweil, J.: Physikalische Probleme der Inkohlung. Brennstoff-Chemie 36 (1955) 1/11.

[8] Karweil, J.: Die Metamorphose der Kohlen vom Standpunkt der physikalischen Chemie. Z. deutsche geol. Ges. 107 (1955), 132/39.

[9] Sommers, H. und Peters, W.: Die Kinetik der Kohleoxidation bei mäßigen Temperaturen. Chemie-Ingenieur-Technik 26 (1954), 441/53.

[10] George, D. und Karweil, J.: Das Verhalten von feinstem Kohlestaub in der Wirbelschicht. Freiberger Forschungshefte A 262 (1962), 21/26.

[11] Münzer, H. und Peters, W.: Zur Kinetik der Kohleoxidation im Temperaturbereich 30 °C bis 100 °C. Brennstoff-Chemie 46 (1965), 399/402.

[12] Včelàk, V.: Die Bestimmung der Oxidationsstufe von Braunkohle mittels Detektion freigesetzter gasförmiger Kohlenwasserstoffe. Vortrag Jahrestagung 1967 der DGMK Hamburg.

[13] Kitagawa, T.: 10. Int. Conf. of Directors of Safety in Mines Research. Pittsburgh, 28. Sept./2. Okt. 1959.

[14] Pursall, B. R. und Ghosh, S. K.: Mining M. I. 7th Jan., 1965 Meeting.

Discussion

W. Flaig: Sie erwähnten, daß die Oxydationsreaktion im Kohlekorn stattfindet. Die damit verbundene CO_2-Bildung könnte dann über eine Dekarboxylierung von Carbonsäuren erklärt werden. Haben Sie Zahlen dafür?

H. Jüntgen: Ja, die Luftoxydation von Steinkohle bei mäßigen Temperaturen ist in verschiedenen Arbeiten von Kröger et al. [1] sowie von Peters et al. [2, 3] eingehend studiert worden. Wir selbst haben 1964 [4] u.a. die Entgasung von oxydierten Steinkohlen untersucht. Danach verändert eine längere Luft-Oxydation (72 h bei 230 °C, Korngröße $<60\ \mu$) die Gasbildung bei Pyrolyse in folgender Weise:

	Gasabspaltung (g Gas/100 g Kohle)			
	CO	CO_2	CH_4	C_2H_6
unbehandelte Kohle	2,49	1,23	6,08	0,85
oxydierte Kohle	9,15	21,26	1,93	0,04

Die gleichzeitige Zunahme der CO- und CO_2-Abspaltung weist unseres Erachtens darauf hin, daß in der Steinkohle nach Oxydation Anhydride von Carbonsäuren vorliegen. So führt die von uns studierte thermische Zersetzung von Perylentetracarbonsäureanhydrid [5] zur gleichzeitigen Bildung von CO und CO_2 im Temperaturbereich zwischen 450 und 550 °C.

[1]   Kröger, C. und Bürger, H.: Brennstoff-Chemie **40** (1959) 76.

[2]   Sommers, H. und Peters, W.: Chemie-Ingenieur-Technik **54** (1954) 444/53.

[3]   Münzer, H. und Peters, W.: Erdöl und Kohle **19** (1966) 417/21.

[4]   Jüntgen, H. und Traenckner, K. Chr.: Brennstoff-Chemie **45** (1964) 105/14.

[5]   Van Heek, K. H., Jüntgen, H., Peters, W.: Brennstoff-Chemie **48** (1967) 163/70.

P. H. Given: In your argument you treat the so-called "frequency factor" as independent of temperature. In the time scale of a laboratory reaction this is usually valid. But the factor is in fact temperature-dependent, and I should have thought that this fact would be relevant in attempts to extrapolate laboratory kinetic data to much lower temperatures and long periods in geological time. It is clear that the pre-exponential term will become of relatively greater importance as we consider lower and lower temperatures.

H. Jüntgen: Die Reaktionsgeschwindigkeitskonstante ist nach Arrhenius gegeben durch

$$k = k_0\, e^{-E/RT} \tag{1}$$

mit

k   Reaktionsgeschwindigkeitskonstante

k_0 Frequenzfaktor

E   Aktivierungsenergie

T   abs. Temperatur

R   allgem. Gaskonstante

Für den Frequenzfaktor monomolekularer Reaktionen gilt nach M. Polanyi und E. Wigner (Z. Phys. Chem. A 139 (1928) 446)

$$k_0 = \frac{2\nu E}{RT} \tag{2}$$

ν = Schwingungsfrequenz der intramolecularen Schwingungen.

Er ist also in der Tat temperaturabhängig. Jedoch ist diese Temperaturabhängigkeit geringfügig und fällt gegenüber der Temperaturabhängigkeit des zweiten Faktors in Gleichung (1) kaum ins Gewicht. Das möge an folgendem Beispiel gezeigt werden:

Wir vergleichen die Größe von k_0 und $e^{-E/RT}$ bei 450 °C = 723 °K (Temperatur des Maximums der Entgasungsgeschwindigkeit T_M bei m = 1 °C/min) und bei 125 °C = 398 °K (T_M bei m = 10^{-11} °C/min) (s. dazu Bild 4). Es ergibt sich:

	723 °K	398 °K
k_0	1	1,81
$e^{-E/RT}$	1	$5 \cdot 10^{-9}$

k_0 ist bei Übergang von der höheren auf die niedrigere Temperatur um ca. 80 % angewachsen, dagegen ist der Faktor $e^{-E/RT}$ fast um 10 Zehnerpotenzen abgesunken.

Daher verschiebt die geringfügige Temperaturabhängigkeit des Frequenzfaktors das Extrapolationsergebnis nur wenig. Viel größeren Einfluß hat jedoch die Tatsache, daß die Gasbildung aus Steinkohlen kein einheitlicher chemischer Prozeß ist und aus zahlreichen Parallel-Reaktionen mit *unterschiedlichen* Werten für Frequenzfaktor und Aktivierungsenergie besteht. Diese Tatsache ist aber bei der entwickelten Theorie über den Zusammenhang von Pyrolyse und Inkohlung berücksichtigt worden.

The Origin of Gases of Mud Volcanoes and the Regularities of their powerful Eruptions

Vasily A. Sokolov, Ziya A. Buniat-Zade, Artem A. Goedekian, Farid G. Dadashev

IGIRGI, Scientific Council of Academy of Sciences USSR on the origin of petroleum
Moscow, USSR.

The mud volcanoes, from which methane mixed with other gases is erupted, are spread only on the area of basins with large thickness of sedimentary rocks. The formation of gases of mud volcanoes is caused by peculiarities of transformation of organic matter of sedimentary rocks at their submersion to $10-12$ km and deeper.

The greatest interest present the mud volcanoes of the South-Caspian basin in which thickness of sedimentary rocks, by seismic data, reaches $20-25$ km and where some hundreds of mud volcanoes on the land and on the bottom of the Caspian sea are known. In the composition of gases of mud volcanoes the main component is methane, the content of which is usually $90-95$ %.

At the quiet activity of mud volcanoes the quantity of gases thrown off is not large, although from several mud volcanoes this quantity reaches $1-3$ thousands m^3 and sometimes more during a day. Eruptions of mud volcanoes takes place from time to time. The quantity of gas thrown off during one eruption may be very large and may reach some hundred millions of m^3 in $1-2$ days. The gas erupted usually catches fire.

Summarising the data on the activity of mud volcanoes during the past 155 years, established the significant regularities in the eruptions, connected with tectonic movements of Main Caucasus. The large eruptions of any mud volcano are repeated in about $50-65$ years.

The paper contains the data on the composition of gases of mud volcanoes, their distribution on the area of basins, the peculiarities of their eruptions, the conditions and theory of formation and migration of gases at large depth in the sedimentary rocks.

The mud volcanoes and the gas eruptions that accompany them are a very interesting phenomenon, the study of which throws a light upon some features of hydrocarbon gas and petroleum formation and migration.

The peculiarity of mud volcanoes is the release of large quantities of hydrocarbon gas. Such mud volcanoes with powerful eruptions of gases are known only on the areas of basins with large thickness of sedimentary rocks.

A typical example is the South-Caspian basin, covering most of Azerbaijan, the southern part of the Caspain Sea and West Turkmenistan. In Azerbaijan more than 200 mud volcanoes are known. Several mud volcanoes occur in Turkmenistan. Some mud volcanoes are located on the bottom of the Caspian sea.

The intensity of gas seepages from the mud volcanoes varies. Some mud volcanoes in quiet state expel several m³ of gas, others sometimes 1–3 thousands m³ during 24 hours. Eruption of mud volcanoes take place from time to time. The volume of gases expelled can be very great.

We describe below some examples of such eruptions, accompanied by the expulsion of some millions or even hundred millions m³ of gas.

Fig. 1

Eruption of mud volcane on the bank of Makarow. Below, on the right Baku is seen (Photo made by V. I. Kousovenkov)

Eruption of mud volcano on the bank of Makarov, located in the sea at the distance of 20 km from the coast opposite Baku, took place on 15th November 1958 (Fig. 1). According to the observers' determinations, the height of the gas column originally thrown out and flaming was estimated as several km. Later the flame had the diameter of 120 m and height of 500 m. The volume of gas expelled by the eruption was estimated by G.P. Tamrazjan as 300 million m³. The volume of gas expelled by the eruption of Great Kjanizdag mud volcanoe was estimated by V.A. Gorin approximately as 100 million m³. At the eruption of Tauragay mud volcano the volume of gas was evaluated by F.G. Dadashev approximately as 500 million m³.

The eruption of Irantekjan mud volcano took place at night on 6th October 1965. The observers state that they first heard the underground rumbling and after that the explosion took place; the column of flame rose to a height of 100 to 150 m over the mountain. The vicinity of the volcano for 10–15 km around was brightly lightened. The temperature of the atmosphere rose so much, that it was hard to breath near the borehole, which was located within 1 km of the center of eruption. The height of the flame fell to 90–100 m in 20–30 min. after the beginning of the eruption and the high temperature decreased near the volcano. Mud breccia had been expelled from the volcano along with the burning gas. By 4–5 o'clock in the morning on the 7th October the intensity of mud volcano eruption had slightly decreased. The flame rose only to a height of 10–20 m. The mud volcano threw out vast volumes of mud breccia (about 1.5 million t) which filled the crater and moved along down the flank of the volcano. The extent of the largest flow of breccia is suggested to be 1600–1800 m.

The mud volcano Achzevir rises approximately 150 m above the surrounding flat land. An underground shock occurred on the 7th July 1964, after which within some minutes large fissures were formed with considerable (2–3 m) displacement of separate blocks. Subsequently abundant faults and fissures mottled all the surface. The fissures conspicuously continued to increase; separate blocks an plates continued to slide and break up. The gas did not ignite. These facts suggest that tectonic processes are mainly responsible for the origin and eruptive activity of mud volcanoes.

The eruption of mud volcano of cape Alijat took place on 20 March 1967. The observers relate that at first they felt an underground shock and heard rumbling. Apparently because of displacement of rock blocks and the high pressure of the gas, the "stopper" consisting of hardened breccia remaining in the vent of the volcano after the previous eruption, was instantaneously knocked out. From the top of the volcano a strong stream of immediately ignited gas was thrown out. The orange-red flame of burning gas rose to a height of 100–200 m. In addition to the large quantity of hydrocarbon gas about, two million ton of solid products was thrown out during the eruption.

The composition of the gases of mud volcanoes was studied by V.A. Sokolov in the years 1935–1938. Besides methane the heavy gaseous hydrocarbons and other components were determined. The content of heavy gaseous hydrocarbons in the gases of the mud volcanoes of the South-Caspian basin was very small. The composition of gases of mud volcanoes of Kerch-Taman basin (between the Black Sea and the Sea of Azov) was also studied. In this basin there are few mud volcanoes and their eruptions are less powerful than those in the South-Caspian basin. In the composition of the gases of Kerch-Taman mud volcanoes, methane was also the main component and the content of hydrocarbons $C_2 - C_4$ was very low. It is interesting that in the composition of gases of Tarchan mud volcano on Kerch peninsula the main component was carbon dioxide. An important content of carbon dioxide was observed in the gas of mud volcano Shugo on Taman peninsula. The composition of gases of several mud volcanoes is presented in Table I.

Table I.   Composition of gases of mud volcanoes.

The name of mud volcano	Composition of gas, %			
	CO_2	CH_4	$C_2 - C_4 +$	N_2 + rare gases
Azerbaijan				
Shichi-Kaja	0,7	97,4	0,002	1,9
Gulbacht	0,8	95,4	0,002	3,8
Ilanli	1,4	93,8	0,007	4,8
Dashgil	3,5	95,9	0,4	0,2
Koturdag	0,9	96,3	0,004	2,4
Bulla	0,5	98,9	0,18	0,4
Los	3,4	94,0	0,034	2,6
Kerch-Taman basin				
Tarchan group, far situated volcano	92,5	7,5	–	–
Karabetowka	31,5	65,6	0,002	–
Gnilaja	–	98,2	0,20	1,6

Table II.   Limits and content distribution of main components of mud volcanoes gases.

Component	Limits of content, %	Quantity of analysis
Methane	< 80	8
	80–90	27
	90–95	40
	> 95	65
Heavy gaseous hydrocarbons	$< 0,1$	83
	0,1–0,3	22
	0,3–1,0	19
	$> 1,0$	16
Carbon dioxide	$< 1,0$	30
	1,0–3,0	52
	3,0–5,0	29
	$> 5,0$	29

A study of the gases of the mud volcanoes of the South-Caspian basin has recently been carried out by F.G. Dadashev (1963, 1967). The results of these investigations, presented in Table II, also show that the main component of the gases of mud volcanoes is methane, the content of which is mostly higher than 90 %. The content of hydrocarbons $C_2 - C_4$ is mostly less than 0.1 %. The analogous data on the composition of gases from mud volcanoes in West Turkmenistan were obtained by I.S. Starobinetz.

It is evident that the hydrocarbon gases of mud volcanoes rise from very deep sedimentary rocks. It is proved by the eruptions of mud volcanoes. Only at the very high gas pressures such as those corresponding to a depth of 10–12 km or more, are such powerful expulsions of gas – up to a height of several kilometers – possible (Fig. 1). During eruptions of mud volcanoes very deepseated rocks are also thrown out.

The composition of the gases is also evidence that they are formed at great depth in accordance with the zonality of hydrocarbon formation through the section of sedimentary rocks (V.A. Sokolov, 1948, 1964, 1965). The section is subdivided into 4 zones (Fig. 2). The upper-biochemical-zone stretches from the earth surface to a depth of 0.2–0.5 km. In this zone methane and carbon dioxide are mainly formed by biochemical processes. However, the heavy gaseous and light liquid hydrocarbons typical of petroleum are practically not formed. The biochemical methane migrates into the atmosphere.

Chemical reactions leading to the formation of hydrocarbons resulted from rise of temperature and influence of catalysis (that is in the termocatalytic zone) began to play an important role at a depth of 1–1.5 km. For these reasons a part of section from the depth of 100–200 m down to the depth of 1–1.5 km is called an intermediate zone, where biochemical processes die out, but the rate of thermocatalytical processes is still slow.

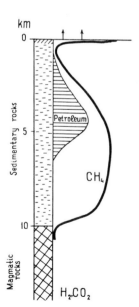

Fig. 2
Vertical zonality of hydrocarbon formation

The intensity of the conversion of organic matter into hydrocarbon compounds continuously increases with increasing depth and rising temperature. Although the chemical processes involved in the alteration of organic matter take place at a shallow depth – from the surfache – the rate of these reactions is very slow. At the geothermal gradient 33°/km and the depth of 1.5 km the temperature is considered to be 50 °C and during geological time the thermocatalytic processes, leading to the generation of hydrocarbons, began to play a certain role. At the depth of 6–7 km and at the same geothermal gradient temperature rises up to 200 °– 230 °C. Calculations based on the equation of Arrhenius show that only methane remains stable at such a temperature. The other light petroleum hydrocarbons occur only as admixture.

The thermocatalytic zone is characterized by the formation both of petroleum and hydrocarbon gas. The thermocatalytic zone is divided into an upper or petroleum-gaseous zone and a lower or methane zone (deeper than 6–7 km), due to a wide difference of temperature through the section of sedimentary rocks. The physical state of hydrocarbons changes with increasing depth, where solubility of liquid hydrocarbons is more complete in compressed gases, with the result that gas-condensate deposits have formed.

Specific conditions at a depth of 12–14 km favour the conversion of water into gas phase. The zone deeper than 12–14 km, where the temperature is higher than 374 °C, should be specified as a separate zone of "water gas". Specific feature of this zone is considered to be the high migration ability of such water gas together with other gaseous components.

The above-mentioned zonality (Fig. 2) represents only the generalized scheme, characterizing the process of hydrocarbon formation through the section of sedimentary rocks. The depth of each zone differs in the various regions (for instance, the depth of beginning of methane zone) depending on the value of the geothermal gradient, as well as on the catalytic influence of enclosing rocks. The boundary of each zone varies in accordance with geological and geochemical conditions; the transition from one zone into the next is gradual.

Zonality of hydrocarbons generation seems to be more obvious within the deepest depressions, where the thickness of sedimentary series varies up to 10–15 km and more. All types of above-mentioned zones are represented therein.

A typical example of such depressions is considered to be the South-Caspian basin, which is regarded as probably the deepest of all depressions known at present. In this basin the thickness of Meso–Cenozoic rocks reaches 20–25 km according to geophysical data. Fig. 3 represents a schematic geological profile through the South-Caspian basin compiled by A.A. Geodekjan, V.A. Nicolenko and K.V. Timarev from deep seismic sounding data, obtained from different institutions.

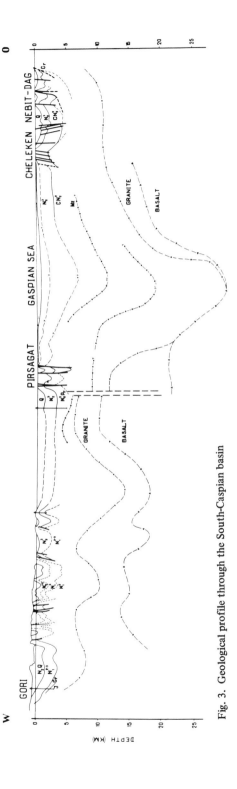

Fig. 3. Geological profile through the South-Caspian basin

It has been shown that granites in the basement are overlain by highly metamorphosed Paleozoc rocks which underlie the Mesozoic and Cenozoic rocks. Abundant rich oil deposits are confined to the productive series (Middle-Pliocene) in the South-Caspian basin. Productive strata occur at a depth of 4.5–5 km and more; their thickness reaches 4–5 km and more in several areas. Productive series are divided into the upper and lower groups separated by well-marked interruption.

Numerous tectonic deformations within the South-Caspian basin serve as paths favourable to vertical migration. For these reasons there are numerous oil and gas shows at the surface in the South-Caspian basin. Outcrops of oil- and gas-bearing rocks are observed in several areas. Sometimes oil and gas accumulations occur at shallow depth. These accumulations originate through migration from depth. The gas content suggests that the gas is of thermocatalytic, not biochemical origin. Gases contained in both the upper and the lower horizons are composed of heavy hydrocarbons in considerable quantities (3–7 %), which cannot be attributed to biochemical processes.

The thermocatalytic zone of the South-Caspian depression is characterized by the occurrence of numerous oil and gas deposits. The most investigated by drilling of deep wells are the series with thickness up to 5 km. For these series the ratio of gas content to petroleum rises with depth (F.G. Dadashev, 1965). The increase in the coefficient of gas content in petroleum in connection with the increase in depth on the Apsheron peninsula can be seen from the following data:

Upper group of productive series . . . . 43 m^3/t
Lower group of productive series . . . . . . 148 m^3/t
Gas-condensate deposit Zyrya . . . . . .
(the depth of 4.3–4.8 km) . . . . more than   10,000 m^3/t
Gases from mud volcanoes . . . . more than 100,000 m^3/t.

The increasing gas content of the petroleum with increase in depth has been reported for the petroleum deposits in the USA. For the Gulf coast the petroleum content at a depth of more than 6.1 km is unimportant (H.K. Hudson, 1963).

The deepest Cenozoic and Mesozoic rocks contain the hydrocarbon gas which is displayed by eruptions of mud volcanoes. Fragments of Mesozoic rocks are often thrown out during these eruptions.

In the zone of "water-gas", which occurs in the lower horizons of section of the South-Caspian basin, all sedimentary rocks serve as a single reservoir due to gaseous state of water. Tectonic movements have been considered to be the cause of "water-gas" breaking into the upper strate. Perhaps such breaking is the reason for the eruptive activity of mud volcanoes.

The composition of the gases from mud volcanoes suggested that their formation took place within the methane zone. The main component of these gases is methane.

The content of heavy gaseous hydrocarbons is small, nearly 10^{-1} %, thus approximately ten times less than in gases of petroleum deposits, confined to the thermocatalytic zone, located in the upper horizons of section. Petroleum has been observed only in rare cases and in small quantities during the eruption of mud volcanoes. Probably this petroleum is carried away by gas and mud breccia during their movement through oil-bearing rocks of upper zones. The high CO_2 content of the gases from the above-mentioned volcanoes is probably connected with the supply of underground water saturated in CO_2.

Some investigators have suggested that the mud volcanoes as well as the gases expelled from them, are caused by magmatic processes. But the comparison of composition of gases of mud volcanoes with the magmatic gases released from the lava lakes and fumarolic gases show their great difference. In Table III the available data have been summarized and the average composition of magmatic and fumarolic gases is indicated, based on numerous gas analyses from the Kamchatka, Japan and other active volcanic areas. The average composition of gases from petroleum deposits and mud volcanoes of the South-Caspian basin are given in this table for comparison. The main components of magmatic gases are CO_2, H_2, HCl and SO_2. The CO_2 content in fumarolic gases increases with decreasing temperature. During migration of magmatic gases in the rocks the chemically unstable components enter

Table III. The mean composition of magmatic and fumarolic gases in comparison with gases of petroleum pools and mud volcanoes of Azerbaijan.

Gases	Composition of gases, %							
	CO_2	CO	H_2	SO_2 + H_2S	HCl+ HF	CH_4	C_2–C_5	N_2
Gases from lava lakes of volcanoes	33.0	1.0	29.0	13.0	21.0[1])	traces	–	3.0
Fumarolic gases (more than 400 °C)	52,3	2.0	10.6	15.1	18.0	traces	–	2.0
Fumarolic gases (100–400 °C)	76.3	1.3	0.9	13.0	7.0	traces	–	1.5
Gases from thermal springs (100 °C and less)	93.3	1.1	0.1	3.0	0.3	traces	–	2.2
Gases from petroleum pools of Azerbaijan	2.5	–	–	–	–	92.5	4.0	1.0
Gases from mud volcanoes of Azerbaijan	3.0	–	–	–	–	93.7	0.3	3.0

[1]) The content of HCl and HF with some other components is only approximate.

into reactions and CO_2 becomes the dominant component. The carbon dioxide content in the thermal springs located within volcanic areas often reaches 95–98 % and more. Methane and other gaseous hydrocarbons are practically absent. Only occasionally does the methane content reach up to 1–2 % or a little more, but it is probably the result of synthesis from CO and H_2, which took place after the releasing of gases. In fumarolic gases the methane content is also unimportant. It is probable that availability of methane as an admixture is a result of the action of hot gases on the organic matter dispersed in the sedimentary rocks, where gases entered during migration.

At the same time gases of mud volcanoes are considered to be typical hydrocarbon gases similar in composition to the other gases from petroleum and gas deposits, confined to the sedimentary rocks. The high methane content as well as the low content of homologues of methane in the gases of mud volcanoes are the main specific features caused by thermodynamic conditions occurring in the methane zone in sedimentary rocks.

The arrangement of mud volcanoes suggests that they are formed mainly within the thick succession of sedimentary rocks. F.G. Dadashev (1967), who studied the distribution and arrangement of mud volcanoes within the South-Caspian depression, suggested that activity of mud volcanoes decrease as one approaches the axial zone of the Main Caucasus Ridge. The conspicuous majority of mud volcanoes, more than 95 % (with the exception of several small mud volcanoes, arranged on the Cretaceous rocks) are confined to the outcrops of Tertiary rocks. The intensity of gas ejection here is high, as well as the quantity of observed eruptions of volcanoes during the last 150 years. These are not specific features of Caucasus mud volcanoes only, but are characteristic of the mud volcano areas of Turkmenistan and Sakhalin. All these areas are characterized by regularly decreasing quantities of mud volconaoes up to their complete disappearance in connection with decreasing of depth of crystalline basement rocks and with appearance of igneous rocks. Particularly in the southwestern direction from Azerbaijan, the thickness of Tertiary rocks decreases and igneous facies appear in the lower horizons of section, which is the reason for the complete disappearance of mud volcanism. If the mud volcanism had been connected with magmatic centres – then it would be the reverse, i.e. mud volcanoes would be confined to the areas, where the thickness of sedimentary series was small and the crystalline basement rocks occurred near the surface.

It is obvious that the confinement of mud volcanoes to the deep depression is not accidental. Besides the South-Caspian depression, mud volcanoes occur only in depressions where the thickness of sedimentary series varies within 10–12 km and more (e.g. Kerch-Taman basin, Mexican bay, Irrawaddy/Andaman basin and some others). The South-Caspian depression is the most important as regards the quantity of mud volcanoes and the intensity of their eruptive activity. In this respect the South-Caspian depression is unique due to the fact that it has the greatest thickness of sedimentary rocks and vast volumes of gases, generated in the lower zones of section.

The mud volcanoes located in the South-Caspian basin have ejected great volumes of gases into the atmosphere during the period of geological time. The total quantity of gases ejected during the Quaternary period (1 million years), taking into account only the quiet state of mud volcanoes, is not less than 4.10^{10} t of gases. The total quantity of gases ejected during the Quaternary period from the volcanoes including powerful eruptions reach approximately 10^{11} t. It has been established that mud volcanoes occurred within the South-Caspian basin not only during the Quaternary period, but even earlier. Thus the total quantity of gases ejected from the mud volcanoes can be evaluated as $10^{11} - 10^{12}$ t (A. A. Geodekjan, 1967, 1968).

Investigations carried out by V.A. Gorin and Z.A. Buniat-Zade (1968), summarizing the data on the activity of mud volcanoes located in the Azerbaijan during the last 155 years (1810–1965), at the same time establish the significant regularities in the eruption activity of these volcanoes.

The powerful eruptions of mud volcanoes took place on Apsheron peninsula, on Kobistan territory situated on south and on neighbouring sea areas. The most active are the mud volcanoes situated on faults. So, for example, the mud volcanoe Lockbatan during the mentioned period (155 years) had erupted 16 times.

In general 137 powerful eruptions of 51 mud volcanoes took place in these territories during the 155 years. On powerful eruption of mud volcano takes place on the average once in 58 years.

The regularity of the activity of the whole system of mud volcanoes lies in the fact that the centre of activity moves consistently from the north edge of the basin to the south. The frequency of eruptions during this movement at first increases, reaches the maximum and afterwards decreases. After this the centre of activity moves abruptly northwards and the process begins again. These movements of gas-volcanic activity are apparently connected with definite tectonic impulses from the Main Caucasus.

References

Geodekjan, A.A. 1967: Investigations of balance and scales of petroleum and gas formation. Origin of petroleum and gas. Nedra, Moscow.

Geodekjan, A.A. 1968: The scales of formation petroleum and gas in South-Caspian basin. Origin of petroleum and gas. Nauka, Moscow.

Gorin, V.A., Buniat-Zake, Z.A. 1968: The regularities of gaspetroleum volcanism of west edge of South-Caspian basin. Origin of petroleum and gas. Nauka, Moscow.

Dadashev, F.G. 1963: Hydrocarbonic gases from mud volcanoes of Azerbaijan. Aserneshr, Bacu.

Dadashev, F.G. 1967: About the origin of gases of mud volcanoes. Origin of petroleum and gas. Nedra, Moscow.

Hudson, H.K. 1963: Is the song of plenty a siren song. Oil and gas Journal, N 24, 61.

Sokolov, V.A. 1948: Qutlines of the origin of petroleum. Gostoptechizdat, Moscow.

Sokolov, V.A. 1964: The modern ideas on the origin and migration of petroleum and gas. New investigations on the origin of petroleum and gas. Zniteneftegas, Moscow.

Sokolov, V.A. 1965: The processes of petroleum and gas formation. Nedra, Moscow.

Über den Ursprung des Stickstoffs in den Kohlen

Wolfgang Flaig

Institut für Biochemie des Bodens der Forschungsanstalt für Landwirtschaft
Braunschweig-Völkenrode
Braunschweig, Germany

After the explanation of the most important conditions for humification and for coalification some porperties of the proteins for these processes are mentioned, because amino acids can be isolated after hydrolysis of coal material.

Phenols derived from lignin or synthesized by micro-organisms fix nitrogenous compounds in the course of their transformation during humification. By means of experiments with ^{14}C-labelled compounds the transformation of the phenols is elucidated, because the extent of fixation of the nitrogenous degradation products of proteins depends upon the constitution of the phenols or quinones respectively.

Besides addition of amino acids by phenols also oxydative deamination of amino acid occurs during autoxidation. Details are reported on the basis of investigations with labelled compounds. Thereby the different reactions of 1,2-di- and 1,2,3-triphenols or 1,3-di- or 1,3,5-triphenols are described.

Furthermore the possibility that the formation of nitrogenous heterocyclics takes place during these reactions is mentioned.

Presumably carbohydrates or their degradation products participate in the fixation of nitrogen, especially when processes occur at temperatures of 200 °C, as it is the case in the course of coal formation.

Nach Erläuterung der wichtigsten Bedingungen für die Humifizierung und die Kohlebildung wird auf einige Eigenschaften der Proteine für den Verlauf dieser Prozesse eingegangen, da nach Hydrolyse von Kohlenmaterial Aminosäuren isoliert werden können.

Phenole, die aus dem Lignin der Pflanze kommen, sowie solche, die von Mikroorganismen synthetisiert werden, fixieren stickstoffhaltige Verbindungen im Verlauf ihrer Umwandlung während der Humifizierung.

Die Umwandlung dieser Phenole wird anhand von Versuchen mit ^{14}C-markierten Verbindungen näher beschrieben, da das Ausmaß der Fixierung von stickstoffhaltigen Abbauprodukten der Proteine von der Konstitution der Phenole bzw. Chinone abhängt.

Außer der Addition von Aminosäuren an Phenole findet während der Autoxydation auch deren oxydative Desaminierung statt. Hierüber werden Einzelheiten auf Grund von Untersuchungen mit markierten Verbindungen berichtet. Dabei wird auf die unterschiedliche Reaktionsweise von 1,2-Di- oder 1,2,3-Tri- bzw. 1,3-Di- oder 1,3,5-Triphenolen eingegangen.

Ferner wird auf die Möglichkeiten der Bildung von Stickstoffheterocyclen bei diesen Reaktionen hingewiesen.

Vermutlich beteiligen sich auch Kohlenhydrate oder deren Spaltstücke an der Fixierung von Stickstoff, insbesondere dann, wenn, wie bei der Kohlebildung, Prozesse bei Temperaturen bis zu 200 °C ablaufen.

Das Ausgangsmaterial für die Bildung der Kohlen war die pflanzliche Substanz. Die Veränderungen, die mit dieser vorgingen, hingen von den jeweils herrschenden Bedingungen ab. Das Verhältnis der ursprünglichen Zusammensetzung der Inhaltsstoffe der pflanzlichen Substanz läßt sich nicht mit großer Genauigkeit angeben; es wird jedoch auch damals die Cellulose den Hauptteil ausgemacht haben, während das Lignin zwischen 5–30 % und Proteine nur zu wenigen Prozenten vorhanden waren. Alle anderen organischen Pflanzeninhaltsstoffe treten in der Regel um 1 % oder weniger auf. Die einzigen pflanzlichen Inhaltsstoffe, die Stickstoff enthalten und mehr als ein Prozent ausmachen, sind die Proteine bzw. deren Bausteine wie Peptide und Aminosäuren.

Der ursprünglich verhältnismäßig hohe Gehalt an Cellulose oder anderen Kohlenhydraten in den Pflanzen ist in den Kohlen nicht mehr feststellbar. Es müßten daher im Verlauf der Umwandlung der pflanzlichen Substanz in Kohle chemische Veränderungen mit den Kohlenhydraten vor sich gegangen sein, die zu deren Abbau führten. Auch die anderen Pflanzeninhaltsstoffe, wie Lignin und Proteine haben Umwandlungen erfahren. Der Abbau des Lignins verläuft langsamer als der der Kohlenhydrate. Die pflanzlichen Proteine werden bei den Umwandlungsprozessen durch die Tätigkeit der Mikroorganismen weitgehend verändert; bei diesen

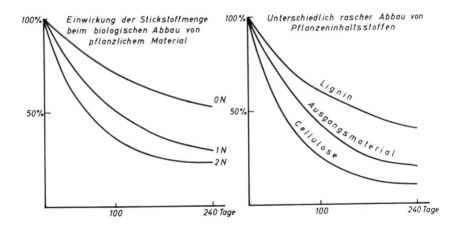

Fig. 1. Unterschiedlich rasche Abnahme der Gesamtpflanzensubstanz der Cellulose und des Lignins im Verlauf des mikrobiellen Abbaus. Erhöhung der Geschwindigkeit der Zersetzung von pflanzlichem Material durch Zugabe von Stickstoffsalzen in unterschiedlicher Höhe

Vorgängen werden durch die Mikroorganismen wieder neue Proteine gebildet. Da vor allem die Mikroorganismen bei den anfänglich noch vollkommen oder teilweise aeroben Bedingungen an den Umwandlungsvorgängen stark beteiligt sind, ist die verhältnismäßig starke Abnahme der Kohlenhydrate wie Cellulose sowohl damit erklärbar, daß diese als Kohlenstoffquelle zur Aufrechterhaltung des Energiestoffwechsels genutzt und zu Kohlendioxid veratmet wird, als auch, daß diese zum Aufbau der Körpersubstanz der Mikroorganismen dient.

Das Lignin wird langsam zersetzt und nimmt im Verlauf der Zeit auch ab.

Ein begrenzender Faktor für die Geschwindigkeit des mikrobiellen Abbaus der verschiedenen Pflanzeninhaltsstoffe ist der den Mikroorganismen zur Verfügung stehende Stickstoff. Dieser stammt weitgehend aus den pflanzlichen Proteinen. Nur ein geringer Anteil wird mikrobiell aus der Luft gebunden oder mit den Niederschlägen angeliefert.

Die Gegenwart von für die Mikroorganismen verwertbaren Stickstoffquellen beschleunigt nicht nur die Zersetzung des pflanzlichen Materials sondern auch die von Lignin merklich. Der prozentuale Anteil an Fraktionen, der mit den Methoden zur Isolierung von Lignin wie z.B. 72 % Schwefelsäure erhalten wird, nimmt in dem zersetzten Pflanzenmaterial laufend zu. Die auf diese Weise erhaltenen Fraktionen entsprechen in ihrer chemischen Zusammensetzung nicht mehr dem ursprünglichen Lignin und werden daher von uns als „Ligninfraktionen" bezeichnet. Der Gehalt dieser Fraktionen an Methoxylgruppen ist geringer, der an Sauerstoff und vor allem der an Stickstoff höher als im ursprünglichen Lignin der Pflanzen (Flaig, Schobinger und Deuel 1959).

Die größere Abbaugeschwindigkeit der Cellulose ist ein Beitrag zur Erklärung der beobachteten erhöhten aromatischen Struktur der Kohlen gegenüber dem pflanzlichen Ausgangsmaterial. Da jedoch auch Lignin einem Abbau unterliegt, haben wir diesen mit ^{14}C-markierten synthetischen Ligninen (Haider 1965) durch Weißfäulespilze untersucht. Die synthetischen Lignine wurden nach der Methode von Freudenberg (1956, 1962) durch Polymerisation von Coniferylalkohol einzeln oder im Gemisch mit weiteren Ligninbausteinen wie p-Cumaralkohol sowie Sinapinalkohol in Gegenwart von Phenoloxydasen dargestellt. Diese synthetischen Lignine besitzen weitgehend die Eigenschaften der aus verschiedenen Pflanzen isolierten (Kratzl, Billek, Klein und Buchtela 1957, Freudenberg 1964, Freudenberg und Harkin 1964).

Wie aus dieser Tabelle hervorgeht, findet zu Beginn des Abbaus der Polymerisate aus Coniferylalkohol eine stärkere Aufspaltung des Benzolringes als ein Abbau der Kohlenstoffatome der Seitenkette oder der Methoxylgruppe statt. Nach wenigen Wochen nehmen jedoch die Werte für die Ringkohlenstoffatome ab, während die für die Methoxyl- und Seitenkettenkohlenstoffatome zunehmen.

Die schon zu Anfang verhältnismäßig hohen Werte für die Verwertung der Kohlenstoffatome der Methoxylgruppe weisen darauf hin, daß die Spaltung der Methyläther eine wichtige Reaktion bei dem mikrobiellen Abbau der Lignine zu sein
scheint.

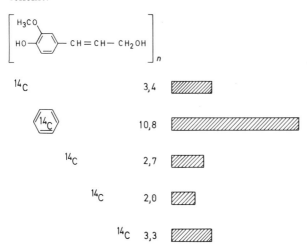

Fig. 2. Prozentuale Mengen an abgespaltenen Kohlenstoffatomen in Form von Kohlendioxid
aus Polymerisaten von verschieden markierten Coniferylalkohol durch Pleurotus ostreatus
nach 10 Tagen (nach Haider 1965)

Es sei nochmals darauf hingewiesen, daß der Methoxylgehalt der Ligninfraktionen
im Verlauf der Humifizierung stetig abnimmt.

Durch die Spaltung der Methyläther können o-Diphenole entstehen, die mit stickstoffhaltigen Verbindungen reagieren können.

Diese Versuche zeigen damit, daß der Abbau des Lignins nicht an den Seitenketten
seiner Bausteine beginnt, sondern daß durch die Ringspaltung die Struktur des
Ligninmoleküls zunächst gelockert wird. Dadurch werden größere oder kleinere
Bruchstücke des Lignins gebildet, die entweder einem weiteren mikrobiellen Abbau
unterliegen oder sich an anderen Reaktionen beteiligen, die noch zu besprechen
sind.

Lignin und dessen Spaltstücke sind jedoch nicht die einzigen Möglichkeiten, die zu
der aromatischen Struktur der Kohle beitragen. Durch milden, oxydativen (Farmer
und Morrison 1964, Morrison 1963) und durch reduktiven (Burges, Hurst and
Walkden 1964) Abbau von Huminsäuren werden phenolische Spaltstücke erhalten,
die Hydroxylgruppen auch in m-Stellung besitzen. Diese können sowohl als Fla-
vanoide oder ähnliche Verbindungen aus den Pflanzen stammen als auch durch
mikrobielle Synthese entstanden sein.

Haider und Martin (1967) und Martin, Richards und Haider (1967) haben die mikrobielle Synthese derartiger Phenole über den Stoffwechsel von Pilzen untersucht.

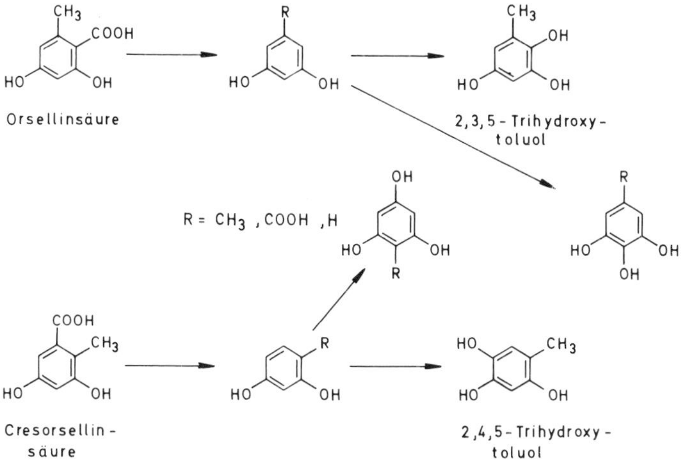

Fig. 3. Synthese von Phenolen durch Epicoccum nigrum und deren Umwandlung

An dem Beispiel von Epicoccum nigrum soll die Bildung von phenolischen Verbindungen durch Mikroorganismen näher erläutert werden. Die aus Glukose als Kohlenstoffquelle aus aliphatischen Vorstufen entstehenden Ausgangsverbindungen, Orsellinsäure und Cresorsellinsäure werden in den Kulturlösungen durch Oxydation der Methylgruppen zu Carboxylgruppen oder durch Decarboxylierung sowie durch Hydroxylierung in verschiedene Phenole umgewandelt, die zwei oder drei Hydroxylgruppen in m-Stellung besitzen. Im Verlaufe der Hydroxylierung entstehen auch Phenole mit Hydroxylgruppen in 1,2,3- oder 1,2,4-Stellung. Der letztere Befund war insofern von Bedeutung, als nur diese Phenole in der Lage sind, mit stickstoffhaltigen Verbindungen, die aus den Proteinen stammen, zu huminsäureähnlichen Substanzen zu reagieren.

Im folgenden sollen einige Reaktionen erwähnt werden, die gleichzeitig für die Ausbildung der aromatischen Struktur und für die Fixierung von Stickstoff in Kohlen herangezogen werden können.

Bei der Besprechung des Abbaus von Lignin wurde erwähnt, daß dabei niedermolekular Phenole entstehen. So sind bei der Humifizierung von Pflanzenmaterial (Maeder 1960, Flaig 1962), oder auch in Torf (Belau 1967) Ligninspaltstücke wie Ferulasäure, Vanillinsäure, p-Hydroxybenzoesäure, in Böden auch Protocatechusäure (Bruckert, Jacquin und Metche 1967) und einige andere Phenole nachgewiesen worden.

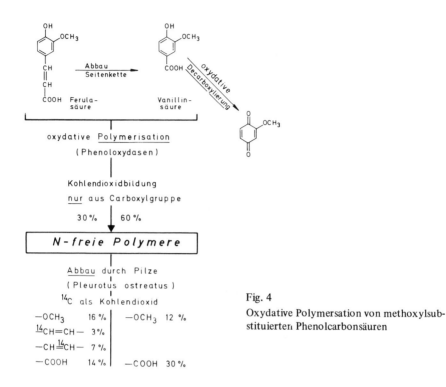

Fig. 4

Oxydative Polymersation von methoxylsubstituierten Phenolcarbonsäuren

Das unterschiedliche Verhalten der Ligninspaltstücke hängt davon ab, ob sich in o-Stellung zur phenolischen Hydroxylgruppe eine Methoxylgruppe oder eine zweite Hydroxylgruppe befindet.

Die methoxylsubstituierten Spaltstücke unterliegen einer oxydativen Polymerisation in Gegenwart von Phenoloxydasen aus Mikroorganismen. Hierfür sind die Beispiele Ferulasäure und Vanillinsäure aufgeführt. Während der Polymerisation wird Kohlendioxid abgespalten. Die entstehenden stickstofffreien Polymerisate werden in Kulturen von Weißfäulepilzen, wie Pleurotus ostreatus, abgebaut. Dabei werden die Kohlenstoffatome der Seitenkette und das der Methoxylgruppe unterschiedlich rasch verwertet, wie wir mit Hilfe von ^{14}C-markierten Verbindungen nachgewiesen haben (Haider, Lim und Flaig 1962, 1964). Durch oxydative, enzymatische Decarboxylierung entsteht aus Vanillinsäure Methoxy-benzochinon-1,4 oder dessen Dimeres wie auf verschiedenen Wegen von Sundman und Haro (1966) und Flaig und Haider (1961a) gezeigt werden konnte.

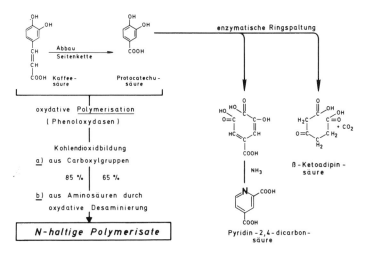

Fig. 5. Oxydative Polymerisation von o-Diphenolcarbonsäuren und deren Reaktion mit stickstoffhaltigen Verbindungen

Als Beispiel für die oxydative Polymerisation von o-Diphenolcarbonsäuren werden Protocatechusäure und Kaffeesäure erwähnt. In Gegenwart von Phenoloxydasen entstehen unter Abspaltung von Kohlendioxid aus der Carboxylgruppe Polymerisate (Fall a). In Gegenwart von Aminosäuren oder Peptiden (Fall b) findet eine zusätzliche Bildung von Kohlendioxid im Verlaufe von deren oxydativer Desaminierung statt. Die gebildeten Polymerisate sind in diesem Falle stickstoffhaltig, während sie bei den methoxylsubstituierten stickstofffrei waren.

Bei der enzymatischen Oxydation von Protocatechusäure wird β-Ketoadipinsäure gebildet (Stanier und Ingraham 1954, McDonald, Stanier und Ingraham 1954, Gross, Gafford un Tatum 1956, Ottey und Tatum 1956, Flaig und Haider 1961b), die von den Mikroorganismen als Kohlenstoffquelle gut verwertbar ist. Die Spaltung von Protocatechusäure scheint eine wichtige Reaktion bei der Umwandlung von aromatischen Verbindungen aus dem Lignin in aliphatische zu sein.

Trippett, Dagley und Stopher (1960) fanden eine andere enzymatische Aufspaltung von Protocatechusäure mit zellfreien Extrakten aus Pseudomonas sp., die zu einem Muconsäuresemialdehyd führt. In Gegenwart von Ammoniak bildet sich auf nicht enzymatischem Wege Pyridin-2,4-dicarbonsäure. Diese Reaktion kann als ein Weg zur Fixierung von Stickstoff in heterocyclischen Verbindungen angesehen werden.

Bevor auf die Reaktion eingegangen wird, die die Umsetzungen von Phenolen mit stickstoffhaltigen Verbindungen aus den Proteinen betreffen, sei noch erwähnt,

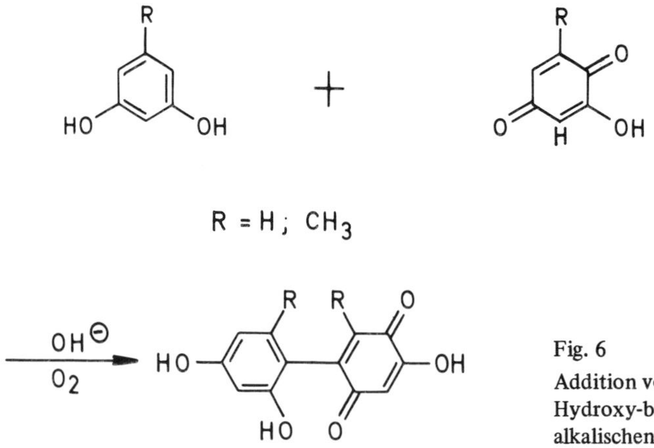

R = H ; CH₃

Fig. 6
Addition von Resorcinderivaten an
Hydroxy-benzochinon-1,4 bei der
alkalischen Autoxydation

daß auch solche Phenole, die in m-Stellung Hydroxylgruppen besitzen, wie sie beispielsweise in den Kulturen von Epicoccum nigrum gefunden werden, nicht polymerisieren, sich aber durch Addition an Chinone bei der Bildung von polycyclischen
Kondensationsprodukten beteiligen können. Hierzu sind von Musso et al. (1964)
Untersuchungen durchgeführt worden.

Da über die Fixierung von Stickstoff an Kohlenhydraten oder an deren Spaltstücken
während der biologischen Phase der Kohlebildung kaum etwas bekannt und diese
verhältnismäßig wenig wahrscheinlich ist, werden zunächst die möglichen Reaktionen der Phenole mit stickstoffhaltigen Verbindungen aus Proteinen näher erläutert.

Ausführliche Untersuchungen (Haider, Frederick und Flaig 1965) haben gezeigt,
daß bei pH-Werten zwischen 6,5 und 8 nur einige der Phenole, die zu Chinonen
oxydiert werden können, Aminosäuren, Peptide oder Proteine im Verlauf der
enzymatischen Oxydation addieren können.

Bei Substitution mit einer Methoxylgruppe in o-Stellung zur phenolischen OH-
Gruppe findet in oxydierendem Medium keine Addition von Aminosäuren statt,
obwohl bekannt ist, daß diese phenolischen Verbindungen über semichinoide
Radikale polymerisieren.

Die Ester von Aminosäuren, wie Glykokolläthylester, reagieren mit Benzochinon-
1,4 zu einer kristallinen Verbindung, dem entsprechenden 2,5-Diglycino-benzochi-
non-1,4, während die Aminosäuren selbst stark braun gefärbte, in ihren Eigenschaften den Huminsäuren vergleichbare Polymere ohne merkliche Bildung von
Kohlendioxid und Ammoniak ergeben.

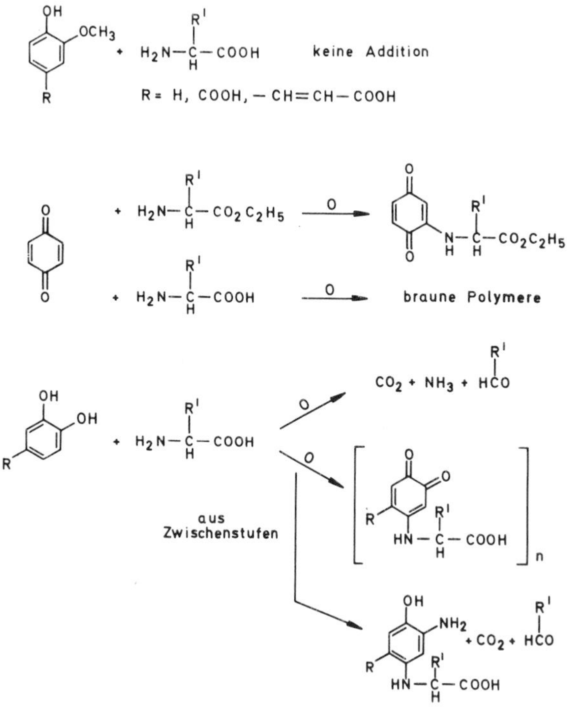

Fig. 7
Möglichkeiten der Addition von Aminosäuren an Phenole in oxydierendem Medium

Benzochinone-1,2 reagieren mit Aminosäuren ebenfalls zu dunkelbraun gefärbten Substanzen. Hierbei wird ein Teil der Aminosäuren gleichzeitig in Kohlendioxid, Ammoniak und in eine Carbonylverbindung aufgespalten.

Die Reaktion kann in zwei Teilreaktionen aufgeteilt werden, in

1) die oxydative Desaminierung der Aminosäuren zu Ammoniak, Kohlendioxid und einer Carbonylverbindung
2) eine nucleophile Addition der Aminosäure an das Chinon und anschließende Polymerisation.

Die Geschwindigkeit der Reaktionen zwischen den beiden Partnern hängt von der Substitution der 1,2-Diphenole sowie von der Konstitution der Aminosäuren ab.

Es wurde auch beobachtet, daß je nach Konstitution der Phenole entweder die Addition oder die oxydative Desaminierung bevorzugt abläuft.

Sehr ausführliche Untersuchungen (Haider, Frederick und Flaig 1965) mit Aminosäuren, die entweder an der Carboxylgruppe oder an einem der aliphatischen Kohlenstoffatome ^{14}C-markiert waren, haben ergeben, daß in den Reaktionsansätzen eine größere molare Menge an abgespaltenem Kohlendioxid als an Ammoniak gefunden wird.

Dieser Befund weist darauf hin, daß der aliphatische Carbonsäurerest der Aminosäure nach der nucleophilen Addition abgespalten wird, während die Aminogruppe
am Ring verbleibt und Aminophenole bzw. Aminochinone entstehen. Derartige
stickstoffhaltige Phenole können in oxydierendem Medium Kondensationsreaktionen eingehen, wobei nach Modelluntersuchungen Phenazine oder im Falle von
Hydroxy-chinonen Phenoxazone entstehen.

Die Bildung derartiger stickstoffhaltiger Heterocyclen könnte neben dem Stickstoff der nicht abhydrolysierbaren N-terminalen Aminosäuren, die an den Phenol-
bzw. Chinonring gebunden sind, zur Deutung des heterocyclischen Stickstoffs in
den Huminsäuren herangezogen werden.

Die Addition von Ammoniak an Benzochinone-1,4 oder -1,2 ist nur bei pH-Werten
über 8 in vitro festgestellt worden. Der höhere Druck und die höhere Temperatur
über die langen Zeiträume während der Kohlebildung schließen jedoch nicht aus,
daß die Umsetzungen mit Ammoniak auch bei niederen pH-Werten ablaufen.

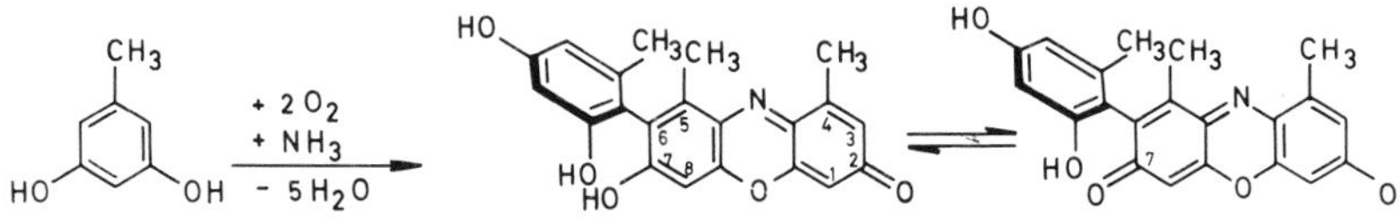

Orceinfarbstoffe ;   Phenoxazone

Fig. 8. Bildung von Stickstoffheterocyclen aus Resorcinderivaten und Ammoniak bei PH-
Werten über 8 in Gegenwart von Sauerstoff (Beecken et al. 1961)

Die Umsetzungen von m-Diphenolen mit Ammoniak laufen ebenfalls nur bei pH-
Werten über 8 ab. Die chemische Konstitution der dabei entstehenden Stickstoffheterocyclen sind aufgeklärt worden (Beecken et al. 1961).

**Verteilung der Funktionen des Stickstoffs in den Huminsäuren mit zunehmender
Inkohlung**

Huminsäuren aus:

Boden, Torf, Kohlen

Abnahme

a) Gesamtstickstoff
b) Prozentgehalt an α-NH_2-Stickstoff

Zunahme

a) Prozentgehalt heterocyclischen Stickstoffs

Wie das Schema zeigt, nimmt der prozentuale Gehalt an Stickstoff in den Huminsäuren mit zunehmender Inkohlung ab. Der Gehalt an α-Aminostickstoff am Gesamtstickstoff wird in der gleichen Richtung geringer, während der Gehalt an heterocyclischem Stickstoff zunimmt.

Die bisherigen Überlegungen treffen hauptsächlich für die biologische Phase der Kohlebildung unter aeroben Bedingungen zu. Über einen gewissen Zeitraum einer aeroben-anaeroben Phase werden vergleichbare Umsetzungen noch stattfinden können. In der anaeroben Phase müßten für die Addition der stickstoffhaltigen Verbindungen und die anschließende Bildung von Heterocyclen an Stelle des gasförmigen Sauerstoffs Verbindungen zugegen sein, die zur Abgabe von Oxydationsäquivalenten geeignet sind. Hierüber liegen jedoch keine Untersuchungen vor.

In der anaeroben Phase, bei der ein Anstieg der Temperatur und des Druckes stattfindet, können weitere Kondensationsreaktionen unter Dehydration eintreten, die zur Bildung von Heterocyclen führen. Diesen Schluß kann man ziehen, da bei der trockenen Destillation von Steinkohle eine größere Anzahl von 5- und 6-gliedrigen Stickstoffheterocyclen erhalten werden.

Bei höheren Temperaturen besteht auch die Möglichkeit, daß Zuckerspaltstücke mit Ammoniak zu Heterocyclen reagieren.

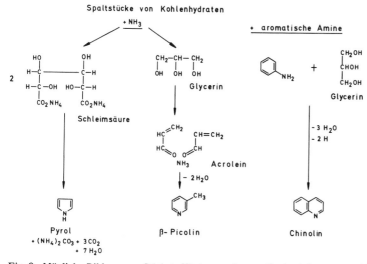

Fig. 9. Mögliche Bildung von Stickstoffheterocyclen aus Spaltstücken von Kohlenhydraten und Ammoniak im Verlauf der Kohlebildung

Einige Beispiele für die Bildung von Pyrrol-, Pyridin- und Chinolinderivaten sind in der Abbildung aufgeführt. Die Bildung weiterer polycyclischer Stickstoffheterocyclen könnte möglich sein, da Haworth mit Cheshire und anderen Mitarbeitern (1967) bei der Zinkstaubdestillation von Huminsäuren aus Böden neben polycyclischen Kohlenwasserstoffen auch geringe Mengen an Carbazol, Acridin und Benzacridinen festgestellt hat. Diese könnten jedoch auch erst im Verlauf der Zinkstaubdestillation bei der angewandten Temperatur von 500 °C entstanden sein.

Zusammenfassung

Faßt man die Ausführungen zusammen, so stammt letzten Endes der Stickstoff in den Kohlen aus den Proteinen der Pflanzen. Diese werden jedoch größtenteils über den Stoffwechsel der Mikroorganismen in arteigene Proteine oder andere Stickstoffverbindungen umgewandelt. Bei den Umsetzungen von Aminosäuren oder Peptiden mit Phenolen aus Fragmenten des Lignins, phenolischen Inhaltsstoffen oder solchen, die durch Mikroorganismen gebildet werden, entstehen bei 1,2-Diphenolen stickstoffhaltige Kondensationsprodukte sowie nachgewiesenermaßen auch Ammoniak.

Während der anaeroben Phase der Kohlebildung können mit der Zunahme von Temperatur und Druck die durch die Enzyme der Mikroorganismen gebildeten Kondensationsprodukte aus Aminosäuren und Phenolen weitere Reaktionen eingehen. Diese führen auf Grund von Modelluntersuchungen zu polycyclischen Stickstoffheterocyclen.

Bei höheren Temperaturen ist es zusätzlich noch wahrscheinlich, daß auch Spaltstücke der Zucker mit Ammoniak zu Stickstoffheterocyclen reagieren. Einige der Reaktionen werden in Analogie zu Untersuchungen in vitro angeführt, da wegen der langen Zeiträume im Verlauf der Kohlebildung keine andere Möglichkeit besteht. Es bleiben jedoch noch verschiedene Probleme zur Aufklärung der Vorgänge für die Bindung des Stickstoffs in den Kohlen ungelöst, die einer weiteren Bearbeitung wert sind.

Literatur

Beecken, H., Gottschalk, E. M., v. Gizycki, U., Krämer, H., Maassen, D., Matthies, H. G., Musso, H., Rathjen, C. und Zahorsky, U. I.: Orcein und Lackmus. Angew. Chem. 73, 665–673 (1961).

Belau, L.: Chemische Untersuchungen heimischer Torfbildner – ein Beitrag zur Kenntnis der Umwandlung von Pflanzenstoffen unter natürlichen und künstlichen Bedingungen. Dissertation Rostock (1967).

Bruckert, S., Jacquin, F. et Metche, M.: Contribution a l'étude des acides phénols présents dans les sols. Bulletin de l'Ecole Nationale Supérieure Agronomique de Nancy IX, 73–92 (1967).

Burges, N. A., Hurst, H. M. and Walkden, B.: The phenolic constituents of humic acid and their relation to the lignin of the plant cover. Geochimica et Cosmochimica Acta 28, 1547–1554 (1964).

Cheshire, M. V., Cranwell, P. A., Falshaw, C. P., Floyd, A. J. and Haworth, R. D.: Humic Acids-II. Structure of humic acids. Tetrahedron 23, 1669–1682 (1967).

Farmer, V. C. and Morrison, R. I.: Lignin in Sphagnum and phragmites and in peats derived from these plants. Geochimica et Cosmochimica Acta 28, 1537–1546 (1964).

Flaig, W.: Über den Einfluß von Verbindungen aus gerottetem Stroh auf den pflanzlichen Stoffwechsel. Symposio Humus and Plant Praha, Brno. 28. IX. – 6. X. 1961, 67–73 (1962).

Flaig, W. und Haider, K.: Reaktionen mit oxydierenden Enzymen aus Mikroorganismen. Planta Medica, Z. f. Arzneipflanzenforsch. 9, 123–139 (1961a).

Flaig, W. und Haider, K.: Die Verwertung phenolischer Verbindungen durch Weißfäulepilze. Arch. Mikrobiologie 40, 212–223 (1961b).

Flaig, W., Schobinger, U. und Deuel, H.: Umwandlung von Lignin in Huminsäuren bei der Verrottung von Weizenstroh. Chem. Ber. 92, 1973–1982 (1959).

Freudenberg, K.: Lignin im Rahmen der polymeren Naturstoffe. Angew. Chem. 68, 84–92 (1956).

Freudenberg, K.: Forschungen am Lignin. Fortschritte der Chemie organischer Naturstoffe 20, 41–72 (1962).

Freudenberg, K.: Entwurf eines Konstitutionsschemas für das Lignin der Fichte. Holzforschung 18, 3–9 (1964).

Freudenberg, K. und Harkin, J. M.: Ergänzung des Konstitutionsschemas für das Lignin der Fichte. Holzforschung 18, 166–168 (1964).

Gross, S. R., Gafford, R. D. and Tatum, E. L.: The metabolism of protocatechuic acid by Neurospora. J. Biol. Chem. 219, 781–796 (1956).

Haider, K.: Untersuchungen über den mikrobiellen Abbau von Lignin. Zbl. Bakteriol. Parasitenkunde, Infektionskrankh. und Hygiene 198, 308–316 (1965).

Haider, K. and Martin, J. P.: Synthesis and transformation of phenolic compounds by Epicoccum nigrum in relation to humic acid formation. Soil Sci. Soc. Amer. Proc. 31, 766–772 (1967).

Haider, K., Frederick, L. R. and Flaig, W.: Reactions between amino acid compounds and phenols during oxidation. Plant and Soil XXII, 49–64 (1965).

Haider, K., Lim, S. und Flaig, W.: Untersuchungen über die Einwirkung von Mikroorganismen auf ^{14}C-markierte phenolische Verbindungen. Landw. Forschung 15, 1–9 (1962).

Haider, K., Lim, S. und Flaig, W.: Experimente und Theorie über den Ligninabbau bei der Weißfäule des Holzes und bei der Verrottung pflanzlicher Substanz im Boden. Holzforschung **18**, 81–88 (1964).

Kratzl, K., Billek, G., Klein, E. und Buchtela, K.: Über das Verhalten von markiertem Coniferin in der verholzenden Pflanze. Mh. Chemie **88**, 721–734 (1957).

McDonald, D. L., Stanier, R. Y. and Ingraham, J. L.: The enzymic formation of β-carboxymuconic acid. J. Biol. Chem. **210**, 809–820 (1954).

Maeder, H.: Chemische und pflanzenphysiologische Untersuchungen mit Rottestroh. Dissertation Giessen (1960).

Martin, J. P., Richards, S. J. and Haider, K.: Properties and decomposition and binding action in soil of "humic acid" synthesized by Epicoccum nigrum. Soil Sci. Soc. Amer. Proc. **31**, 657–662 (1967).

Morrison, R. I.: Products of the alkaline nitrobenzene oxidation of soil organic matter. J. Soil Sci. **14**, 201–216 (1963).

Musso, H., Gizycki, Z. v. Zahorsky, U. I. und Bormann, D.: Die Bildung von Hydroxyl-Chinonen durch Addition von Phenolen an Chinone. Annalen der Chemie **676**, 10–20 (1964).

Ottey, L. and Tatum, E. L.: Protocatechuic acid oxidase of Neurospora. J. Biol. Chem. **223**, 307–311 (1956).

Stanier, R. Y. and Ingraham, J. L.: Protocatechuic acid oxidase. J. Biol. Chem. **210**, 799–808 (195

Sundmann, V. and Haro, K.: On the mechanism by which cyclolignanolytic argrobacteria might cause humification. Finska Kemists Medd. **75**, 111–118 (1966).

Trippett, S., Dagley, S. and Stopher, D. A.: Bacterial oxidation of protocatechuic acid. Biochem. J. **76**, 9 p (1960).

Discussion

M. Teichmüller: Wir haben heute von Dr. Karweil gehört, daß während der Inkohlung viel Stickstoff abgegeben wird. Man findet ja auch viel absorbierten N_2 in den Kohlen. Man kennt nach den Untersuchungen von Dr. Flaig jetzt recht gut die Bildung stickstoffhaltiger Substanzen in Torfen und Kohlen. Weiß man auch in welcher Form der Stickstoff aus den doch recht stabilen cyclischen Verbindungen der Kohle wieder abgegeben wird?

W. Flaig: Vermutlich wird der heterocyclisch gebundene Stickstoff nur durch Oxydationsvorgänge als molekularen Stickstoff abgespalten werden können. Die Oxydationsäquivalente könnten dabei auch aus sauerstoffhaltigen Verbindungen stammen. Versuche zu diesem Problem sind noch nicht gemacht worden.

P. H. Given: It has long been appreciated that coals contain an unexpectedly large amount of nitrogen, in view of the fact that relatively few cells in the higher plants are protoplasmic and therefore contain nitrogen. Dr. Flaig has suggested very plausible mechanisms by which nitrogen (presumably from bacterial and fungal sources) can become fixed in humic substances. But there is also more organic sulphur then one would expect in coals. I have wondered whether sulphur is fixed at the same time and by the same mechanism as nitrogen, perhaps in the form of cystine or cysteine. What does the author think?

W. Flaig: The sulfur-containing amino acids are also fixed by quinones formed by oxydation of the phenols. In some cases nitrogen and sulfur containing heterocycles are known.

J. Connan: Do you think that similar mechanism can occur in the incorporation of nitrogen in the insoluble organic matter of sedimentary rock (kerogen).

W. Flaig: The same mechanism is also possible for the formation of the substances which you mentioned.

Carbon Isotopic Study of Hydrocarbons in Italian Natural Gases

Umberto Colombo [1]), Franco Gazzarrini [1]), Roberto Gonfiantini [2]), Ezio Tongiorgi [2])
and Luigi Caflisch [3])

[1]) Montecatini Edison S. p. A., Istituto Ricerche "G. Donegani"
   Novara, Italy
[2]) Laboratorio di Geologia Nucleare Università di Pisa
   Pisa, Italy
[3]) Roma, Italy

About a hundred gas samples were collected and studied from different wells in a multilayer gas field of Southern Italy. The reservoir is constituted by alternating sand an clay layers of Pliocene age. The total volume of gas accumulated in the sand traps is on the order of several billions cubic meters.

Methane is associated with variable amounts of ethane and higher hydrocarbons. In some of the traps nitrogen and carbon dioxide are also present in the gas. The δC^{13} values of methane range from -70 to -50 per mil (PDB) in samples containing over 80 % CH_4, while δC^{13} as high as -40 per mil were found in samples containing carbon dioxide as the main component.

Considering the field as a whole, the carbon isotopic composition of CH_4 is closely related to the ethane/methane ratio. Both δC^{13} of methane and the ethane/methane ratio tend to decrease going from the water-saturated sediments towards the structurally highest parts of the traps.

The chemical and isotopic data obtained are discussed in terms of the processes of origin and migration of the hydrocarbons. Migrational factors and, in particular, aqueous phase diffusion, are believed to play a major role in determining the chemical and isotopic distributions found.

Introduction

At the Paris meeting of organic geochemistry (1964), the Authors, in collaboration with G. Sironi, reported the results of chemical and carbon isotopic analysis of some natural gases from fields of Southern Italy and Sicily. δC^{13} variations of methane as high as 30 per mil were observed among the gas samples analyzed. Such variations were found to be related to the content of ethane and higher hydrocarbons in the gases: the C^{13} content of methane increased regularly with decreasing $CH_4/C_2H_6^+$ ratio.

In the same paper, the Authors reported briefly the results of some simplified laboratory experiments, carried out with the gas chromatographic technique, which indicated clearly the possibility of obtaining significant isotopic fractionations in the flow of methane through columns filled with sand, limestone and various clays.

On the basis of all the data then available, the Authors concluded that the isotopic distributions found in the natural gases studied, could be explained by either of the following hypotheses:

1) the methane in any given natural gas has an isotopic composition which results from the admixture of an isotopically lighter bacterial methane, with a heavier methane, formed together with higher hydrocarbons in chemical processes;
2) the observed isotopic distribution is the result of fractionation processes occurring during the migration of the gases.

Isotopic variations in CH_4 due to differences in genetic conditions were already known from the work of Craig (1953), Silverman and Epstein (1958), Wasserburg et al. (1963), Nakai (1960), etc. The role of migrational processes in determining the isotopic fractionation of methane was pointed out for the first time by the Authors. Other investigators (Müller and Wienholz, 1967: May et al., 1967; Galimov, 1967) have thereafter brought further evidence in favour of an isotopic fractionation of methane during the migration of natural gas. In particular, Müller and his coworkers have stressed the importance of adsorption and desorption processes, while Galimov has suggested that solubilization and desolubilization of the methane isotopic species during their migration through wet rocks are primarily responsible for the fractionation observed.

Isotopic fractionation in methane from different occurrences has been explained by Sackett et al. (1966, 1968) in terms of genetic processes, assuming, in agreement with Silverman (1964), that methane is formed in the thermal cracking of petroleum ("maturation"). In such a process, the important factors are: the temperature at which methane is formed, and the strength of terminal carbon-carbon bonds in the parent organic material. Migration, according to Sackett, is not regarded as a mechanism for isotopic fractionation, but rather "as a mean of moving the isotopically light gases, initially formed in source rocks, out into potential reservoirs".

Working on methane occurrences associated with German coal seams, the Authors, in collaboration with G. Kneuper and M. and R. Teichmüller (1966), have concluded that the broad distribution of the isotopic composition of methane in the different horizons, is to be attributed mainly to postgenetic processes related to the migration of the gas, and in particular to adsorption by the coal.

Recently, Stahl (1968) has reported a geochemical and isotopic study of some natural gases from North West Germany, reaching some very interesting conclusions about the roles played by genetic and migrational processes in determining the present geochemical and isotopic distribution.

It thus appears that both genetic and migrational factors may give reason for the wide isotopic distribution of methane in natural gases.

It should, however, be recognized that nearly all published information refers to a very limited number of samples for each particular gas accumulation, and that isotopic data have been used mostly in connection with general geochemical problems.

The Authors feel that a better understanding of the significance of isotopic data can be achieved through detailed work, where the isotopic tool is used together with other geologic and geochemical data.

Therefore, they have undertaken the study of a relatively small, but geologically interesting methane field in Southern Italy. In this paper isotopic and other analytical data on the gas from different producing layers of the field are reported, and an interpretation is given, consistent with the known geologic situation.

Experimental

1. Geologic description of the gas field

A recently discovered gas field in Southern Italy was chosen for this investigation. Commercial production in the field has started only after the completion of the sampling program concerning this work.

The traps which constitute the field are of mixed type.

Stratigraphic, structural and hydrodynamic factors play important roles in the intrapment of the hydrocarbons.

The field is developed in a sequence of Pliocene sands and shales filling up a relatively large basin along the Apennines trend (Fig. 1). The substratum and the Eastern flank of the basin are represented by Miocene or Mesozoic limestones. The Western flank, on the contrary, is formed by the overthrusted shaly formations of the Apennines. Such overthrusts, in their movement towards North-East, cover partially the Pliocene sediments, truncating the deepest layers and defining the boundary of the sandy sedimentation of the highest layers: in fact, sandy sedimentation of the highest layers: in fact, sandy layers become thinner until they pinch out approaching the averthrust.

The average thickness of the Pliocene sequence is 2000–2500 meters, about one third of it being constituted by the sandy intercalations uniformly distributed. Three main sandy complexes have been identified on the basis of their mineralization: complex A, saturated with fresh water; complex B, mineralized with methane; and complex C, containing carbon dioxide with varying amounts of CH_4 and higher hydrocarbons. Such three complexes are subdivided in layers to which have been assigned numbers increasing from top to bottom. As it appears from Figure 1, the sandy layers pinch out also Eastwards without, however, coming in contact with the limestone formations uplifting in the same direction.

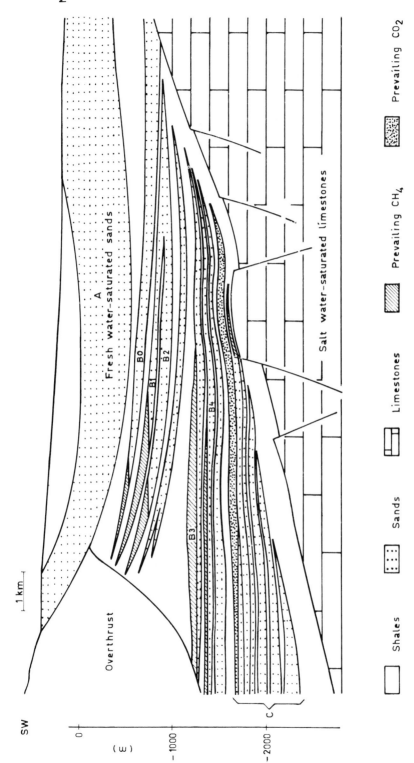

Fig. 1. Simplified stratigraphic profile of the gas field

Therefore, with the exception of a few small faults, the communication of fluids between the Pliocene sands and the underlying limestones may take place only through the shaly intercalations. The sands, still rather incoherent in the uppermost layers, are shaly and more and more cemented in the B layers, until they become true sandstones in the C layers. Their porosity ranges from 25 % in the B layers to about 15 % in the sands immediately overlying the limestones.

Permeability varies in the same general direction, ranging from 1000–3000 md to only 10–40 md. Each sandy layer corresponds, in a more or less complete degree, to a sedimentary cycle beginning with coarse, very permeable sands, and ending with silts and shaly sands characterized by a very low permeability.

The complexes B and C can be considered, as shown in Fig. 1, as being two big lenticular bodies plonging towards opposite directions and mineralized with gas in their structural highest positions.

From a hydrodynamic viewpoint, it should be pointed out that the sands of complex A, outcropping towards Southwest, are saturated with water down to a depth of about 700 meters. Below this depth the layers B, C and the underlying limestones are saturated with a water having a salinity averaging 26 000 ppm of sodium chloride.

The sketch of Figure 2 represents the static pressure-depth relationship in the field, with an indication of the pseudopotentiometric values of the different layers. It

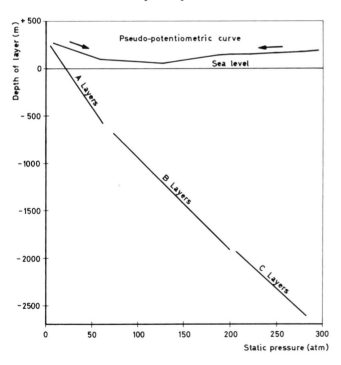

Fig. 2

Static pressure-depth relationship and scheme of hydro-dynamic potential in the A, B, C layers

appears that the methane-mineralized B layers are characterized by the lowest pseudopotentiometric values, a condition which may have favoured the accumulation
of hydrocarbons in these layers. The fresh water of the near-surface strata does, in
fact, consitute an efficient hydrodynamic seal.

The carbon dioxide mineralization in the underlying C layers is not rare in this
region, where the sandy reservoirs are in direct contact with a thick limestone sequence.

As far as naphthogenesis is concerned, it should be observed that the Pliocene shaly
sediments contain enough organic matter (about 1 % by weight of residual organic
carbon) to account for the generation of the hydrocarbons entrapped in the intercalated sandy layers.

2. Samples and analytical procedures

88 gas samples were collected from a total of 47 wells distributed throughout the
field. Gas samples from different layers and from different wells in the same layer
were obtained. All samples were collected during production tests, paying attention
that the actual sampling takes place only when the gas composition has attained the
equilibrium value.

The chemical analysis of the gas samples was performed by gas chromatography,
and the carbon isotopic composition of methane, after its separation from CO_2
and from higher hydrocarbons, was carried out with the methods described in detail
in a previous paper (Colombo et al., 1964). Isotopic data are expressed in δC^{13} %,
using, as reference, the PDB standard. The standard error of δC^{13} values, resulting
from the whole sequence of processing and analytical operations, was found to be
of ± 0.3 %.

Results

The data on chemical composition of the gas samples are reported in Table I, along
with the results of carbon isotopic analysis of the methane.

Most of the samples are from the layers B of the field, characterized by a high methane content (with only few exceptions, CH_4 is always higher than 85 %). In these
samples, CO_2 is generally lower than 1 %, while nitrogen varies from 0.2 % to about
18 %.

The isotopic composition of the methane in samples from the layers B ranges from
-46 to -70. The most negative values were found in the samples coming from rather
small, high pressured, lenticular sands intercalated within the B layers (samples 76
+ 83).

The most positive isotopic values vere found in samples taken in the immediate
proximity of an oil mineralization present locally in B4 layer.

Table I. Chemical and isotopic data of gas samples from a gas field in Southern Italy

| Sample No. | Well No. | Depth below sea level m | Chemical composition | | | | | C_2/C_1 x 10^4 | δC^{13} ‰ CH_4 |
			C_1	C_2	C_3^+	CO_2	N_2		
Layer B 0									
1	W 8	508	92.51	1.67	0.24	0.00	5.58	181	−58.0
2	W 10	259	90.19	1.81	0.00	0.00	8.00	201	−53.1
3	W 10	330	91.01	1.64	0.06	0.00	7.29	180	−57.1
4	W 12	406	93.52	1.28	0.20	0.00	5.01	137	−58.4
5	W 15	311	91.58	1.57	0.07	0.00	6.38	171	−57.4
6	W 15	372	92.16	1.44	0.06	0.00	6.34	156	−57.6
Layer B 1									
7	W 6	673	88.50	2.36	0.28	0.00	8.86	267	−55.5
8	W 8	602	92.48	1.38	0.18	0.02	5.58	149	−58.1
9	W 11	651	88.44	2.30	0.28	0.41	8.57	260	−55.6
10	W 13	678	89.23	2.27	0.22	0.00	8.28	254	−55.7
11	W 20	540	93.93	1.62	0.47	0.00	3.98	172	−60.0
12	W 26	599	93.70	1.57	0.59	0.00	4.14	168	−60.2
Layer B 2									
13	W 1	684	90.65	2.30	0.27	0.04	6.74	254	−57.6
14	W 2	614	92.45	1.56	0.21	0.05	5.71	169	−57.3
15	W 5	638	92.52	1.73	0.27	0.00	5.48	187	−56.2
16	W 7	629	91.03	1.54	0.21	0.00	7.22	169	−57.4
17	W 7	692	89.53	1.55	0.56	0.00	8.36	173	−57.4
18	W 11	720	88.59	2.26	0.26	0.00	8.89	255	−55.4
19	W 14	699	88.42	2.23	0.28	0.10	8.97	252	−56.2
20	W 19	708	88.30	2.10	0.00	0.07	9.28	238	−55.7
Layer B 1 − B 2									
21	W 4	675	92.58	1.86	0.25	0.02	5.29	201	−58.8
22	W 7	577	92.54	1.42	0.23	0.00	5.81	153	−57.4
23	W 10	669	90.00	1.78	0.55	0.38	7.28	198	−56.3
24	W 15	551	91.99	1.69	0.30	0.06	5.94	184	−58.8
25	W 16	661	91.07	1.94	0.38	0.17	6.42	213	−55.7
26	W 18	626	92.58	1.74	0.36	0.00	5.28	188	−56.9
Layer B 3									
27	W 7	1169	94.98	0.90	1.24	0.00	2.88	95	−61.7
28	W 7	1201	93.98	1.18	1.48	0.00	3.36	126	−59.7
29	W 9	1151	96.12	0.55	0.82	0.00	2.44	57	−61.8
30	W 9	1232	95.01	0.76	1.07	0.00	3.16	80	−60.4
31	W 10	1185	94.67	0.87	1.34	0.00	3.11	92	−58.6
32	W 14	1191	93.08	1.16	1.30	0.00	4.46	125	−59.8
33	W 15	1209	92.91	1.30	0.00	0.00	5.79	140	−55.2

Sample No.	Well No.	Depth below sea level m	Chemical composition					C_2/C_1 x 10^4	δC^{13} CH_4
			C_1	C_2	C_3^+	CO_2	N_2		
34	W 17	1234	88.29	1.85	2.10	0.00	7.66	210	-57.3
35	W 18	1191	92.38	1.07	1.97	0.23	4.34	116	-59.0
36	W 21	1224	92.05	1.18	1.58	0.00	5.19	128	-59.6
37	W 23	1216	91.22	1.23	1.65	0.00	5.90	135	-59.4
38	W 24	1229	92.25	1.01	1.30	0.07	5.37	109	-60.4
39	W 25	1188	93.74	1.20	1.35	0.05	3.66	128	-60.6
40	W 26	1125	89.97	1.60	1.87	0.03	5.53	178	-57.6
41	W 27	1206	94.32	1.16	2.28	0.00	2.24	123	-60.5
42	W 27	1227	91.31	1.36	1.78	0.00	5.55	149	-59.2
43	W 31	1209	98.34	0.18	0.26	0.29	0.92	18	-60.8
44	W 32	1231	91.94	1.36	2.32	0.02	4.36	148	-60.4
45	W 33	1230	81.98	2.34	3.04	0.03	12.61	285	-55.0
46	W 34	1200	98.61	0.17	0.26	0.00	0.96	17	-61.8
47	W 35	1193	90.02	1.12	1.45	0.24	7.17	124	-60.6
48	W 36	1229	82.48	2.85	3.67	0.00	11.00	346	-55.7
49	W 37	1220	86.46	2.07	2.56	0.07	8.84	239	-58.2
50	W 40	1226	95.77	0.58	0.73	0.08	2.85	61	-62.1
51	W 44	1228	94.98	0.70	1.97	0.00	2.35	74	-63.4
Layer B 4									
52	W 28	1297	93.71	1.77	1.54	0.03	2.94	189	-57.7
53	W 29	1204	89.83	1.91	2.34	0.08	5.84	213	-56.9
54	W 30	1294	87.59	1.72	2.30	0.00	8.39	196	-57.2
55	W 31	1262	93.26	0.99	1.94	0.00	3.81	106	-59.7
56	W 31	1282	89.95	1.47	2.07	0.60	6.51	163	-58.6
57	W 31	1288	88.33	1.77	2.42	0.07	7.41	200	-57.6
58	W 32	1286	83.00	2.32	2.36	0.98	11.34	280	-55.5
59	W 34	1260	89.10	1.34	2.14	0.14	7.28	150	-58.3
60	W 35	1270	82.16	1.91	1.96	10.09	3.78	232	-53.0
61	W 37	1307	63.51	2.77	4.12	12.78	16.82	436	-49.3
62	W 38	1240	90.52	1.04	1.25	0.00	7.19	115	-59.7
63	W 39	1245	83.34	2.52	2.83	0.10	11.21	302	-56.5
64	W 40	1248	83.35	2.35	3.78	0.10	10.42	282	-55.2
65	W 40	1260	76.70	3.04	3.16	0.18	16.92	396	-52.1
66	W 40	1288	77.91	3.22	3.27	0.13	15.47	413	-53.3
67	W 41	1265	81.80	2.10	2.48	0.24	13.38	257	-55.0
68	W 42	1245	93.05	0.83	0.80	0.05	5.27	89	-60.6
69	W 43	1308	73.62	3.71	4.59	0.57	17.51	504	-46.4
70	W 44	1282	51.97	2.28	2.95	28.08	14.72	439	-49.4

| Sample No. | Well No. | Depth below sea level m | Chemical composition | | | | | C_2/C_1 x 10^4 | δC^{13} ‰ CH_4 |
			C_1	C_2	C_3^+	CO_2	N_2		
Layer B 5									
71	W 22	1311	98.89	0.16	0.24	0.05	0.63	16	−61.2
72	W 23	1313	99.24	0.15	0.12	0.09	0.40	15	−60.3
73	W 24	1305	99.17	0.13	0.12	0.07	0.51	13	−61.1
74	W 25	1310	98.92	0.21	0.28	0.07	0.52	21	−61.4
75	W 26	1314	99.06	0.18	0.26	0.16	0.45	18	−59.3
Lenticular sands									
76	W 3	1217	99.15	0.13	0.02	0.05	0.62	13	−67.4
77	W 3	1242	99.44	0.10	0.04	0.06	0.36	10	−69.5
78	W 9	756	96.44	0.58	1.04	0.00	1.94	60	−63.8
79	W 9	764	96.64	0.05	0.08	0.00	0.23	5	−66.7
80	W 30	1181	94.57	0.80	0.74	0.03	3.86	85	−61.8
81	W 38	1315	99.37	0.10	0.15	0.12	0.26	10	−65.5
82	W 38	1325	99.50	0.11	0.22	0.15	0.02	11	−65.0
83	W 41	800	98.82	0.22	0.00	0.06	0.90	22	−67.5
Layer C									
84	W 40	1454	2.27	0.13	0.08	95.78	1.74	573	−42.9
85	W 40	1490	1.04	0.05	0.59	97.59	0.73	481	−42.2
86	W 45	1575	5.94	0.21	0.71	92.04	1.10	353	−52.4
87	W 46	1555	39.75	2.75	4.10	40.89	12.51	692	−41.1
88	W 47	1664	35.68	1.82	1.38	49.71	10.51	510	−46.4

The gas samples from the underlaying layers C contain large amounts of CO_2 plus N_2 and a relatively high ratio C_2H_6/CH_4. The methane associated with this gas has, in general, higher δC^{13} values with respect to the gas of the B layers. A few isotopic analyses of the CO_2 from layers C were performed and δC^{13} values from −5 to −9 were found.

An overall relationship was found to exist in the field between the isotopic composition of the methane, and the C_2H_6/CH_4 ratio. Such relationship, illustrated in the curve of Figure 3, covers all the samples analyzed, irrespectively of their stratigraphic position, and it confirms the trend previously observed by the Authors in other Italian gas fields. A considerable variation in both chemical and isotopic composition of the gas is observed even within each layer. This is shown in Figures 4 and 5, where the data from layers B3 and B4, are reported. The above mentioned relationship between the chemical and isotopic composition appears even more sharply than in Figure 3.

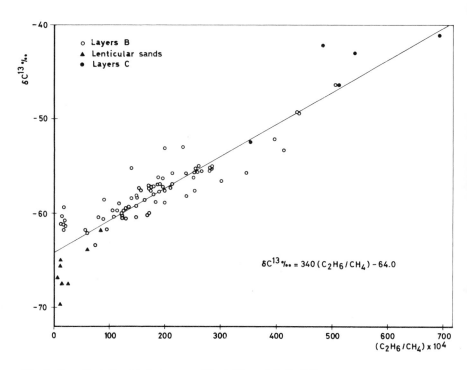

Fig. 3. Overall relationship between $\delta\,C^{13}$ of CH_4 and C_2H_6/CH_4

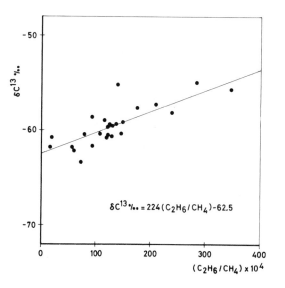

$$\delta C^{13}\,{}^o\!/_{oo} = 224\,(C_2H_6/CH_4) - 62.5$$

Fig. 4

Relationship between $\delta\,C^{13}$ of CH_4 and C_2H_6/CH_4 in the layer B 3

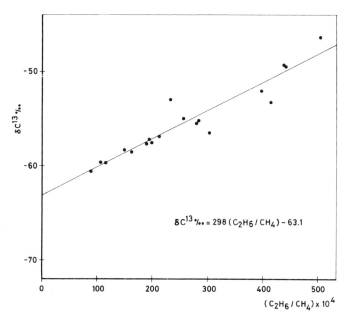

Fig. 5. Relationship between δC^{13} of CH_4 and C_2H_6/CH_4 in the layer B4

The data reported in Table I indicate clearly that there is no significant overall relationship between the chemical and isotopic composition of the gas and the depth from which samples were taken. However, a relationship was observed between depth and δC^{13} within each layer, where the isotopically lighter values are preferentially associated with the higher structural positions. The relationship is detectable also if one considers only the samples taken at different depths of one layer from a single well (see wells W7, W9, W27 and W31, W40 in the layers B3 and B4 respectively). Figure 6 is reported to illustrate, as an example, the above mentioned relationship. In the Figure the iso-δC^{13} curves in the layers B4 and B5 are presented, together with the isobates of the top of these layers. These data indicate that each permeable layer, isolated from the others by a shaly intercalation, behaves like an independent medium for the migration of hydrocarbons.

In the course of the present research, some attempts were made to correlate the isotopic data with the petrophysical properties of the reservoir. Unfortunately only a few permeability data (measured directly on cores) were available, therefore in most cases permeability was evaluated from either pressure buildup curves or electric logs. The data thus obtained suggest that the isotopic ranges are widest in the layers characterized by higher degrees of heterogeneity in the permeability. Also, it was found that the isotopically lighter methanes are associated with the lower permeability layers. Both trends, which could have a general significance, should be confirmed by further studies on different gas fields.

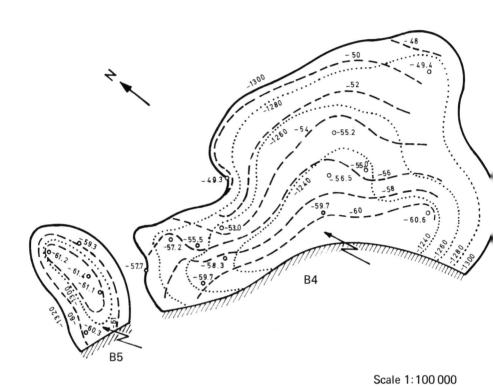

Scale 1:100 000

Isobates of the top of the layers

Iso δC^{13} of methane

Permeability barrier

Base of the gas-mineralized zone

Fig. 6. Structural map of the layers B4 and B5 and distribution of $\delta\ C^{13}$ in methane

Discussion

The results of this investigation, summarized in the preceding paragraph, could in principle be explained by either genetic or migrational factors.

The dual genesis hypothesis, already mentioned by the Authors (1964, 1965) in connection with a previous work, could still be invoked to explain the correlation found in the present study, between the chemical composition of gas and C^{13} content of methane. However, the fact that the whole sequence of sands in this basin is heavily mineralized with gas, and the consideration that most of the methane generated microbially in sediments is, as a rule, lost to the atmosphere during the initial stages of compaction, lead to consider as extremely unlikely that microbial processes are responsible for the genesis of a significant portion of the methane in this basin.

Furthermore, the following equation was derived with the method of least squares from the data reported in Figure 3:

$$\delta C^{13} \permil = (340 \pm 35) \frac{[C_2 H_6]}{[CH_4]} - (64.0 \pm 0.7)$$

Considering that the range of variation of the ethane to methane ratio in the field is practically from 0 to 0.05, the above equation would indicate that each methane sample results from the admixture of an isotopically light bacterial methane with a δC^{13} value of -64.0, with a heavier methane, associated with higher hydrocarbons, having a δC^{13} value of -47. Because the mean value of methane δC^{13} in the field is -58, the above relationship would suggest that about 2/3 of the gas volume in the field has a bacterial origin, which appears extremely unlikely.

Considering now the hypothesis advanced by Sackett et al. (1966, 1968), it should be observed that such hypothesis can give reason for the wide range of δC^{13} of methane, but in order to explain how the ethane/methane ratio could vary in the natural gases parallel with the isotopic composition of methane, one should admit that the rate of formation of ethane is much slower than that of methane. Kinetic data on the formation of methane and ethane in thermal cracking processes from natural organic material are missing in the literature. The above hypothesis, however, is in contrast with the fact that the bond dissociation energy for the group $-CH_3$ is slightly higher than that for the group $-C_2 H_5$ (Benson, 1965). In addition, the work of Jüntgen (1967) on the formation of methane and ethane during the cracking of low-rank coals indicates that the rates of formation of ethane and methane are quite comparable.

These considerations do not necessarily rule out the importance of genetic factors in determining the chemical and the isotopic composition of natural gases. It is known (see for example Erdman 1967) that methane can be produced by a variety of a biogenic reactions in the sediments, starting from such parent materials as carotenoids, steroids, aminoacids, carbohydrates, paraffins. Some of such reactions give rise also to ethane and higher hydrocarbons, some others generate only CH_4. These latter reactions are believed to proceed at a faster rate until completion after a few thousand years and probably most of the methane produced in these early diagenetic stages of the organic matter is lost to the atmosphere. Thus, on the basis of the available data, it appears that genetic processes are unable to explain in a simple way the regularities of chemical and isotopic distributions found in the present work.

Let us now discuss to possible role of migrational factors in determining the chemical and isotopic compositional trends found in the present study. It should be pointed out that the physical processes involved in migration of hydrocarbons are believed to be rather complex, and are still not well understood. A thorough discussion of migrational processes has been made by Sokolov at al. (1963) and more recently by Baker (1967). We shall consider only those processes which are likely to cause isotopic fractionation of the migrating species, particularly in the case of low molecular weight hydrocarbons, such as methane.

Adsorption and desorption of the gas molecules have been studied by May et al. (1967) in the laboratory: these Authors have found, in methane flow experiments through a column filled with the molecular sieves, that the mobility of $C^{13}H_4$ was higher than that of $C^{12}H_4$, because this latter component is adsorbed more readily at the solid's surface. These results seemed to find confirmation in the field data reported by Müller and Weinholz (1967), who studied the chemical and isotopic composition of the two-layer gas field of Langensalza in Thuringia. It is interesting to remark that the lower layer of the field, enriched in $C^{12}H_4$, is also characterized by an enrichment of higher hydrocarbons with respect to the upper layer. In other words, the relationship existing at the Langensalza field between chemical and isotopic composition seems to be opposite to that observed in the present study. Therefore, it is legitimate to assume that the migration mechanisms in the two fields are quite different, and therefore that adsorption processes play little if any role in our case.

Solubilization and desolubilization of methane in water saturated sand has been studied by Galimov (1967) who found that the $C^{13}H_4$ migrated through the water-wet medium at a greater velocity. This effect was attributed to the greater rate of solubilization of $C^{12}H_4$ with respect to $C^{13}H_4$, which resulted in an apparent increase of mobility of this latter compound. Galimov's data, however, appear to be largely due to kinetic factors, because of the relatively high flow velocity of the gas. In the present study, as discussed in the preceding paragraph, the lightest methanes were found to be associated preferentially with the highest structural positions in the traps, i.e. in the positions farthest from the water-surface. This seems to indicate that the process considered by Galimov has not played an important part in this case, otherwise the lighter methanes should have been found in the position nearer to the water saturated portions of the layer.

Among the physical processes that may cause isotopic fractionation during migration of natural gas, diffusion is certainly one of the most relevant. Diffusion phenomena are favoured by the existance, in many reservoirs, of permeability variations due to differences in the clay content or to differences in texture and microfractures of reservoir rocks. Such permeability variations, in effect, behave as more or less efficient barriers, which prevent the turbulent non-fractionating mixing of fluids, while favouring diffusive processes.

The rate of diffusion of a gaseous compound is inversely proportional to the square root of its mass. It follows, then, that the diffusion rate of $C^{12}H_4$ is greater than those of $C^{13}H_4$ and of C_2H_6. In the present case, the range of variation of the C_2H_6/CH_4 ratio is too wide compared to that of δC^{13} of methane in order to be explained by gaseous diffusion processes, taking into account the relative ratio of the diffusion coefficients of the migrating species $C^{12}H_4$, $C^{13}H_4$, C_2H_6.

Hydrocarbon diffusion in the aqueous medium has been widely investigated in the recent years (Antonov, 1954; Witherspoon and Saraf, 1965; Witherspoon et al., 1968; Bonoli and Witherspoon, 1968), in connection with the present trend of geochemical thought of the predominant role of water in the migration of hydrocarbons (Meinschein, 1959; Baker, 1967; Roberts, 1967; Colombo and Gazzarrini, 1968; Meinhold, 1968).

The experimental data available indicate that the diffusion coefficient of methane in aqueous solution is higher than that of ethane by a factor of 1.23 at temperatures up to 80 °C. Data on the diffusion coefficient of $C^{13}H_4$ in aqueous solution are still missing in the literature, however it is reasonable to assume that $C^{13}H_4$ diffuses at a slower rate than $C^{12}H_4$. In order to explain by this mechanism the differences in the observed ranges of C_2H_6/CH_4 ratio and of methane isotopic composition, the difference in the diffusion coefficient should be very small compared to the mass differences of the two isotopic species of methane. It should be kept in mind that diffusion coefficients are believed to be related mostly to molecular volumes; furthermore, their possible dependence on the mass is probably affected by the fact that hydrocarbons diffuse in water as solvated species. A major contribution for the solution of this problem could be given by direct experimental determinations of the diffusion coefficient of $C^{13}H_4$ in water.

From a qualitative point of view, diffusion in the aqueous medium seems to explain satisfactorily the relationships observed in this gas field. Diffusion explains also why the isolated lenses, separated from the other layers by more efficient barriers, contain the isotopically lightest methanes. An overall analysis of the chemical and isotopic compositions of the gas in this field, in terms of the diffusion mechanism, suggests that the accumulation process has not reached stationary state conditions, and that the layers B represent the frontal zone of the migrating current.

Conclusions

The data on the chemical and isotopic composition of the gas in a Southern Italian Pliocene field suggest that migrational factors are primarily responsible for the isotopic and chemical differentiation of the gas within the field. The isotopic distribution suggests, in particular, that the trap is immature and that the migrational process is still taking place. The detailed isotopic analysis of methane in gas fields could thus be an useful tool to establish the degree of maturity of any given trap, and could, under favourable conditions, supply valuable information on the direction of migration. The data analyzed in the present study support the idea that hydrocarbon migration takes place in the aqueous vehicle. To confirm this conclusion, is the agreement between chemical and isotopic data on one hand, and the distribution of hydrodynamic potential on the other, which both seem to indicate conditions favourable to the accumulation of hydrocarbons in the low potential B layers of the field.

Acknowledgements: The Authors are grateful to Mr. G. Ferrero for his valuable assistance in the laboratory work.

The work carried out in the Laboratorio di Geologia Nucleare dell'Università di Pisa was supported by the contract CNEN/CNR No. 115/1159/3033.

References

Antonov, P. L. (1954): On diffusion permeability of some argillaceous rocks. Geochemical Methods of Oil and Gas Detection, Gostoptekhisdat.

Baker, E. G. (1967): A geochemical evaluation of petroleum migration and accumulation. In Fundamental Aspects of Petroleum Geochemistry (edited by Nagy, B. and Colombo, U.), Elsevier Publishing Co., Amsterdam, pp. 299–329.

Benson, S. W. (1965): Bond Energies. J. Chem. Education, 42, 502–518.

Bonoli, L. and Witherspoon, P. A. (1968): Diffusion of paraffin, cycloparaffin and aromatic hydrocarbons in water and some effects of salt concentration. Forth International Meeting on Organic Geochemistry, September 16–18, 1968, Amsterdam (in press).

Colombo, U., Gazzarrini, F., Gonfiantini, R., Sironi, G., Tongiorgi, E. (1964): Measurements of C^{13}/C^{12}, isotope ratios on Italian natural gases and their geochemical interpretation. Advances in Organic Geochemistry, 1964, Pergamon Press, Oxford, pp. 279–292 (1966).

Colombo, U., Gazzarrini, F., Sironi, G., Gonfiantini, R., Tongiorgi, E. (1965): Carbon isotope composition of individual hydrocarbons from Italian natural gases. Nature, 205, No. 4978, pp. 1303–1304.

Colombo, U., Gazzarrini, F., Gonfiantini, R., Kneuper, G., Teichmüller, M. and Teichmüller, R. (1966): Carbon isotopic study on methane from German coal deposits. Advances in Organic Geochemistriy, 1966, Pergamon Press, Oxford, pp. 1–26 (1968).

Colombo, U., Gazzarrini, F. (1968): A contribution to the understanding of hydrocarbons migration and accumulation. Paper presented at "All-Union Conference on Origin of Oil and Gas", Moscow, January 1968 (to be translated into Russian and published with Proceedings).

Craig, H. (1953): The geochemistry of the stable carbon isotopes. Geoch. et Cosmoch. Acta, 3, 53–92.

Erdman, J. G. (1967): Geochemical origins of the low molecular weight hydrocarbon constituents of petroleum and natural gases. Proceedings of Seventh World Petroleum Congress, 2, 13–24, Elsevier Publishing Co. Ltd.

Galimov, E. M. (1967): Carbon isotopic variation in methane flowing through wet rocks (in Russian), Geokhimia 12, 1504–1505.

Jüntgen, H. (1967): Rate of heating as the dominating factor in coal pyrolysis. Paper presented at the Gordon Conference, New Hampton (USA).

May, F., Freund, W., Müller, E. P., Dostal, K. P. (1967): Modellversuche zur Deutung des Migrationsverhaltens von Erdgasen. 5. Arbeitstagung über stabile Isotope, Leipzig.

Meinhold, R. (1968): Über den Zusammenhang geothermischer, hydrodynamischer und geochemischer Anomalien und deren Bedeutung für die Klärung der Entstehung von Erdällagerstätten. Z. angew. Geol., 14, Heft 5, 233–240.

Meinschein, W. G. (1959): Origin of petroleum. Bull. A. A. P. G., 43, 925–943.

Müller, P., Wienholz, R. (1967): Bestimmung der natürlichen Variationen der Kohlenstoffisotope in Erdöl- und Erdgaskomponenten und ihre Beziehung zur Genese. Z. angew. Geol. 13, Heft 9, 456–461.

Nakai, N. (1960): Carbon isotope fractionation of natural gas in Japan. J. of Earth Sciences, Nagoya University, 8, 174–80.

Roberts, W. H., III (1967): Hydrodynamic analysis in petroleum exploration. In Enciclopedia del petrolio e del gas naturale: Ente Nazionale Idrocarburi, Rome, V, 617–636.

Sackett, W. M., Nakaparksin, S. G. and Dalrymple, D. (1966): Carbon isotope effects in methane production by thermal cracking. Advances in organic geochemistry, 3 (1968).

Sackett, W. M. (1968): Carbon isotope composition of natural methane occurrences. Bull. A. A. P. G., 52, 853–857.

Silverman, S. R. and Epstein, S. (1958): Carbon isotopic compositions of petroleums and other sedimentary organic materials. Bull. Am. Ass. Petr. Geol., 42, 998–1012.

Silverman, S. R. (1964): Investigations of petroleum origin and evolution mechanisms by carbon isotope studies. Isotopic and Cosmic Chemistry, edited by H. Craig, S. L. Miller and G. J. Wasserburg, North-Holland Publ. Co., Amsterdam, 92–102.

Sokolov, V. A., Zhuse, T. P., Vassojevich, N. B., Antonov, P. L., Grigoriyev, G. G. and Kozlov, V. P. (1963): Migration processes of gas and oil, their intensity and directionality. World Petrol. Congr., Proc., 6th, Frankfurt, 1963, 1:493–505.

Stahl, W. (1968): Kohlenstoff-Isotopenanalysen zur Klärung der Herkunft nordwestdeutscher Erdgase-Dissertation, Technischen Hochschule Clausthal.

Wasserburg, G. J., Mazor, E. and Zartman, R. E. (1963): Isotopic and chemical composition of some terrestrial natural gases. Earth Science and Meteoritics, North-Holland Publ. Co., Amsterdam, 219–240.

Witherspoon, P. A. and Saraf, D. N. (1965): Diffusion of methane, ethane, propane, and n-butane in water from 25 to 43°. J. Phys. Chem., **69**, 3752–3755.

Witherspoon, P. A., Bonoli, L. and Sahores, J. J. (1968): Results on the measurement of diffusion coefficients for paraffin, aromatic, and cycloparaffin hydrocarbons in water. Paper presented at All-Union Conference on Origin of Oil and Gas, Moscow, USSR, January 1968 (to be translated into Russian and published with Proceedings).

Discussion

W. G. Meinschein: I am surprised that the solution–desolution process would led to a preferential concentration of $C^{13}H_4$ in gases furtherest from the source. We have considered the migration of methane in ground waters for many years. We have always assumed that physical laws, namely Henry's law, would require that $C^{12}H_4$ would be more mobile than $C^{13}H_4$ in ground waters.

F. Gazzarrini: A thorough study of the solution-desolution process in terms that may be considered as relevant to the problem of hydrocarbon migration has not been made yet. The data reported in our paper were obtained by Galimov in underground storage experiments. We have performed, in our laboratory, some kinetic solutilization-desolubilization experiments with methane in water at low pressures, and obtained data in agreement with Galimov. The enrichment in $C^{13}H_4$ in the gas phase is attributed to a kinetic effect, due to the higher rate of solubilization of $C^{12}H_4$.

These experiments have, however, a rather limited significance, because data under equilibrium condition would appear to be more relevant to the geologic problem.

Our field data fully agree with the assumption of Dr. Meinschein that $C^{12}H_4$ is, in nature, more mobile than $C^{13}H_4$. Our interpretation, on the basis of the data now available, is in favour of a diffusion mechanism, but we cannot exclude that future work on equilibrium solubilization of isotopic species of methane may indicate a contribution of this mechanism to the complex process by which hydrocarbons migrate.

Stable Carbon Isotope Compositions of Graphite and Marble in the Deposit of Kropfmühl/NE Bavaria

Contribution to the discussion of graphite genesis

Paula Hahn-Weinheimer, Gudrun Markl and Helmut Raschka

Forschungsstelle für Geochemie, Technische Hochschule
München, Germany

33 samples of graphite and marble were collected from catazonal metamorphic Precambrian rocks – gneisses, amphibolites and marbles – which had been subjected to repeated events of metamorphism and tectonism.

The δC^{13} ratios of graphite samples (corrected to the Chicago PDB standard) range between $-10\%o$ and $-26\%o$, those in carbonate samples between $-2\%o$ and $-22\%o$. The isotope ratios are compared with existing data on those of carbonaceous and carbonate carbon. Relations between the isotopic ratios of graphite, the compositions of country rock and tectonic movements were found. Several theories to the genesis of graphite are discussed with regard to the formation from biological or nonbiological matter.

The variation of isotope compositions of elementary and carbonate carbon is studied by a model calculation of isotope fractionation reactions from which it is inferred that graphite may possibly be formed by the Boudouard reaction $2CO \rightleftharpoons CO_2 + C$.

Introduction

It has been shown (Hahn-Weinheimer, 1965) that the stable isotopic compositions of coexisting graphite- and carbonatebearing metamorphic rocks can be similar. The C^{13}-contents of carbonate amount to those of graphite of biogenic origin, whereas graphites in marbles show an enrichment of C^{13}. Therefore it seems probable that the C^{13}/C^{12} ratios are connected with the genesis of graphite and limestone. For this study samples of graphite, crystalline limestone and graphitic rocks were systematically collected in the graphite mine of Kropfmühl near Passau (Figure 1).

Stable Carbon Isotope Measurements

The graphite containing rock samples were prepared differently according to their graphite content. First, all samples were crushed to pieces of $1/2$ to $1\,cm\,\phi$ by a jaw breaker. Samples with a high percentage of graphite were pulverized manually, at first in a steel mortar and then in an agate mortar. Limestone and silica rock samples were ground in a disk mill with corundum disks and afterwards pulverized down to a grain size of $50-150\,\mu$ in a swinging mill with an agate insertion.

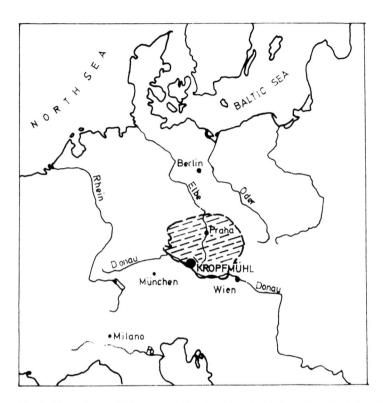

Fig. 1. Map of Central Europe with Kropfmühl in the Moldanubian Block (hatched area)

The carbonate was decomposed by conc. H_3PO_4 in an apparatus similar to that of J.M. McCrea (1950). CO_2 was used for the mass spectrometric measurement of the C^{13}/C^{12} ratio. As chemical reactions may cause an isotopic fractionation it is possible that the CO_2 produced by an incomplete decomposition of carbonate samples has a C^{13}/C^{12} ratio different from that of the original carbonate sample. With this method of CO_2-preparation no isotopic fractionation in connection with incomplete decomposition could be traced. Temperature dependence of the isotope ratio was not found in the range from $18°$ to $40°$. The H_2S of samples rich in sulphide was precipitated by 10% copper acetate in dil. HCl. The solubility product of CuS $(2 \cdot 10^{-47}$ at $16-18\,°C)$ is rather small; CuS already precipitates in acid solution. An acid solution was used to be sure that nothing of the CO_2 was lost by forming copper carbonate.

The rock powder was heated in HCl (3:1) for decarbonatisation and isolation of elementary carbon. After dismounting the solution was decanted and the precipitate sucked on an asbestos plate. The carbonate-free rock powder was dried in a porcelain vessel in CO_2-free atmosphere.

The graphite was combusted in a tubular furnace V at 1 000 °C in an oxygen stream (excess of oxygen) with an atmospheric superpressure of ca. 20 Torr. (first part of Figure 2). In the second part of Figure 2 a subpressure is produced by a membrane pump XV. Part 1 and part 2 are connected by a pressure adjusting valve. The CO_2-O_2 mixture coming from the tubular furnace is passing a trap VIII cooled by liquid nitrogen. The CO_2 is condensed whilst the oxygen is pumped off by the membrane pump. The CO_2 is transferred to tube X being evacuated to high vacuum and cooled by liquid nitrogen. Samples with sulphur content produce SO_2 (boiling point -10 °C). This gas is condensed in two cold traps VI at a temperature of ca. -20 to -30 °C. In tube VII which is filled with $Mg(ClO_4)_2$ water is absorbed. The blind can be neglected when using sample quantities with a graphite content > 4 mg.

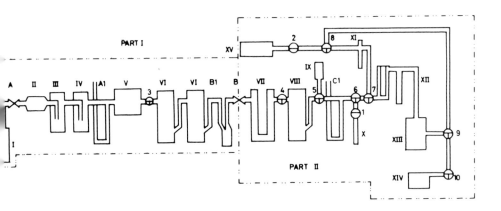

Fig. 2. Schematic diagram showing the graphite combustion arrangement

I	Oxygen Tank	A, B	Dosage Valves
II	Combustion Trap	A1, C1	Mercury Columns
III	Bottle with 30 % KoH	B1	Pressure Adjusting Valve
IV	Bottle with conc. H_2SO_4		
V	Furnace		
VI	Cold Traps (- 20 °C)		
VII	Tube with $Mg(ClO_4)_2$		
VIII	Cold Trap (Liquid N_2)		
IX	Pirani Gauge		
X	Sample Tube for CO_2		
XI, XII	Vapour traps		
XIII	Diffusion Pump		
XIV	Rotary Pump		

For the measurement of the C^{13}/C^{12} ratios of CO_2 a mass spectrometer of Varian Mat, M 86, with double inlet system (viscous gas inlet) and a double collector was used. By means of a special compensating connection for signals coming from both collectors the mass ratio 45/44 can directly be determined.

For the C^{13}/C^{12} ratios the following mass ratios of CO_2 were determined:

$$45/44 \; = \; (C^{13}O_2^{16} + C^{12}O^{16}O^{17})/C^{12}O_2^{16} \tag{a}$$

$$46/(44 + 45) \; = C^{12}O^{16}O^{18}/(C^{12}O_2^{16} + C^{13}O_2^{16} + C^{12}O^{16}O^{17}) \tag{b}$$

(for oxygen correction)

These ratios were measured for sample and standard alternatively

$$\delta C^{13} = \left[\frac{(45/44)_{Sample}}{(45/44)_{Standard}} - 1 \right] \cdot 1000 \quad (\%o)$$

The reduction factors of the working standard $-$ CO_2 Linde puriss. $-$ compared with the $BaCO_3$ standard Stockholm (Wickman, 1956) are:

$$\frac{(45/44)_{Stockholm}}{(45/44)_{Linde}} = 0.9955$$

$$\frac{(46/(44 + 45))_{Stockholm}}{(46/(44 + 45))_{Linde}} = 0.9922$$

Thus, the working standard has a favourable C^{13}/C^{12} ratio being only slightly different from the Stockholm ratio. The PDB standard (Chicago) differs from the Stockholm standard by $\delta C^{13} = -10.3 \%o$.

Due to the precision of the recorder the mass ratios can be determined with an error of 0.05% for the ratios 45/44 and 46/(44 + 45) (compensation measurement with double collector, sample versus standard). Each sample was measured twice for the average. The reproducibility of the mass spectrometric measurement was 0.1% re

Coefficient of variation for chemical preparation: $s = \pm 0.05 \%$ for the 45/44 ratios of carbonate; $s = \pm 0.14 \%$ for that one of graphite. Each sample was prepared twice. The average of the mass ratio was recalculated to the δC^{13} value of the PDB standard

The special construction of the double collector complicates the measurements of contaminated samples. The collector for the rare isotope (mass 45) is a Faraday cage. At both sides of this cage a graphite plate is mounted, representing the collector for the abundant isotope (mass 44). As this collector is rather large its mass dissolving power is poor: it records the sum of the intensities in the mass ranges from 39 to 44 and from 46 to 49. Possible contaminations of the samples $-$ p.e. air (Ar, mass 40) or SO_2 (SO, mass 48) $-$ falsify the measured 45/44 ratio. It appears too small as the denominator is the sum of the mass intensities mentioned above. In these cases a correction formula was used to find the true isotope ratios.

R' is the true isotope ratio.

$$R' = \frac{I(45)_P/I(44)_P}{I(45)_S/I(44)_S} \qquad (1)$$

In fact, the following ratio is measured (g):

$$R = \frac{I(45)_{g,P}/I(44)_{g,P}}{I(45)_{g,S}/I(44)_{g,S}} \qquad (2)$$

$I(45)$ intensity of mass 45, etc.
Index P   sample
Index S   standard

B_p, B_S are the sum of the intensities of the contamination products (39 to 43 and 46 to 49) for sample and standard respectively.

Simultaneously the background intensities of mass 44 and 45 in the analyser are considered:

$$a = \text{background intensity of mass 45}$$
$$b = \text{background intensity of mass 44}$$
$$I(45)_{g,P} = I(45)_P + a$$
$$I(44)_{g,P} = I(44)_P + B_P + b$$
$$I(45)_{g,S} = I(45)_S + a$$
$$I(44)_{g,S} = I(44)_S + B_S + b \qquad (3)$$

(3) in (2):

$$R = \frac{I(45)_P + a}{I(45)_S + a} \cdot \frac{I(44)_S + b + B_S}{I(44)_P + b + B_P} \qquad (4)$$

The two factors of (4) can be developed in a series:

$$\frac{I(45)_P + a}{I(45)_S + a} = \left[\frac{I(45)_P + a}{I(45)_S}\right] \cdot \left[1 - \frac{a}{I(45)_S} + \left(\frac{a}{I(45)_S}\right)^2 - \ldots\right] \qquad (5)$$

$$\frac{I(44)_S + b'}{I(44)_P + b' + \Delta B} = \left[\frac{I(44)_S + b'}{I(44)_P}\right] \cdot \left[1 - \frac{b' + \Delta B}{I(44)_P} + \ldots\right] \qquad (5)$$

with the abbreviation used:

$$b' = b + B_S$$
$$\Delta B = B_P - B_S$$

Terms $\leqslant 10^{-4}$ may be neglected here as we have a mass spectrometric error of about 10^{-3}.

When

$$\frac{a}{I(45)_S} \leqslant 10^{-2} \quad \text{and} \quad \frac{b' + \Delta B}{I(44)_P} \leqslant 10^{-2},$$

the series can be stopped after the second term. At the compensation measurement
the pressure of sample and standard gas in the analyser is adjusted such that equation
(6) is valid:

$$I(44)_S + b' = I(44)_P + b' + \Delta B \tag{6}$$

With (5) in (4) and the condition (6) the correction formula is:

$$R' = R - \frac{a}{I(45)_S} + \frac{I(45)_P}{I(45)_S} \cdot \left[\frac{\Delta B}{I(44)_P} + \frac{a}{I(45)_S} \right] \tag{7}$$

on condition that

$$\frac{a}{I(45)_S} , \quad \frac{b' + \Delta B}{I(44)_P} \leqslant 10^{-2} \tag{8}$$

ΔB and a were measured with the single collector method. The correction formula
proved to be useful in its range of validity. The error of the corrected compensation
measurement is higher than normal as the correction terms can only be determined
by single collector measurement.

If the intensities of the contaminating masses are set zero the correction formula for
background intensitites of mass 44 and 45 in the mass analyser is:

$$R' = R - \frac{a}{I(45)_S} \cdot \left[1 - \frac{I(45)_P}{I(45)_S} \right] = R - C$$

With correction term C the background can be tested for undisturbed compensation
measurement: If $C < 10^{-3}$ the background in the analyser is to be neglected.

Summary of Geology

The Prevariscan series in the area of Kropfmühl consist of paragneisses with frequent
intercalations of graphitic gneiss, marble and amphibolite (Figure 3). The widespread
cordierite-bearing biotite-plagioclase gneisses show a granoblastic schistose texture,
they originate from clay and marl sediments. Schistosity disappears with increasing
migmatisation. The paragneisses frequently contain graphite in small layers, little
patches or as euhedral or anhedral ragged crystals. According to Maucher (1936) the
frequently tectonically reworked graphite is found in the intergranular film of adjacent minerals without any displacement; graphite, however, may be included in
quartz and feldspar.

Furthermore flakes and layers of graphite may occur in horizons of marble up to 10 m
thick which can be traced in the area of Kropfmühl up to a length of 10 km. Skarns
may contain graphite. Quite frequently graphite occurs in marble as so-called flinz-
graphite, representing flakes with an average diameter of 1 mm.

In the surroundings of Kropfmühl and Pfaffenreuth graphite layers are replaced by
seams more than 1 m thick. The seams contain 20–50% C, and pyrite and pyrrhotite
as a common association. Pyrite and pyrrhotite are encountered as single grains or

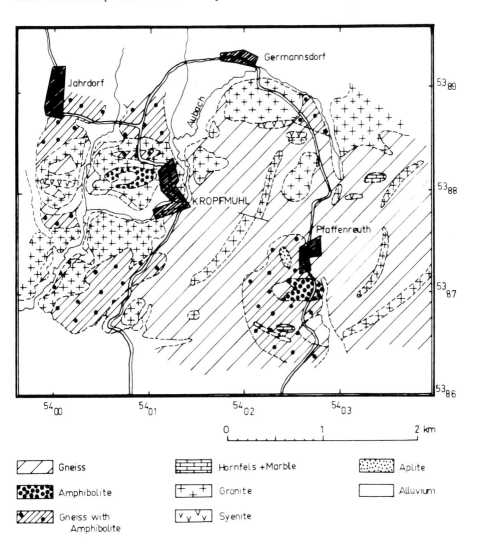

Fig. 3. Geological map of the area of Kropfmühl (after L. Ritter 1951)

as enriched layers in graphitic gneisses and marbles. Graphite, pyrrhotite and pyrite underwent the same tectonic processes, i.e. they were already formed before the last movement of Variscan orogeny. Graphite seams mainly occur in gneiss but they are as well connected with crystalline limestone. With regard to the whole area of Kropfmühl graphite layers are associated with horizons of marble. In local concern, i.e. in the mine, however, marble may occur below or above the graphite seams. They may pass through both marble and gneiss. The features of the occurrence of graphite and limestone are manifold. The graphite seams are folded with axes striking from E to W, plunging towards the W. They are predominantly concordant, but may divide into series of lenses. Intense tectonic movements caused the varying thickness of incompetent graphite seams, the formation of discordant (graphite) veins and the enrichment in anti- and synclines. Such processes caused too that the graphite layers are penetrated by lumps of country rock being transformed to balls and spindles with polished surfaces. Such phenomena are specifically developed in amphibolites.

The Variscan granites penetrated the graphite seams and their adjacent country rocks discordantly, they are younger than the graphite. The granites invaded the rock series of Kropfmühl as sills, dykes and laccoliths of minor extent. The graphite seams are displaced for 5–20 m along the postgranitic steeply dipping dykes of hornblende-porphyry[1]). Along the contacts the seams are dragged, graphite and adjacent rocks are transformed to mylonitic rims. Such processes may have pressed the graphite into the granite and porphyry.

In the discussion about the mutual relations between stable carbon isotopic compositions of graphite and crystalline limestone and their geology the history of the Prevariscan rock series should be taken into consideration. According to Davis and Schreyer (1962) the geological evolution began with sedimentation of marine clays, marls, carbonates and euxinic sediments. This sedimentation was contemporaneous with a submarine volcanic activity. These rocks were folded, metamorphosed and partially migmatised under catazonal conditions in Prevariscan and Variscan orogenic cycles. Posttectonic intrusions of granites, followed by swarms of basic dykes, are the last interesting events.

Sampling Technique and Results

All samples of graphite and carbonate were systematically taken at almost the same depth in the mine of Kropfmühl for investigation of local and regional inhomogeneity. By sampling underground (Luger adit, cross adit 10) no weathering has to be taken into account. Samples Nos.18 and 19 were purposely collected in a weathered zone of gneiss. The locations of the samples are indicated in Figure 4; origins and characteristics are described in Table 1. 3–5 kg from each station were taken.

1. Primarily the local inhomogeneity of the C^{13}/C^{12} ratios at one station was interesting. Therefore we collected six, respectively five samples (Nos. K 5a–5f; Nos. K 10a–10e) in distances of 25 cm from footwall to the hanging at localities

---

[1]) Porphyry is used for the term "Porphyrit" of Maucher, describing an altered dioritic rock containing needles of hornblende in a finegrained groundmass.

N   S

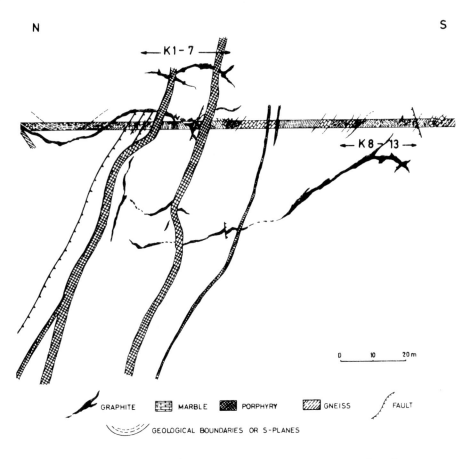

Fig. 4. Geological section at Adit Luger, Crossadit 10. K 1–13: Localities of specimens

No. K 5 and No. K 10. No. K 5 lies in the NS-profile in gneiss, quite remote from any other country rock. Station No. K 10 is situated in amphibolite. δC^{13} values of these samples with regard to their distances from the rock wall are shown in Figure 5.

Graphite from gneiss is with 7‰ enriched in C^{12} compared with that from amphibolite. Besides the isotopic compositions vary more in amphibolite than in gneiss: coefficient of variations is ±9.1 % rel. and 5 % rel. higher than in gneiss (± 3.7 % rel.). The samples of the centre of the seams are isotopically the lightest ones, this is valid for both, amphibolite and gneiss.

Table 1. Description of samples and carbon isotope compositions of graphites and carbonates

	Samples	Sample No. of the mine	Country Rock	Sample Description	δC^{13} Graphite ‰	δC^{13} Carbonate ‰
NS Profile	1	K 1	Porphyry	Graphite	−23	
	2	K2	Porphyry	Graphite with calcite	−20	+ 7
	3	K 3	Gneiss, centre of seam	Graphite	−24	
	4	K4	Gneiss, near Granite contact	Graphite and limestone	−24	−14
	5	K 5	Gneiss	Graphite	−24	
	6	K 6	Gneiss	Graphite and limestone	−21	− 9
	7	K 7	Crystalline limestone	Limestone with flakes of graphite	−21	− 9
EW Profile	8	K 8	Gneiss, folded	Graphite	−15	
	9	K 9a	Gneiss, hanging	Graphite and limestone	−17	− 2
	10	K 9b	Gneiss, foot wall	Graphite with limestone	−21	
	11	K 10	Amphibolite	Graphite	−17	
	12	K 11a	Gneiss	Graphite	−20	
	13	K 11b	Gneiss	Graphite and limestone	−21	−14
	14	K 12a	Amphibolite, centre of seam	Graphite	−21	
	15	K 12b	Amphibolite, centre of seam	Graphite and limestone	−21	− 7
	16	K 13a	Amphibolite with graphitic rim	Graphite	−15	
	17	K 13b	Amphibolite with graphitic rim	Graphite with limestone	−22	−22
	18		Weathered gneiss	Graphite	−24	
	19		Weathered gneiss	Graphite	−23	
	20		Gneiss ⎫ Barbara	Finegrained graphite	−26	
	21		Gneiss ⎬ Mine,	Finegrained graphite	−25	
	22		Gneiss ⎭ Ficht	Finegrained graphite with limestone	−25	
	23		Banded Gneiss	Graphite and pyrrhotite	−14	
	24		Marble	"Flinz" Graphite	−10	− 2

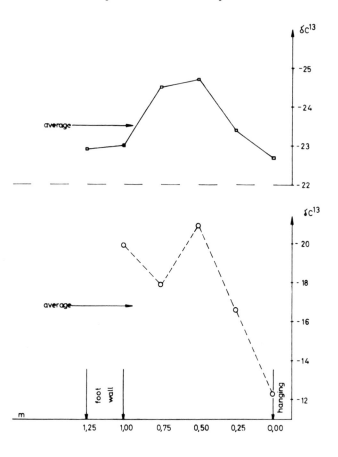

Fig. 5
Variation of the carbon isotope compositions in the cross sections of two graphite seams (in gneiss: □, in amphibolite: ○)

2. The inhomogeneity in regional concern was determined in the material of thirteen localities: Nos. K 1–K 7 are situated W of crossadit 10; Nos. K 8–K 13 lie farther to the S (Figure 4). The variation of the δC^{13} values of the samples from the mine Kropfmühl (Nos. 1–17) and of some additional samples from the surroundings (Nos. 18–24) are tabulated in Table 1. Decimals of values are rounded off. The coefficient of variation of the seventeen graphite samples from the mine amounts to ± 15.2 % rel.

3. For evidence of change in carbon isotopic composition during metamorphism of country rock the following samples were determined: Nos. K 1 and K 2 from porphyry; No. K 4 from gneiss, which is already not far from the granite contact. From eight samples from gneiss, six are from normal folded gneiss (Nos. K 3, K 5, K 11a, 20, 21, 22) whereas three samples (Nos. K 8, K 9a, K 9b) were collected in more intensely folded gneiss. The country rock of pyrrhotite (No. 23) rich in

graphite is a banded gneiss; this graphite is remarkable because of its enrichment in C^{13}. A similar enrichment in C^{13} can be noted for No. 24 "Flinzgraphit"; for the marble associated the δC^{13} value amounts to -2‰, until now commonly regarded as typical for marine origin.

The second series of five samples (Nos. K 10, K 12a, K 12b, K 13a, K 13b) from amphibolites show characteristics of a still more intense deformation compared with the gneisses. From Table 1 the ranges of δC^{13} of graphite samples are elucidated in dependence of the rock type and its deformation (Table 2).

Table 2. Range and average of carbon isotope compositions of graphite in dependence of the country rock

Rock Type	range δC^{13} ‰	n	average δC^{13} ‰
porphyry	−20 to −23	2	−22
normal gneiss	−20 to −26	6	−24
folded gneiss	−15 to −21	3	−18
amphibolite	−15 to −22	5	−18
crystalline limestone	−17 to −24	7	−21

Table 2 shows that by more intense tectonic movements in gneisses and amphibolites graphite carbon became enriched in C^{13} by removal of C^{12}. The amphibolite with a graphite bearing rim (No. K 13a) shows the strongest enrichment in C^{13} in graphite of the mine (−15‰). From the similar value −14‰ of sample No. 23 with pyrrhotite some relations between both observations may be suggested. The late porphyry intrusions have not affected the original isotopic composition anymore.

4. The frequent association of marble and graphite was favourable for a comparison of the isotopic compositions of elementary and carbonate carbon. The elementary carbon of seven samples (Nos. K 4, K 6, K 7, K 9a, K 11b, K 12b, K 13b) containing crystalline limestone from the mine varies between −17‰ and −24‰ (Table 2); all samples are considerably lighter than the associated carbonate carbon.

The seven marble analyses cover the wide range from −2 to −22‰ if the value of the calcite from porphyry (No. K 2) with +7‰ is not included. This heavy carbon of calcite may probably be explained by contamination of pit water. The coefficient of variation of the δC^{13} values of carbonates amounts to ±58% rel., being considerably higher than that one of graphites: ±15.2% rel.

Sample No. K 13b is conspicuous by identical δC^{13} values for graphite and limestone (−22‰). It is an example for the case that the difference in isotopic composition between coexisting graphite-carbonate pairs may decrease. The deviation between the δC^{13} values of graphite (Gr.) and carbonate (Carb.) can be expressed by the characteristic value Δ (Hahn-Weinheimer, 1965).

Δ is defined:

$$\Delta = (\delta C^{13})_{Carb.} - (\delta C^{13})_{Gr.} \quad \%_0$$

In good approximation can be written:

$$(\delta C^{13})_{Carb.} - (\delta C^{13})_{Gr.} \approx \left[\frac{(C^{13}/C^{12})_{Carb.}}{(C^{13}/C^{12})_{Gr.}} - 1 \right] \cdot 10^3$$

In Figure 6 the isotopic compositions of graphite and crystalline limestone in dependence of country rock are compiled.

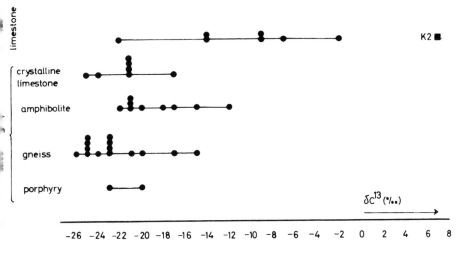

Fig. 6. Carbon isotope compositions of graphite and crystalline limestone in dependence of country rock

Discussion

The isotopic compositions of the 33 graphite samples vary between $-10\%_0$ and $-26\%_0$. This rather large variation does not definitely indicate a biological or non-biological origin (Rankama, 1954). Isotopic fractionation has to be taken into account for all probabilities of graphite formation. The difficulty to calculate the equilibrium constants for reactions of hydrocarbons to graphite is known, and our knowledge about fractionation for an isotope exchange reaction between graphite and native carbon is almost none. The change of the original atmosphere (Suess, 1962) brought about CO and CO_2 reacting according to Boudouard equation, in which isotopic fractionation is envolved. Probable fractionation processes for the formation of carbon from carbonoxyde will be presented at the end of this paragraph.

Evidence from the variation of C^{13}/C^{12} ratio in graphite is provided by the following considerations.

a) Graphite may have originated in organic matter. Differentiation between inorganic and biogenic carbon may have started with photosynthesis and vital processes in Precambrian times. Recently the existence of primitive terrestrial life has apparently been confirmed by the discovery of bacteria, algal rests and spores in the 2150-million year-old sediment series of the Witwatersrand and in other 3000-million-year-old rocks of South Africa (Prashnowsky et al., 1967). If it is suggested that the lighter carbon isotope was preferably incorporated in organisms in this early period of the earth and the carbon cycle gradually came into existence, enrichment in C^{12} in those early fossils seems probable. The bulk of our isotopic data on graphite and the assumed Algonkian age of the Kropfmühl deposit do not contradict to that statement. The δC^{13} values of graphites from Precambrian limestones from various European regions fall in the range $-5\%o$ to $-28\%o$ (Hahn-Weinheimer, 1965) and agree with our present results.

Graphite may be derived from kerogen. Hydrocarbons are produced by changes of kerogen, the major organic constituent of sediments, whose ultimate residue is graphitic carbon (Abelson, 1959, 1967). But the content of organic matter of Precambrian shales is considerably small. Cloud et al. (1965) do not regard the existence of hydrocarbons extracted from shales as conclusive for biological origin of carbon, notwithstanding that the enrichment of C^{12} is diagnostic of it.

The graphite and pyrite containing material may as well be interpreted as nonbiogenic colloidal substance. According to these authors the biological origin of carbon from more than 2000-million-year-old rocks has not unequivocally been proved. The discovery of fossil bacteria is indeed a strong argument, but the conclusive evidence of the nonbiological development of organisms is still missing.

Silverman's (1964) investigations of the origin and evolution of petroleum by carbon isotope studies are indicatory of the genesis of graphite. Petroleum formation processes from organic substances are connected with isotope fractionation. The C^{13}/C^{12} ratios of petroleums are lower than these of the organisms from which they supposedly derived, but similar to the ratios of lipid fractions. Thus, petroleum obviously forms selective accumulation or chemical transformation of C^{12}-enriched constituents of organic matter. Analyses of narrow distillation fractions of liquid petroleum and isotopic analyses of the separated fractions show correspondingly progressive increases in boiling points and C^{13}/C^{12} ratios. The residues left behind and rich in conjugated polyenes and aromatics become isotopically heavier. Asphalt or graphite can be assumed as final residues depending on the maturation and post-depositional processes of the original organic matter. As petroleums (according to Silverman -22.2 to $-29.4\%o$ for marine sediments, and -29.9 to $-32.5\%o$ for non-marine sediments) are always isotopically lighter than their corresponding residues, we may conclude from the isotopic range ($-14\,‰$ to $-22\,‰$) of Kropfmühl graphite that it is derived from biogenic matter whose marine or nonmarine origin cannot yet be established.

b) The C^{13}/C^{12} ratios of graphite containing marble from the mine vary between -2 and $-22\,‰$. The rather high amount of C^{12} probably excludes a marine origin. The isotopic range of marbles partially overlaps that one of corresponding graphite (-15 to $-24\,‰$). For sample No. K 13b the identical value of $-22\,‰$ was found. The tendency of overlapping may be discussed from two aspects:

1) Graphitic and carbonate carbon originated of a common biogenic source. Isotopic ratios changed by postdepositional events and fractionation.

2) The assimilation of isotope ratios in graphitic and carbonate carbon occurred by metamorphic or tectonic movements which caused the loss of the original indication of biogenic or nonbiogenic origin.

Isotopic changes of elementary and carbonate carbon are theoretically possible in a broad range which is shown by a model calculation for isotopic fractionation reactions. Hence it can be followed that the theory of genesis of graphite from limestone – as formerly proposed by geologists – should be revised.

Strens (1965) recently drew the conclusion for the Southwaite graphite deposit/ Borrowdale that CO deposited carbon by the Boudouard reaction catalysed by pyrite.

We calculated the reaction chain of carbon formation from calciumcarbonate in a very simplifying manner. At $900-1000\,°C$ and atmospheric pressure $CaCO_3$ decomposes:

$$CaCO_3 \rightarrow CaO + CO_2 \tag{1}$$

In the presence of ferrous iron, notably pyrite or pyrrhotite, CO_2 is reduced to CO:

$$3\,FeO + CO_2 \rightarrow Fe_3O_4 + CO \tag{2}$$

If CO is transferred from the reaction zone to cooler regions chemical equilibrium between CO, CO_2 and C will come about (Boudouard reaction):

$$CO_2 + C \rightleftharpoons 2CO \tag{3}$$

For these three reactions fractionations of carbon- and oxygenisotopes are possible; oxygen fractionations are not considered; the magnitude of carbon fractionations can approximately be determined by the Boudouard reaction. Equation (3) is split into four partial reactions:

$$C^{12}O_2 + C^{12} \rightleftharpoons C^{12}O + C^{12}O \tag{a}$$

$$C^{12}O_2 + C^{13} \rightleftharpoons C^{12}O + C^{13}O \tag{b}$$

$$C^{13}O_2 + C^{13} \rightleftharpoons C^{13}O + C^{13}O \tag{c}$$

$$C^{13}O_2 + C^{12} \rightleftharpoons C^{12}O + C^{13}O \tag{d}$$

The Arrhenius equation was used for the calculation of the ratios of the velocity constants k (Brodsky, 1961) for the equation pairs (a), (b) and (a), (d) respectively reaction (c) was disregarded because this reaction occurs rarely in nature.

According to Brodsky (1961) the Arrhenius equation can be applied for certain heterogenic reactions. Carbon was assumed not to have already properties typical for the solid state. The equilibrium constants K at 720 °C for reactions (a), (b) and (a), (d) respectively are:

$$\frac{\overleftarrow{k}_a/\overleftarrow{k}_b}{\overrightarrow{k}_a/\overrightarrow{k}_b} = \frac{K_b}{K_a} = 1.011 \; ;$$

$$\frac{\overleftarrow{k}_a/\overleftarrow{k}_d}{\overrightarrow{k}_a/\overrightarrow{k}_d} = \frac{K_d}{K_a} = 0.964 \; .$$

In reaction (b) equilibrium is shifted to the right side compared with that one of reaction (a). The "fractionation factor" K_b/K_a is 1.011 which implies a depletion of C^{13} in elementary carbon compared with the C^{13}/C^{12} ratio of the original CO (equation (2)). Likewise $K_d/K_a = 0.964$ causes an enrichment of C^{12}. These result imply enrichment of C^{12} in carbon compared with the original CO. If an initial δC^{13} range for CO_2 (equation (2)) is assumed to be $+4$ to -4% (marine limeston related to PDB) the evaluated δC^{13} range for carbon varies between -8 and -16% on condition that reaction (2) is complete

From this theoretical change of isotope composition may be concluded that enrichment of C^{12} is possible for graphite formed from carbonate source material. If this reaction trend is continued enrichment in C^{12} will finally pretend a biogenic origin of graphite.

Thus, the final decision on the genesis of Kropfmühl graphite is difficult in the present state of investigation.

Acknowledgements: This work was carried out by the support of the Bundesministerium für Wissenschaftliche Forschung. It is a pleasure to thank this institution, further Dipl.-Berging. K. Erhard/Kropfmühl AG for the help of collecting the samples and Mrs. H. Messerschmitt and K. Gerwert for technical help.

References

Abelson, P. H. (1959): Geochemistry of organic substances. Researches in Geochemistry I, 79–103. John Wiley and Sons, New York.

Abelson, P. H. (1967): Conversion of biochemicals to kerogen and n-paraffins. Researches in Geochemistry II, 63–86. John Wiley and Sons, New York.

Brodsky, A. E. (1961): Isotopenchemie. Akademie-Verlag, Berlin 1961.

Cloud jr., P. E., Gruner, J. W. and Hagen, H. (1965): Carbonaceous rocks of the Soudan iron formation (Early Precambrian). Science 148, 1713–1716.

Davis, G. L. and Schreyer, W. (1962): Altersbestimmungen an Gesteinen des ostbayerischen Grundgebirges und ihre geologische Deutung. Geol. Rundschau 52, 146–169.

Hahn-Weinheimer, P. (1965): Die isotopische Verteilung von Kohlenstoff in Marmor und anderen Metamorphiten. Geol. Rundschau 55, 197–209.

Hoering, T. C. (1967): The organic geochemistry of Precambrian rocks. Researches in Geochemistry II, 87–111. John Wiley and Sons, New York.

Maucher, A. (1936): Die Entstehung der Passauer Graphitlagerstätten. Chemie der Erde 10, 339–365.

McCrea, J. M. (1950): On the isotopic chemistry of carbonates and a paleotemperature scale. J. Chem. Phys. 18, 849.

Prashnowsky, A. A. and Schidlowski, M. M. (1967): Investigation of the Pre-Cambrian Thucholithe Nature 216, 560–563.

Rankama, K. (1954); The isotope constitution of carbon in ancient rocks as an indicator of its biogenic or non-biogenic origin. Geochim. Cosmochim. Acta 5, 142–152.

Silverman, S. R. (1964): Investigations of petroleum origin and evolution mechanisms by carbon isotope studies. Isotopic and cosmic chemistry, 92–102. Amsterdam.

Strens, R. G. J. (1965): The graphite deposits of Seathwaite in Borrowdale, Cumberland. Geol. Mag. Harford, 393–406.

Suess, H. E. (1962): Thermodynamic data on the formation of solid carbon and organic components in primitive planetary atmospheres. J. Geophys. Res. 67, 2029–2034.

Wickman, F. E. (1956): The cycle of carbon and the stable carbon isotopes. Geochim. Cosmochim. Acta 9, 136–153.

Discussion

J. Jedwab: A-t-on observé des structures organisées en section polie dans la graphite de Kropfmühl?

P. Hahn-Weinheimer: No polished sections were studied. These sections were studied by A. Maucher, but no organised structures are mentioned.

Racemisation of Amino Acids on Silicates

Hans Kroepelin

Institut für Chemische Technologie der Technischen Universität Braunschweig
Braunschweig, Germany

The temperature of the complete decomposition of amino acids arises up to 150 degrees centigrade, when these acids are inserted into the silicates e.g. montmorillonite.

In posidonia shales we have found 19 amino-acids. One can assume, that these amino-acids partly are also bound in the crystal lattice of the silicate minerals. It is an important purpose to determine the optical rotation of these acids. For the interpretation of the results, we should answer the question the rotating power is it influenced or not by an interaction between the amino acids and the silicate lattices.

We have adsorbed L(-)leucine on montmorillonite and heated different times at temperatures between 100° and 200 °C. The leucine has been extracted by water, purified with ion exchangers from certain products of decomposition and controlled by thin-layer chromatography. After 25 hours the molar rotating power of the heated L(-)leucine was 80 % of the original value at 100°, 24 % at 150 °C. The racemisation was finished after 100 hours at 100°, after 6 hours at 200 °C.

So, we are very sorry, that the rotating power of amino-acids from very old stones or from meteorites cannot decide whether or not these amino-acids are biogenic.

At the Paris meeting (1966) I discussed in my paper that amino acids adsorbed on silicates, are influenced in two opposite directions.

a) Part of the acid is thermally decomposed with a higher reaction rate than in the crystalline state.

b) An other part is protected against decomposition.

The lowest temperature at which the last traces of the amino acids have disappeared, when the system is heated during 170 hours is marked in Figure 1. The best protector is montmorillonite.

We have repeated such experiments several times.

Figure 2 shows, as a function of time, the percentage of the not decomposed amount of several amino-acids adsorbed on kaolinite and kept at 180 °C. Figure 3 shows a corresponding experiment with the acids adsorbed on montmorillonite.

It there is so strong an interaction between the lattice of the silicates and the amino-acids, the question arises whether a racemisation of amino-acids on silicates, e.g. montmorillonite, is possible and which are the conditions for this racemisation. As leucine is well stabilised on silicates and it is the most abundant amino-acid in posidonia shales, and as montmorillonite is the best stabilising silicate, we made the experiments with l(-)leucine on montmorillonite.

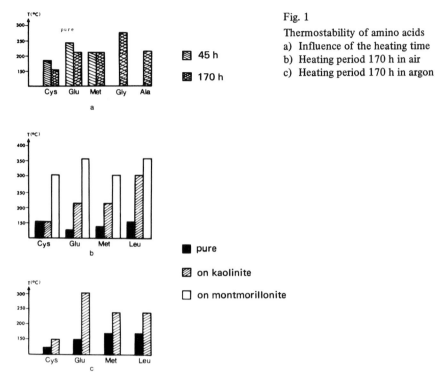

Fig. 1
Thermostability of amino acids
a) Influence of the heating time
b) Heating period 170 h in air
c) Heating period 170 h in argon

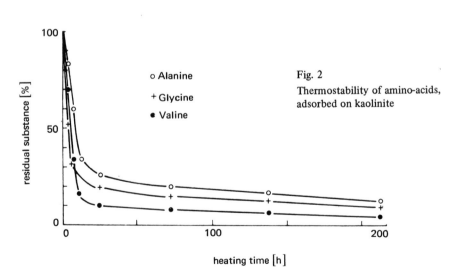

Fig. 2
Thermostability of amino-acids,
adsorbed on kaolinite

o Alanine
+ Glycine
• Valine

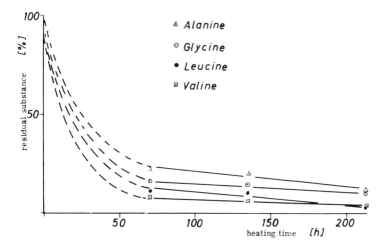

Fig. 3. Thermal decomposition on montmorillonite Temperature 180 °C

Leucine and montmorillonite are mixed in the ratio 1:20, wetted with water and dried at 70 °C, well ground to a fine powder and then heated in an argon-atmosphere. After heating, the samples have been extracted with a great amount of water. The solution is concentrated in a vacuum evaporator. The amino-acid is separated from the products of decomposition by means of an ionexchange-column. The amount of chemically unchanged amino-acid is determined with ninhydrine. The purity of the leucine is proved by thin-layer-chromatography before and after heating.

Figure 4 gives as a function of time the percentage of leucine which does not decompose on montmorillonite at 100°, 150° and 200 °C respectively. The ratio decomposed to protected acid depends on the temperature. The slope of the curve after 50 or 100 hours is very small. This is even true at 200 °C, although the amount of the protected acid is small (only 1.6 %); the further decomposition of this rest is extremely slow.

The optical rotation is measured with a photo-electric polarimeter having a sensitivity of a few thousandths of a degree. Figure 5 shows how the optical rotation decreases as a function of time during heating at a constant temperature of 150 °C. The values of the rotation are given for a constant concentration of 10 mg leucine in 1 cm^3 water. The optical rotation becomes zero after heating for 80 hours. The amount of the acid on montmorillonite which did not decompose after this period of time is 57 % of the original substance.

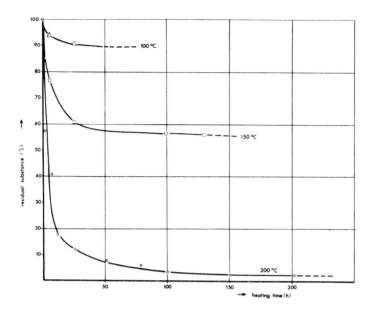

Fig. 4. Thermal decomposition of leucine

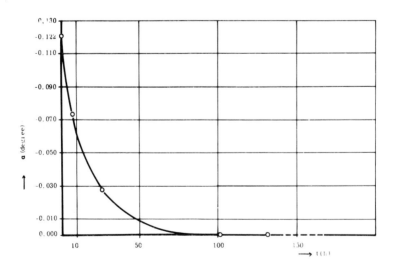

Fig. 5. l-leucine on montmorillonite
Decrease of the optical rotation a (degree) by heating at 150 °C as a function of the heating time t (h)

The curves in Figure 6 show the decline of the optical rotation as a function of temperature, the heating time being kept constant. For the two curves, the heating times are 6 hours and 25 hours respectively. In the middle part, the slope of the curves is similar.

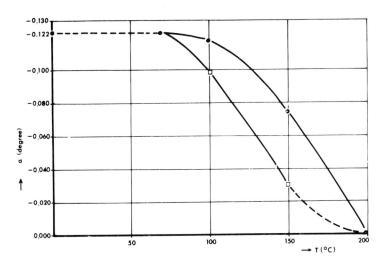

Fig. 6. l-leucine on montmorillonite
Decrease of the optical rotation α (degree) by heating to different temperatures T (°C).
Heating time   6 h (left)
                   25 h (right)

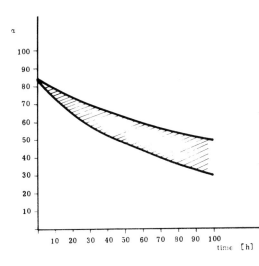

Fig. 7

Angle of rotation α (degree) measured with solutions of L(+)-isoleucine in water after heating with montmorillonite at 150 °C versus the time of heating (h). Heated for 10 hours to 180 °C : α = 0.005 grd

Experiments with 1(-) iso-leucine give similar results (Figure 7). The hatched area indicates that the accuracy of the determination of the concentration was not very good. Generally the process of racemisation is of similar character as for 1(-) leucine.

It is well known, that natural amino-acids can undergo racemisation during chemical treatment. The hydrolysis of natural polypeptides often affects the rotation of the isolated amino-acids. Also during the synthesis of peptides, even if the acids are fixed on ion-exchangers, the configuration is sometimes changed.

One of the earliest papers we know on this subject was written in 1922 by W. F. Hofmann and R. A. Gortner [1]. These authors have boiled cystine in a solution of 20 % hydrochloric acid in water. The decrease of the specific rotation was 38 % after 12 hours, 76 % after 24 hours, and 76 % after 48 hours. Other authors [2, 3, 4] have isolated from these solutions the d-, l-, and meso-cystine.

We have identified the reaction products eluted from ion-exchangers with ammonia by thin-layer-chromatography only. Ninhydrine gives the same blue-violet colour not only with amino-acids, but also with amines. May be, that in this way we not only determined the concentration of an amino-acid, but as well of an amine formed from the amino-acid by decarboxylation. We added the corresponding amines to our solutions of the amino-acids. When a mixture of n-propanol-formic acid-water (40:20:10) is used as eluent, the amines remain at the starting point of the chromatogram. So, indeed, the determination of the concentration of the l-leucine is accurate.

A second objection: is the racemisation really effected in a specific manner by the silicates? We should remember the racemisation by acids.

A third objection: is not the observed racemisation only caused by high temperatures?

To reject these objections, solutions of l(-) leucine in water are heated during 25 hours at temperatures of 150°, 180°, and 200 °C. The results are given in the following Table 1.

Table 1. Deterioration and racemisation of l(-) leucine dissolved in water, after heating for 25 h (quartz-vessel)

Temperature °C	Concentration mg/cm^3	Optical rotation		
		calculated °	measured °	measured for a concentration of 10 mg/cm^3
not heated	10	-0.124	-0.122	-0.122
150			-0.101	> -0.101
180	6.58	-0.080	-0.005	-0.0076
200	6.58	-0.080	-0.003	-0.0045

Decomposition occurs and racemisation too. After heating for 25 hours at a temperature of 200 °C, the optical rotation is only 6 % of the original one.

But if we compare the experiments with water and montmorillonite at 150 °C, we are shure, that the silicate acts as a specific catalyst. After 25 hours the optical rotation of l-leucine adsorbed on montmorillonite, is reduced to 25 % of the initial one. Heated in water, the l-leucine shows an optical rotation of 80 % of the initial one.

Such laboratory experiments are necessary in order to be able to decide whether or not amino-acids, isolated from rocks or extraterrestrial material are biogenic. We are very sorry to say, however, that the answer to this fundamental question cannot be given by measuring the optical rotation. Even if we are sure that the origin is biogenic, − as in sedimentary rocks − we may find amino-acids, not having the expected optical rotation.

Still worse: may be we will find amino-acids in rocks having an inverse optical rotation. This is possible, if the biogenic acids have undergone a racemisation on silicates, and the l(-) forms are subsequently eaten by bacteria. We are very curious, what will be found in the future.

References

[1]   W. F. Hoffmann and R. A. Gortner: Journ. Chem. Soc. 44 (1922) 341.
[2]   L. Hollander and V. du Vigneaud: J. Biol. Chem. 94 (1931) 243.
[3]   M. S. Loring and V. du Vigneaud: J. Biol. Chem. 107 (1934) 267.
[4]   J. Andrews: J. Biol. Chem. 97 (1932) Proc. XIX.

Discussion

M. Bajor: Leucin kommt in fossilen Sedimenten zum größten Anteil nicht im freien Zustand, sondern in Kombination, chemisch gebunden mit anderen organischen Verbindungen (Aminen, Aminosäuren, Aldehyden, etc.) vor. Daher könnte ja sein, daß die optische Aktivität des Leucins im gebundenen Zustand während der Diagenese von den Silikaten nicht beeinträchtigt wird. Man sollte vielleicht das Drehvermögen der Aminosäuren und deren Veränderung durch silikatisches Material bei der Erhaltung in gebundenem Zustand ebenfalls untersuchen.

H. Kroepelin: Vor einem Versuch kann man nichts sagen, nur alles vermuten. Es handelt sich bei unseren Versuchen um die ersten Schritte zur Feststellung einer neuen Tatsache und zur Klärung des chemischen Mechanismus.

P. H. Given: Your finding of easy racemization of amino acids on clays surprises me in view of the recent results of Kvenvolden. He extracted amino acids from various ancient rocks (including the fig tree chert), converted them to trifluoro acet-amides-2-butanol esters. The 2-butanol was optically active, and so the optical isomers of each amino acid were separable by gas chromatography. He found the peaks corresponding to the L-acids, and only very small peaks due to the D-acids. He believed that the latter might have been due to a little racemization in the chromatographic column.

Organische Aminoverbindungen in den Gas- und Flüssigkeitseinschlüssen uranhaltiger Mineralien und deren Bedeutung für Transportreaktionen in hydrothermalen Lösungen

Reimar Kranz

Institut für Physikalische Chemie der Kernforschungsanlage Jülich GmbH
Jülich, Germany

The remmants of a former crystallization event have remained trapped in the gas and liquid inclusions of minerals. It is therefore understandable that these inclusions have aroused increasing interest. One hopes, from the analysis of these inclusions, to gain a new insight into the chemistry of the gases and solutions which are present during mineral formation. The gases and liquids present as inclusions in the crystal lattice of mineral samples were extracted by grindling under vacuum, and finally subjected to gas-chromatographic and mass-spectrometric analysis. While primarily inorganic gases and traces of hydrocarbons were obtained from all minerals, measurable quantities of organic amino-compounds as amines and nitriles of low molecular weight could be detected in uraniferous minerals and in radium bearing feldspar samples. Furthermore in some highly radioactive feldspar samples from the uranium bearing Co-Ni-Ag-veins of Wittichen in the Black Forest, some amino-acids could be found. Always a streight dependence of the appearance of organic matter especially of amino-groups on the uranium, thorium and radium content was detected.

Further discussions will be about the influence of these compounds on the solubility and recrystallisation of mineral material. Some model-experiments prove the large solubility of mineral matter in very dilute solutions of amines, aminoacids and nucleic-acids. The influence of such transport reactions on the distribution of the radioactive nuclides of the uranium and thorium series, and the age determinations by lead-lead and uranium-lead methods will be mentioned.

The investigations prove the hypothesis that the organic substances found are due to radiation-chemical products formed from high volatile hydrocarbons, ammonia and water inside the mineral inclusions, and that even amino-acids could be formed in this way during geological time.

Bei der Durchsicht organisch-geochemischer Literatur ist es erstaunlich festzustellen, daß bisher fast ausnahmslos sedimentäres oder meteoritisches Material auf organische Bestandteile untersucht wurde, während primäre Mineralien und Gesteine von vornherein aufgrund ihrer angenommenen magmatischen Entstehungsweise und der damit verbundenen hohen Temperaturbelastung während der Genese für wenig lohnende Untersuchungsobjekte gehalten wurden. Selbst die gut bekannten hochmolekularen Kohlenwasserstoffe und Bitumen hydrothermaler Gänge, wie z.B. Kohlenblenden von Kongsberg oder die meist hoch uranhaltigen Carburane und Tucholithe sind bis heute nur wenig bearbeitet und ihre Herkunft und Genese ungeklärt. Während für die uranhaltigen Tucholithe allgemein strahlenchemische Polymerisationsreaktionen angenommen werden, werden über die Bildung und

Ablagerung der Kohlenblenden und denen ähnlicher asphaltartiger Substanzen die
unterschiedlichsten Meinungen vertreten: Von der Hydrierung kohliger Substanz
unter magmatischen Bedingungen bis hin zur Beteiligung juveniler Kohlenwasserstoffe in hydrothermalen Lösungen.

In den vergangenen Jahren sollte daher untersucht werden, in wie weit organische Verbindungen an der Füllung der Gas- und Flüssigkeitseinschlüsse in primären Mineralien
beteiligt sind, und welche Rolle ihnen bei der Mineralbildung oder -umbildung zufällt.
schließlich finden wir gerade in diesen Gaseinschlüssen Restphasen eines ehemaligen Kr
stallisationsgeschehens, und wir dürfen hoffen, aus der Analyse dieser Einschlüsse zu
neuen Einblicken in die Chemie der bei der Mineralbildung vorhandenen Gase und Lös
gen zu gelangen; zu Kenntnissen, die für die Erforschung der Bildungsbedingungen der
Mineralien und Gesteine von grundlegender Bedeutung sind.

Bei der Vakuumextraktion der in Flußspäten des Wölsendorfer Reviers eingeschlossene
Gase und anschließender massenspektrometrischer Analyse fanden sich neben den beka
ten anorganischen Gasen Helium, Wasserstoff, Argon, Stickstoff, Kohlendioxid und
Wasser auch erhebliche Mengen niederer Kohlenwasserstoffe; in den uranführenden dur
len Fluorit-Varietäten konnten darüber hinaus meßbare Mengen fluorierter Kohlenwass
stoffe neben Sulfuryl- und Thionylfluorid und Spuren niedermolekularer organischer
Amine bestimmt werden [5, 7]. Mit verfeinerten Analysenmethoden, u.a. durch Kombi
nation von Gaschromatograph und Massenspektrometer [8] gelang es in der Folgezeit,
solche organischen Verbindungen in einer Vielzahl von Mineralien zu beobachten. Beso
ders beachtenswert erscheint das Vorkommen organischer Stickstoffverbindungen (Am
und Nitrile) in Silikaten [6]. Radiochemische Uran- und Thoriumanalysen zeigten eine
direkten quantitativen Zusammenhang zwischen dem Vorkommen organischer Substan
(insbesondere der Amino-Verbindungen) und dem Uran- und Thoriumgehalt der Minera
lien. Eine abiogene strahlenchemische Bildung dieser Verbindungen aus primär vorhand
Ammoniak und einfachen Kohlenwasserstoffen muß daher angenommen werden.

Aus diesen Ergebnissen wuchs zwangsläufig die Frage, ob eine solche strahlenchemische
Synthese organischen Materials in der Erdkruste im Beisein von Wasser auch noch zu
höhermolekularen Verbindungen führen kann. An einigen hoch uranhaltigen Flußspäte
wie auch an uran- bzw. radiumhaltigen Feldspäten der Schwarzwälder Granite wurde da
versucht, Aminosäuren analytisch abzutrennen und dünnschichtchromatographisch zu
bestimmen. Diese Versuche befinden sich erst im Anfangsstadium, jedoch zeichnet sich
das Vorhandensein von Aminosäuren in uranhaltigem Material deutlich ab. So konnten
Glykokoll, Alanin und Aminobuttersäure nachgewiesen werden; das Vorkommen von
schwefelhaltigen Aminosäuren wie Methionin ist wahrscheinlich. Eine optische Aktivit
konnte nicht beobachtet werden. In inaktivem Material wurden bisher keine derartigen
Verbindungen gefunden.

Wenn wir aber in diesen Gas- und Flüssigkeitseinschlüssen Restphasen einer ehemaligen
Kristallisationslösung vorfinden, so war weiter zu fragen, welche Rolle diesen organisch
Verbindungen bei der Mineralbildung oder -umbildung zufällt. Am Beispiel des Feldspa

konnte eine bedeutende Steigerung der Löslichkeit anorganischen Materials bei Anwesenheit organischer Aminoverbindungen (Amine, quarternäre Ammoniumsalze, Aminosäuren und Nucleinsäuren) gezeigt werden [6]. Ganz allgemein ist die Frage nach der Löslichkeit schwer löslicher Substanzen bei Gegenwart biogener Materie von grundsätzlicher Bedeutung für die Biochemie der Pflanzenernährung, und wurde erstmals 1952 von I. Mandl und Mitarbeitern [10] und 1955 von W.D. Evans [13] diskutiert. Schließlich assimilieren Pflanzen mit großer Leichtigkeit schwer lösliche oder bei den herrschenden Bedingungen im Ackerboden nahezu unlösliche anorganische Substanz, die als Inkrustation an Zellwänden oder auch im Innern der Zellen rekristallisiert. Es schien daher interessant, den Einfluß hochmolekularer Amino-Verbindungen auf Löslichkeit und Transport von Uran und

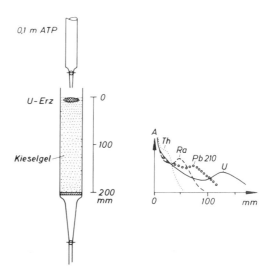

Bild 1

Die Löslichkeit von Pechblende in einer 0,1 m ATP-Lösung und die Differentiation des Urans von seinen Folgenukliden in einer Kieselgelsäule

seinen Folgeprodukten zu prüfen. Bild 1 zeigt die improvisierte Versuchseinrichtung mit dem Ergebnis. Eine etwa 20 cm lange Glasröhre war mit Kieselgel (Kieselgel 0,1–0,2 mm zur Chromatographie, Merck) gefüllt; auf der Oberfläche befand sich eine kleine Menge (etwa 500 mg) pulverisierte Pechblende bzw. ein stark uranhaltiger Granit aus dem Nebengestein der Witticher Gänge. Aus einer Bürette tropfte eine 0,1 molare Adenosintriphosphatlösung mit einer Geschwindigkeit von ca. 0,2 ml pro Minute auf die Säule auf. Um bakterielle Veränderungen der ATP-Lösung zu vermeiden, wurde der Versuch in einer Sterilbox durchgeführt. Nach etwa einer Woche Versuchsdauer wurde die Säulenfüllung in einzelne Schichten unterteilt und jeweils deren Gehalt an Uran, Thorium - 230, Radium -226 und Blei -210 radiochemisch bestimmt. Aufgetragen wurden im Diagramm die Aktivitäten der einzelnen Radionuklide gegen den Ort ihrer Fixierung im Kieselgel, d.h. in Abhängigkeit von ihrer Verteilung in der Säule nach dem Versuch. Die Löslichkeit des Uranpecherzes ist, wie zu erwarten war, beträchtlich. Unter den geschilderten Versuchsbedingungen wird Uran am weitesten transportiert, Thorium am wenigsten; es befindet

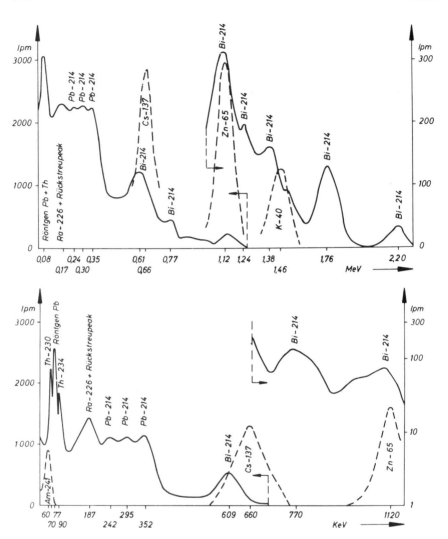

Bild 2 a, b. γ-Spektren von Uranpecherzen (^{137}Cs, ^{65}Zn, ^{40}K als Energiemarken gestrichelt gezeichnet)

sich nach der Versuchsdurchführung noch fast am Ursprungsort. Diese unterschiedlich Wanderungsgeschwindigkeiten hängen selbstverständlich in hohem Maße von den Abs tionseigenschaften der Säule, vom p_H-Wert der Lösungen sowie von den sonst an dies Vorgängen beteiligten Lösungspartnern ab.

Derartige Lösungs- und Diffusionsvorgänge finden sich jedoch genauso in der Natur w und man muß sich gerade bei der Prospektion von Uranerzen sehr vor Trugschlüssen l

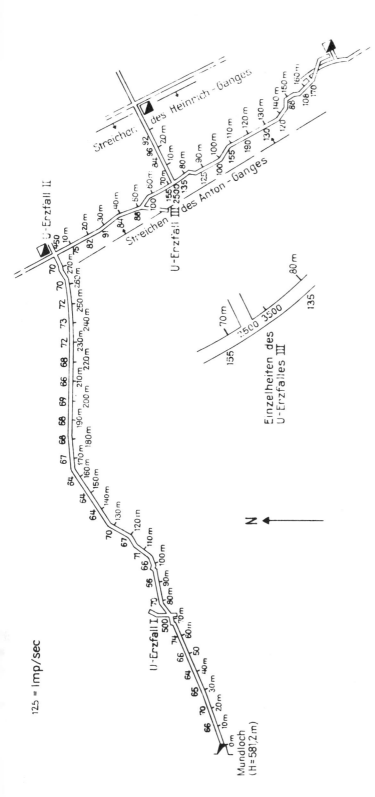

Bild 3. Scintillometer-Aufnahme des unteren Stollens der Grube Anton im Heubachtal (Schwarzwald) — aus F. Kirchheimer, 1953

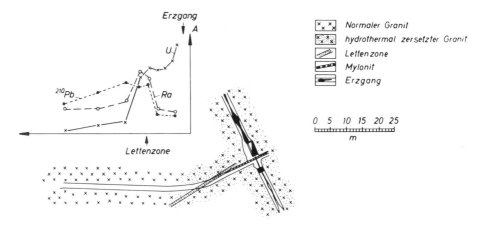

Bild 4. Ausbildung des Anton-Ganges am Stollenkreuz

Die Uranprospektion geschieht seit jeher meist radiometrisch, d.h. durch Aufnahme v
Aktivitätsprofilen entlang vorhandener Bergwerksschächte oder Stollen. Bei der Eichv
der Strahlenmeßgeräte in Uranäquivalenten wird hierbei stillschweigend vorausgesetzt
daß sich das Uran mit Gesteinskörper mit seinen radioaktiven Folgenukliden im Gleic
gewicht befinden, d.h. daß seit der Erzabscheidung im heutigen Zustand, zumindest iเ
den vergangenen 500.000 Jahren, keine chemischen Veränderungen eingetreten sind.
Hinzu kommt, daß bei Szintillometeraufnahmen einzig das kurzlebige [214] Bi, ein direk
Folgenuklid des Radiums, als energiereicher γ-Strahler zur Aktivitätsmessung beiträgt
(Bild 2a, b).

Ein Beispiel einer solchen Feldvermessung zeigt eine Aufnahme des Antonstollens im
Heubachtal (Wittichen, Schwarzwald), die 1953 von F. Kirchheimer [4] durchgeführt
wurde (Bild 3).

In Bild 4 sind die Verhältnisse am Stollenkreuz, also am Uranerzfall 2, noch einmal hฺ
gezeichnet. An dieser Stelle wurden vor etwa 7 Jahren bei einer Grubenbefahrung anl
lich einer anderen geochemischen Untersuchung eine Reihe von Proben aus dem Urar
fall 2 und aus dem Stollenprofil genommen. Die Ergebnisse der Uran-, Radium- und
Radiobleianalysen sind im Diagramm darüber aufgetragen. Man findet hier im Prinzip
genau das gleiche Bild der Nuklidverteilung des Laborversuches, wenn auch die Letteเ
wie zu erwarten, die klaren Verhältnisse des Modells etwas verwischt.

Über die absoluten Mengen gelösten und an anderer Stelle erneut abgeschiedenen Maฺ
können noch keine verbindlichen Angaben gemacht werden. Die hierzu erforderlicheเ
aktivierungsanalytischen Arbeiten befinden sich z. Z. in Vorbereitung. Es ist zu hoffeฺ
nach Abschluß dieser Untersuchungen auch Lösungs- und Diffusionsgeschwindigkeitฺ
den Halbwertzeiten der betreffenden Radionuklide, den radioaktiven Ungleichgewichฺ
und den Entfernungen vom Haupterzträger rechnerisch ermittelt werden können.

Bei der Bearbeitung von Material einer alten, nicht mehr im Abbau stehenden Grube ist trotz sorgfältiger, auf möglichst frisches Material ausgerichteten Probennahme, stets die Möglichkeit einer starken Beeinflussung der Elementverteilung durch jüngste Verwitterungseinflüsse gegeben. Besonderen Einfluß übt die aus der Oxydation sulfidischer Erze freigesetzte Schwefelsäure aus, die in den Grubenwässern erhebliche Konzentrationen erreichen kann (E. S. Bastian und J. M. Hill [1]; F. W. Clarke, 1924 [2]). Um Irrtümer und Trugschlüsse ausschließen zu können, wurde daher nicht nur der Laborversuch mit 0,1 m Schwefelsäure wiederholt, sondern insbesondere auch aus dem Wittichener Granit Feldspat und Glimmer durch mikroskopische Auslese der Mineralien abgetrennt und in den Mineralfraktionen die Verteilung von Radium und Radioblei gemessen.

Schon im Modellexperiment zeigten sich auffallende Unterschiede. Während mit ATP-Lösung nach dem Versuch sämtliche Zerfallsnuklide des Urans wie in einem Chromatogramm über die Kieselgelsäule verteilt waren, wurde mit Schwefelsäure ausschließlich das Uran in erheblicher Menge gelöst, während Radium und auch Radioblei im Erz zurückblieben. Beide Elemente werden aufgrund der Schwerlöslichkeit ihrer Sulfate sofort im Erz fixiert, wo sie sich im Verhältnis zum Uran stark anreichern. Diese Ergebnisse stehen in völligem Einklang mit den Untersuchungen von G. Phair und H. Levine (1953) [11], die darüber hinaus noch feststellten, daß das Uran-Sauerstoff-Verhältnis der Pechblende großen Einfluß auf die Löslichkeit und Wegfuhr von Uran in schwefelsauren Lösungen hat.

Auch die Nuklidverteilung in Felspat und Glimmer des Witticher Granits sprechen gegen eine nur durch Verwitterungseinflüsse hervorgerufene Elementverteilung. Auffallend ist vor allem der relativ hohe Radiumgehalt der Kalifeldspäte, der den der Glimmer um 80–100 % übertrifft.

Ein geochemischer Stofftransport in der obersten Erdkruste unter Mitwirkung organischen Materials ist daher nicht auszuschließen. An die Auswirkungen hierbei eintretender Nuklidverschiebungen auf die Ergebnisse der Altersbestimmung nach den Uran-Blei- bzw. Blei-Blei-Methoden sei erinnert.

So wird z.B. für das Kupfer-Uranyl-Phosphat, Torbernit, genau wie für das primäre Uranpecherz fast der Gleichgewichtswert an Radium von etwa $3,4 \cdot 10^{-7}$ g Ra/gU angenommen. 1959 stellte W. Küttner [9] einen strahlungsinduzierten α, β-Modifikationswechsel bei Bestrahlungsversuchen mit Röntgen- und γ-Strahlung fest, der bei einer absorbierten Strahlendosis von etwa $1,7 \cdot 10^{12}$ MeV $\cdot$ g^{-1} erfolgt. Diese Beobachtung der α, β-Umwandlung des Orthotorbernits $(Cu (UO_2)_2 (PO_4)_2 \cdot 12 H_2O)$ gestattet es, die mögliche maximale „Lebensdauer" des α-Orthotorbernits zu bestimmen, aus der sich auch weitreichende genetische Schlußfolgerungen ziehen lassen.

Die Eigenstrahlung des Urans im radioaktiven Gleichgewicht beträgt 47,4 MeV pro Zerfall $^{238}U = {}^{206}Pb + 8 \, {}^4He$ und 45,2 MeV pro Zerfall $^{235}Pb + 7 \, {}^4He$; entsprechend einer Strahlendosis von $1,94 \cdot 10^{13}$ MeV/Jahr $\cdot$ g Natururan. Bezogen auf das Mineral Torbernit (ca. 50 % U) bedeutet dies eine ständige Jahresdosis von mindestens $8,5–9,0 \cdot 10^{12}$ MeV/g, wenn man nur den Anteil der α-Teilchen in Betracht zieht. Im α-Orthotorbernit kann

demzufolge ein radioaktives Gleichgewicht nicht erreicht werden. Die α, β-Umwandlu
vollzieht sich bereits vor Erlangung eines nur angenäherten Gleichgewichtes. Radioch
mische Untersuchungen der Radiumverteilung in einem Torbernitkriställchen zeigten
dann auch eine deutliche Radiumanreicherung in der Randzone des Kristalls, währen
das Kristallinnere fast völlig frei von Radium war (Bild 5). Die Zerfallsprodukte des U
insbesondere das langlebige Radium, die aus der Umlagerung primären Pecherzes in d
pseudohydrothermalen Lösungen vorhanden waren, wurden demnach erst in der letz
Mineralisationsphase abgeschieden. Eine Zerlegung des im Granit primär eingesprengt
Uranpecherzes durch kalte oder wenig temperierte Wasser ist nach den beschriebenen
Untersuchungen durchaus möglich.

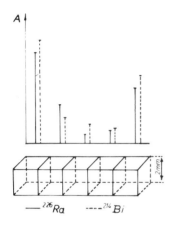

Bild 5
Radium-Verteilung im Torbernit

Über die Lösungs- oder Ionenaustauscheigenschaften der kohligen Substanzen hydrothermaler Mineralisationen liegen bis heute keine detaillierten Untersuchungen vor. E
mikroskopische Arbeiten bestätigen jedoch auch hier den großen Einfluß dieser Verb
dungen auf die Beweglichkeit des Urans. Besonders eindrucksvolle Beispiele für die M
lisation des Uranpecherzes durch organische Substanz gibt M. Schidlowski (1966) [12
seiner Studie über die radioaktiven Bestandteile der Witwatersrand-Konglomerate. Er
beobachtete zunächst das schon vielfach beschriebene Eindringen tucholithartiger
kohliger Substanz auf kataklastischen Sprüngen in die Pechblende-Körnchen. Diese Tu-
cholith-Äderung ist jedoch nur das Anfangsstadium eines Verdrängungsprozesses, an
dessen Ende die völlige Weglösung des primären Pecherzes steht. Der ganze in Auflös
befindliche UO_2-Körper wird hierbei von einer Tucholithhülle überzogen, an deren O
fläche wiederum oft ein Teil des verdrängten Pecherzes als sekundäres Uranmineral
(Brannerit, UTi_2O_6) nach kurzer Wanderung wieder abgeschrieben wird.
Bei dieser Tucholithisierung, die nach Schidlowskis Beobachtungen oft in einer völlig
Verdrängung der primären Pechblende durch die als Tucholith verfestigten organisch

Verbindungen endet, handelt es sich um den Abbau und Wegtransport einer festen Mineralphase, also um einen echten Lösungsmechanismus, der offensichtlich durch die Anwesenheit organischer Materie stark begünstigt wird. Aus der Tatsache, daß die das Uranpecherz verdrängenden Kohlenwasserstoffe selbst nur unbedeutende Spuren von Uran enthalten, zieht Schidlowski den Schluß, daß die kohlige Substanz nur katalytisch an diesen Vorgängen beteiligt war und sog. „metallorganische" Verbindungen eine untergeordnete Rolle spielten. Diese Ansicht ist sicher richtig vom Standpunkt der Fixierung des Urans durch Adsorption. Für die Mobilisierung und den Transport des Urans trifft sie jedoch nach den geschilderten Versuchsergebnissen nicht zu. Im Gegenteil, das Uran wird mit großer Wahrscheinlichkeit als metallorganischer Komplex gelöst und abgeführt. Bei diesem Vorgang ist ebenfalls keine Urananreicherung in der organischen Matrix zu erwarten, da diese die Chelatbildner liefert, die das Uran ständig in Lösung halten. Eine Wiederausscheidung ist erst außerhalb der Tucholithsubstanz unter veränderten chemischen Bedingungen möglich, wie dies auch teilweise beobachtet wird.

Aus den beschriebenen Ergebnissen ist nun aber zu folgern, daß hochmolekulare, scheinbar biogene organische Substanzen auch innerhalb der Gesteine der oberen Erdkruste durch strahlenchemische und thermische Reaktionen aus primär vorhandenen einfachen Kohlenwasserstoffen, Ammoniak (bzw. Stickstoff und Wasserstoff) und Wasser gebildet werden können, die dann später unter geeigneten Umständen wieder mobilisiert werden können und dann aufgrund ihrer löslichkeitssteigernden Wirkung zum Transport anorganischer Materie beitragen. Eine endgültige Lösung aller hier aufgeworfenen Fragen bleibt sicherlich einer zunächst noch fernen Zukunft vorbehalten. Auf jeden Fall aber werden systematische Arbeiten auf diesem neuen Gebiet der Geochemie Antwort auf manches bisher ungelöste Problem nicht nur der Mineral- und Lagerstättengenese, sondern auch der Biochemie auf die Frage nach der Evolution biogener Materie geben.

Literatur

[1] E. S. Bastian und J. M. Hill: U.S. Geol. Survey Prof. Paper **94**, 379 S (1917).

[2] F. W. Clarke: U.S. Geol. Survey Bull. **770**, 841 S. (1924) 5. Auflage.

[3] W. D. Evans: Trans. Inst. Met. **65**, 13 (1955).

[4] F. Kirchheimer: Abh. Geol. Landesamt Baden-Württemberg **1**, 1 (1953).

[5] R. Kranz: Naturwissenschaften **54**, 469 (1967).

[6] R. Kranz: Ber. d. Deutschen Keramischen Ges. **44**, 430 (1967).

[7] R. Kranz: Institution of Mining + Metallurgy, Transactions B, **77**, 26 (1968).

[8] R. Kranz: Meßtechnik **6**, 121 (1968).

[9] W. Küttner: Hamburger Beiträge zur angewandten Mineralogie **2**, 116 (1959)

[10] I. Mandl, A. Grauer und C. Neuberg: Biochim. Biophys. Acta **8**, 654 (1952).

[11] G. Phair und H. Levine: Econ. Geology **48**, 358 (1953).

[12] M. Schidlowski: N. Jb. Miner. Abh. **105**, 55, 183, 310 (1966). Contr. Mineral. and Petrol. **1**
365 (1966).

Discussion

J. Jedwab: E. Welin (1966) a montré que les matieres organiques trouvées dans la mine de Bolide en association avec de l'uranium et du thorium ont un âge très récent de quelques dizaines de mill d'années. Il est d'autre part fréquent que l'on observe à l'intérieur de minérieur de minéraux hy thermaux des inclusions liquides secondaires dont les températures de décrépitation sont beau plus basses que celles des inclusions primaires . Il est donc possible que les acides aminés trouvé dans la présente étude proviennent principalement de solutions vadoses.

R. Kranz: Selbstverständlich ist bei einer derartigen Untersuchung auch an sekundäre Einschlüsse denken, deren Inhalt aus vadosen Lösungen stammen könnte. Wir sind dieser Frage nachgegangen. der Herkunft aus vadosen Wässern sollten die gefundenen Aminosäuren eine optische Aktivität zei die nicht nachgewiesen werden konnte. Auch ist der quantitative Zusammenhang zwischen dem A treten organischer Aminoverbindungen und dem Uran- und Thoriumgehalt der Mineralien besond auffällig. Wir halten daher eine strahlenchemische Entstehung dieser organischen Verbindungen au primär vorhandenen leichten Kohlenwasserstoffen, Wasser und Ammoniak, bzw. Stickstoff und W stoff, für sehr wahrscheinlich.

Coloration rose-carmin d'une sepiolité eocene, la quincyte, par des pigments organiques

Marcel Louis[1]), Claude-Jean Guillemin[2]), Juan-Carlos Goni[2]) et Jean-Paul Ragot[2])

[1]) Institut Français du Pétrole
Rueil-Malmaison, France

[2]) Bureau de Recherches Géologiques et Minières
Orléans, France

Echantillonnée dans une formation éocène lacustre de la région de Quincy (Cher, France), la quincyte est une variété de sépiolite colorée en rose-carmin par une substance organique.

La quincyte se trouve à l'état dispersé dans le ciment et dans les accidents siliceux d'un calcaire bréchiforme; aussi l'étude de sa coloration a-t-elle nécessité des opérations de concentration.

La substance organique colorant la quincyte n'a pu être extraite qu'en détruisant par HF la fraction argileuse du complexe. L'étude chimique préliminaire de cette substance indique qu'elle est constituée par plusieurs pigments organiques dont le spectre dans le visible est différent de celui des grandes classes de pigments naturels connus: porphyrines, pigments biliaires, caroténoïdes . . . Par ailleurs, ces pigments se trouvent associés dans la roche à une fraction huileuse, dans laquelle l'acide O. phtalique a pu être identifié.

The quincyte has been sampled in an eocene lacustral formation of Quincy's country (Cher-France). It is a variety of a sepiolite coloured pink-carmine by an organic substance.

The quincyte is dispersed in the siliceous concretions appearing in a limestone breccia and in its cement; so, the study of its coloration has required processes of concentration.

The organic substance colouring the quincyte has been isolated only by destruction of the argillaceous fraction of the complex by H. F. The preliminary chemical analysis of this substance indicates that it is made up by several organic pigments which have visible spectra different from porphyrin's spectra. Moreover, this pigments are associated in the rock sample with an oily substance in which O. phtalique acide has been identified.

Introduction

La quincyte [1]) est une variété de sépiolite colorée en rose-carmin par une pigmentation de nature organique.

---

[1]) Appellation et orthographe originales de M. Berthier 1825, reprises par A. Lacroix 1893.

Echantillonnée dans des dépôts lacustres éocènes (Ludien) de la région de Quincy (Cher, France), dépôts qui s'étendent sur plusieurs km² (Fig. 1), elle se trouve a l'état dispersé dans un calcaire grumeleux bréchiforme qu'elle colore nettement en rose sur une épaisseur de 0,5 à 1 m.

Sa teneur dans la roche est d'environ 0,5 %; par endroit, elle peut atteindre 3 %.

Des accidents siliceux présentent également des teintes roses plus ou moins prononcées dont la nature était inconnue, jusqu'à présent, et qui sont dues, comme dans les faciès calcaires, à une fine dispersion de quincyte.

L'étude de cette association remarquablement stable au cours des temps géologiques d'une sépiolite et d'une substance organique colorante a nécessité:

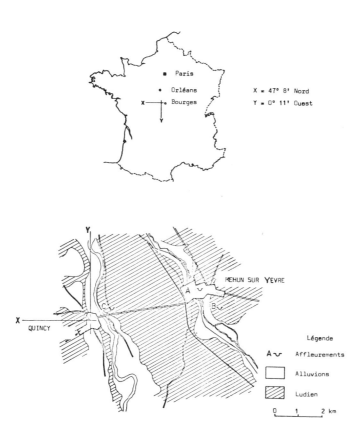

Fig. 1. Localisation des affleurements de quincyte (Situation en France et extrait de la Carte Géologique au 1/80 000e – feuille de Bourges)

a) des opérations de concentration de la fraction argileuse colorée: quincyte proprement dite,

b) des opérations d'extraction et de purification de la substance organique colorant la quincyte,

c) un essai de détermination chimique de cette substance colorante.

I. Observation microscopiques

a) Faciès calcaire (Photo 1)

Examinée en plaque mince, la quincyte apparait localisée dans de fines vacuoles de recristallisation d'un calcaire grumeleux (Photo 2). Sa teinte reste prononcée; elle est translucide et d'aspect "fluidal" ; son faciès fibreux apparait nettement en lumière polarisée.

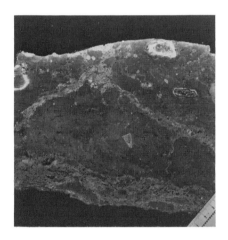 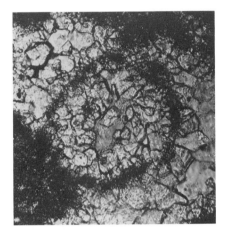

Photo 1
Calcaire lacustre de la région de Quincy, coloré par la quincyte. (Affleurement A Fig. 1)

Photo 2
Quincyte localisée dans une vacuole de recristallisation d'un calcaire grumeleux (Photo 1). Lumière polarisée. G. X. 400 environ.

b) Accidents siliceux

La quincyte est connue des gemmologues en tant que variété d'opale rose (Cavenago-Bignami S. 1965), sans que soit précisé sa relation avec la sépiolite rose de même appellation.

D'autres opales roses ont été découvertes en Californie; elles sont localisées, toutefois, dans un contexte volcanique, sans rapport avec celui de la quincyte (Baker, C. 1911, Dibbelee, T. 1968).

En ce qui concerne les échantillons d'opale rose, homogène, provenant de la région de Quincy, il est très difficile d'y déceler la quincyte au microscope; cette identification n'a été possible que dans certains échantillons où des ilots de recristallisation de l'opale en quartz (Fig. 2) ont concentré la quincyte.

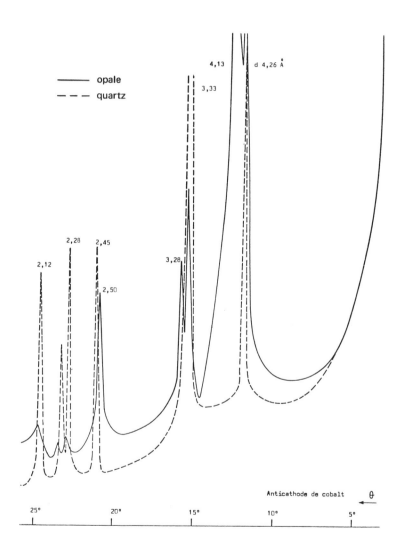

Fig. 2. Courbes diffractométriques par réflexion des R. X. de l'opale et du quartz

II. Methodes de concentration de la quincyte

a) Méthodes chimiques

Ces méthodes consistent à détruire la phase carbonatée des faciès calcaires contenant la quincyte par $CH_3 COOH$ ou HCl (20 % environ, et à froid). Cette méthode présente le grave inconvénient de libérer une certaine quantité d'huile présente dans la roche. L'huile libérée se fixe à la quincyte au cours de l'attaque de la roche et se mêle à la substance colorante dont elle gène considérablement la purification.

b) Méthodes physiques

La découverte d'un affleurement de calcaire rose, profondément touché par l'altération météorique, nous a amenés à envisager une séparation mécanique de la quincyte, hors de la roche qui la contient. En effet, à cet endroit, la quincyte se trouve sous forme de cristaux de quelques centaines de microns alors que la gangue calcaire est devenue assez friable (Photo 3).

Après une série d'essais, une méthode de séparation par tamisage, élutriation et battée, a permis d'obtenir un concentré ne contenant plus que 30 % environ de calcaire (Photo 4). Cette phase carbonatée résiduelle a été éliminée par HCl, sans attendre la mise au point d'une technique de séparation physique plus poussée qui sera nécessaire pour parfaire l'étude des pigments.

La quincyte ainsi obtenue reste mélée d'une peu de quartz et d'illite (Fig. 3); mais sa pollution par des huiles étrangères provenant de la roche est très réduite.

Photo 3
Calcaire enrichi en quincyte à la suite d'une dissolution partielle par les eaux de pluie (Affleurement C Fig. 1)

Photo 4
Quincyte isolée de sa gangue calcaire (Photo 3) par voie mécanique. G. X. 200 environ

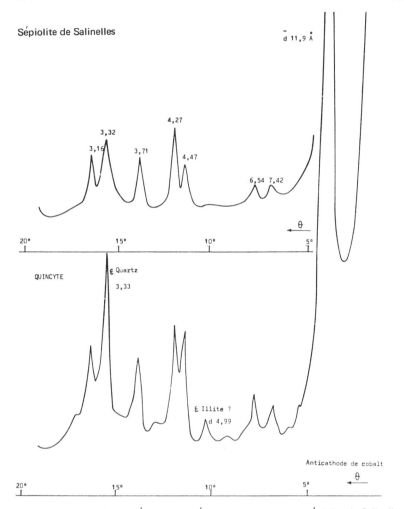

Fig. 3. Courbes diffractométriques par réflexion des R. X. de la sépiolite de Salinelles (Gard) et de la quincyte

III. Stabilité de la coloration de la quincyte

Sur le terrain, la quincyte frappe par la vivacité de sa teinte. Elle apparait absolument inaltérée par les agents atmosphériques. Au laboratoire, elle résiste parfaitement au divers traitements chimiques que nous avons fait subir à la roche: HCl concentré et chaud ne la dégrade que partiellement; seul HF permet de la détruire à froid, et de libérer ainsi sa substance colorante, soluble dans les solvants organiques. L'action directe des solvants organiques sur la quincyte, même au Soxhlet, est sans effet.

a) Essais thermiques

Chauffé progressivement, la quincyte passe du rose-carmin au rose-violacé vers 250 °C; elle conserve cette teinte jusqu'à 325 °C environ, puis la coloration disparait.

b) Comparaison avec le " Bleu des Mayas "

Les propriétés de la quincyte sont à rapprocher de celles qui ont été décrites à propos du " Bleu des Mayas " (Guettens, R. 1962, Van Olphen, 1966). Ce pigment serait constitué par un mélange remarquablement stable d'indigo et d'argile fibreuse: attapulgite et sépiolite. La mélange résiste aux acides minéraux concentrés, et à la chaleur, jusqu'à une température de 250 °C environ.

c) Nature du complexe sépiolite-substance colorante organique

La sépiolite, comme l'attapulgité, présente une structure en " rubans " qui offre en coupe l'aspect d'un empilement de briques creuses (Fig. 4). Cette disposition

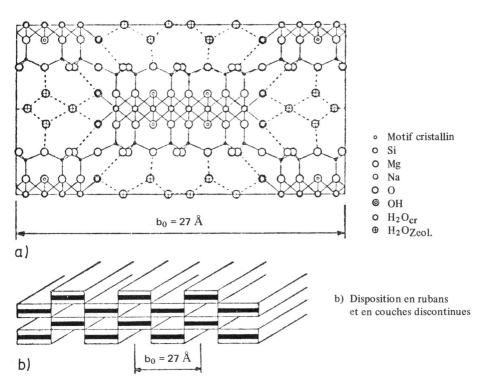

o   Motif cristallin
o   Si
o   Mg
o   Na
o   O
⊚   OH
o H_2O_{cr}
⊕ $H_2O_{Zeol.}$

$b_0 = 27$ Å

a)

b) Disposition en rubans et en couches discontinues

b) $b_0 = 27$ Å

Fig. 4. Schéma de la structure de la sépiolite. Extrait de Preisinger A. 1963 et Vivaldi J. 1960

en couches discontnues crée des espaces vides, ou canaux, occupés par de l'eau zéolithique; elle est responsable des surfaces spécifiques très élevées (150 m^2/g) mesurées pour la sépiolite.

En ce qui concerne le "Bleu des Mayas", les auteurs pensent que la molécule d'indigo est trop grosse pour se loger dans les canaux de la sépiolite, et qu'en raison de la faible capacité d'échange de ce minéral pour l'indigo, ce dernier serait adsorbé à la surface externe des particules. Cette interprétation est en accord avec le fait que la teinte est irrégulièrement répartie dans le "Bleu des Mayas": de nombreuses particules sont uniquement frangées de bleu à l'extérieur.

Ce n'est pas le cas de la quincyte dont la teinte, parfaitement uniforme, suggère une association intime et spécifique du pigment organique et de la sépiolite; il serait intéressant de pouvoir préciser cette association en vue d'applications industrielles, par exemple.

IV. Extraction et purification la substance colorante de la quincyte

a) Quincyte extraite par voie chimique

Le résidu insoluble de l'attaque par HF de la quincyte obtenue par élimination chimique de la phase carbonatée de la roche donne un extrait soluble dans le M. A.B.[1]), extrait constitué à plus de 90 % par une huile qui rend très délicate les opérations de purification de la substance colorante proprement dite. Le spectre dans le visible des produits colorés obtenus est masqué partiellement par ces huiles étrangères.

Un essai de purification a été entrepris en extrayant sélectivement au Soxhlet la fraction huileuse, d'abord, la substance colorante, ensuite, après traitement progressif de la quincyte par des solutions d'HCl de plus en plus concentrées et chaudes. Le spectre dans le visible de la substance colorante s'en trouve nettement amélioré (Fig. 5).

b) Quincyte extraite par voie physique

La quincyte concentrée à 70 % par élutriation et battée, livre une substance colorante dont la qualité du spectre dans la visible après purification (Fig. 6) est encore amélioré (Fig. 7). Cette méthode de concentration encore imparfaite, est certainement celle qui devra être retenue pour une étude chimique approfondie de la substance organique colorant la quincyte, et, surtout, pour une étude cristallographique visant à préciser le mode d'association de ces deux produits.

---

[1]) M.A.B.: Mélange triple contenant 15 % de méthanol, 15 % d'acétone et 70 % de benzène.

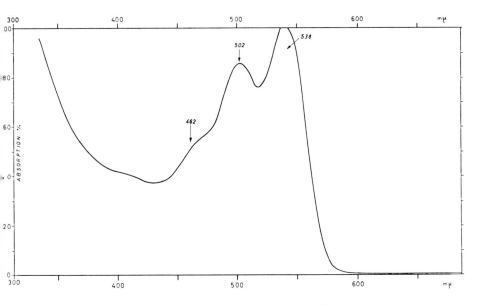

Fig. 5. Colorant obtenu par dégradation progressive de la quincyte à HCl concentré et chaud
(Sol. M. A. B.)

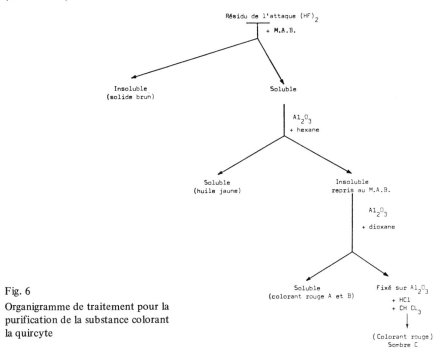

Fig. 6

Organigramme de traitement pour la
purification de la substance colorant
la quircyte

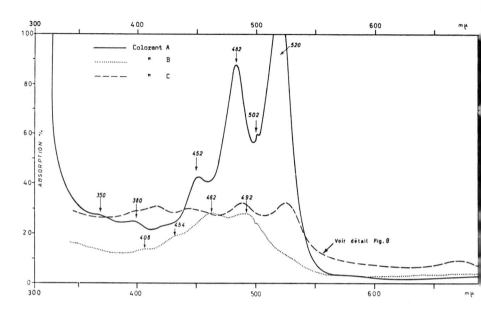

Fig. 7. Colorants obtenus à partir de la quincyte concentrée par voie mécanique (Sol. dioxane)

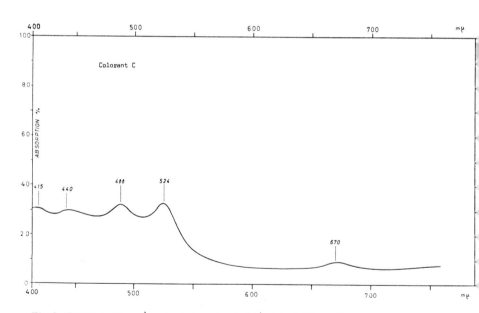

Fig. 8. Colorant obtenu à partir de la quincyte (Détail de la Figure 7)

V. Etude chimique preliminatre de la substance colorante de la quincyte

Du produit solide brun-rouge résultant de l'attaque fluorhydrique de la quincyte, nous avons cherché à extraire le colorant.

A la suite d'essais préliminaires, nous avons adopté le mode opératoire schématisé sur la Figure 6. La fraction soluble a été extraite par le mélange triple M.A.B. Après concentration, la solution colorée a été placée sur une colonne d'alumine Brockmann. Une première élution à l'hexane enlève une huile jaune pâle, peu visqueuse.

De l'alumine colorée en rose, le dioxane a permis d'éluer, en deux portions, A et B, la plus grande partie du colorant. Toutefois, il reste encore un anneau rouge violacé sur la colonne, que d'autres solvants n'arrivent pas à enlever. En détruisant l'alumine par l'acide chlorhydrique, on a pu mettre ce colorant C en solution dans le chloroforme.

Les spectres dans le visible sont reportés sur les Figures 7 et 8.

Le colorant A présente une forte bande à 520 mμ, une autre moins forte à 482, une troisième plus petite à 452 mμ, et encore deux plus faible à 380 et 350 mμ.

Le colorant B donne deux bandes à 492 à 462 mμ ayant sensiblement les mêmes intensités. Il y a encore deux bandes plus faibles à 434 et 408 mμ. A noter que ce colorant donne une solution fluorescente dans le dioxane.

Le colorant C est le seul qui présente une bande à 670 mμ. Les deux autres bandes se trouvent à 524 et 480, puis deux autres plus faibles à 440 et 415 mμ.

Aucune de nos substances ne présentent les bandes caractéristiques des porphyrines, entre 550 et 635 mμ (Fig. 9). Les spectres IR, ne sont pas non plus identiques.

La phycoérythrine, que l'on trouve dans les eaux rouges de certains lacs des Alpes suisses montrent aussi des bandes au-dessus de 550 mμ. Elle n'est donc pas présente dans la quincyte.

Le colorant B possède deux bandes (434 et 462) voisines de celles du carotène β (437 et 462), mais les autres sont différentes. Par ailleurs, le colorant A montre deux bandes (452 et 482) voisines de celles de l'extrait de gytthia (tourbe lacustre) qui est lui aussi un mélange.

Quant à l'huile jaune éluée à l'hexane, elle présente un indice de saponification élevé = 353. Les acides séparés sont en majorité des solides blancs. On a pu isoler l'un d'entre eux; il a pour composition: C = 57,20 %, H = 3,73 %, O = 38,63 %. Poids moléculaire 158.

Son spectre infra-rouge correspond à celui de l'acide phtalique. Ce dernier a, en effet, une composition très voisine: C = 57,83 %, H = 3,61, O = 38,55. Poids moléculaire 166.

L'acide isolé donne avec la résorcine une magnifique fluorescence, (fluorescéine); il s'agit donc de l'acide ortho-phtalique.

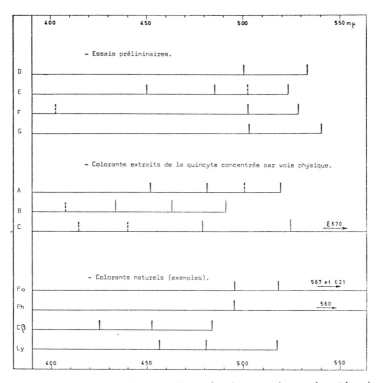

Fig. 9. Spectres dans le visible des diverses fractions organiques colorant la quincyte
Comparaison avec les spectres de colorants connus

A-G: Rouge ± orangé: Colorants de la quincyte. Sol. dioxane
P_o: Rouge violacé: Etioporphyrine. Sol. dioxane
Ph: Rouge: Phycoérythrine. Sol. HCl 5 %
C: Orange: Carotène β. Sol. hexane
Ly: Rouge orangé: Lycopène. Sol. hexane

Cette étude est incomplète et bien des points sont encore à préciser. Cependant
on peut déjà entirer quelques remarques importantes.

1) La couleur de la quincyte est due à plusieurs colorants.

2) Ces matières colorantes ne sont pas de porphyrines, comme différents auteurs
(Deribere, M. 1961) l'avaient supposé.

3) La présence d'acide organique incite à supposer une origine végétale à ces colorants. Les traces de racines observées dans la roche (faciès vermiculé) appuient
cette opinion.

4) Ces substances sont intimement fixées sur la sépiolite qui les a protégées de
l'altération pendant 40 millions d'années environ.

5) L'acide 0. phtalique a été reconnu. Il a jusqu'à présent, rarement été signalé dans les substances fossiles. Il a été trouvé dans une asphaltite uranifère (Pierce A., Mytion, J. et Barnett, P. 1958), dans une huile brute de Uinta (Phillips, A. et Berger, A. 1958). L'un de nous (Louis, M.) l'a isolé du pétrole d'Hassi Messaoud et mis en évidence dans plusieurs autres.

Cet acide n'existe pas à l'état libre dans le monde vivant; il provient sans doute de l'oxydation de molécules aromatiques existant dans les organismes végétaux (lignine par exemple: Polonowski, M. et Lespagnol, A. 1941). Sa présence révèle un milieu oxydant à un moment donné de l'histoire du sédiment.

On peut comparer notre observation à celle de Burlingame, A. (1968), qui a trouvé des acides benzène dicarboxyliques et des phénols dans le schiste de Green River. Ce schiste, d'âge Eocène, provient aussi d'un milieu lacustre, comme la quincyte.

Conclusion

L'étude de la quincyte peut donner des informations inédites pour la reconstitution géochimique, voie paléobotanique, d'un milieu de sédimentation lacustre ancien; des informations relatives à la génèse des sépiolites peuvent également être apportées.

Si la nature chimique des pigments organiques reste à préciser, la présence d'acide 0. phtalique constitue déjà une donnée nouvelle intéressante; d'autres acides organiques doivent pouvoir être encore identifiés.

Enfin, l'association sépiolite-pigment organique qui a pu se maintenir pendant quelques 40 millions d'années et résister aux agents atmosphériques à l'affleurement, est un sujet d'étude à retenir; il s'apparente à celui qui a déjà été posé par le " Bleu des Mayas " .

Remerciements: Nous prions les personnes des Départements " Géochimie " et " Physique Analytique " de l'I. F. P., celles des Départements " Laboratoires " et " Géologie " du B. R. G. M. qui nous ont apporté leur concours dans ce travail, de trouver ici l'expression de notre gratitude.

Bibliographie

Baker, C. L. (1911): Notes on the later Cenozoic history of the Mohave Desert region in south eastern California. Bull. Depart. geo.-Univ. of California. 6, n° 15, pp. 33–383.

Berthier, M. P. (1825): Examen de la substance rose de Quincy. Annales des Mines 10, 242.

Burlingame, A. L., Haug, P. A., Schnoes, K. H., et Simoneit, B. B. (1968): Fatty acides derived from the Green River formation oil shale. 4th international meeting on organic geochemistry.

Cavenago-Bignami, S. (1965): Gemmologia. Hoepli Milan.

Deribere, M. (1961): La fluorescence des porphyrines concentrées dans les éléments minéraux d'origine biologique. Bull. Soc. fr. de Miner. et Crist. 84, pp. 94–95.

Dibblee, T. W. (1968): Fremont Peak and Opal Moutain Quadrangles, 188, pp. 60–61. Calif. Div. Mines and Geology.

Gettens, R. J. (1962): Maya Blue: An unsolved problem in ancient pigments. American Antiquity. 27 n° 4.

Lacroix, A. (1893): Minéralogie de la France et de ses colonies. Baudry-Beranger Paris.

Olphen, V. (1966): Maya Blue: A clay organic pigment? Science. 154, p. 645.

Philips, H., Berger, A. (1958): Isolement et identification d'un ester de l'acide phtalique dans une huile brute américaine. Geochimica et cosmochimica acta. 15, p. 51.

Pierce, A., Mytton, J., Barnett, P. (1958): Geochemistry of uranium in organic substances in petroliferous rocks. 2me conf. ONU. Peaceful uses of atom. energy. 2, 192.

Polonowski, M., Lespagnol, A. (1941): Chimie organique biologique.

Preisinger, A. (1963): Sepiolite and related compounds: Its stability and application. Proc. 10 the. conf. of Clays and Clay mineral 12. pp. 365–370 Pergamon Press.

Vivaldi, J. L., Gonzales, J. L.: A random intergowth of sepiolite and attapulgite. Proc. 9 th. Nat. Conf. of clays and clay minerals 9, pp. 592–602, Pergamon Press.

Discussion

R. E. H. Göhring: I wonder you know the publication by Mr. Hunneman of the possibilities of contamination by phtalates from polyvinylchloride. We know from experience that the use of polyvinylchloride sample bags already brings about the contamination of samples with phtalates which are present as softeners in the plastic material.

J. P. Ragot: Connaissant ce risque de pollution, nous avons évité d'utiliser dans nos expériences des solvants contenus dans des récipients en matière plastique; en effect celle-ci renferme souvent du phtalate de butyle et isooctyle.

Accumulation of Microelements in Peat Humic Acids and Coal

Alexander Szalay and Marie Szilágyi

Institute of Nuclear Research of the Hungarian Academy of Sciences
Debrecen, Hungary

V.M. Goldschmidt observed in the thirties high geochemical accumulation of microelements in coals. He assumed three possible explanations for them.

He missed the uranium accumulation in coals, because spectral analytical technique is not sensitive for U. U content of Hungarian coals was discovered by the senior author in 1949 and very soon confirmed by observations on coals in many parts of the world. Experiments of the senior author clarified the cause of this accumulation. U is accumulated from very dilute solutions by the cation exchange properties of insoluble humic acids in peat. The accumulation can be characterized by a very high geochemical enrichment factor (GEF) of $10,000:1$.

Further experiments revealed that this cation exchange process is identical with that known for microelements in soil science – e.g. exchange of Ca^{2+} versus K^+ etc. –, but the GEF is very high for elements of high atomic weight and valence.

In the course of the recent 15 years the sorption on peat of a great number of elements throughout the periodic system was investigated in this institute. Insoluble humic acids behave as a natural organic cation exchange resin of the carboxylated type. This exchange phenomenon is of general validity for the accumulation of many minor elements in peat, in the hydrogeochemical cycle.

The bottleneck of this accumulation process is the low concentration of the element in natural waters and not the ion exchange sorption which is a very efficient process, collecting by a high GEF.

But returning again to the observations of Goldschmidt we must realise that many of the minor elements accumulated in coal are not cations at all and only the accumulations of cations can be explained by the simple cation exchange process.

Vanadium and molybdenum are usually associated with uranium in coals in Hungary and elsewhere. Both elements have only anionic migrating form at the conditions prevailing in natural waters. Our laboratory experiments demonstrated that when their migrating forms (VO_3^-, MoO_4^{2-}) come into contact with insoluble humic acids, they are reduced into their cationic forms: VO^{2+}, Mo^{5+} and these forms are strongly fixed by cation exchange. In this way even amphoteric elements with anionic migrating form might accumulate in peat after reduction.

Many minor elements are accumulated in these ways by the insoluble humic acids in peat and coal and at the same time natural waters are depleted of them.

This phenomenon is responsible according to our observations for the starvation or deficiency of plants on several micronutrients (Cu, Zn, Mn, Co, Mo) on peat fields, of which about 50 million hectars exist in Europe, Further, this process might have a role in the geochemical deficiency of the ocean waters in U, Th and many other heavy cations.

Introduction

To begin with, may we remind you of some pioneering discoveries concerning the association of microelements with fossil organic substances. By microelements we mean those occuring in the earth-crust at several ppm range of average concentration and we speak about an association if the accumulation in the organic substance exceeds the Clarke-number of the microelement by orders of magnitude.

Some observations are represented in Table I.

Table I. Some discoveries concerning the enrichment of microelements in fossil organic matter.

Author	Year	Observations
H.M. Thompson and J.T. Way	1850	Cation exchange of Ca^{2+}, K^+ and (NH_4^+) in fertile soil
F. Hess	1914	Enrichment of U and V in fossil plant parts in Colorado sandstone
W.J. Vernadsky	1915	Enrichment of U and V in asphalts
F. Beyschlag	1921	U, Cu and other enrichments in peat
V.M. Goldschmidt and Cl. Peters	1933–37	Enrichment of Be, B, Sc, Co, Ni, Zn, Ga, Ge, As, Mo, Ag, Cd, Pb, Bi, etc (not U) in coals.
A.H. Westergard	1941–44	U-content of alum shales in Sweden
A. Szalay	1949–50	U in coals in Hungary
Many authors, Atoms for Peace Conferences I. and II. Geneva	1955–58	U in various bioliths in many places of the world

Cation exchange properties of the fertile soil had been observed already by Thompson and Way in England concerning NH_4^+, K^+ and Ca^{2+} (H.S. Thompson 1850, J.T. Way 1850). They observed some kind of retention resp. exchange of these cations for one another.

F. Hess observed a strong accumulation of U, V and Mo in fossil wood logs embedded into Colorado sandstones (F. Hess 1914).

Vernadsky in 1915 observed (W.J. Vernadsky 1930) the enrichment of U in asphalts.

In 1921 F. Beyschlag found U-occurence in peat (F. Beyschlag 1921).

Goldschmidt observed in the thirties the enrichment of many microelements in coals (V.M. Goldschmidt et al. 1933). He failed to observe U, probably because the spectral analytical method is not sensitive for this element.

U concentration had been observed by Westergard in the kolm lenses of Cambrian-Ordovician alum shales in Sweden (A.H. Westergard 1944a, 1944b). Enrichment of U in subbituminous coals was observed by A. Szalay in Hungary in 1949

(A. Szalay 1952c, 1964). A great number of similar observations have been reported by many authors on the first and second conferences on "The Peaceful Uses of Atomic Energy", in Geneva in 1955 and 1958 (Geneva 1956, Geneva 1958). Modern radiometric methods revealed many associations of U with bioliths (coals, antrim shales and Chattanooga shales in the U.S.A., etc.). Authors and papers are very numerous and it is not the prupose of this paper to provide a full account of them. Some excellent survey papers appeared in the Geneva Volumes (loc. cit) and in the professional papers of the Geological Survey of the U.S.A. (J.D. Vine, 1962).

These empirical observations in Table I seemed to be quite independent from one another. They relate to very different types of rocks and soil, geological ages and different microelements. The primeval forms of plant life developed tremendously in the course of evolution since the precambrian ages up to the age of more recent coals and peats, into higher forms of plant life. Some of the microelements in coal are cations, some of them transitory elements or even anions. So it is understandable that no scientist thought or dared to link them all by a single comprehensive explanation.

F. Hess already in 1914 and W.J. Vernadsky in 1930 emphasized the association of U and V with fossil organic substances, but the question of the causal relationship remained open.

V.M. Goldschmidt gave some explanations for the enrichment of some microelements in coal. He laid special stress on the role of uptake of nutrient and ballast elements by living plants with subsoil water and the deposition of them in the twigs and leaves. It is certain that micronutrients and some ballast elements are transported by this mechanism to the soil surface, where a local enrichment of Cu, Zn, Mn, Mo, B etc. is observable and this amount is steadily in the turnover of vegetation (V.M. Goldschmidt 1937). Another explanation by him was adsorption in the surface of precipitating Mn and Fe hydroxides, or the precipitation by a special local chemical environment, e.g. anaerobic rotting of plant substances under water and the precipitation by the developing H_2S, etc.

The Role of Humic Acids in the Enrichments

Here we should like to give an account of our experimental investigations in Debrecen, which revealed the role of humic acids in the enrichment of U and other microelements in fossil plant substances and bioliths and which link these phenomena by a single quantitative law of broad validity in the biosphere.

After the discovery of U in subbituminous coals in Hungary, the senior author started soon a series of experiments in order to find an explanation for these enrichment phenomena in bioliths, because he thought they could be traced down to a common basic phenomenon. The accumulation of U might have nothing to do with life processes, it must happen on the surface of dead plant substances, moldering under water. He supposed that if this concentration process had functioned in so various forms of plant material in the course of so different geological ages it consequently must do so even nowadays.

It was astonishing to observe that a lignite powder or peat sample sorbed U so quickly even from very dilute aqueous solutions that it virtually disappeared from the water within one minute. The phenomenon demonstrated strikingly regular features which could be graphically represented by a regular sorption isotherm (A. Szalay 1954a, 1954b), (Fig. 1). This isotherm can be characterized mathematically by two numerical constants. The measured points can be well fitted with a Langmuir equation for a sorption isotherm:

$$N = \frac{N_\infty \cdot a \cdot c}{1 + a \cdot c}$$

where c is the concentration of U in water, N in peat.

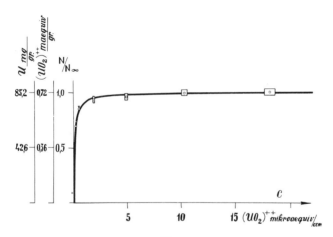

Fig. 1. Sorption isotherm of UO_2^{2+} ion on a pliocene lignite at pH = 5. Abscissa: equilibrium concentration of UO_2^{2+} in water. Ordinate: equilibrium concentration of UO_2^{2+} in the lignite

One of the numerical constants (N_∞) is the sorption capacity of the given peat in milliequivalent/g, the other one ($N_\infty \cdot a$) is the equilibrium distribution coefficient of the cation between the peat and aqueous phases at very low concentrations. We can call it the "Geochemical Enrichment Factor" (G.E.F.).

$$\text{G.E.F.} = \frac{N}{c} = N_\infty \cdot a$$

Both constants are remarkably well defined. Among the investigated rather numerous peat, lignite and subbituminous coal samples the saturation capacity for UO^{2+} varied between 0,7 − 2 m-equiv./g values (Fig. 2). The G.E.F. is very high, about 10.000 for UO_2. Investigations by radioisotope exchange and other methods clarified that the enrichment process is a pure cation exchange phenomenon and it takes place in the insoluble humic acids in peat or coal. In fact, insoluble humic acids are natural cation exchange resins, and in this respect they are similar in behaviour to synthetic exchange resins of the carboxylated polyaromatic type. They are the main constituents of peat. They originate in the lignin part of plants, forming an intermediate state in the course of fossilization to coal. Fig. 3 demonstrates schematically the structural unit of an insoluble humic acid after W. Fuchs (W. Fuchs 1931). It consists of a polyaromatic skeleton of high chemical resistance against microbial attack under unairated conditions and having some polar groups on it. The carboxylic groups dissociate at pH values 3 or higher and their H^+ can be exchanged for other cations. This exchange is responsible for the enrichments. Asphalts contain many carboxyl groups and the enrichments of U in them, observed by Vernadsky, can be explained by this fact.

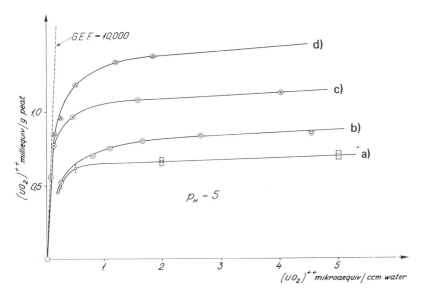

Fig. 2. Sorption isotherms of UO_2^{2+} ions on various humic acid preparations at pH = 5. Ordinate: equilibrium concentration of UO_2^{2+} in the solid phases; Abscissa: equilibrium concentration of UO_2^{2+} in water

a) Pliocene lignite. b, c, d) Quaternary Holocene phragmites peats

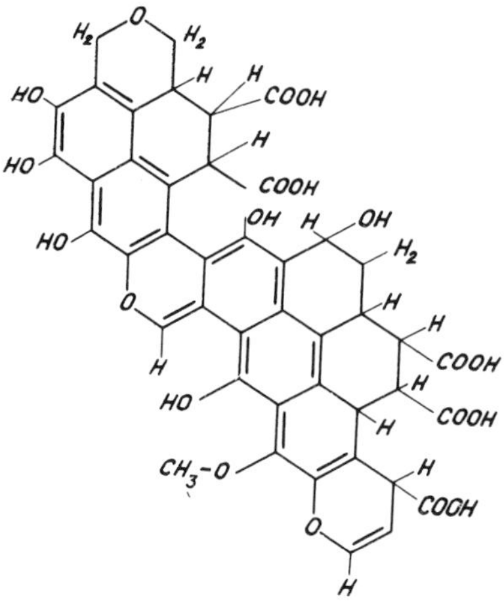

Fig. 3
Chemical schema of a structural unit of humic
acids after Fuchs

Further experiments revealed that this cation exchange process is identical with the
one known qualitatively for macroelements in soil science (e.g. exchange of Ca^{2+}
versus K^+ etc.), but the G.E.F. is very high for elements of high atomic weight and
valency.

We investigated experimentally further (I. Szabó 1958, A. Szalay et al. 1961a,
A. Szalay et al. 1961 b), in the course of the recent 15 years, the sorption of a great
number of elements on peat throughout the periodic system (Fig. 4). Table II
demonstrates the G.E.F. for some of them.

This exchange phenomenon is the cause of the accumulation of many microelements in peat in the hydrogeochemical cycle. The low concentration of the elements
in natural waters is the bottleneck of this accumulation process and not the ion
exchange sorption which is a very efficient collecting process, characterized by a
high G.E.F. The total amount of organic substances accumulated in the biosphere
consists, to a large extent, of insoluble humic acids and its amount far exceeds that
of living substances. This law of hydrogeochemistry explains the seemingly independent facts of Table I as consequences of a single cation exchange phenomenon.
There are some microelements, however, which must be investigated and explained
in detail.

This cation exchange phenomenon accumulates only cations and so the accumulation of those elements, the migrating form of which is an anion, cannot be explained by it. Transitory elements like V and Mo, observed already by early explorers
to be strongly associated with U and organic substances migrate definitely only in
their highly soluble anionic forms in natural waters, such as VO_3^- and MoO_4^{2-}.

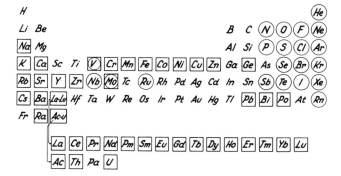

Fig. 4. Interaction of insoluble humic acids with elements of the periodic table. Elements sorbed in squares, those certainly not sorbed in circles. V and Mo sorbed after reduction of anionic migrating form. Others not investigated yet

Table II. Approximate G.E.F. values for some microelements in peat.

Investigated in laboratory			Migrating form
ion form	G.E.F.	at pH	
UO_2^{2+}	$1 \cdot 10^4$	5.0	UO_2^{2+}
Fe^{3+}	$2.65 \cdot 10^4$	4–4.5	Fe^{2+}
Fe^{2+}	$9.1 \cdot 10^2$	4–4.5	Fe^{2+}
Ni^{2+}	$4.51 \cdot 10^2$	4–4.5	Ni^{2+}
La^{3+} (rare earths)	$2.3 \cdot 10^4$	5.0	La^{3+}
Ba^{2+}	cca. 10^4	5	Ba^{2+}
Mn^{2+}	$5.0 \cdot 10^3$	5.0	Mn^{2+}
Cu^{2+}	$2.38 \cdot 10^3$	4–4.5	Cu^{2+}
Co^{2+}	$6.9 \cdot 10^3$	4.6	Co^{2+}
VO^{2+}	$5.0 \cdot 10^4$	5.0	VO_3^-
MoO_4^{2-}	$2.0 \cdot 10^2$	4.0	MoO_4^{2-}
Zn^{2+}	$8.6 \cdot 10^3$	5.0	Zn^{2+}
Zr^{4+}	$> 10^4$	1	

Many of the further accumulating elements observed are definitely not cations
at all (e.g. As, Se etc.). We investigated with M. Szilágyi at first V and Mo because
their association with U in bioliths is very striking (A. Szalay et al. 1967, M. Szilágyi
1967).

These two elements have the common chemical property that they are easily reduced
from their migrating anionic forms VO_3^-, MoO_4^{2-} into cationic forms VO^{2+} and
Mo^{5+}.

Ample laboratory experimental evidence has been found that this happens when
natural waters carrying vanadate and molibdate anions come into contact with peat.
Peat reduces them to cation forms and strongly fixes the cation form by the already
known cation exchange process. This occurs even under airated conditions. In this
way even amphoteric elements with anionic migrating form might accumulate in
peat after reduction. A future investigation of some other elements of this kind is
intended.

The following can be said about the accumulation of Se and As in coals. It is well-
known that bioliths contain always a large amount of Fe which accumulated partly
by cation exchange. We do not speak about an enrichment, because Fe is very
abundant in the earthcrust.

H_2S develops from organic materials which rot in the anaerob zone (reduction
zone) under the water horizon. This H_2S reacts with the iron-humate (Fe^{2+} in
cation exchange binding). In fact, the so called "meadow ore" rich in iron-humate,
is used industrially for the purification of city gas from H_2S and mercaptanes. In
the course of mineralization pyrite is produced. Now AsH_3, H_2Se are certainly
produced from their anionic migrating forms AsO_4^{3-} and SeO_4^{2-} at the same reduction potential which is sufficient for the production of H_2S.

It can be assumed that when the traces of AsH_3 and H_2Se diluted with a larger
amount of H_2S come into contact with the iron-humate content of peat, at first
ironselenide and arsenide reactions occur and selenopyrite and arsenopyrite are
produced in the course of mineralization. The high As and Se enrichment in some
coals could be probably located in these minerals. This type of concentration should
be effective even for Te, but Te is a very rare element and therefore it probably has
never been investigated and detected in coals. In this type of enrichment of anionic elements, the cation exchange properties of humic acids have only an intermediate role i.e. they present the ion exchangefixed Fe^{++} ions (ferro-humate) for the
sulfidization reaction.

Additionally, it is well-known that several nutrient elements, micronutrients and
ballast-elements are taken up by living plants and Goldschmidt's explanation is certainly valid for them. This explains the accumulation of B, because according to
our experiments humic acids do not fix boric acid at all. Some nutrient elements

(Fe), and particularly micronutrients (Cu, Zn, Mn, Mo), can be fixed in both ways, and there might be a competition between the biological need for uptake by living plants and the retention by humic acids in the soil.

Depletion of Microelements from Waters by Humic Acids

Humic acids are very abundant in nature and they exert by their cation exchange property a strong concentration effect upon micrometals of higher atomic weight and valency. They must at the same time deionize, deplete natural waters which have been in contact with tehm and exert herewith a negative, depletion effect on the cation content of natural waters. Investigations in this direction of depletion effects have been started.

Recently we investigated the retention of plant micronutrients by insoluble humic acids and observed a high retention for Mn, Fe, Zn, Cu and somewhat less for Mo (A. Szalay et al. 1968a, 1968b). In fact, the retention is strong enough to cause a deficiency or starvation of plants on peat- and moorlands with a high humic acid content. The retention of Cu by soils of high organic content is already known in many parts of the world, e.g. reclamation lands in Holland, in the extended moorlands in Northern Europe and the USSR. Laboratory observations have been published for the sorption of Cu on peat by Manskaya et al. (S.M. Manskaya et al. 1960) and by Ling Ong et al. (H. Ling Ong et al. 1966). We are very glad to be able to measure quantitatively and understand scientifically the retention of micronutrients on moorlands leading to deficiency symptoms of plants (A. Szalay et al. 1968b). 50 million acres of such lands exist in Europe alone (incl. the European part of the USSR), not to mention the extended moor- and peat-fields of the USA, Canada, British Columbia, etc. New agricultural experiments have been started in Hungary in order to overcome the starvation of plants and increase the fertility of such soils.

A further hypothetical generalization of this law is possible in this negative, depletion sense. It is a well-known fact that there is a large deficiency in the geochemical balance of the content of the ocean waters in heavy cations. They did not accumulate substantially during geological eons be evaporation of river waters feeding the oceans. Although there exist other explanations for this deficiency (e.g. adsorption on precipitating Mn and Fe hydroxides) the missing elements can be found enriched in the organic sediments of the river deltas and lagoons, and in the fossil organic substances of the bioliths, e.g. black marine shales. It is quite probable that the heavy cation content of the river waters is already fixed on transported humic particles and settles down in the delta regions and lagoons. At this moment this is merely a hypothesis and it needs experimental proof in the future.

Summary

Many observations concerning the enrichment of various microelements in various types of fossile organic material can be explained by a single phenomenon: the cation exchange property of insoluble humic acids.

U and many other cations are accumulated by this exchange property with a geo-chemical enrichment factor (G.E.F.) of about 10.000 in the humic acids of peat.

Some microelements which have anion migrating forms (e.g. V and Mo) are at first reduced by the humic acids to cations and fixed in the cation form afterwards.

As and Se are probably fixed under anaerob (rotting) conditions by way of their volatile hydrogene compounds as arsenopyrite and selenopyrite, in the course of sulidization, in the iron-humate content of peat.

The depletion of water in a peat-soil from its microelements causes deficiency of plants in micronutrient elements. Humic acid particles transported by rivers pro-bably deplete the waters from their heavy cation content and so humic acids might have a significant role in the deficiency of the cation balance of the oceans.

References

Beyschlag, F.; (1921): Z. pr. Geol. loco cit. W.J. Vernadsky, Geochemie, Akademische Verlagsgesellschaft M.B.H. Leipzig (1930) p. 266.

Fuchs, W.; (1931): Die Chemie der Kohle, J. Springer, Berlin.

Goldschmidt, V.M.; (1937): Journ. of the Chem. Soc. p. 655.

Goldschmidt, V.M. and Cl. Peters; (1933): Nachr. Ges. Wiss. Göttingen, Math.-physik. Klasse,
III. 38; IV. 40; p. 371.

Hess, F.; (1914): Econ. Geol. 9, p. 686.

Ling Ong, H. and Vernon E. Swanson; (1966): Econ. Geol. 61, p. 1214.

Manskaya, S.M., T.V. Drozdova, M.P. Emel'yanova; (1960): Geokhimiya No. 6, p. 529.
(in Russian)

Proc. of the Intern. Conf. on the Peaceful Uses of Atomic Energy vol. 6 (1956). United Nations,
New York.

Proc. of the 2nd United Nations Intern. Conf. on the Peaceful Uses of Atomic Energy vol. 2
(1958). United Nations, Geneva.

Szabó, I.; (1958): Comm. Third Math.-Phys. Class Hung. Acad. Sci. 8, p. 393. (in Hungarian).

Szalay, A.; (1952): Comm. Sixth Techn. Sci. Class. Hung. Acad. Sci. 5, p. 167. (in Hungarian).

Szalay, A.; (1954a): Acta Geol. Hung. 2, p. 299.

Szalay, A.; (1954b): Comm. Third. Math.-Phys. Class Hung. Acad. Sci. 4, p. 327. (in Hungarian).

Szalay, A.; (1964): Geochim. et Cosmochim. Acta 28, p. 1605.

Szalay, A. and M. Szilágyi; (1961a): Comm. Third Math.-Phys. Class Hung. Acad. Sci. 11, p. 47.
(in Hungarian).

Szalay, A. and M. Szilágyi; (1961b): Acta Phys. Hung. 13, p. 421.

Szalay, A.and M. Szilágyi; (1967): Geochim. et Cosmochim. Acta 31, p. 1.

Szalay, A. and M. Szilágyi; (1968a): Comm. Fourth Agricult. Class Hung. Acad. Sci. 27, p 109.
(in Hungarian).

Szalay, A. and M. Szilágyi; (1968b): Plant and Soil, 29, no. 2. Oct. 1968. p.

Szilágyi, M.; (1967): Geokhimiya No, 12. p. 1489. (in Russian)

Thompson, H.S.; (1850): J. Roy. Agr. Soc. England 11, p. 68.

Vernadsky, W.J.; (1930): Geochemie in ausgewählten Kapiteln, Akademische Verlagsgesellschaft
M.B.H. Leipzig, p. 266.

Vine, J.D.; (1962): G.S. Prof. Paper 356-D., U.S. Govern. Print. Off. Washington, p. 113.

Way, J.T.; (1850): J. Roy. Agr. Soc. England 11, p. 313.

Westergard, A.H.; (1944a): Sver. geol. undersökning, ser. C, no 459, p. 13.

Westergard, A.H.; (1944b): Sver. geol. undersökning, ser. C, no 463, p. 18.

Discussion

M. Schidlowski: Did you ever observe newly-formed, proper uranium minerals within the carbonaceous materials which you used for your experiments?

A. Szalay: I used non uraniferous young peat in the cation exchange experiments. Secondary mineralisation occurs slowly in uraniferous coals.

J.C. Goni: Avez-vous une idée sur le mécanisme de réduction de l' AsO_4^{3-} à AsH_3?

A. Szalay: Non.

J.C. Goni: Avez-vous purifié les acides humiques de la tourbe?

A. Szalay: Non, nous avons travaillé sur la tourbe "tel quel".

P.H. Given: I was surprised by your finding that humic acids do not fix boron. In view of what Dr. Flaig has told us about the role of phenols, including *ortho*-dihydroxy-benzenes, in the formation of humic acids, I would have expected that boron would be fixed as a chelate complex. The stable complexes of boron with cis-*ortho*-dihydroxy compounds are well known in analytical chemistry.

A. Szalay: According to our experiments boron acid is not fixed by insoluble humic acids in an aqueous slurry. Other fixation mechanisms in the whole soil organic komplex are not excluded herewith.

Critical Remarks on a postulated Genetic Relationship between Precambrian Thucholite and Boghead Coal

Manfred Schidlowski

Mineralogisch-Petrographisches Institut, Universität Heidelberg
Heidelberg, Germany

An interpretation of the thucholite or *"carbon"* occurrences within the South African Witwatersrand System as altered Precambrian boghead coal does not stand up to critical examination. It can be demonstrated that the textural relationship between the uraninite-bearing carbonaceous substances and certain sapropelic coals is a fortuitous one, since sections of fibrous thucholite cut skew to the main direction of the fibres display a similar fabric as boghead coal. Whereas in boghead coal the long axes of the deformed algae are roughly parallel to the bedding, the lentiform ends of the thucholite fibres encountered in polished sections are skew to the stratification. A comparison of the trace elements as well as of the carbon isotope composition is also not suggestive of a genetic relationship. The δ^{13}C-values encountered within the carbonaceous matter (–27 to –33 % as an average) indicate that the material is related to oil and asphalt rather than to coal.

Introduction

It is generally known that carbonaceous matter or *thucholite* [1]) is a common and very widespread constituent of the economically important Precambrian conglomerates from the Blind River and Witwatersrand districts in Canada and South Africa respectively. During the last two decades, the South African occurrences (which are connected with the gold- and uranium-bearing reefs of the Witwatersrand System) have, in particular, attracted considerable scientific interest. After Davidson and Bowie (1951), Ramdohr (1955), and Liebenberg (1955) had laid the foundations for a more scientific approach to the thucholite problem by the application of reflected light microscopy, further investigations carried out in recent years have contributed other important data relative to the origin of these carbonaceous substances. Although research is still in progress, a remarkable consensus of opinion has as yet been reached between the various investigators working on the spot. It is generally accepted by most students that the carbonaceous materials are derived from originally gaseous or liquid hydrocarbons that percolated through the strata and were consequently polymerized by ionizing radiation emanating from the uraninite fraction of the conglomerates (Davidson and Bowie, 1951;

---

[1]) The term "thucholite", consisting of the chemical symbols of the main constituting elements (Th, U, C, H, O), has been introduced by Ellsworth (1928) for uraninite-bearing carbonaceous materials.

Ramdohr, 1955, 1958; Liebenberg, 1955; Schidlowski, 1966 b). As this process of polymerization entailed a transition into the solid state, the mobile hydrocarbons were fixed in close proximity to the sources of radiation, i. e., the radioactive minerals. Accordingly, the association between uraninite and polymerized hydrocarbons is very intimate in the Witwatersrand conglomerates. Detrital grains of uraninite are often surrounded by secondary aureoles of carbonaceous matter; the latter also enters the grains along cracks and fissures and finally tends to replace them (Fig. 1). In an advanced state of replacement the primary uraninite phase has almost wholly been resorbed or "digested" by the organic materials except for very small relict-bodies floating within the latter (Fig. 2).

The mechanism of uraninite replacement within the "carbon" groundmass has been exhaustively dealt with elsewhere by the author (1966 b). The radiochemical aspects of the problem, in particular the experimental foundations of the process of radiolytic polymerization of simple (mostly unsaturated) hydrocarbons by α- and γ-radiation, have been set out by Lind and Bardwell (1926), Lind (1928), and Colombo et al. (1964).

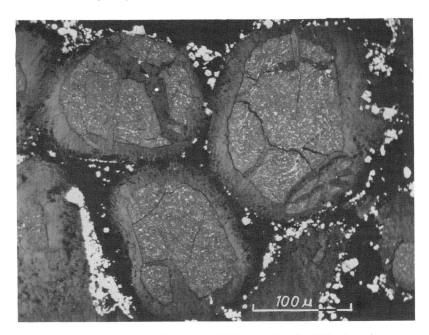

Fig. 1. Detrital grains of uraninite, surrounded by aureoles of solid hydrocarbons or "carbonaceous matter" (the latter showing different shades of grey due to pronounced reflection pleochroism). The grains are gradually being replaced by the hydrocarbons along cracks and fissures. Note dust-like inclusions of radiogenic galena (PbS, white) within uraninite. From "B" Reef, Loraine Gold Mines, Orange Free State; oil immersion.

Fig. 2. Warty granules of carbonaceous matter within which uraninite has been resorbed except for small angular relict bodies. The uraninite relics exhibit the common dusting with minute specks of galena. From Basal Reef, Virginia, Orange Free State; oil immersion.

Recently Snyman (1965) has questioned the concept of a radiogenic origin of the solid hydrocarbons from the Witwatersrand, advancing instead the theory that the carbonaceous materials represent altered Precambrian boghead coal. This hypothesis is somewhat appealing, since it seems to support most decidedly a biogenic derivation of the thucholite which had already been advocated by early geologic investigators (*inter alia*, Sharpe, 1949). Snyman's reasoning is based on micromorphological, chemical, and trace element data. Since the latter two do not furnish convincing evidence to support his thesis, I propose to confine myself mainly to a critical review of the morphological or coal petrographic criteria which seem indeed – at least at first sight – to suggest genetic affiliations between thucholite and the common type of boghead coal.

Microscopic or Coal Petrographic Criteria

Before entering upon a discussion of Snyman's arguments, some additional information on the thucholite aggregates of the Witwatersrand conglomerates should be given. Since the detrital uraninite grains (cf. Fig. 1) are mostly concentrated at the footwalls of the individual reefs as part of the heavy suite, the hydrocarbons are also preferably accumulated in these lowermost layers, on account of their fixation by radioactive emanations. The footwalls of highly uraniferous reefs are, therefore, often characterized by "carbon" seams sometimes more than 1 cm thick within which the original uraninite fraction has been almost completely dissolved; as a rule, only small irregular relics of the mineral (cf. Fig. 2) have survived the resorption process. A characteristic feature of these seams is their peculiar fibrous or columnar fabric. The fibres have a medium thickness of about 0.5 mm and are ± perpendicular to the bedding planes (Fig. 3), as already stressed by

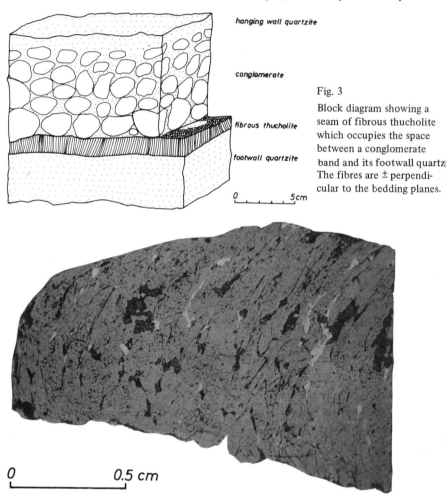

hanging wall quartzite

conglomerate

fibrous thucholite

footwall quartzite

0   5cm

Fig. 3

Block diagram showing a seam of fibrous thucholite which occupies the space between a conglomerate band and its footwall quartz The fibres are ± perpendicular to the bedding planes.

0   0.5 cm

Fig. 4. Polished surface of a thucholite aggregate cut parallel to the columnar texture. The space between the individual "carbon" fibres is often occupied by sulfides and gold (white) or silicate minerals (dark). From "B" Reef, Loraine Gold Mines, Orange Free State.

Liebenberg (1955, p. 133). The textural habit in general (Fig. 4) is similar to that of other fibrous minerals like gypsum, amphibole, etc., which are also often found to occupy intrastratal partings in sedimentary rocks. The origin of the columnar "carbon" aggregates obviously has to be explained in terms of fibrous growth as described by Mügge (1928) for a great variety of minerals. A detailed account of mineral composition and fabric of these thucholite seams has been recorded elsewhere (Schidlowski, 1966 c).

During a microscopic investigation of such "carbon" layers Snyman (1965) has come to observe various types of roundish or oval structures reminding him of algal colonies as usually encountered in boghead coal (Figs. 5 and 6). In first approximation, the resemblance is indeed striking, as a comparison with a similar sketch of a polished section of a genuine boghead coal will prove (Fig. 7). The experienced microscopist familiar with the topic will, however, note very soon that *these peculiar internal structures represent nothing but the ends of individual thucholite fibres which are cut in different angles to the main axis of the fibrous texture (Fig. 8).*

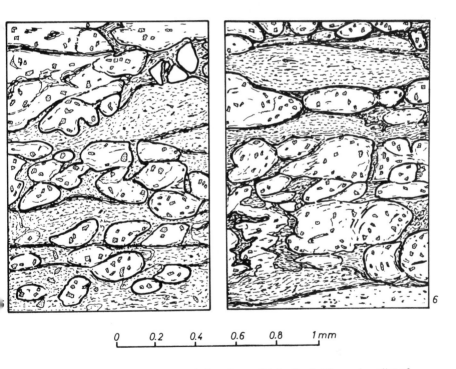

0   0.2   0.4   0.6   0.8   1 mm

Figs. 5 and 6. Thucholite aggregates consisting of roundish bodies (with angular relics of uraninite) and elongated patches, the latter being extremely porous. From Vaal Reef, Klerksdorp area (drawn after photomicrographs presented by Snyman, 1965).

Polished sections of columnar thucholite cut in these directions always furnish elongated or roundish bodies of the type depicted by Snyman (1965, Plates II and III) and explained by him as deformed algae. These textures are well known by the microscopic worker, as they or similar ones are met with in practically every section of the fibrous variety of carbonaceous matter (Fig. 9). The occurrence of indisputable flow structures within the "carbon" aggregates (Snyman, p. 228) is, in this particular case, not necessarily an additional argument for a derivation of the organic material from sapropelic coal. Flow laminations which could figure well as text-book examples are very common within fibrous thucholite. The textures observed are often comparable with those encountered in partially mobilized metamorphic rocks (Fig. 10). The flow directions as visible under the microscope always coincide with the direction of the fibres; the latter are — as already stressed before — more or less perpendicular to the enclosing bedding planes (Fig. 3).

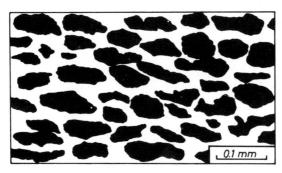

Fig. 7. Schematic sketch of a polished section of boghead coal displaying lentiform algal bodies (dark) within a groundmass of micrinite (white). The lenticular forms are due to compaction which the primarily roundish algae have undergone; the long axes of the bodies are parallel to the bedding. Note certain morphological analogies between this picture and the internal fabric of thucholite aggregates as depicted in Figs. 5, 6, and 9.

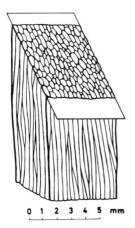

Fig. 8

Schematic block diagram showing an aggregate of fibrous thucholite cut in a skew angle to the fibre direction. On the section plane, the fibre ends show up as lentiform bodies. Attention is called to a fortuitous similarity between these cross-sections (and their real counterparts as displayed in Figs. 5 and 6) and certain internal structures of boghead coal (cf. Fig. 7).

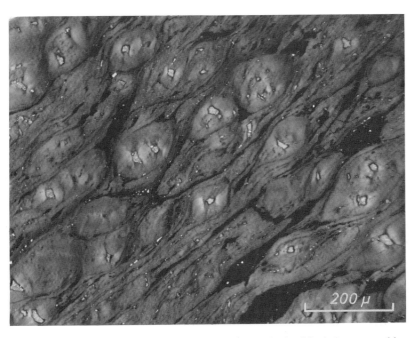

Fig. 9. Thucholite aggregate showing a phacoidal fabric, the lenticles being arranged here almost parallel to the fibrous texture. Numerous relics of uraninite give rise to radioactive haloes within which the reflectivity of the carbonaceous material is markedly increased. From "B" Reef, Loraine Gold Mines, Orange Free State; oil immersion.

Unfortunately, Snyman (1965, p. 235) received his thucholite samples already as polished blocks and had no possibility to collect the specimens himself underground; otherwise he would have certainly noticed the obvious geometric relationship between the columnar fabric and the putative algal structures reminding him of boghead coal. In the case where material comes from a collection and is submitted to the microscopic investigator already as polished sections, this relationship is usually obliterated, unless the thucholite seam is associated with some country rock indicating its original footwall or hanging wall. As Snyman's specimens obviously did not include attachments of country rock [2]), he is unable to furnish details about the orientation of his supposed algal structures in their primary sedimentary environment. This orientation is, however, decisive, since the long axes of the deformed

---

[2]) Carbonaceous matter usually fills fissures along the parting plane between the conglomerates and their respective footwall rocks (cf. Fig. 3); the coherence of these *carbon fillings* with the bordering rock material is always very weak, especially in the case of major seams. Sampling intact thucholite specimens along with the neighbouring sediments is, therefore, very difficult. Thus most thucholite specimens found in professional or amateur collections are devoid of wall-rock attachments.

Fig. 10. Carbonacous matter displaying distinct flow lamination around inclusions of sphalerite. The flow direction is parallel to the fibrous texture of the thucholite aggregate. From "B" Reef, Loraine Gold Mines, Orange Free State; oil immersion.

algae within boghead coal are *parallel to the bedding (Fig. 7), whereas the lenticular cross-sections of the fibre ends of columnar thucholite are skew or sometimes almost vertical to the latter (Fig. 8).* Only the poorly defined and untypical thucholite bodies referred to by Snyman as *type I* are reported to be roughly parallel to the stratification (p. 227).

Accordingly, the morphological evidence for a derivation of carbonaceous matter from sapropelic coal proves to be untenable. Furthermore, the statement by Snyman (p. 233) that there is no replacement of uraninite by hydrocarbons in the case of the thucholite cannot be accepted. Since Snyman has exclusively examined the *massive* variety of *carbon* and never the minute granules or *"fly spots"* loosely scattered in the rock (the accumulation of which eventually gave rise to the massive variety), he records only *one single picture of a continuously progressing process of replacement without realizing, that this picture represents already the final stage of uraninite replacement.* Only the investigator familiar with the whole sequence of successive replacement stages will note that the very small angular uraninite bodies occurring within thucholite are relics of bigger detrital grains measuring originally between 100 and 120 microns across (cf. Fig. 1). The single stages of this replacement process have been described in detail in a previous paper by the author (1966 b). Replacement of uraninite by organic substances may sometimes even be

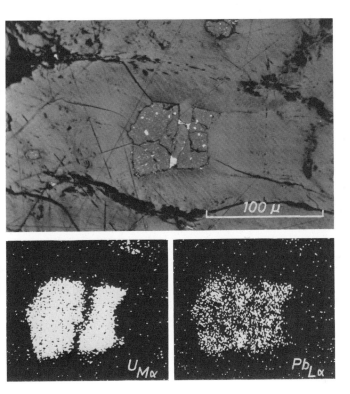

Fig. 11. Fragments of a primary detrital uraninite grain (upper picture), being replaced by solid hydrocarbons; the latter show different shades of grey due to reflection pleochroism. The particles are in the state of "floating apart" within the carbonaceous matter. The white specks within the uraninite consist of galena (PbS) which has formed from radiogenic lead; the mineral has been partially "sweated out" and accumulated within the "carbon" occupying the interstices between the UO_2-fragments. – Below: Microprobe scanning pictures showing the distribution of uranium and lead within the uraninite particles and their surroundings. From "B" Reef, Loraine Gold Mines, Orange Free State (optical picture taken in oil immersion).

observed within the massive "carbon" variety (Fig. 11). The interpretation advanced by Snyman shows that even a good observer may be led to wrong conclusions when tackling a problem just from *one side*, without being sufficiently acquainted with other aspects of the topic.

Besides, Snyman (p. 234) obviously sustains the concept first proposed by Koen (1961) that the UO_2 fraction of the Witwatersrand conglomerates has formed by precipitation of uraniferous solutions in pre-existing carbonaceous sediments, that is, the putative boghead coals [3]). Two facts, however, militate against this theory.

First, the resulting UO_2-variety should have been colloform *pitchblende* formed at low temperature and not coarse crystalline *uraninite* characteristic of pegmatite (i.e., high temperature) deposits. Even if a later recrystallization should be responsible for the present form of the mineral, the thorium content could still be expected to fall within the range normally found in pitchblende (< 0.5 %). Actually, the uraninite fraction of the Witwatersrand conglomerates contains between 2 and 3 % thorium (Liebenberg, 1955, p. 126; Schidlowski, 1966 a, p. 190). This does by no means favour a low-temperature origin. A Th-tenor of this order is typical for pegmatitic uraninite.

Secondly, it is wellnigh impossible to get the well-rounded detrital uraninite grains as encountered in the conglomerates by a sedimentary reworking of the angular UO_2-particles present in the thucholite. In an attempt to explain the abraded nature of the majority of uraninite particles not associated with *"carbon"*, Koen (196 p. 43) as well as Snyman (1965, p. 234) have advocated the possibility of such reworking processes. It can be easily demonstrated, however, that this theory does not stand up to critical examination. According to Snyman (p. 228), the average diameter of the angular uraninite particles occurring within the thucholite is usually below 35 microns. According to my own experience, this is true in the overwhelming majority of cases; very seldom the particles are more than 50 microns across (cf. Figs. 2 and 9). The water-worn detrital uraninite grains, on the other hand, have

---

[3]) It should be mentioned here that this type of uranium fixation in organic substances is by far the most common one, being responsible for the formation of many economically important uranium deposits. For instance, the famous uranium province of the Colorado Plateau has been mostly formed in this way (Gruner, 1955). The concentration of uranium is effected here by precipitation of U^{+6} (carried by weathering solutions in the form of the uranyl complex, $[U^{VI}O_2]^{+2}$) as U^{+4} in the reducing environment of decompositing organic substances, mostly of coal. Consequently, the low-temperature, cryptocrystalline variety of $U^{IV}O_2$, *pitchblende,* is formed which is characterized by a very low Th-content (< 0.5 %). Hence, in this particular case uranium is precipitated because of a change of the redox potential, whereas in the case of the Witwatersrand deposits migrating hydrocarbons have come to assemble around pre-existing uranium minerals as a result of radiolytic polymerization. Although both processes eventually have the same result, namely, a close association between uranium and organic substances, the respective *mechanisms of fixation* as well as the *materials fixed* are quite different. For the enrichment of uranium in coal the cation exchange properties of humic compounds also seem to play a decisive role (cf. paper by Szalay and Szilagyi in this volume).

a medium diameter between 100 and 120 microns (Fig. 1). It is, therefore, impossible that these *major* uraninite particles have formed by attrition of the *smaller* ones. On the contrary, the small particles represent relict-bodies of the big detrital grains which have been partially replaced by hydrocarbons.

Chemical Criteria

Chemical data advanced to support a possible derivation of thucholite from boghead coal do in no way provide clear-cut evidence. A comparison of ultimate analyses of thucholite with those of sapropelic coals (Snyman, 1965, Table I) reveals a distinct hydrogen deficit in the case of thucholite. This deficit is accounted for by Snyman by a subsequent dehydrogenation due to irradiation by uraninite. A comparison of the trace elements occurring in carbonaceous matter and coal presents further difficulties for a boghead coal theory, which are fully realized by Snyman *("no single coal is known of which the trace element content is similar to that of thucholite in all respects",* p. 232). The following table compiled by the latter author serves as an excellent illustration of how big the differences are, particularly with regard to the gold, thorium, and rare earths contents.

Table 1. Comparison of trace elements from Witwatersrand thucholite and coal (after Snyman, 1965).

	Thucholite		Coal
	per cent	cations in p. p. m.	cations in p. p. m.
U_3O_8	8.48	71 900	0 – 25 600
PbO	1.84	17 100	10 – 41 000
			(assuming 10 % ash)
ThO_2	0.27	2 370	– –
Rare earths	0.07	± 700	present
P_2O_5	0.15	654	100 – 1 300
Au	0.28	2 800	0 – 10
TiO_2	0.94	564	120 – 1 500

Investigations carried out recently on the carbon isotope composition of Witwatersrand thucholite (Hoefs and Schidlowski, 1967; Hoering, 1967) have raised additional objections to a genetic affiliation between these substances and coal. With few exceptions, the δ^{13}C-values of carbonaceous matter lie between –27 and –33 %, whereas the respective values for coals are between –21 and –27 % with an average at about 24.2 % (Craig, 1953). Thucholite of the so-called "Carbon Leader" from the Western Witwatersrand has even furnished δ^{13}C-values of about –37 % (Hoering, 1967, p. 92; cf. Table 2). Since all carbon isotope studies recorded in the literature have shown that the isotopic composition of coal is hardly affected by geologic age, the δ^{13}C-values of thucholite seem to suggest that the material is related to oil and asphalt rather than to coal. In particular, the coincidence of the thucholite values with those normally found for crude oils (Eckelmann et al., 1962; Kvenvolden and Squires, 1967) is very striking. Table 2 lists all δ^{13}C-values of Witwatersrand thucholite hitherto known.

Table 2. δ^{13}C-values of thucholite samples from Upper-Witwatersrand conglomerates or *reefs* based on Solenhofen standard (N. B. S. isotope reference sample No. 20).

Reef	Mining company	δ^{13}C [‰]	Reference
Basal	Virginia	−22.4	Hoefs and Schidlowski, 1967
Basal	Virginia	−22.9	Hoefs and Schidlowski, 1967
"B"	Loraine	−27.1	Hoefs and Schidlowski, 1967
Carbon Leader	?	−27.36	Hoering, 1965/1966
Carbon Leader	East Daggafontein	−27.69	Hoering, 1967
Basal	Free State Geduld	−30.3	Hoefs and Schidlowski, 1967
"B"	Loraine	−30.5	Hoefs and Schidlowski, 1967
Basal	President Brand	−30.9	Hoefs and Schidlowski, 1967
Basal	Western Holdings	−32.8	Hoefs and Schidlowski, 1967
Carbon Leader	West Driefontein	−35.22	Hoering, 1967
Carbon Leader	West Driefontein	−37.15	Hoering, 1967

Origin of the Hydrocarbons

As has been set out in the foregoing pages, there is no convincing evidence indicating that boghead coal is the parent material of the uraniferous "carbon" assemblages within the Witwatersrand deposits. Microscopic as well as carbon isotopic data most decidedly confirm the view hitherto held, namely, that the assemblages constitute radiolytic polymerizates of gaseous and/or liquid hydrocarbons.

With regard to the source of these primary hydrocarbons Davidson and Bowie (1951) maintained that they were derived from the Karroo coal measures overlying parts of the Witwatersrand Basin. As has been shown convincingly by Ramdohr (1955, p. 30) and Liebenberg (1955, p. 190), this explanation is incompatible with geologic as well as ore-microscopic observations. Since the underlying basement rocks could also hardly have discharged carbonaceous emanations, the hydrocarbons must be regarded as being indigenous to the Witwatersrand System and, accordingly, more or less contemporaneous with the rocks now containing their polymerized derivatives. The accumulation of vast amounts of carbonaceous substances within the sequence is likely to suggest a flourishing primitive life during Witwatersrand times (> 2.15 x 10^9 years ago). The biogenic nature of the primary hydrocarbons is, furthermore, substantiated by micropaleontological, carbon isotope, and biochemical data. For exhaustive information on these questions the reader is referred to the papers by Schidlowski (1965), Hoefs and Schidlowski (1967), Prashnowsky and Schidlowski (1967), and Oberlies and Prashnowsky (1968).

References

Colombo, U., Denti, E. and Sironi, G. (1964): A geochemical investigation upon the effect of ionizing radiation on hydrocarbons. J. Inst. Petrol. 50, 228–237.

Craig, H. (1953): The geochemistry of the stable carbon isotopes. Geochim. Cosmochim. Acta 3, 53–92.

Davidson, C. F. and Bowie, S. H. U. (1951): On thucholite and related hydrocarbon-uraninite complexes, with a note on the origin of the Witwatersrand gold ores. Bull. Geol. Surv. Gt. Brit. 3, 1–18.

Eckelmann, W. R., Broecker, W. S., Whitlock, D. W. and Allsupp, J. A. (1962): Geological note on implications of carbon isotope composition of total organic carbon of some recent sediments and ancient oils. Bull. Am. Assoc. Petrol. Geol. 46, 699–704.

Ellsworth, H. V. (1928): Thucholite, a remarkable primary carbon mineral from the vicinity of Parry Sound, Ontario. Am. Mineral. 13, 419–439.

Gruner, J. W. (1955): Concentration of uranium by carbon compounds. Econ. Geol. 50, 542–543.

Hoefs, J. and Schidlowski, M. (1967): Carbon isotope composition of carbonaceous matter from the Precambrian of the Witwatersrand System. Science 155, 1096–1097.

Hoering, T. C. (1965/1966): Criteria for suitable rocks in Precambrian organic geochemistry. Ann. Rpt. Director Geophys. Lab. Carnegie Inst., Washington, 1965–1966, 365–372.

Hoering, T. C. (1967): The organic geochemistry of Precambrian rocks. In: P. H. Abelson (ed.), Researches in Geochemistry 2, 87–111.

Koen, G. M. (1961): The genetic significance of the size distribution of uraninite in Witwatersrand bankets. Trans. Geol. Soc. S. Afr. 64, 23–46.

Kvenvolden, K. A. and Squires, R. M. (1967): Carbon isotopic composition of crude oils from Ellenburger Group (Lower Ordovician), Permian Basin, West Texas and Eastern New Mexico. Bull. Am. Ass. Petrol. Geol. 51, 1293–1303.

Liebenberg, W. R. (1955): The occurrence and origin of gold and radioactive minerals in the Witwatersrand System, the Dominion Reef, the Venterdsorp Contact Reef, and the Black Reef. Trans. Geol. Soc. S. Afr. 58, 101–227.

Lind, S. C. (1928): The chemical effects of alpha-particles and electrons. Reinhold Publ. Corp., New York.

Lind, S. C. and Bardwell, D. C. (1926): The chemical action of gaseous ions produced by alpha-particles. IX. Saturated hydrocarbons. J. Am. Chem. Soc. 48, 2335–2351.

Mügge, O. (1928): Über die Entstehung faseriger Minerale und ihrer Aggregationsformen. N. Jb. Miner. Geol. (A) 58 (Beil.-Bd.), 303–348.

Oberlies, F. and Prashnowsky, A. A. (1968): Biogeochemische und elektronenmikroskopische Untersuchung präkambrischer Gesteine. Naturwissenschaften 55, 25–28.

Prashnowsky, A. A. and Schidlowski, M. (1967): Investigation of pre-Cambrian thucholite. Nature 216, 560–563.

Ramdohr, P. (1955): Neue Beobachtungen an Erzen des Witwatersrandes in Südafrika und ihre genetische Bedeutung. Abh. dt. Akad. Wiss. Berlin, Kl. Chem. Geol. Biol. 1954, Nr. 5.

Ramdohr, P. (1958): New observations on the ores of the Witwatersrand in South Africa and their genetic significance. Trans. Geol. Soc. S. Afr. (Annexure) 61, 50 p.

Schidlowski, M. (1965): Probable life forms from the Precambrian of the Witwatersrand System (South Africa). Nature 205, 895–896.

Schidlowski, M. (1966 a): Beiträge zur Kenntnis der radioaktiven Bestandteile der Witwatersrand-Konglomerate, I. Uranpecherz in den Konglomeraten des Oranje-Freistaat-Goldfeldes. N. Jb. Miner. Abh. 105, 183–202.

Schidlowski, M. (1966 b): Beiträge zur Kenntnis der radioaktiven Bestandteile der Witwatersrand-Konglomerate. III. Kohlige Substanz ("Thucholith"). N. Jb. Miner. Abh. 106, 55–71.

Schidlowski, M. (1966 c): Mineralbestand und Gefügebilder in Faseraggregaten von kohliger Substanz ("Thucholith") aus den Witwatersrand-Konglomeraten. Contr. Mineral. Petrol. 12, 365–380.

Sharpe, J. W. N. (1949): The economic auriferous bankets of the Upper Witwatersrand Beds and their relationship to sedimentation features. Trans. Geol. Soc. S. Afr. 52, 265–300.

Snyman, C. P. (1965): Possible biogenetic structures in Witwatersrand thucholite. Trans. Geol. Soc. S. Afr. 68, 225–235.

Carbon Polytypism in Meteorites

Gennady P. Vdovykin

V.I. Vernadsky Institute of Geochemistry and Analytical Chemistry, Academy of Sciences of the USSR
Moscow, USSR

Carbon is present in meteorites in various forms – as free carbon (diamond and graphite), complex organic compounds, carbides, carbonates, gaseous materials. The investigation of carbon polytypism in meteorites is of great interest for the elucidation of carbonaceous material transformation under different natural conditions and for clearing up the conditions of meteorite formation.

The structural peculiarities of diamonds from meteorites (and of the cohenite Canyon Diablo) bring evidence that the diamonds in ureilites have formed at a collision of asteroid bodies in space. Diamonds in the meteorite Canyon Diablo have formed during the meteorite fall to the Earth. This is confirmed by the presence of a hexagonal diamond-lonsdalite in meteorites. We have identified lonsdalite in the meteorite Novo Urei.

In some meteorites besides graphite with a hexagonal structure graphite of a cubic morphology, cliftonite, is known. According to our investigations cliftonite from the meteorite Canyon Diablo does not differ by its structure from graphite of the meteorites Yardymlinsky and Burgavli. Cliftonite has formed from cohenite under conditions of low pressure.

Organic compounds are represented in carbonaceous chondrites by hydrocarbons, aminoacids, a high molecular organic matter, etc. All these compounds are of an extraterrestrial radiogenic origin. The chemical similarity of these materials with terrestrial biogenic compounds evidence that the biogenic evolution in terrestrial environments has to be regarded as a part of a general process of carbonaceous compound transformation in nature.

Carbon is present in meteorites in various forms – as free carbon (diamond and graphite), as complex organic materials, carbides, carbonates, gaseous compounds. Elementary carbon in meteorites has different modifications. In particular it is in the form of diamond, not only well-known cubic diamond, but also the hexagonal diamond. Graphite is represented by micromonocrystals of the hexagonal system. In some meteorites carbon having graphite structure is known but its grains have a cubic morphology.

The different forms of carbon in meteorites reflect the genesis of meteoritic material. The investigation of carbon polytypism in meteorites is of great interest for the elucidation of carbon material transformation under various natural conditions and for clearing up the conditions of meteorite formation [1–3].

Of especial interest in the cosmochemistry of carbon are diamonds, graphite and organic materials in meteorites. We have investigated these carbon forms in meteorites of various types [1–5 etc.].

Diamonds were for the first time established by M.V. Erofeev and P.A. Lachinov as long ago as in 1888 in the stony meteorite Novo Urei which they ascribed to the group of achondrites-ureilites. A long time diamonds in meteorites were considered as indicators of high pressures and temperatures which had taken place at great depths in a meteorites primary body of planet size [6].

Many investigators have shown that diamonds are contained in three stony meteorites-ureilites and in the iron meteorite Canyon Diablo.

Small samples of the three ureilites were given to us from the meteorite collection of the Academy of Sciences, USSR; a diamond from the meteorite Canyon Diablo was kindly sent to us by Prof. C.B. Moore from the meteorite collection of Nininger (Arizona, USA).

All the three ureilites – Novo Urei, Dyalpur, Goalpara – have a very similar structure, mineral and chemical composition. They contain olivine, less pigeonite (amounting to 90–93 wt. %), nickel – iron – kamacite (3–6 %), troilite FeS (∼ 1.7 %), chromite $FeCr_2O_4$ (traces), carbon matter. Carbon matter in ureilites is represented by diamond and graphite, being present in thin intergrowths. Organic compounds, hydrocarbons of the paraffin series, are present in small amounts (0.02–0.06 %).

Black diamond – graphite intergrowths of an irregular form measuring up to 0.3–0.9 mm, not being decomposed in acids, are more or less evenly distributed in ureilites (Fig. 1). Diamond is present in them approximately in equal proportion with graphite. Small amounts of fine kamacite, troilite and chromite are scattered in these intergrowths. The diamond of ureilites does not differ in its structure from terrestrial diamonds. But in these intergrowths a hexagonal diamond, lonsdalite, is present which is not known under terrestrial conditions. R.E. Hanneman with collaborators [7] synthesized lonsdalite from graphite during impact and found it in the ureilite Goalpara. We have identified the admixture of lonsdalite in diamonds of the meteorite Novo Urei (2,4).

We have obtained a pure diamond fraction after release from other mineral components by melting the powder of the meteorite Novo Urei with Na_2O_2 at 600–700 °C. The fraction which remained after melting consisted of whitish/light-gray diamond particles of an irregular form. Each particle is an aggregate of diamond micromonocrystals of a < 1 μ size (Fig. 2). The elementary cell of the diamond a = 3.552 Å. The total amount of diamonds in the three ureilites does not exceed 200 carats.

With the purpose of determining defects in the structure of meteoritic diamond we have investigated a pure diamond fraction from the meteorite Novo Urei by the EPR and IR spectroscopy methods. On the EPR spectrum superfine structure of three components became apparent. Fission ($\Delta H/2$ = 33.6 Oersted) had the same

Fig. 1
a) Diamond – graphite intergrowths in the stony meteorite Novo Urei, and
b) their X-ray pattern (FeK$_a$)

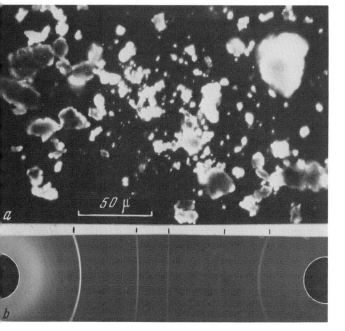

Fig. 2
a) Pure diamond fraction in the meteorite Novo Urei, and
b) its X-ray pattern (CuK$_a$)

value as for the donor nitrogen of the terrestrial diamond (Fig. 3). On the IR spectrum of the diamond fraction absorption lines became apparent at 500 cm^{-1} and one particularly intense line at 900–1300 cm^{-1}. This confirms the presence of nitrogen admixture in the structure of meteoritic diamond. It may be considered that the meteoritic diamond is characterized by non-uniformities in the structure, at least partially being conditioned by the presence of donor nitrogen. This may bear witness to genetic interrelations between the diamonds of ureilites and the carbonaceous material of stony meteorites – carbonaceous chondrites, which also contains nitrogen in its composition.

Genetic interrelations between ureilites and carbonaceous chondrites become especially apparent according to our investigation data of the isotopic composition of their carbon. Ureilites and carbonaceous chondrites are in comparison with other meteorites enriched by the heavy ^{13}C isotope [8]. The δ ^{13}C value is in the

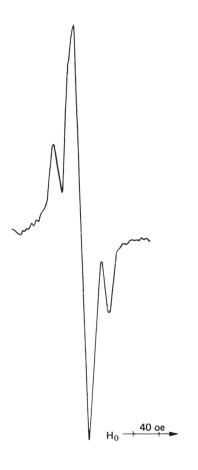

H_0 $\xrightarrow{\quad 40 \text{ oe} \quad}$

Fig. 3
EPR spectrum of diamond of the meteorite Novo

meteorite Novo Urei — 7.1 and in the meteorite Goalpara — 8.4 per mille (data are reduced to the PDB standard) (Table I). By their isotopic composition the elementary forms of the meteorite Novo Urei carbon approach the total carbon, for diamond $\delta^{13}C = -5.7$ ‰. But the carbon of organic material has in comparison with them $\delta^{13}C = -27.7$ ‰.

Table I. Isotopic composition of carbon of ureilites Novo Urei and Goalpara.

Meteorites	Fractions of carbon matter	Content in the meteorite, %	$\delta^{13}C$, ‰
Novo Urei	Total carbon	2,23	− 7,1
	Intergrowths of diamond with graphite	2,17	− 6,3
	Pure diamond fraction	1,00	− 5,7
	Organic matter	0,06	−27,7
Goalpara	Total carbon	1,54	− 8,4

Ureilites and carbonaceous chondrites are similar in many other aspects [2]. They contain a greater amount of carbon, but little FeS, metallic Fe, alkaline elements, etc. However, unlike carbonaceous chondrites ureilites are intensively recrystallized. The achondrite structure is typical of them. The silicate grains in them are broken, a polycrystal character is typical of kamacite grains. All this, as well as the presence of diamonds with a hexagonal structure and the oriented character of diamond microcrystals in diamond-graphite intergrowths permit us to conclude that ureilites have formed from the material of carbonaceous chondrites during the collision of asteroid bodies in space. During the impact, diamonds crystallized in ureilites from the carbonaceous material of carbonaceous chondrites.

In iron meteorites diamonds are only known in the coarse Canyon Diablo octahedrite, which fell in Arizona (USA) about 50 000 years ago. When falling this meteorite formed the Arizona (Barringer) meteoritic crater measuring more than 1200 m and being of depth up to 180 m. The meteorite Canyon Diablo and the diamonds in it were detected as long ago as 1891.

The diamond grain from the Canyon Diablo meteorite investigated by us had an irregular, more or less rounded form, was of a brownish-dark-grey colour and 5 mm in size. It was intersected by thin veins consisting of iron oxides. Therefore, under no great mechanical action the grain broke into angular fragments (Fig. 4). The roentgenometric investigation bears witness to the fact that this is an aggregate of fine intergrown microcrystals of diamond with graphite admixture. Iron oxides are also present being represented by hydrogoethite (Table II). The grains were treated

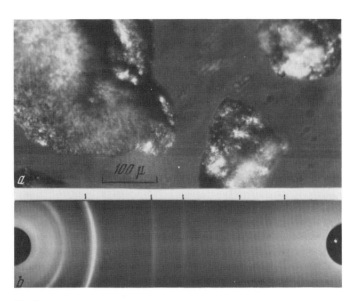

Fig. 4
a) Diamond grains from the iron meteorite Canyon Diablo and
b) its X-ray pattern (CuKα)

Table II. Material composition of diamond-containing grains in the meteorite Canyon Diablo.

Meteorite Canyon Diablo									
Intergrowths of diamond with graphite, containing brown iron oxides		Intergrowths of diamond with graphite, treated with HCl		Diamond		Graphite		Hydrogoethite	
I	$\dfrac{d\alpha}{n}$	I	$\dfrac{d\alpha}{n}$	I	$\dfrac{d\alpha}{n}$	I	$\dfrac{d\alpha}{n}$	I	$\dfrac{d\alpha}{n}$
6	4,17	–	–	–	–	–	–	10	4,18
9	3,29	9	3,29	–	–	10	3,37	3	3,39
1	2,660	–	–	–	–	–	–	8	2,690
1	2,447	–	–	–	–	–	–	10	2,450
10	2,069	10	2,069	10	2,05	5	2,044	–	–
1	1,723	–	–	–	–	8	1,691	8	1,719
1	1,502	–	–	–	–	–	–	4	1,510
7	1,258	7	1,255	5	1,26	8	1,231	1	1,266
1	1,179	–	–	–	–	7	1,155	–	–
5	1,076	5	1,073	4	1,072	1	1,051	–	–
2	0,885	1	0,883	1	0,885	–	–	–	–
4	0,818	2	0,818	2	0,813	3	0,800	–	–

Table III. Roentgenometric data of diamonds of the iron meteorite Canyon Diablo.

hkl	I	$\dfrac{d\alpha}{n}$	a, Å	I	$\dfrac{d\alpha}{n}$	a, Å
111	10	2,069	3,583	10	2,069	3,583
220	7	1,258	3,557	7	1,255	3,559
311	5	1,076	3,549	5	1,073	3,549
400	2	0,885	3,540	1	0,883	3,538
331	4	0,818	3,555	2	0,818	3,555
			3,557			3,557

with hydrochloric acid. Roentgenometric examination has shown that the remaining particles are diamond with graphite admixture. The elementary cell of diamond from the meteorite Canyon Diablo is a = 3.557 Å (Table III).

Investigations of the diamonds of the Canyon Diablo meteorite, carried out by other authors, also bear witness to the fact that diamonds in this meteorite are always met in polycrystalline aggregates and not in the form of large crystals. A hexagonal diamond – lonsdalite has been established in them [7], which bears witness to the shock origin of diamonds in this meteorite. By this the diamonds of Canyon Diablo and the diamonds of ureilites are similar. But in Canyon Diablo the diamond intergrowths are of a considerably greater size and in them diamond quantitatively predominates over graphite. The Canyon Diablo meteorite has possibly undergone a more intensive shock than ureilites. An investigation of cohenite in a diamond-containing sample, carried out by us, has shown that this meteorite fragment had undergone a shock pressure up to 1 megabar. This agrees with data of many other investigators.

Diamonds are only contained in small fragments of the Canyon Daiblo meteorite found on the rim of the Arizona meteoritic crater. In large fragments of the meteorite found in the plain surrounding the crater, diamonds are lacking. A distinct dependence has been established between the location of diamond-containing fragments of this meteorite, the recrystallization degree of these fragments and the content of cosmogenic isotopes of rare gases [9, 10 etc.]. This correlation clearly proves that the diamonds in the Canyon Diablo meteorite were formed when the meteorite hit the Earth.

The carbon source during the crystallization of Canyon Diablo diamond is discussed. It is thought that the carbon source could be either graphite or cohenite. We have investigated the isotopic carbon composition of the Canyon Diablo diamond. The $\delta^{13}C$ value for it is -5.8 ‰. In its isotopic carbon composition the diamond of Canyon Diablo is similar to graphite but differs from cohenite (Table IV). It is most likely that graphite was the parent carbon during crystallization of the Canyon Diablo diamond.

Table IV.   Isotopic composition of carbon of the meteorite Canyon Diablo and other iron meteorites.

Meteorites	Carbon matter	$\delta\,^{13}C, \%_0$	Source of data
Canyon Diablo (USA)	diamond	$-5,8$	this work
Canyon Diablo (USA)	graphite	$-6,0$	[11]
Canyon Diablo (USA)	graphite	$-6,3$	[12]
Canyon Diablo (USA)	cohenite	$-17,9$	[12]
Odessa (USA)	graphite	$-5,2$	[11]
Toluca (Mexico)	graphite	$-5,2$	[11]
Yardymlinsky (USSR)	graphite	$-5,0$	our data, 1967 [8]

Hence, the diamonds in the iron Canyon Diablo meteorite were formed from graphite when the meteorite hit the Earth. At the moment of the impact pressures exceeded 1 megabar.

Graphite is the most widespread form of carbon in meteorites. In iron meteorites graphite nodules often have a rounded form, their sizes reach some cm. In nodules carbon usually associates with troilite and other accessory minerals.

The roentgenometric and electronographic investigation carried out by us on graphite from nodules of the Yardymlinsky and Burgavli iron meteorites have shown that in its structure meteoritic graphite does not differ from terrestrial graphite. These graphites also have equal hardness (10 kg/mm^2). Organic material (~ 0.04 per cent) represented by paraffin hydrocarbons is contained in graphite of these meteorites [2]. Paraffin hydrocarbons are also present in the graphite of Canyon Diablo [13].

Rarely elementary carbon occurs in meteorites in the form of grains of cubic morphology. This carbon is named the mineral cliftonite. We have investigated cliftonite from the Canyon Diablo meteorite, which Dr. B. Mason (USA) had kindly sent us. In its structure this mineral is similar to graphite of other iron meteorites (Yardymlinsky and Burgavli).

It was thought that cliftonite in meteorites could have formed as a pseudomorph of graphite after diamond; from this one could conclude that diamonds had formed in the planetary body from which the meteorites were derived. But such a possibility was not confirmed. Recently Brett and Higgins [14] have experimentally shown that cliftonite is actually formed during decay of cohenite under conditions of low pressures.

Meteorites of a very rare type, carbonaceous chondrites, are enriched in *organic compounds*. In contrast to other meteorites they contain a great amount of easily volatile elements: C – up to 4.8 per cent, H – up to 2.4 per cent, S – up to 6.7 per cent, as well as N, O, etc. These elements enter the composition of minerals typical of carbonaceous chondrites — hydrous iron — magnesium silicates (chlorite — serpentine), carbonates, sulfates, elementary sulfur. Carbonaceous chondrites contain up to 7 per cent of organic compounds [2, 13, 15, 16 etc.].

We have investigated organic compounds in the carbonaceous chondrites Orgueil, Mighei, Staroye Boriskino, Cold Bokkeveld, Murray, Groznaya [2].

It has been found that organic compounds are more or less evenly distributed in meteorites being present in interchondrule space as well as within the chondrules. The main part of the carbonaceous matter of these meteorites is represented by organic material of polymeric character having a condensed aromatic structure. Its elementary composition is characterized by a high degree of oxidation and by the presence of chlorine [2]. According to our infrared spectroscopy data CH-groups, hydroxyl and carbonyl groups are noted in the composition of this material. Structural investigations have shown that this main part of the carbon matter is a mixture of compounds of different degree of crystallinity — from amorphous high-molecular organic matter to partially graphitized material. In carbonaceous material of these meteorites, free organic radicals have been established by the EPR method the stability of which is accounted for by the delocalization of uncoupled π-electrons in complicated aromatic structures.

In the high-molecular organic material are distributed bitumen-like components which are extracted from meteorites by organic solvents. The content of the bitumen-like components makes up $\sim$ 10 per cent of the total carbonaceous matter. They are a mixture of organic compounds of hydrocarbon (n-paraffins, cycloparaffins, aromatics) and non-hydrocarbon character. Among the aromatics individual polynuclear hydrocarbons have been identified such as anthracene, 1,12-benzperylene, 3,4-benzpyrene, perylene, coronene.

Many investigators have studied this material. It has been shown that carbonaceous chondrites contain besides hydrocarbons carboxilic acids, amino acids, carbohydrates, nitrogen cyclic compounds.

All the organic compounds which have been established in meteorites are also known in terrestrial conditions. As the organic compounds in conditions of the Earth have passed through living matter it seems that it could be thought by analogy that the organic matter in meteorites is also of a biogenic nature. But such a conclusion would be premature for the following reasons:

1. There are organic matters in diamond-containing meteorites, in some ordinary chondrites, in graphite nodules of iron meteorites. Organic compounds are form part of the carbon matter of meteorites.

2. Particularly enriched in organic compounds are carbonaceous chondrites. Organic matter is contained in them both in the interchondrule space and within the chondrules. In carbonaceous chondrites an increase of organic compound content is

distinctly observed in parallel with the content increase of the easily volatile elements entering the composition of many mineral phases. This indicates that the formation of organic compounds occurred parallel with the forming of the whole material of carbonaceous chondrites.

3. Organic matter of meteorites is characterized by a heightened chlorine content.

4. The composition of the organic matter of meteorites is simpler than the composition of terrestrial biogenic matters.

5. Optical activity is not characteristic of organic matters inherent in meteorites. Metal-porphyrin complexes have yet not been established for certain.

6. The organic matter of meteorites is substantially enriched in deuterium in comparison with the organic matter of rocks.

These peculiarities of abundance and composition of organic matters bear witness to the fact that in meteorites the organic compounds are of an extraterrestrial abiogenic nature. The possibility of an abiogenic synthesis of complicated organic compounds from elementary precursors is actually confirmed by a great amount of recent experimental work.

Hence, the formation of organic compounds in carbonaceous chondrites most likely occurred at the early formation stage of the whole matter of these meteorites. This conclusion is of great importance when we consider the primary organic compounds in conditions of the Earth and their chemical evolution preceding the appearance of living matter [3, 17, 18].

Recent investigations of the composition of meteorites [19, 20, 21] give evidence of the fact that the bodies primary to meteorites were of no great size. They could not gravitatively retain on their surface the easily volatile elements which on Earth escape in the degassing process and enter into the composition of the atmosphere and hydrosphere — the environment necessary for the evolution of living matter. The transformation of carbon matter in asteroid bodies occurred in a chemical way. Nevertheless certain organic materials in meteorites are similar to terrestrial organic materials of a biogenic nature (Table V).

The general similarity of the organic compounds of meteorites formed by abiogenic synthesis from simple initial material and the terrestrial organic compounds of biogenic nature witness to the similar character of carbon matter transformation irrespective of the location of their transformation (under terrestrial conditions or under conditions of bodies being parent for meteorites), as well as of the origin of organic compounds (abiogenic or biogenic). The biogenic evolution under terrestrial conditions has possibly to be considered as a part of the general process of carbon matter transformation in nature [2, 3, 18].

Table V. Transformation of organic compounds [18].

Necessary conditions of organic compound formation	Conditions of the primary synthesis of organic compounds	Established products of sinthesis	Conditions of further transformation of organic compounds and its products	
1. Initial elements and chief molecules: C (CH_4, CO, CO_2) N (NH_3, HCN) H (H_2) O (H_2O) S (H_2S) P (H_3PO_4)	Radiogenic synthesis of organic compounds in the process of agglomeration of bodies being parent for meteorites (carbonaceous chondrites)	Hydrocarbons Aromatic acids Fatty acids Amino acids Carbohydrates Nitrogen cyclic compounds Sulfur-containing compounds High-molecular organic matter	Crushing of the bodies being parent for meteorites Irradiation of meteorites in space by cosmic rays	
2. Energy sources 3. Mineral catalysts	Degassing under conditions of the Earth. Formation of the hydrosphere, the atmosphere (and the Earth's crust). Chemical evolution of organic compounds	Not precisely established	Formation of the biosphere. Living matter: proteins, carbohydrates, fats a.o., water	Transformation during burial in sediments. Organic matter of rocks: Hydrocarbons Aromatic acids Fatty acids Amino acids Carbohydrates Nitrogen cyclic compounds Porphyrins a.o. Polymeric organic matter
	Synthesis of organic matters in laboratory conditions	Hydrocarbons Organic acids Amino acids Carbohydrates Nitrogen cyclic compounds Porphyrins, etc.	During heating – highmolecular organic compounds: Polysaccharides Proteins Nucleic acids	

References

[1] Vdovykin, G.P.: In book "Problems of geochemistry", Moscow, "Nauka", 1965.

[2] Vdovykin, G.P.: Carbon matter of meteorites (organic compounds, diamonds, graphite). Moscow, "Nauka", 1967.

[3] Vdovykin, G.P.: In book "Physics of the planets", Alma-Ata, "Nauka", 1967.

[4] Vinogradov, A.P., Vdovykin, G.P.: Geochemistry, 8, 743, 1963.

[5] Vdovykin, G.P.: Meteoritica, 23, 69, Taurus Press, 1965.

[6] Urey, H.C.: Astrophys. J., 124, 623, 1956.

[7] Hanneman, R.E., Strong, H.M., Bundy, F.P.: Science, 155, N 3765, 1967.

[8] Vinogradov, A.P., Kropotova, O.I., Vdovykin, G.P., Grinenko, V.A.: Geochimia, 3, 267, 1967.

[9] Heymann, D., Lipschutz, M.E., Nielson, B., Anders, E.: J. Geophys. Res., 71, 619, 1966.

[10] Moore, C.B., Birrell, P.J., Lewis, C.F.: Geochim. Cosmochim. Acta, 31, 1885, 1967.

[11] Nichiporuk, W., Chodos, A.A.: J. Geophys. Res., 64, 2451, 1959.

[12] Craig, H.: Geochim. Cosmochim. Acta, 3, N 2–3, 1953.

[13] Nooner, D.W., Oró, J.: Geochim. Cosmochim. Acta, 31, 1359, 1967.

[14] Brett, R., Higgins, G.T.: Science, 156, 819, 1967.

[15] Nagy, B.: Endeavour, 27, 81, 1968.

[16] Hayes, J.M.: Geochim. Cosmochim. Acta, 31, 1395, 1967.

[17] Vdovykin, G.P.: In book "The origin of life in space", Moscow, Acad. Sci. USSR, 1963.

[18] Vdovykin, G.P.: In book "Abiogenesis and the first stages of life evolution", Moscow, "Nauka", 1968.

[19] Mason, B.: Meteorites. J. Wiley and sons, N.Y.-L., 1962.

[20] Anders, E.: Space Sci. Rev., 3, N 5–6, 1964.

[21] Vinogradov, A.P.: Pure and Appl. Chem., 10, N 4, 1965.

List of Delegates

Abderahim, A.:
Soc. Nat. de Recherche et d'Exploitation
des Pétroles en Algérie,
Alger, Algeria

Albrecht, P.:
Institut de Chimie de la Faculté des
Sciences,
Strasbourg, France

Aldershoff, W. G., Drs.:
Koninklijke/Shell Exploratie en Produktie
Laboratorium,
Rijswijk, The Netherlands.

Alpern, B.:
Centre d'Etudes et Recherches des Char-
bonnages de France,
Verneuil-en-Halatte, Creil (Oise), France

Alturki, Y. I.:
School of Chemistry, University of Bristol,
Bristol, U. K.

Bajor, M., Dr.:
Bundesanstalt für Bodenforschung,
Hannover, Germany

Bayliss, G. S., Dr.:
Esso Production Research Co.
Houston, Texas, USA

Benaissa, B.:
Soc. Nat. de Recherche et d'Exploitation
des Pétroles en Algérie,
Alger, Algeria

Berg, M. H. J. van den:
Geologisch Instituut, Universiteit Utrecht,
Utrecht, The Netherlands

Bestougeff, M.:
Compagnie Française des Pétroles,
Paris, France

Bonoli, L.:
Istituto di Ricerche "G. Donegani",
Novara, Italy

Boschke, F., Dr.:
Springer Verlag,
Heidelberg, Germany

Boylan, D. B., Dr.:
Organic Geochemistry Unit, School of
Chemistry, University of Bristol,
Bristol, U.K.

Brongersma-Sanders, M., Mrs. Dr.:
Geologisch en Mineralogisch Instituut,
Universiteit Leiden,
Leiden, The Netherlands

Buchta, H., Dr.:
Oesterr. Mineralölverwaltung AG
Vienna, Austria

Burlingame, A. L., Prof:
Space Sciences Laboratory, University of
California,
Berkeley, Cal.,USA

Byramjee, R.:
Compagnie Française des Pétroles,
Paris, France

Califet-Debyster, Mrs. Y.:
Institut Français du Pétrole,
Rueil-Malmaison, France

Claret, J.:
Société ELF pour la Recherche et
l'Exploitation des Hydrocarbures,
Paris, France

Combaz, A.:
Compagnie Française des Pétroles,
Bordeaux, France

Connan, J.:
C. R. P. – S. N. P. A.,
Pau, France

Cooper, B. S.:
Organic Geochemistry Unit, The University
of Newcastle-upon-Tyne
Newcastle-upon-Tyne, U. K.

Correia, M.:
Institut Français du Petrole,
Rueil-Malmaison, France

Cox, R.:
Organic Geochemistry Unit, University of
Bristol,
Bristol, U. K.

Douglas, A. G.:
Organic Geochemistry Unit, The University
of Newcastle-upon-Tyne,
Newcastle-upon-Tyne, U. K.

Dreier, W. F., Dr.:
Mobil Research & Development Corp.
Geneva, Switzerland

Dungworth, G.:
Organic Geochemistry Unit, The University
of Newcastle-upon-Tyne,
Newcastle-upon-Tyne, U. K.

Dupuy, J. P.:
Esso REP,
Bègles, France

Ebhardt, G., Dipl. Geol.:
Universität Würzburg,
Würzburg, Germany

Eglinton, G., Dr.:
Organic Geochemistry Unit, University of
Bristol,
Bristol, U. K.

Eisma, E., Drs.:
Amsterdam, The Netherlands

Engelhardt, E. D., Drs.:
Koninklijke/Shell Exploratie en Produktie
Laboratorium,
Rijswijk, The Netherlands

Feugère, G.:
Géoservices,
Paris, France

Firth, J. N. M.:
Organic Geochemistry Unit, The University
of Bristol,
Bristol, U. K.

Flaig, W., Prof. Dr.:
Institut für Biochemie des Bodens der
Forschungsanstalt für Landwirtschaft
Braunschweig-Völkenrode, Germany

François, C.:
Soc. Nat. de Recherche et d'Exploitation
des Pétroles en Algérie,
Alger, Algeria

Gaertner, H. R. von, Prof.:
Bundesanstalt für Bodenforschung,
Hannover, Germany

Gazzarrini, F., Dr.:
Istituto di Ricerche "G. Donegani",
Novara, Italy

Gedenk, R., Dr.:
Deutsche Erdöl AG,
Wietze, Germany

Geodekian, A. A., Dr.:
Academy of Sciences USSR,
Moscow, USSR

Gérard, R. E.:
Géoservices,
Paris, France

Given, P. H., Prof.:
Pennsylvania State University,
University Park, Pennsylvania, USA

Glezer., Mrs.:
Moscow, USSR

Göhring, K. E. H., Dr.:
Koninklijke/Shell Exploratie en Produktie
Laboratorium
Rijswijk, The Netherlands

Goni, J. C., Dr.:
Bureau de Recherches Géologiques et
Minières,
Orléans-La Source, France

Gransch, J. A.:
Koninklijke/Shell Exploratie en Produktie
Laboratorium,
Rijswijk, The Netherlands

Groot, K., de Ir.:
Koninklijke/Shell Exploratie en Produktie
Laboratorium,
Rijswijk, The Netherlands

Grossin, M., Mrs.:
Compagnie Française des Pétroles,
Paris, France

Gulyaeva, L. A., Mrs.:
Moscow, USSR

Gutjahr, C. C. M., Dr.:
Koninklijke/Shell Exploratie en Produktie
Laboratorium,
Rijswijk, The Netherlands

Hahn, J., Dr.:
Institut für Chemische Technologie,
Technische Universität
Braunschweig, Germany

Hahn-Weinheimer, P., Mrs. Dr.:
Forschungsstelle für Geochemie, Tech-
nische Hochschule,
München, Germany

Happel, L., Dr.:
Universität München,
München, Germany

Havenaar, I., Ir.:
Koninklijke/Shell Exploratie en Produktie
Laboratorium,
Rijswijk, The Netherlands

Heller, W., Dr.:
Chirurgische Universitätsklinik Tübingen,
Tübingen, Germany

Hobson, G. D., Dr.:
Imperial College of Science and Technology,
London, U. K.

Hood, A., Dr.:
Shell Development Co, Exploration and
Production Research Centre,
Houston, Texas, USA

Humalda van Eysinga, F. W. B. van:
Elsevier Publishing Company,
Amsterdam, The Netherlands

Hunneman, D. H.:
Organic Geochemistry Unit, University of
Bristol,
Bristol, U. K.

Jedwab, J., Dr.:
Université Libre de Bruxelles,
Bruxelles, Belgium

Jonathan, D.:
Société ELF pour la Recherche et l'Exploi-
tation des Hydrocarbures,
Paris, France

Jüntgen, H., Dr.:
Bergbauforschung GmbH,
Essen, Germany

Karweil, J., Dr.:
Bergbauforschung GmbH,
Essen, Germany

Kisch, H. J., Dr.:
Geologisch en Mineralogisch Instituut,
Universiteit, Leiden,
Leiden, The Netherlands

Knoche, H.:
Institut de Chimie de la Faculté des Sciences,
Strasbourg, France

Kranz, R., Dr.:
Institut für Physikalische Chemie der Kern-
forschungsanlage Jülich GmbH,
Jülich, Germany

Kroepelin, H., Prof. Dr.:
Technische Universität,
Braunschweig, Germany

Kulbicki, G., Dr.:
Société Nationale des Pétroles d'Aquitaine,
Pau, France

Leplat, P.:
Labofina, S. A.,
Bruxelles, Belgium

Le Tran Khanh, Dr.:
Société Nationale des Pétroles d'Aquitaine,
Pau, France

Leythaeuser, D., Dr.:
Geologisches Institut, Universität Würzburg,
Würzburg, Germany

Louis, M., Dr.:
Institut Français du Pétrole,
Rueil-Malmaison, France

Marchand, A., Prof.:
Institut de Magnétochimie "Brivazac",
Université de Bordeaux,
Pessac, France

Meinschein, W. G., Prof.:
Department of Geology, Indiana University,
Bloomington, Ind., USA

Morrison, J.:
Oil and Gas Journal
Zoetermeer, The Netherlands

Murris, R. J.:
N. V. Nederlandse Aardolie Maatschappij,
Assen, The Netherlands

Neglia, S., Dr.:
Servizio Geochimica e Laboratori AGIP,
Milano, Italy

Neumann, H. J., Dr.:
Institut für Chemische Technologie, Tech-
nische Universität,
Braunschweig, Germany

Newman, G. H.:
Consulting Geologist Cabeen Expl. Corp.,
North Hollywood, California, USA

Petrov, Al. A., Prof. Dr.:
IGIRGI,
Moscow, USSR

Philippi, G. T., Dr.:
Shell Dev. Co., Expl. and Prod. Res. Centre,
Houston, Texas, USA

Porrenga, D. H., Dr.
Koninklijke/Shell Exploratie en Produktie
Laboratorium,
Rijswijk, The Netherlands

Posthuma, J., Dr.:
Koninklijke/Shell Exploratie en Produktie Laboratorium
Rijswijk, The Netherlands

Postma, H., Prof. Dr.:
Nederlands Instituut voor Onderzoek der Zee,
Den Helder, The Netherlands

Powell, T. O.:
Organic Geochemistry Unit, The University of Newcastle-upon-Tyne,
Newcastle-upon-Tyne, U. K.

Prashnowsky, A., Dr.:
Geologisches Institut der Universität Würzburg,
Würzburg, Germany

Ragot, J. P.:
Bureau de Recherches Géologiques et Minières
Orléans-La Source, France

Raschka, H., Dr.:
Forschungsstelle für Geochemie, Technische Hochschule München,
München, Germany

Robinson, Sir Robert:
"Shell " Research Ltd,
London, U. K.

Roucaché, J. Mrs.:
Institut Français du Pétrole,
Rueil-Malmaison, France

Sarmiento, R., Dr.:
Esso Production Research Company, European Laboratories,
Bègles, France

Schenck, P. A., Drs.:
Koninklijke/Shell Exploratie en Produktie Laboratorium,
Rijswijk, The Netherlands

Schidlowski, M., Dr.:
Mineralogisch-Petrographisches Institut, Universität Heidelberg,
Heidelberg, Germany

Shoresh, R.:
The Institute for Petroleum Research & Geophysics,
Azor, Israel

Simoneit, B. R.:
Space Sciences Laboratory, University of California,
Berkeley, Cal.,USA

Smith, J. W.:
CSIRO,
Chatswood, NSW., 2067, Australia

Sokolov, V., Prof.:
Scientific Council on the Origin of Petroleum,
Moscow, USSR

Speers, G. C.:
B. P. Research Centre,
Sunbury-on-Thames, U. K.

Szalay, A., Prof. Dr.:
Institute of Nuclear Research of the Hung. Academy of Sciences,
Debrecen, Hungary

Szilágyi, M., Mrs. Dr.:
Institute of Nuclear Research of the Hung. Academy of Sciences,
Debrecen, Hungary

Szumlas, F., Dr.:
I. T. C.
Delft, The Netherlands

Teichmüller, M., Mrs. Dr..
Geologisches Landesamt Nordrhein West-falen,
Krefeld, Germany

Thiadens, A. A., Dr.:
Geologische Stichting,
Haarlem, The Netherlands

Thomas, F. C., Dr.:
B. P. Research Centre,
Sunbury-on-Thames, U. K.

Tissot, B. P.:
Institut Français du Pétrole,
Rueil-Malmaison, France

Tobback, P., Dr.:
Dept. of Geology and Geophysics, University of Minnesota,
Minneapolis, Minnesota, USA

Trichet, J.:
Ecole Normale Supérieure
Paris, France

Verdurmen, E. A. Th., Dr.:
Laboratorium voor Isotopen-Geologie,
Amsterdam, The Netherlands

Vuchev, V., Dr.:
Geological Institute, Bulgarian Academy
of Sciences,
Sofia, Bulgaria

Wehner, H., Dipl. Geol.:
Niedersächsisches Landesamt für Boden-
forschung,
Hannover, Germany

Weide, B. van der:
Société Nationale des Pétroles d'Aquitaine,
Pau, France

Welte, D. H., Dr.:
Chevron Oil Field Research Co.,
La Habra, Cal., USA

Whitehead, E. V.:
B. P. Research Centre,
Sunbury-on-Thames, U. K.

Wollrab, V., Dr.:
Institute of Organic Chemistry and Bio-
chemistry, Czechoslov. Academy of Science,
Prague, Czechoslovakia

Wszolek, P. C., Miss.:
Space Sciences Laboratory, University of
California,
Berkeley, Cal.,USA

Zhuze, T. P., Mrs.:
Moscow, USSR

Name Index

The list includes the names of the delegates and authors and refers to the papers and the discussions.

Abderahim, A. 605
Albrecht, P. 605
Aldershoff, W. G. 605
Alpern, B. 605
Alturki, Y. I. 227, 605

Bajor, M. 226, 354, 372, 542, 605
Bayliss, G. S. 268, 605
Benaissa, B. 605
Berg, M. H. J. van den 605
Bestougeff, M. 331, 344, 605
Bonoli, L. 373, 605
Boschke, F. 605
Boylan, D. B. 227, 239, 240, 605
Bratt, J. M. 167
Brongersma-Sanders, M. 605
Buchta, H. 605
Buniat-Zade, Z. A. 279, 473
Burlingame, A. L. 85, 129, 131, 166, 239, 605
Byramjee, R. 155, 319, 330, 331, 605

Caflisch, L. 499
Califet-Debyster, Y. 385, 605
Claret, J. 605
Colombo, U. 499
Combaz, A. 605
Connan, J. 498, 605
Cooper, B. S. 605
Correia, M. 303, 318, 605
Cox, R. 605

Dadashev, F. G. 473
Deroo, G. 345
Douglas, A. G. 605
Dreier, W. F. 605
Dungworth, G. 606
Dupuy, J. P. 606
Durand, B. 345

Ebhardt, G. 606
Eglinton, G. 1, 157, 181, 226, 227, 606
Eisma, E. 606
Engelhardt, E. D. 606
Espitalie, J. 345

Fabre, M. 241
Feugère, G. 355, 606
Firth, J. N. M. 606
Flaig, W. 470, 485, 498, 578, 606
François, C. 606

Gaertner, H. R. von 155, 425, 606
Gazzarrini, F. 499, 516, 606
Gedenk, R. 606
Geodekian, A. A. 279, 473, 606
Gérard, R. E. 355, 372, 606
Given, P. H. 226, 427, 470, 498, 572, 578, 606
Glezer, 606
Göhring, K. E. H. 226, 268, 318, 330, 566, 606
Gonfiantini, R. 499
Goni, J. C. 553, 578, 606
Gransch, J. A. 606
Groot, K. de 606
Grossin, M. 606
Guichard-Loudet, N. J. 241
Guillemin, C. J. 553
Gulyaeva, L. A. 606
Gutjahr, C. C. M. 606

Hahn, J. 606
Hahn-Weinheimer, P. 517, 533, 606
Hanbaba, P. 459
Happel, L. 606
Haug, P. A. 85
Havenaar, I. 606
Heller, W. 226, 217, 240, 607
Henderson, W. 181
Hobson, G. D. 607
Hood, A. 302, 607
Humalda van Eysinga, F.W.B. van 607
Hunneman, D. H. 157, 166, 268, 566, 607

Jedwab, J. 533, 552, 607
Jonathan, D. 607
Jüntgen, H. 441, 459, 470, 471, 607

Karweil, J. 59, 354, 498, 607
Kirkwood, S. 167
Kisch, H. J. 407, 425, 607
Kisielow, W. 289, 302
Knoche, H. 607
Kranz, R. 543, 552, 607
Kroepelin, H. 129, 166, 535, 542, 607
Kulbicki, G. 607

Lacaze, J. 303
Leplat, P. 607
Le Tran Khanh, 607

Leythaeuser, D. 429, 441, 607
Louis, M. 129, 344, 553,

Marchand, A. 607
Markl, G. 517
Marzec, A. 289, 302
Meinschein, W. G. 129, 2 607
Morrison, J. 607
Murris, R. J. 318, 607

Nagy, B. 209
Nagy, L. A. 209
Neglia, S. 607
Neumann, H. J. 607
Newman, G. H. 607

Oudin, J. L. 385

Pelet, R. 345
Petrov, Al. A. 401, 607
Philippi, G. T. 25, 607
Porrenga, D. H. 607
Posthuma, J. 608
Postma, H. 47, 608
Poulet, M. 303
Powell, T. O. 608
Prashnowsky, A. 608
Pustilnikova, S. D. 401

Ragot, J. P. 553, 608
Raschka, H. 517, 608
Robinson, Sir Robert 60
Roucaché, J. G. 241, 25 318, 608

Sarmiento, R. 608
Schenck, P. A. 259, 261 608
Schidlowski, M. 578, 57
Schnoes, H. K. 85
Shoresh, R. 608
Simoneit, B. R. 85, 129, 608
Smith, J. W. 608
Sokolov, V. A. 279, 372 608
Speers, G. C. 608
Swain, F. M. 167
Szalay, A. 567, 578, 608
Szilágyi, M. 567, 608
Szumlas, F. 608

Teichmüller, M. 155, 16 498, 608

Thiadens, A. A. 608
Thomas, F. C. 608
Tichomolova, T. V. 401
Tissot, B. P. 345, 354, 608
Tobback, P. 167, 608
Tongiorgi, E. 499
Trichet, J. 608

Vasse, L. 319, 331
Vdovykin, G. P. 593
Verdurmen, E. A. Th. 608
Vuchev, V. 609

Wehner, H. 443, 609
Weide, B. van der 385, 609
Welte, D. H. 259, 268, 269, 330, 429, 443, 609

Whitehead, E. V. 129, 240, 268, 318, 609
Witherspoon, P. A. 373
Wollrab, V. 181, 609
Wszolek, P. C. 129, 131, 155, 609

Zhuze, T. P. 609

Subject index

Abietic acid 5
Abiogenic lipids 19
− processes 5
Acacus formation 321, 322
Acetate/malonate biogenesis 6
Achondrites 594, 597
Acid-hydrolyzable sugars 174
Acid, branched-chain 87, 133, 151
−, normal carboxylic 133, 137, 144, 151, 265
Activation energy 169, 176, 465
Adiantane 192, 194
Adsorption process 500
AgNO$_2$ thin layer chromatography 203
Algae 8, 15, 86, 182, 185, 189, 203
Algal colonies 583
− mat 8
− sources 202
Alkanes 2, 309, 394, 400
−, branched 189, 198, 202, 203, 402, 403
−, −, see also isoparaffins
−, cyclic 86, 182, 189, 193, 198, 202, 203
−, isoprenoidal 86
−, normal 27, 202, 241−258, 261−268, 269, 323, 388, 400−403, 429
−, −, determination of, by gas chromatography 241−258
−, −, distribution of, in relation to coal rank 434
−, in gas from coals 448
Alkylation processes 6
Alkylbenzoporphyrins 87
Ambreane 200

Amino-acids 535, 544
−, addition of, to quinone 492
Amino compounds 543
α-amylase 167, 169, 174
β-amylase 167, 169, 174
Analcime and low coal rank 407, 415, 417, 420, 421
Ancient biological residues 227
Angiosperms 185
Annularia 167
Apennines trend 501
Apiezon L 189, 203
Aquatic organisms 189
Aquatic plants 268
Arabinose 167, 170
Arborane 185
Arenes, diffusion of, in water 374
Aromatics 11
Aromatic acids 151
− carbon atoms 291, 298, 299
− carboxylic acids 87
− C-H stretching vibrations 294
− hydrocarbons 255, 291, 394, 399
− profiles 323, 327
Arrhenius equation 169, 280, 532
Arsenic, enrichment of, in coals 568, 574, 576
Asphalthenes 388, 393, 394, 399, 400, 590
ATP 217

Bacteria 39
Basin, South-Caspian 473−484
Bauerane 188

Becker-Ryhage separator 204
Bentonite 21
Benzene, diffusion of, in brines 373−376
Benzoquinone 492, 493
Biochemical productivity 63
− zone 477
Biogenic lipids 19
Biolipids 7
Biological marker 1, 181
Biologically produced carbon skeletons 269, 276
Biopolymers 157
Bitumen in meteorites 601
Bituminous shale, Monte San Giorgio 217
− Tertiary, Messel 218
Black shales, Devonian 175
Blind River 579
Boghead 579
Botryococcus braunii 133
Boudouard reaction 517
Brown coal 65
− seams, weathered zones 459
− Tertiary 217, 218
Burial metamorphism and coalification 407, 408, 409, 411, 421, 422
Butane, diffusion of, in brines 374

C = C skeletal vibrations 294
C^{13}/C^{12} isotope analysis 269
Calamites 167, 170, 172, 174, 175
− duboisi 170, 172, 174
− Suckowi 170, 172, 174,
− −, carbohydrate content of 175
Callixylon 167, 170

Capillary columns 12, 188, 203
Capillary column gas liquid chromatography (GLC) 188, 189, 195
— gas chromatography-mass spectrometry (GC-MS) 11, 188, 198, 204, 211
Carbohydrates of early Paleozoic plant fossils 168
— protected by mineral matter 175
—, separation of, by gas chromatography 168
— yields 167
Carbon, forms of, in meteorites 593, 600
— isotope composition of Witwatersrand thucholite 589
— isotope analysis 269, 499
— — ratio 517
— Leader 589
— number dominance 68
—, polytypism, in meteorites 593—604
— Skeleton Concept 66
Carbonaceous matter 579
Carbon-carbon bonds, strength of 500
Carbon dioxide 66, 476, 477, 481
Carboniferous 23, 167, 443
— reservoirs 304
Catalytic properties of rocks 282
Cation exchange capacity of insoluble humic acids in peat 567, 574—576
Cellobiose 176
Cellulase 167
Cellulose 168, 174, 486
Chemical fossil 1
— transformation 298
Chemotaxonomy 8
Chemotaxonomic studies 183—188
Chenopodiales 185
Chlorite 407
Chloromethylsilyl ethers 169
Chlorophyceae 131
Chlorophyll 9, 151
Cholestane 4, 86
5 C-cholestane 192, 196, 200, 202, 204
5β-cholestane 192, 200, 202
Cholesterol, absolute stereochemistry of 4
Chondrites, carbonaceous 596, 597, 600—603

Chromic acid oxidation 135
Clay minerals 385
— —, burial-metamorphic modification of 411, 413
Cliftonite in meteorites 593, 600
Clinoptilolite 415, 417
Coal 65, 427, 428
—, aromatic structure of 488
—, composition of gas from 450
—, degassing of 451
—, elementary composition of 444
—, enrichment of microelements in 568, 569
—, formation of, biological phase 492
—, formation of, (Ruhr area) 78
—, genesis of, geochemical phase 460
—, grain size of 466
—, hydrocarbons in 453
—, hydrocarbon content of 445
—, microelements in 567, 568
—, non-lignitic derivatives in 64
—, rate of heating of 464
—, residual gases in 452
—, sapropelic 579, 589
—, spontaneous ignition in 469
—, volatile compounds in 445
— rank
    and burial-metamorphic facies 407—409, 411, 415, 420—422
    and distribution of heavy n-paraffins 434
— rank scale 409—411, 420
Coalification 65, 459
— as burial metamorphic process 407, 408, 409
—, degree of 446, 450
—, rate of 70
Cohenite in meteorites 593, 599, 600
Colorado Plateau 588
Column chromatography 291
Comparative biochemistry 8
Copepods 9
Correlation index 323, 327
Cracking, catalytic 401
—, thermal 401
Cresorsellinic acid 489

Crude oils, see also petroleum 241, 242, 261, 385, 400, 590
—, from Abu Dhabi 332—343
—, Algerian 304
—, analysis of 291, 323
—, evolution of 304
—, fraction C_{10}^+ 309
—, fraction $C_{10}-C_{25}$ 309
—, fraction C_{25}^+ 310
—, genesis of 304
—, Libyan 319
—, metamorphism of 289, 299, 301
—, Middle East 332—343
—, North Saharan 319
—, similarity of infrared spectra of 302
—, sulphur containing 331—343
—, —, characterisation 342
—, —, classification 334, 342
—, —, density 333—335, 338
—, —, evolution 332
Cyclanes 403, 404
Cycloalkanes 188, 193, 203
—, diffusion of, in water 374
Cycloalkylporphyrins 87
Cycloparaffins 252
Cystine 540

Deamination, oxidative 491
Decarboxylation, oxidative 490
Degassing rate 68
Demineralization 9, 89, 134, 139
Drepanophycus spp. 173
Desolubilization of methane 500
Desorption of gas 463
— process 500
—, zone of 76
Devonian 167, 170, 175, 321, 443
— reservoirs 304
Dextrose 176
Diagenesis 155, 181, 182
—, late, see Burial Metamorphism
Diamond 593—595, 598—600
—, hexagonal, in meteorites 593, 594, 597, 599
Dicarboxylic acid 139, 148, 152
Diffusion 282, 284
— coefficient, correlations of 379, 380, 384

— of methane 513
— of gas 463
— in brines of: benzene, butane, ethane, methane, propane 373, 374, 376
—, in the migration of gas 513
— of hydrocarbons in water 373, 380
—, activation energy for 380
—, effect of electrolytes on 373
Dihydrophytol 12
Dihydroxybenzoic acids 491
Disproportionation of hydrogen 292
Dissolved organic carbon, see Organic matter
Distribution of heavy n-paraffins in relation to rank of coal 434
Diterpanes 2

Earth, expansion of the 61, 73
—, polar flattening of the 75
Environment, depositional 76
Enzymatic analyses for monosaccharides 168
Enzymes in bituminous layers 222
Eocene age 86
Equisitum 8, 170
Ergostane 86, 197, 200, 202
Ethane, diffusion of, in brines 373, 374, 375
— methane ratio 499
Ethylene 467
Eucaryotic organisms 168
Even predominance 268
Environmental markers 9
Evolution of plants 185, 203
Expulsion 282
Extraction processes 133

Fatty acids 1, 7, 401
Feldspars 544
Fichtelite 5
Fig Tree Series 210
Flame ionisation detector 203
Fluorescence of Oceanwater 47, 51
Fluorites 544

Fossils 7, 170
—, chemical 1
—, —, in coals 428
Fossil products 181, 182
Freshwater lake sediment 157
Friedelane 188, 195
Friedo rearranged compounds 188
Fungi 182
Furfurals 175

Galactan 167, 170
Galactantype structural polysaccharides 170
Galactose 167, 170
Gammacerane 86, 192, 195, 202
Gas chromatography 10, 90, 227, 241−258, 504
—, capillary 241
—, on polyphenylether columns 200
—, on SE 30 columns 241
—, on SE 52 columns 253
Gas Chromatography-Mass spectrometry 202
Gas-liquid chromatography 137, 198, 202, 203
Gas, composition of, from coals 461
—, decompositional formation 66
— formation 279
— —, from coals 459
— —, influence of oxygen on 466
— —, rate of 461
Gasoline, composition of 401, 402
G. E. F., Geochemical Enrichment Factor 567, 570, 572
— definition 570
— values 571, 573, 576
Geogenetic relationships 5
Geolipids 5
Geothermal gradient 282
Glucopyranose 167, 174
Glucose 167, 169, 170, 176
— in association with Devonian black shale 176
— in association with montmorillonite 176
— degradation 169
— oxidase reagent 169
Glutane 188
Graphite 517
— in meteorites 593, 594, 597−600

Green River formation 86
— shale 15, 182, 189, 193, 198, 202
Greenschist facies and metaanthracite 407, 411, 414, 415
Gutenberg 76
Gymnospermae-Cardaitales 167

Hastinella sp. 173
Hatchettite 23
Heteroatomic plots 93
Heterocyclic compounds 281
—, containing nitrogen 495, 496
Heulandite-clinoptilolite and low coal rank 415, 417, 420, 421
High resolution GLC 197
— MS 91, 137
Hopane 185, 194, 195, 201
Humic acids 494, 496
—, peat, accumulation of microelements in 567
—, peat, interaction with elements of periodic table 573
—, role of, in the enrichment of microelements 569
Hydrocarbon/Carbon ratio 28
Hydrocarbons 1, 401−404, 579
—, aliphatic 393, 394, 400
—, aromatic 255, 291, 394, 399
— (C_2-C_{13}) 280
—, in coals 453
—, diffusion in brines 373, 374
—, diffusion in water 373, 380
—, entrapment of 501
— formation zones 477, 478, 480
—, in gas from coals 448
—, genesis of 306
—, higher than methane 461
—, light, adsorbed on sediment 358
—, —, contained in sea water 355
— in meteorites 593, 594, 600, 601, 603
— from mud volcanoes 473, 476
—, naphthenic 392, 400

–, naphtheno aromatic
309
–, polycyclic 281
–, polymerized 580
–, saturated 241, 291, 299,
301, 309, 323
–, saturated/aromatic ratio
323
–, unsaturated 464, 468
Hydrodynamic factors 501
Hydrogen content of crude
oil 299
Hydrogenation 292
– dehydrogenation reaction
5
Hydrogeochemistry 567, 572
Hydrothermal solutions,
transport reactions in 543
Hydroxy acids 157

Igneous intrusion 19
Illite 407
Immaturity 261, 266
Infra-Red spectra of hydro-
carbons 294, 302
– spectrometry 10
Iron humate peat 574, 576
Isomerisation 401
Isoparaffins 252, 388, 394,
400
Isoprene 19
Isoprenoid 246, 323
– acyclic 2
– biogenesis 6
– hydrocarbons 151
Isoprenoidal acid 87
Isotope fractionation 517
Isotopic composition 4
– composition of carbon
in meteorites 596, 597,
599, 600
– fractionations, during
migration of gas 499
Italian gas fields 499

Kaolinite, disappearance in
high-rank coals 407, 411,
413–415, 422
Karroo coal measures 590
Kerogen 135, 139
– matrix 87
– oxidation 89, 155
– saponification 135, 139
Keto acids 147
Keyser Limestone 173

Kinetics of chemical reactions
460, 461
Kovats indices 189

Langensalza gas fields 512
Lanostane 193, 196
Lanosterol 182
Laser mass spectrometry of
coals 427
Laumontite and coal rank
407, 415, 417, 420–422
Leaf waxes 7
Least square method 299
Leguminales 185
Lepidodendron Sigillaria
167
Lepidophloios 170, 172
Lepidophloios laricinus 172
Leucine 537
Lignin 486, 487
–, degradation products
of 488
–, microbiological degra-
dation of 488
–, synthetic, ^{14}C labeled
487
Lipids 2, 41
–, abiogenic 19
–, biogenic 19
Lipid fraction 281
Living organisms 1
Loganophyton sp. 173
Lonsdalite in meteorites
593, 594, 599
Los Angeles basin 36
Lower Devonian 170
Lower Permian 170
Lupane 86, 185, 193, 195,
201

Magnetism, terrestrial 75
Malabaricane 200
Maltose 176
Mannose 167, 170
Marble 517
Marine foodweb 8
– organism Pachysphaera
pelagica 131
Martian soil 19
Mass spectral fragmentation
patterns 193
– line diagrams 195, 200
Mass spectrometer 189, 195
Mass spectrometry 10, 90,
197, 227, 389, 394, 427,
428
Maturation 21, 181, 182
– of petroleum 40, 261, 266,
500

Mesozoic 306
Meta-anthracite in green-
schist facies 407, 411, 414,
415
Metamorphism 404
–, chemistry of 299
– of crude oil 289, 299, 301
– facies and coal rank
407–409, 411, 420–422
Meteorites 593–604
–, Burgavli 593, 600
–, Canyon Diablo 593, 594,
597–600
–, formation of 593
–, Goalpara 597
–, Novo Urei 593–595, 597
–, Odessa 600
–, Toluca 600
–, Yardymlinsky 593, 600
Methane 66, 279, 280, 284,
461
–, desolubilization of 500
–, diffusion of, in brines
373–375
–, processes in the genesis
of 511
–, solubilization of 500
Microelements, accumulation
of, in peat humic acids
and in coal 567, 576
–, deficiency of, in plants
567, 575
–, definition 568
–, depletion of, in natural
waters 567, 575, 576
Microfossils 132
Micronutrient, deficiency of,
in plants 567, 576
–, fixation of 574, 575
Migration 69, 279, 282, 285
304
– path 327
Migrational processes 500
Mineral facies, burial-metamorphic 415
– assemblages, burial-metamorphic 407–409, 417,
420, 421, 422
Miocene 261
Molecular sieves 11
– 5 Å, 203, 241–258
Molybdenum, association
with uranium 567, 572,
574
–, enrichment 568, 569,
576
–, retention of, by humic
acids 575
Monosaccharide components
167

Montmorillonite 386, 388, 391–394, 399, 400, 537
Moodies Series 210
Moretane 202
Mud Lake 14
Mud volcanoes, Achzevir 475
–, Alijat 475
–, Azerbaijan 473, 476, 483
–, Bank of Makarow 474
–, composition of gas from 475, 476, 481
–, eruptions of 474–476
–, Great Kjanizdag 474
–, hydrocarbons from 473, 476
–, Irantekjan 474
–, Kerch-Taman 475, 476
–, Tauragay 474
Multiflorane 188

Naphthenes 36, 309, 392, 400
Naphthene index 38
Naphthogenesis 504
Naphthoic acids 146
Naphthyl alkanoic acids 137
Natural gases 499
– –, genesis of 500
Neuropteris 167
Nitrogen 66, 283, 476
–, in coal 469, 485, 489
–, in heterocyclic compounds 495, 496
NMR, Nuclear magnetic resonance 11
NMR-spectra of aromatic hydrocarbons 298
Non-marine environment 86
Nor-lanosterol 182
Norphytanic acids 87
Nostoc Muscorum 8
Nutrients 569, 574

Octahedrite in meteorites 597
Odd predominance 261, 276, 434
Oil, see Crude oils
–, see Petroleum
Oil content in the residua 292
–, migration of 69
– Shale 86
Oleanane 185

Olefinic acids 152
Olefins 388, 400
Oleic acid 401
Oligosaccharides 176
Onocerane 195
– II 192
– III 192
Onverwacht kerogen 211
– microstructures 212
– pillow-lava, inorganic artefacts in 214
– sedimentary rocks 209
– Series 210
Opal rose, see Quincyte 555
Ordovician 173
Organic carbon, dissolved in the Oceans, see Organic matter
– compounds in plants 486
– material, transformation of 346, 349
Organic Matter dissolved in the Oceans 47–57
– –, concentration 47, 48, 50, 53
– –, composition 47, 48, 55
– –, definition 48
– –, distribution 47, 48
– –, –, vertical 49, 55
– –, origin 48, 51, 52
– –, residence time 48, 52
– –, stability 48
–, particulate in the Oceans 47–54
–, of Precambrian 530
–, production of 47, 52
–, sources of 48–54
–, transformation of 280
Organic rich shales 40
Orsellinic acid 489
Oxidation reaction in coal grain 470
Oxygen, rate of consumption of 47, 50
Oxo-acids 87

Paleochemotaxonomy 157, 183
Paleozoic 306
– plant fossils 170
Paraffins, see Alkanes
Parent ions 198
Paris Basin 346
Peat, microelements in 576
–, tertiary 217, 218
Pectic substances 168
Pentacyclic cycloalkanes 182, 193, 203
– triterpanes 201

Perfluorokerosene 205
Perhydrocarotene 15
Perhydro-β-carotene 86
Permeability of reservoir rocks, in Italien gas fields 509
Permian 170, 261
Petroleum, see also Crude Oils 2, 21, 188, 269, 590
–, accumulation of 282
–, alteration of 279
–, formation of 279, 346
–, genesis of 404
–, influence of pressure on the evolution of 385
–, kinetics and the formation of 352
–, mathematical models in studies of genesis of 353
–, migration of 69, 279
–, origin of 26
–, precursors of 41
–, rate of formation of 346
–, thermal evolution of 385, 400
Phenols 139, 488, 489, 491
–, polymerisation products of 490
– sulfuric acid colorimetric method 168
Phenyl alkanoic acids 137, 146
Phytane 17, 268
Phytanic acid 12, 87
Phytol 9, 12
Phytoplankton 9
Pitchblende 588
Plants 182, 185, 268
–, evolution of 203
–, sterols in 188
–, terrestrial 261, 268
–, wax distribution in 202
Pollution 9
Polycyclic alkanes 182
Polymerized hydrocarbons 580
Polypeptide 5
Polyphenylether, 7-ring 189, 192, 204
Polysaccharides 167, 174, 176
Polytypism of carbon 593
Porphyrin 2, 11, 87, 227
Posidonia shale 217
Postgenetic processes 500
Precambrian 168, 173
– conglomerates 579
Preference of odd numbered n-paraffins 261, 276, 434
Pristane 9, 17, 268
Procaryotic organisms 168

Propane, diffusion of, in
  brines 373—375
Prospecting for uranium
  548
Protozoa 189
Psilophyton 173
Pteridopermatophyta 167
Pteriodophyta-Equisetales
  167
— Lycopodiales 167
— Psilophytales 167
Pterophyta 203
Pyrophyllite and meta-anthra-
  cite rank 407, 411, 413—
  415
Pyrolysis 459

Quaternary carbon atoms
  196
Quincyte 553
Quincyte, natural organic
  pigments in 553—565

Racemisation 535
Radioactive minerals 580
Radiochemical synthesis
  544
Radiolytic polymerization
  580, 588
Radstock, England 170, 175
Rare gases 476
Reaction rate constant 470
—, temperature dependence
  of 471
Resins 5, 393, 394, 399, 400
Retene 5
Retention data 189
Rhamnose 170
Rhynia 167, 170, 172, 174
— gwynne-vaughani 167,
  172, 174
Ring content of hydrocarbons
  294
Rock extracts 262
Rock, magnetic 284, 286
—, sedimentary 210, 285

Saar 448
Salt water 386, 388, 391,
  394, 400
Saponification of kerogen
  135, 139
Sapropelic coals 579, 589
Saturated hydrocarbons 241,
  291, 299, 301, 309, 323
Scottish torbanite 152
Sediments 1, 33, 86, 188,
  261
Sedimentary rocks on earth,
  oldest known 210

Selenium, enrichment of, in
  coals 574, 576
Sepiolite 553
Sicily gas fields 499
Sigillaria cf. approximata
  172
Silurian 173, 321
Silyl ethers 168
Sitostane 86
Solar spots 75
Solubility of inorganic mate-
  rial in the presence of
  organic amino compounds
  545
Solubiiization of methane
  500
Sorption capacity of peat
  570
Sorption isotherm of UO_2 +
  on ignite 570, 571
Sorption, of elements on peat
  567
—, of uranium by peat and
  lignite 570
Soudan shale (Precambrian)
  17
Source rocks 27, 301, 306,
  342, 500
South-Caspian basin 473—484
South Wales coal field 23
Southern Italy gas fields 499
Specific rotation, decrease of
  540
Spectra, EPR, diamond in
  meteorites 594, 596, 600,
  601
—, IR, diamond in meteorites
  594, 596
—, X-ray, diamond in meteorites 595, 597—600
Spectral analyses of aromatic
  hydrocarbons 294
Squalene 182

Stable carbon isotope mea-
  surements 269, 499, 517
Starch 168, 170, 174
Stearic acid 401
Steranes 2, 15, 86, 182, 188,
  192, 193, 196, 200
Steroids 181, 182, 185, 193,
  203
Sterols 36, 151, 203
Stigmastane 192, 196, 200,
  202
Subsidence 282
Subsurface temperature 27
Sugar components 170
Sugars, acid hydrolyzable 174
—, separated by paper chro-
  matography 168

Sulphur in crudes 331—343
—, non-thiophenic 331,
  340, 341
—, thiophenic 339, 340, 342
Swaziland System 210
Syngenetic component 299

Taeniocradia dubia 173
Taraxastane 188
Tasmanites 131
Temperature gradient 38
— history 41
— range of coalification
  464
— range of pyrolysis 464
Terpenoidal hydrocarbons
  (C_{40}) 86
Terrestrial plants 261, 268
Tetracyclic alkanes 182, 193,
  203
Tetrahydrophenanthrene
  391
Tetralin 391
Tetraterpenoidal alkanes 86
Thallophyta 185
Thermal alteration 21
— cracking of petroleum 599
— decomposition 27, 176
— degradation of glucose
  167, 169
Thermocatalysis 280, 282,
  401
Thermocatalytic processes
  478—480
— zone 478—480
Thin layer chromatography
  10
Thin sections 132
Thiourea adduction 11
Thucholite 579, 589
Toarcian 346
Torbanite 133, 152, 549
Trace elements 589
— —, see also microelements
Transformation, internal, of
  oil 292
— of organic matter 280
Transport reactions in hy-
  drothermal solutions
  543
Trenton Limestone 173
Tricyclic alkanes 182, 193,
  200, 203
Trimethylsilyl ethers 168
Trimerophyton robustius
  167
Triterpanes 2, 15, 86, 182,
  185, 188, 192, 193, 197
Triterpenoids 9, 181, 182,
  185, 193, 203

Ultrasonic agitation 134
Ultraviolet spectra 302
— spectra of aromatic
   hydrocarbons 295
— and visible spectrocopy
   11
Unsaturated esters 10
Uraninite 580
— bearing carbonaceous
   substances 579
Uranium, accumulation of,
   in coals 567, 569, 576
—, association of, with
   bioliths 569, 574
—, enrichment of 568, 569
— fixation in organic substances 588
— in Hungarian coals 567—
   569

— minerals, occluded liquids
   in 543
— minerals, occluded gas in
   543
—, prospecting for 548
—, sorption of, by peat and
   lignite 570, 571
—, transport of 545
Uranyl complex 588
Urea adduction 11, 135, 271
Ureilites, Dyalpur 594
—, Goalpara 594
—, Novo Urei 594
Ursane 185

Vanadium, association with
   uranium 567, 572, 574
—, enrichment of 568, 576

Venturi basin 36
Virginia Argillite 173

Water, liquid structure of
   384
—, self-diffusion coefficients
   of 381
Wax, leaf 7
—, plant 202
Witwatersrand thucholite
   589

X-ray crystallography 11
Xylans 170
Xylose 167, 170

Zeolites and coal rank 407—421